SOLID STATE
PHYSICS

A SELECTED LIST OF OTHER PRENTICE-HALL TECHNICAL BOOKS

Elements of Atomic Physics, Peaslee and Mueller
Fundamental Formulas of Physics, Menzel editor
Fundamentals of Quantum Mechanics, Persico
High Energy Particles, Rossi
Introduction to Experimental Physics, Fretter
Introduction to Nuclear Engineering, Murray
Mathematical Methods for Scientists and Engineers, Smith
Modern Physics, Van Name
Nuclear Radiation Physics, 2d ed., Lapp and Andrews
Nuclear Reactor Physics, Murray
Procedures in Experimental Physics, Cartwright, Strong, et al.
Quantum Chemistry, Pitzer
Quantum Theory, Bohm
Transistor Electronics, Lo, Endres, Zawels, Waldhauer
  and Cheng

SOLID STATE

PHYSICS

By

ADRIANUS J. DEKKER

PROFESSOR, DEPARTMENT OF ELECTRICAL
ENGINEERING, UNIVERSITY OF MINNESOTA

Englewood Cliffs, N.J.
PRENTICE-HALL, INC.

Library of Congress Catalog Card No.: 57-8688

First printing.............. May, 1957
Second printing......... January, 1958
Third printing......... February, 1959

PRINTED IN THE UNITED STATES OF AMERICA
82197

PREFACE

THE purpose of this book is to introduce the reader to the study of the physical properties of crystalline solids. It is based on notes which I used for lectures in the Physics Department of the University of British Columbia, Canada, and in the Electrical Engineering Department of the University of Minnesota.

My aim has been to write an introductory text suitable for senior undergraduate and beginning graduate courses on the solid state in physics, engineering, chemistry, and metallurgy. Also, I have attempted to make it suitable for self study by scientists in industrial laboratories interested in the physical properties of solids. The widely varying background of the anticipated groups of readers has affected the organization and presentation of the subject matter. The general level of presentation has been kept elementary, with emphasis on the physical reasoning underlying the interpretation of the physical properties of solids. I have made an effort, however, to remain as rigorous and up-to-date as possible within the limits imposed by the level of presentation. The first eight chapters deal with subjects which, at least in an introductory text, can be discussed without reference to the details of the electronic structure of solids. Prerequisite for understanding this part of the book is an elementary knowledge of statistical thermodynamics and of the quantized harmonic oscillator. Chapters 9 through 20 deal with the electronic properties of solids and require familiarity with the elements of wave mechanics, although in a number of chapters no explicit use of wave mechanics is made. As a consequence of the organization of the material outlined above, the degree of difficulty tends to increase as one progresses through the book. This in itself does not compel the reader to follow the order in which the various subjects are discussed. In fact, the chapters are organized in groups which could be taken up in any order suitable to serve the particular needs of the instructor or reader.

To some extent, my own interest and taste have determined the choice of material; however, with the possible exception of Chapter 17, the material is basic to a great variety of subjects in the field of solid state.

I am indebted to W. Opechowski for constructive criticism during the preparation of Chapters 10 and 11, and to A. H. Morrish for his comments on other parts of the manuscript. I also wish to acknowledge the cooperation of numerous publishers who kindly permitted me to reproduce illustrations. I am grateful to F. L. Vogel, W. G. Pfann, H. E. Corey, and E. E. Thomas for a micrograph of a lineage boundary in germanium. Finally, I wish to thank my wife for typing the manuscript and for her encouragement.

A. J. Dekker

CONTENTS

Chapter 1

THE CRYSTALLINE STATE

1-1. The crystalline state of solids

The elements and their chemical compounds generally occur in three states of aggregation: the solid state, the liquid state, and the gaseous state. In solids and liquids the distance between neighboring atoms is of the order of a few Angstroms, i.e., they contain 10^{22}–10^{23} atoms per cm^3. This may be compared with a density of about 2.7×10^{19} molecules per cm^3 in a gas at room temperature under one atmosphere, corresponding to an average distance of approximately 30 Å between molecules.

In crystalline solids the atoms are stacked in a regular manner, forming a three-dimensional pattern which may be obtained by a three-dimensional

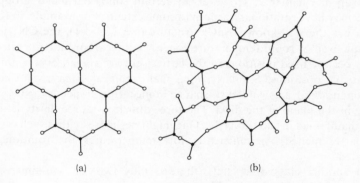

(a)   (b)

Fig. 1-1. Schematic illustration of the difference between a crystal (a) and a glass (b). [After W. H. Zachariasen, *J. Am. Chem. Soc.*, **54**, 3841 (1932)]

repetition of a certain pattern unit; two-dimensional examples are given in Fig. 1-1a and Fig. 1-3. When the periodicity of the pattern extends throughout a certain piece of material, one speaks of a single crystal. In polycrystalline materials the periodicity of structure is interrupted at so-called grain boundaries; the size of the grains in which the structure is periodic may vary from macroscopic dimensions to several Angstroms. When the size of the grains or crystallites becomes comparable to the size of the pattern unit, one can no longer speak of crystals, since the essential feature of a crystal is its periodicity of structure; one then speaks of "amorphous" substances. For most solids the crystalline state is the natural one since the energy of the ordered atomic arrangement is lower than that of an irregular packing of atoms. However, when the atoms are not given an opportunity to arrange themselves properly, by inhibiting their mobility, amorphous material may be formed; an example is amorphous carbon formed as a decomposition product at low temperatures. Certain polymers are composed of very large and irregular molecules and in such cases a crystalline packing is not easily obtained. In other cases, the solid state may correspond to a supercooled liquid in which the molecular arrangement of the liquid state is frozen in; because of rapid cooling and a high viscosity of the liquid, crystals may not have had time to grow and a glassy material results (see Fig. 1-1b). Upon annealing, such glassy substances may crystallize (devitrify), as is well known to any experimentalist who has worked with quartz. In this book we shall be concerned essentially with solids which are generally regarded as crystalline.

Although one usually thinks of a solid as an arrangement of atoms in which the atoms occupy fixed positions relative to each other, this is not necessarily the case. Of course, in any crystal the atoms carry out a vibrational motion about their equilibrium position; this topic will be taken up in Chapter 2. However, in certain solids particular groups of atoms may have rotational freedom to some extent. For example, in KCN, which has the well-known NaCl structure (see Fig. 5-1), the CN^- ion is rotating even at room temperature;[1] neither the carbon nor the nitrogen atoms occupy fixed positions in the lattice, but are spread over a number of possible positions. Similarly, long-chain molecules may rotate about the longitudinal axis and disk-shaped ionic groups such as NO_3^- may rotate in the plane of the disk. The three-dimensional regularity is, however, maintained in such crystals. One might perhaps say that such crystals are partly melted. At sufficiently low temperatures the rotations are inhibited.

In another class of crystals, there is only two- or one-dimensional regularity,[2] viz., in the "liquid crystals." Such substances actually flow and will rise in a capillary tube. Normal crystals exhibit flow only under influence of external forces (see Chapter 3). A few hundred examples of liquid crystals are known, most of them being organic compounds, such as ammonium oleate $C_{17}H_{33}COONH_4$. They will not be discussed in this volume.

Although we shall assume in the present chapter that the crystals under consideration are "perfect," the reader will have ample opportunity in the

---

[1] See, for example, C. W. Bunn, *Chemical Crystallography*, Oxford, New York, 1946, pp. 329–331.

[2] J. D. Bernal and W. A. Wooster, *Ann. Repts. Chem. Soc.*, **28**, 262 (1932); J. T. Randall, *The Diffraction of X-rays and Electrons by Amorphous Solids, Liquids and Gases*, Chapman and Hall, London, 1934; W. Voigt, *Physik. Z.*, **17**, 76, 153 (1917).

remainder of this book to realize that a large number of properties of solids are determined by lattice imperfections such as impurities, vacant lattice sites, atoms in positions where they "should not be" according to the crystal structure, etc. However, since we shall be mainly concerned

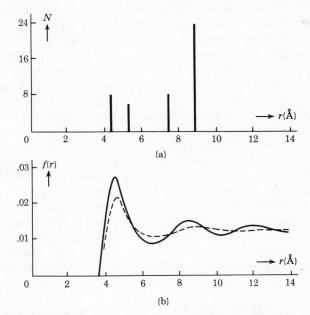

Fig. 1-2. The number of K atoms in metallic potassium is represented in (a) as function of the radial distance from a given K atom (20°C); in (b) the fully drawn and dashed curves represent the density of K atoms $f(r)$ in the liquid at 70°C and 395°C, respectively. [After Thomas and Gingrich, ref. 3]

in this chapter with crystal structures and their determination, such defects may be neglected temporarily.

In liquids, the atoms or molecules are in continual motion, and a crystalline structure is therefore absent. On the other hand, this should not lead one to believe that the arrangement of atoms is completely random. Even in liquids there is a certain amount of order, but it extends over a relatively short distance. To illustrate the difference between the "long-range order" in a crystal and the "short-range order" in a liquid, let us consider potassium in the solid and liquid states. Potassium, like the other alkali metals has the body-centered cubic structure (Fig. 1-4b), the cube edge being 5.344 Å at 20°C. Taking the nucleus of a given K atom in the crystal as origin, suppose we were to plot the number of nuclei of other K atoms as function of the radial distance r from the central atom. We would then obtain a number of vertical lines as in Fig. 1-2a at specific distances from the origin. For example, there are eight atoms at a distance $\frac{1}{2}a\sqrt{3}$, six atoms at a distance a, etc. In the liquid state the situation is rather different. Suppose the origin of the coordinate system is attached to a given K atom and moves with this atom. At a given instant there will be a certain configuration of the other atoms, but the configuration changes continually with time. Taking the time average of these different configurations, one could then plot the average number of nuclei as function of the distance from the central atom. Such information may actually be obtained from X-ray diffraction experiments. Thus, in Fig. 1-2b the fully drawn curve $f(r)$ represents the density of K atoms per Å^3 at 70°C as function of the radial distance from an arbitrary K atom in the liquid;[3] the dashed line corresponds to 395°C. Note that the set of discrete lines of Fig. 1-2a has been transformed into a continuous curve. Also, only the first few "shells" of other atoms are distinguishable in the 70°C curve, whereas in the 395°C curve only the first two are somewhat pronounced. For distances larger than $\sim 10\,\text{Å}$ the curves show little or no structure and the density becomes independent of r; for the crystal, however, the discrete lines extend over the whole piece of material, at least when it is a single crystal. It is of interest to remark that the integral of $4\pi r^2 f(r)$ over the first peak determines the average number of nearest neighbors of the central atom; for the alkali metals we find that this is approximately equivalent to 8 nearest neighbors, as it is in the solid (only there, it is exactly 8).

1-2. Unit cells and Bravais lattices

We shall now discuss somewhat further the periodicity of structure, which is the fundamental feature of a crystal. Consider part of a two-dimensional crystal, the atoms of which are arranged in a pattern as illustrated in Fig. 1-3. Each cluster of atoms (in this case a dot and two open circles) will be referred to as a pattern-unit. It is observed that when a parallelogram such as $ABCD$ is repeatedly translated by the vectors a and b, corresponding respectively to AB and AD, the whole pattern may be obtained; thus $ABCD$ is called a "unit cell." The choice of a unit

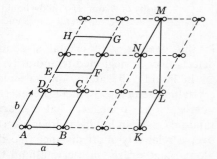

Fig. 1-3. Two-dimensional crystal and various unit cells.

cell is by no means unique; for example, $EFGH$ or $KLMN$ would serve the purpose just as well and so would many others. All three unit cells

---

[3] D. E. Thomas and N. S. Gingrich, *Phys. Rev.*, **56**, 415 (1938); for a review of this topic, see N. S. Gingrich, *Revs. Mod. Phys.*, **15**, 90 (1943).

mentioned contain one pattern-unit, since each of these units located at a corner belongs to four neighboring parallelograms and each pattern unit located at an edge belongs to two parallelograms. The areas of all unit cells containing one pattern-unit are equal. It is usually convenient to choose as a unit cell a parallelogram with the shortest possible sides.

In three dimensions, a similar procedure may be followed by stacking parallelepipeds in a regular manner; a convenient unit cell then contains again pattern-units only at the corners. In some cases, however, there

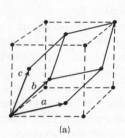 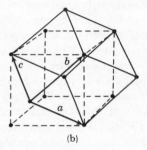

(a)   (b)

Fig. 1-4. The true (fully drawn) and compound (dashed) unit cells of the f.c.c. (a) and b.c.c. (b) lattices.

are reasons, to be given below, for choosing a "compound unit cell" which contains more than one pattern-unit. Consider, for example, the arrangement of atoms in a crystal of nickel, illustrated in Fig. 1-4a. The true unit cell corresponds to the parallelepiped based on the translation vectors a, b, c; it contains Ni atoms only at the corners, i.e., there is one atom per unit cell. On the other hand, the lattice may also be divided into a system of cubes with atoms at the corners and at the centers of the cube faces. It is convenient to consider a cube of this kind as a new "unit cell," even though it contains four atoms and has a volume four times as large as the "true" unit cell. One refers to the face-centered cube loosely as the "unit cell," although strictly speaking this is not correct since it is a combination of four unit cells. The most important reason for choosing the face-centered cube as a new unit cell is that the symmetry properties of the atomic arrangement in nickel are the same as in crystals which have a cube as the true unit cell. In fact, the essential symmetry elements of a simple cube (atoms only at the corners) are four threefold axes running diagonally through the cube; whenever the cube is rotated about any of these axes over 120°, it is brought into a position indistinguishable from the original position. The same symmetry is seen to be possessed by the face-centered cube. Another reason for choosing the compound unit cell is the fact that cubic axes provide a more convenient reference system than those corresponding to a rhombohedron.

In a similar way, the structure of the alkali metals represented in Fig.

1-4b is described as body-centered cubic (b.c.c.); in this case the compound unit cell contains two atoms and is twice as large as the true unit cell based on the vectors a, b, c. The b.c.c. structure also has the required four threefold symmetry axes. The three cubic structures mentioned here (simple, f.c.c., and b.c.c.) are the only possible cubic structures. For example, a cube with atoms at the corners and at the centers of one or two pairs of opposite faces would not have the four threefold symmetry axes, and thus no cubic symmetry.

In order to describe the structure of crystals, Bravais in 1848 introduced the concept of the space-lattice. A space-lattice is a mathematical concept and is defined as an infinite number of points in space with the property that the arrangement of points about a given point is identical with that about any other point. For example, the intersections of the two dashed sets of parallel lines in Fig. 1-3 represent a two-dimensional space-lattice. The intersections of these lines are the lattice points. From symmetry considerations of the type indicated above for the three possible cubic structures, Bravais showed that there exist no more than fourteen space-lattices in three dimensions. In order to specify the arrangement of points in a space-lattice, one introduces a system of axes such as indicated in Fig. 1-5. One distinguishes between seven systems of axes or crystal systems, depending on certain specifications about the lengths of the axes and the angles between them; the seven crystal systems together with the essential symmetry elements are given in Table 1-1. Although we shall not discuss the symmetry properties of crystals here, the elements occurring in the table may be defined.[4] A crystal is said to possess an n-fold rotation axis when rotation over $(360/n)$ degrees brings the crystal into self-coincidence. When a plane can be drawn in the crystal, which contains the center of the crystal, such that one half of the crystal is the reflection of the other half, the crystal is said to have a plane of symmetry. A crystal possesses an inversion center when for each point located at r relative to the center there exists an identical point at $-r$. A rotation-inversion axis exists when the crystal can be brought into self-coincidence by a combined rotation and inversion.

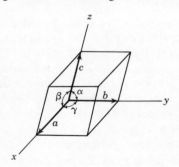

Fig. 1-5. Crystal axes.

The fourteen Bravais lattices or space lattices are represented in Fig. 1-6. Certain unit cells contain only points at the corners; they are

[4] See, for example, A. Schoenflies, *Theorie der Kristall Struktur*, Bornträger, Berlin (1923), or W. Voigt, *Lehrbuch der Kristallphysik*, Teubner, Leipzig and Berlin, 1910.

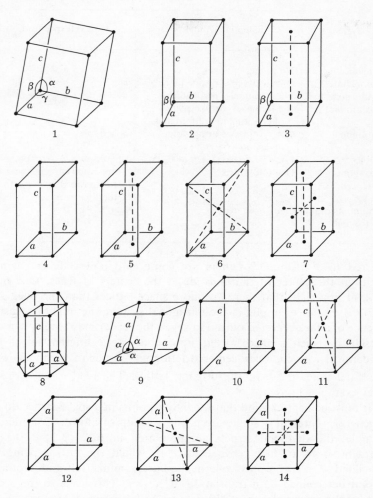

Fig. 1-6. The fourteen Bravais lattices: (1) triclinic, simple; (2) monoclinic, simple; (3) monoclinic, base centered; (4) orthorhombic, simple; (5) orthorhombic, base centered; (6) orthorhombic b.c.; (7) orthorhombic f.c.; (8) hexagonal; (9) rhombohedral; (10) tetragonal, simple; (11) tetragonal, b.c.; (12) cubic, simple; (13) b.c.c.; (14) f.c.c.

Table 1-1. The Seven Crystal Systems and Their Essential Symmetry

System	Essential symmetry	Unit cell specification
Triclinic	No planes, no axes	$a \neq b \neq c$; $\alpha \neq \beta \neq \gamma \neq 90°$
Monoclinic	One 2-fold axis or one plane	$a \neq b \neq c$; $\alpha = \beta = 90° \neq \gamma$
Orthorhombic (rhombic)	Three mutually perpendicular 2-fold axes, or two planes intersecting in a 2-fold axis	$a \neq b \neq c$; $\alpha = \beta = \gamma = 90°$
Tetragonal	One 4-fold axis or a 4-fold inversion axis	$a = b \neq c$; $\alpha = \beta = \gamma = 90°$
Cubic	Four 3-fold axes	$a = b = c$; $\alpha = \beta = \gamma = 90°$
Hexagonal	One 6-fold axis	Three equal coplanar axes a at 120°; fourth axis $c \perp$ to these; $c \neq a$.
Rhombohedral (trigonal)	One 3-fold axis	$a = b = c$; $\alpha = \beta = \gamma \neq 90°$

referred to as "simple." Others are compound unit cells and contain points at the center of the body or at the centers of faces. One might think at first sight that there are more space-lattices than the ones given in Fig. 1-6. For example, in the tetragonal system one might suggest the absence of a face-centered type. However, the reader may readily convince himself that such a lattice would, upon choosing a different set of axes, be identical with the body-centered tetragonal lattice of which the edges are $1/\sqrt{2}$ times those of the original lattice. The reader may consider other examples himself.

It must be kept in mind that the lattice points in a space-lattice do not, in general, represent a single atom but a group of atoms. Consider, for example, the diamond structure represented in Fig. 13-1; it may be represented by an f.c.c. space lattice in which the lattice points are associated with two atoms: one in the lattice point itself and another in a point determined by a translation of $\frac{1}{4}$, $\frac{1}{4}$, $\frac{1}{4}$. This leads to the typical configuration in which any given atom is surrounded by four nearest neighbors occupying the corners of a regular tetrahedron. A discussion of the crystal structure of particular elements or compounds will be postponed until the physical properties of such materials are being considered.

1-3. Miller indices

The lattice points forming a space-lattice may be thought of as occupying various sets of parallel planes; some examples of dividing a lattice into such sets of planes are given in Fig. 1-7. With reference to the axes of the "unit cell," each set of planes has a particular orientation. In order to specify the orientation, one employs the so-called Miller indices; these are defined as follows: Suppose a particular plane of a given set has intercepts pa, qb, and rc with the crystal axes (Fig. 1-8). The Miller indices of the set of planes are then given by three numbers h, k, l such that

$$h : k : l = 1/p : 1/q : 1/r \qquad (1\text{-}1)$$

with the condition that h, k, and l are the smallest integers satisfying (1-1), i.e., h, k, and l have no common factor > 1. We shall adhere to the rather general practice of using the notation (hkl) for a particular set of planes. We emphasize once again that these indices refer not to a particular plane

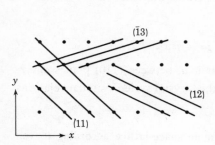

Fig. 1-7. Various ways of dividing a square lattice in atomic planes; the Miller indices are indicated.

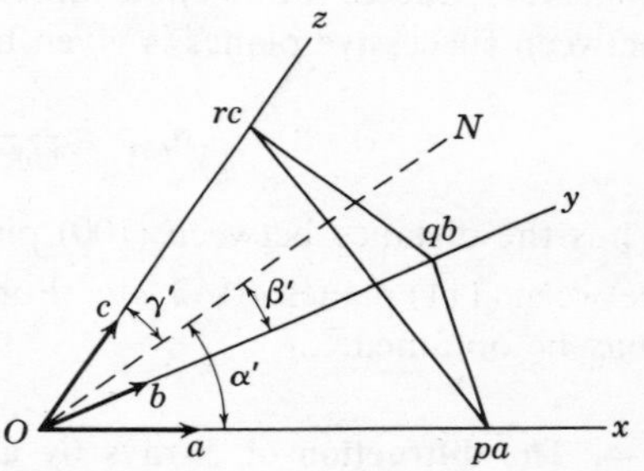

Fig. 1-8. Illustrating a plane with intercepts pa, qb, and rc; ON is the normal to the plane.

but to a set of parallel planes. One or more of the indices may be negative when the corresponding intercepts are negative; they are represented in a form such as this: $(\bar{h}kl)$, $(h\bar{k}\bar{l})$ etc. Miller indices for some planes are given in Fig. 1-7.

When the indices are shown enclosed by braces, such as $\{hkl\}$, they refer to planes which in the crystal are equivalent even though their Miller indices may differ. For example, in a cubic lattice all cube faces are equivalent; in order to specify this group of planes, one writes $\{100\}$, which includes the planes (100), (010), (001), ($\bar{1}$00), (0$\bar{1}$0), (00$\bar{1}$).

In order to specify a certain direction in a crystal, one employs three indices u, v, w enclosed in square brackets $[u, v, w]$; the indices are integers and have no common factor larger than unity. The direction specified by this symbol is obtained as follows: Move from the origin over a distance ua along the a-axis; vb along the b-axis and wc along the c-axis. The vector connecting the origin with the point so obtained is then the direction specified by the symbol $[uvw]$. Thus, in a cubic crystal the direction of the x-axis is indicated by [100], the y-axis by [010], etc. A full set of equivalent directions in a crystal is represented by a symbol of the kind $\langle uvw \rangle$.

We may note here that the Miller indices of a set of planes are related to the direction cosines of the normal to these planes. Denoting the angles between the normal ON in Fig. 1-8 and the crystal axes respectively by α', β' and γ', one obtains the relation

$$\cos \alpha' : \cos \beta' : \cos \gamma' = (1/pa) : (1/qb) : (1/rc)$$
$$= (h/a) : (k/b) : (l/c) \qquad (1\text{-}2)$$

Also, the distance between successive planes in a set (hkl) is determined by the Miller indices. It is evident already from Fig. 1-7 that as the value of one or more of the Miller indices is increased, the distance between the planes is reduced. For a cubic lattice the reader may show that the distance between successive planes is given by

$$d_{hkl} = \frac{a}{(h^2 + k^2 + l^2)^{1/2}} \qquad (1\text{-}3)$$

Thus the distance between (100) planes is a, between (110) planes $a/\sqrt{2}$, between (111) planes $a/\sqrt{3}$, etc. For other crystal systems similar relations may be obtained.[5]

1-4. The diffraction of X-rays by a simple space-lattice according to von Laue

It is well known that when a beam of light passes through a screen containing a regular pattern of holes, interference phenomena may be observed if the distance between the holes is of the same order as the wavelength of the light employed. The diffraction of X-rays by the atoms in a solid is a completely analogous phenomenon, the wavelength of the electromagnetic radiation in this case being of the order of interatomic distances in solids, i.e., of the order of 1 Å. The use of X-rays as a tool for investigating the structure of crystals was first suggested by von Laue in 1912 and was later further developed by W. H. and W. L. Bragg. The principles of X-ray diffraction will now be discussed briefly.

When an electron is subjected to a monochromatic beam of X-rays, the electric field vector of the radiation forces it to carry out vibrations of a frequency equal to that of the incident beam. As a consequence of the acceleration of the electron, it in turn will emit radiation of the same wavelength in all directions. Thus, in an atom all electrons contribute to the scattering of X-rays in this fashion. (Inelastic scattering will be taken up in later chapters.)

A few remarks about the scattering by a single atom may be in order. It is obvious that when the wavelength of the incident radiation is large compared with the dimensions of an atom, the wavelets emitted by the

[5] See for example C. S. Barrett, *Structure of Metals.* 2d ed., McGraw-Hill, New York, 1952, p. 633.

electrons in the atom are nearly all in phase. However, X-rays used in diffraction work have a wavelength of the same order of magnitude as the atomic diameter (this is necessary to obtain a diffraction pattern). Thus the wavelets emitted by the electrons in an atom are in general out of phase. Consequently, these wavelets will partially cancel each other by interference and the amplitude of the radiation scattered by an atom containing Z electrons is less than that scattered by a free electron times the number of electrons in the atom. We can, however, consider the atom as a scattering center with an effective atomic scattering factor f_s which is given by the ratio of the amplitude of the wave scattered by the

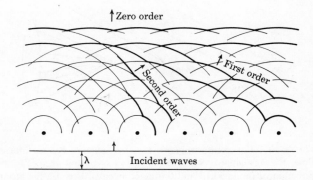

Fig. 1-9. Reinforcement of scattered waves producing diffracted beams of different orders.

atom and that of the wave scattered by a free electron (for the same incident beam). This problem will be discussed further in Sec. 1-6.

In crystals we are concerned with the scattering by a large number of atoms arranged according to a particular pattern. For simplicity, let us consider a one-dimensional row of atoms with interatomic distance a. Assuming the incident wave crests to be parallel to the row of atoms, we obtain a picture such as Fig. 1-9. The envelope of the wavelets emitted by the individual atoms forms new wave crests and we see that besides a beam propagated in the same direction as the incident beam (zero-order) there are a few diffracted beams of other direction (first-order, second-order, etc.). Thus, even though the individual atoms scatter radiation in all directions, there are only a few directions in which these wavelets reinforce each other. The condition for such a diffracted beam to exist may easily be found as follows: In Fig. 1-10, suppose that AB is a wave crest of the incident beam, and CD is a wave crest of the diffracted beam. Then, because a wave crest is an assembly of points of the same phase, we must require that the path difference $(AC - BD)$ shall equal an integer times the wavelength of the beam. Thus a diffracted beam is observed only if

$$a(\cos \alpha - \cos \alpha_0) = e\lambda, \quad \text{with} \quad e = 0, 1, 2, 3, \ldots \qquad (1\text{-}4)$$

For given values of α_0, a, λ, and e there is only one possible value for α. We note that such a value exists only if at the same time $\cos \alpha \leqslant 1$. Suppose then that to a certain value of e there corresponds a value α. The direction of the diffracted beam then forms a cone of directions with the row of atoms as axis, as indicated in Fig. 1-10. Thus a monochromatic

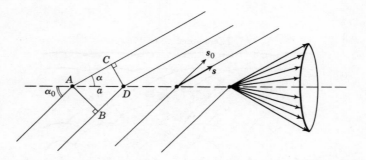

Fig. 1-10. For reinforcement $AC-BD$ should be an integer times the wavelength. The vectors s_0 and s are unit vectors in the direction of the incident and diffracted beams. Because the atoms emit spherical waves, the possible directions of s form a cone about the array of atoms.

X-ray beam falling on a row of atoms gives rise to a family of cones representing the directions of diffracted beams.

Equation (1-4) may also be written in vector notation; if s_0 and s represent unit vectors, respectively, in the direction of the incident and scattered beam (Fig. 1-10), and if a represents the translation from A to D, we have

$$\boldsymbol{a} \cdot (\boldsymbol{s} - \boldsymbol{s}_0) = e\lambda \qquad (1\text{-}5)$$

For a two-dimensional space-lattice, two conditions of the type (1-5) must be satisfied. Each of these conditions gives rise to a set of cones for possible diffracted beams. Hence, if both must be satisfied, only those directions for a diffracted beam are possible that belong to one cone of the first group and to one of the second group. Thus the second condition strongly limits the number of possible diffracted beams, viz., to directions determined by intersecting lines of two direction cones.

Conditions become even more stringent for a three-dimensional lattice. Consider, for example, a simple space-lattice with a unit cell defined by the primitive translations a, b, and c. Then, for diffraction to occur, the following equations for the path differences must be satisfied:

$$a(\cos \alpha - \cos \alpha_0) = a \cdot (s - s_0) = e\lambda$$
$$b(\cos \beta - \cos \beta_0) = b \cdot (s - s_0) = f\lambda \qquad (1\text{-}6)$$
$$c(\cos \gamma - \cos \gamma_0) = c \cdot (s - s_0) = g\lambda$$

where e, f, and g are integers; α_0, β_0, γ_0 and α, β, γ represent, respectively, the angles between the incident and scattered beams and the axes a, b, c. These are the von Laue equations. It must be noted that for a given value of λ and an arbitrary direction of incidence s_0, it is in general not possible to find a direction s which satisfies (1-6). In other words, for a monochromatic X-ray beam falling on a crystal with an arbitrary direction of incidence, in general no diffraction is observed. This may readily be understood by remembering that for a two-dimensional lattice there exist only specific directions for a diffracted beam and these directions are in general not part of the direction cones determined by the third condition required for the three-dimensional case. Thus only for particular angles of incidence will diffraction be observed; it is exactly this limitation that makes X-ray diffraction a useful tool for investigating crystal structures. This point will become more clear when we discuss the Bragg formula below. Before doing this, it may be useful to rewrite (1-6) for the case of a simple cubic lattice. Assuming $a = b = c$, we obtain from (1-6) by squaring and adding

$$2a^2(1 - \cos \alpha \cos \alpha_0 - \cos \beta \cos \beta_0 - \cos \gamma \cos \gamma_0) = \lambda^2(e^2 + f^2 + g^2)$$

Now, if ϕ represents the angle between the incident and scattered beams, we may write

$$2(1 - \cos \phi) = 4 \sin^2 (\phi/2) = (\lambda^2/a^2)(e^2 + f^2 + g^2) \qquad (1\text{-}7)$$

In this form the von Laue equation is closely related to the Bragg formula.

1-5. X-ray diffraction according to Bragg

Bragg considered the problem of X-ray diffraction from a somewhat different point of view. Although in itself it is not completely satisfactory because it involves certain assumptions that are not immediately obvious, it gives results identical with the Laue treatment and is therefore justified. Bragg considers X-ray diffraction from a crystal as a problem of reflection from atomic planes. In Fig. 1-11 consider a set of parallel atomic planes of Miller indices (hkl), the distance between successive planes being d_{hkl}. If we assume with Bragg that an X-ray beam is reflected by an atomic plane according to Snell's law (i.e., incident beam, reflected beam, and normal in one plane, and angle of incidence equals angle of reflection) we see that rays 1 and 2 can reinforce each other in the reflected direction only if their path difference is an integer times λ. This is necessary because wave crests are points of equal phase. Thus from the figure we find as condition for reflection from the set of planes under consideration,

$$2d_{hkl} \sin \theta = n\lambda \quad \text{with} \quad n = 0, 1, 2, 3, \ldots \qquad (1\text{-}8)$$

The value of n indicates the order of reflection. This condition shows immediately that for given values of d_{hkl} and λ, and n having integer values, only a particular angle θ would produce such a reflection. Thus we arrive at the same conclusion as above, viz., that a beam of monochromatic X-rays incident on a crystal with an arbitrary angle θ is in general not reflected. Also, because $\sin \theta \leqslant 1$ and $d \simeq 10^{-8}$ cm, we see that reflection can be observed only for λ of the order

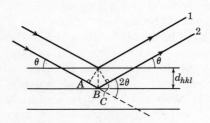

Fig. 1-11. Beams reflected from successive planes will reinforce each other if $AB + BC$ equals an integer times the wavelength; this leads immediately to equation (1-8).

of 10^{-8} cm or less. It is for this reason that X-rays are used in these experiments.

We shall now show that condition (1-8) as given by Bragg is equivalent to (1-6) derived from the von Laue treatment. For simplicity let us consider a simple cubic lattice, so that we must compare (1-7) and (1-8). First of all it is evident from the definition of ϕ and from Fig. 1-11 that $\phi/2 = \theta$. Furthermore, making use of expression (1-3) for the distance between successive planes of Miller indices (hkl) in a cubic lattice, we may write (1-8) as

$$2a \sin \theta = \lambda n(h^2 + k^2 + l^2)^{1/2} \qquad (1\text{-}9)$$

Thus, identifying the integers $e, f,$ and g, respectively, with $nh, nk,$ and nl, a diffracted beam defined in the von Laue treatment by the integers e, f, g may be interpreted as the nth order reflection from a set of planes (hkl) in the Bragg theory. The order of the reflection n is simply equal to the largest common factor of the numbers e, f, g.

1-6. The atomic scattering factor

So far, we have considered only the condition for diffraction from simple structures for which only the corner points of the unit cell are occupied. It will be evident that the intensity of a beam diffracted by an actual crystal will depend on the grouping of atoms in the unit cell and on the scattering power of these atoms. Conversely, the intensity of a diffracted beam should provide information about the configuration of atoms in the unit cell and therefore must be considered an important quantity in X-ray diffraction work. In the present section we shall consider the atomic scattering factor; in the next section the relationship between the intensity of a diffracted beam and the atomic configuration in the unit cell will be discussed.

In the beginning of Sec. 1-5 we mentioned that the atomic scattering factor f_s is defined as the ratio of the amplitude of an electromagnetic wave scattered by an atom and that of a wave scattered by a free electron. To calculate this factor for a given wavelength λ we refer to Fig. 1-12. Let A be the center of the atom and let us consider an incident and a scattered beam making an angle of 2θ with each other. We may then choose the z-axis of a polar coordinate system r, ϑ, ϕ along AN, where AN is the normal to the "reflecting plane" BAC. If the electronic charge distribution of the atom is assumed to be spherically symmetric, a function $\rho(r)$ may be introduced representing the density of electrons at a distance r from the nucleus A. Thus the number of electrons in a

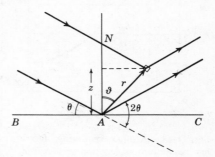

Fig. 1-12. Calculation of the atomic scattering factor. AN is the normal to the reflecting plane BAC. The vectors are all drawn in the plane of the paper, so that the azimuthal angle ϕ has not been indicated.

volume element at r is equal to $\rho(r)r^2\,dr\,\sin\vartheta\,d\vartheta\,d\phi$. Consider now the phase difference between the rays scattered by this element of charge and the rays that would be scattered if the same charge were located in point A. From what has been said in the preceding section it follows that this phase difference is determined only by $z = r\cos\vartheta$, and in fact equal to

$$\varphi = (4\pi z/\lambda)\sin\theta = (4\pi/\lambda)r\cos\vartheta\sin\theta \qquad (1\text{-}10)$$

On the other hand, the absolute value of the amplitude of the scattered wave is of course independent of the location of the charge and simply proportional to the amount of charge. The ratio of the complex amplitude of the wave scattered by the element under consideration and the amplitude of the wave that would be scattered by the same charge in A is thus simply $e^{i\varphi}$. The atomic scattering factor is therefore

$$f_s = \int_{r=0}^{\infty}\int_{\vartheta=0}^{\pi}\int_{\phi=0}^{2\pi} e^{i\varphi}\rho(r)r^2\,dr\,\sin\vartheta\,d\vartheta\,d\phi$$

Substituting (1-10) for φ, the integral becomes

$$f_s = \int_0^{\infty} 4\pi r^2\rho(r)\frac{\sin kr}{kr}\,dr \quad \text{with} \quad k = (4\pi/\lambda)\sin\theta \qquad (1\text{-}11)$$

We note that $\int 4\pi r^2 \rho(r)\,dr$ is equal to the total number of electrons Z in the atom. Hence the atomic scattering factor is equal to Z only for $\theta = 0$, and $< Z$ for all other angles of scattering. From (1-11) it follows that a calculation of f_s requires a knowledge of the charge distribution in the atom. As an example, we give in Fig. 1-13 the atomic scattering factor for magnesium as a function of $(\sin \theta)/\lambda$. The charge distributions on which such curves are based may be obtained from a Hartree approximation or for atoms with a large number of electrons (beyond rubidium) from a statistical atomic model developed by Thomas and by Fermi.[6] In some cases, viz., for solids with simple structures, the atomic scattering factor may be determined experimentally from intensity mea-

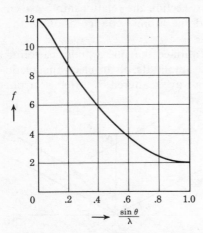

Fig. 1-13. Atomic scattering factor for magnesium as function of $(\sin \theta)/\lambda$, where λ is expressed in Angstroms.

surements. The agreement with the theoretical curves is generally good.

1-7. X-ray intensity and atomic configuration of the unit cell

To illustrate the problem to be discussed here, let us consider a particularly simple example. In Fig. 1-14 let us suppose, to begin with, that only the corners of the cubic unit cell are occupied by atoms. For such a simple cubic lattice, (which, by the way, does not occur in nature) the first-order reflection from the set of planes (001) would be observed for a particular Bragg angle θ, determined in accordance with (1-8) by

$$2d_{001} \sin \theta = 2\,a \sin \theta = \lambda$$

For this reflection, the path difference between rays 1 and 2 is equal to one wavelength. Suppose now, that the unit cell contains also an atom

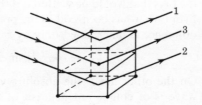

Fig. 1-14. Illustrating that the first-order reflection from the planes {100} is absent in a body-centered cubic lattice. The path difference between 1 and 2 is λ; between 1 and 3 it is $\lambda/2$.

at the center of the cube; we may then ask the question as to how this

[6] For values of the scattering factors of atoms and ions see R. W. James and G. W. Brindley, *Z. Krist.* **78**, 470, (1931); *Internationale Tabellen zur Bestimmung von Kristallstrukturen*, Vol. 2, Bornträger, Berlin, 1935.

will influence the intensity of the first-order reflection mentioned above. Addition of an atom at the center of the unit cell is equivalent to inserting planes halfway between the (001) planes; furthermore, the density of atoms per unit area on these planes is exactly the same as that for the (001) planes. Now, if the path difference between rays 1 and 2 is λ, the path difference between 1 and 3 is $\lambda/2$. From this, it is evident that the intensity of the first-order reflection from the (001) planes in a body-centered cubic lattice is zero, at any rate if all atoms have the same scattering factor. In other words, for an element crystalizing in a b.c.c. lattice, the first-order reflection from planes such as (001) will be absent. Similar considerations may be held for other reflections and other atomic configurations. This leads to a number of characteristic absences from which it is possible to draw conclusions regarding the atomic configuration in the unit cell. If the central atom is different from those at the corners, the intensity of the reflection under consideration will not vanish completely, but will give rise to a relatively weak line. For the second-order reflection, the path difference between 1 and 2 is 2λ, that between 1 and 3 is λ; in that case, then, all rays will reinforce each other and this reflection will be present in the b.c.c. structure.

The problem will now be discussed quantitatively. Let us consider the intensity of an X-ray beam diffracted by a crystal with a unit cell of primitive translations a, b, c. The conditions that must be satisfied for the waves emitted by the atoms at the corners of this unit cell to be in phase are given by (1-6); it will be assumed that these equations are fulfilled. Furthermore, taking a particular corner atom as origin, let the coordinates of the other atoms in the unit cell be represented by vectors of the type

$$r_k = u_k a + v_k b + w_k c \qquad (1\text{-}12)$$

In analogy with the von Laue equations (1-6) it then follows that the phase difference between the beam scattered by atom k and the one scattered by the atom at the origin is given by

$$\phi_k = (2\pi/\lambda) r_k \cdot (s - s_0) \qquad (1\text{-}13)$$

where s_0 and s are unit vectors, respectively, in the direction of the incident and scattered beam. Substituting (1-12) and making use of (1-6), we obtain

$$\varphi_k = 2\pi(u_k e + v_k f + w_k g) \qquad (1\text{-}14)$$

It is convenient to introduce the structure factor F, defined in analogy with the atomic scattering factor as follows: F is the ratio of the amplitude of the wave scattered by all atoms in a unit cell and that scattered by a free electron for the same incident beam. In view of (1-13) the complex amplitude produced by atom k is $f_{sk}e^{i\varphi_k}$ where f_{sk} is the atomic scattering factor for atom k. Thus the structure factor may be written

$$F = \sum_k f_{sk}e^{i\varphi_k} = \sum_k f_{sk}e^{2\pi i(u_k e + v_k f + w_k g)} \qquad (1\text{-}15)$$

where the summation extends over all atoms in the unit cell. In connection with this summation we must emphasize that an atom at a corner belongs to eight unit cells, so that such an atom in the summation counts for only $\frac{1}{8}$. In other words, all atoms at the corners together produce only one term. We may also look at this problem in this fashion: if we add vectorially the amplitudes of the waves scattered by the atoms in a unit cell, we obtain a picture such as in Fig. 1-15, where F is the resultant amplitude. Each amplitude has two components, $f_{sk} \cos \varphi_k$ and $f_{sk} \sin \varphi_k$ and the intensity, which is proportional to the square of the amplitude, then becomes proportional to

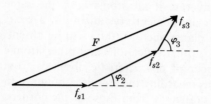

Fig. 1-15. Showing the vectorial addition of the amplitudes of the waves scattered by the different atoms in the unit cell. F is the resultant of the individual f_{sk}'s.

$$F^2 = (\sum_k f_{sk} \cos \varphi_k)^2 + (\sum_k f_{sk} \sin \varphi_k)^2 \qquad (1\text{-}16)$$

This expression is identical with $|F|^2 = FF^*$, where F is given by (1-15) and F^* represents the complex conjugate of F. The values of the φ_k's are given by (1-14).

For the particular case that all atoms in the unit cell are the same, all f_{sk}'s are equal and one may write

$$F = f_s \sum_k e^{2\pi i(u_k e + v_k f + w_k g)} \qquad (1\text{-}17)$$

A simple example may illustrate the conclusions one may draw from the above treatment. For a body-centered cubic lattice of similar atoms, the summations extend over the values $u, v, w = 0, 0, 0$ and $u, v, w = \frac{1}{2}, \frac{1}{2}, \frac{1}{2}$ (all corner atoms together represent one atom). According to (1-14) $\varphi_1 = 0$ and $\varphi_2 = \pi(e + f + g)$. Hence, for a body-centered cubic lattice of similar atoms we have, according to (1-16),

$$|F|^2 = f_s^2 \{[1 + \cos \pi(e + f + g)]^2 + \sin^2 \pi(e + f + g)\}$$

We conclude that if $(e + f + g)$ is odd, $|F|^2 = 0$ and the corresponding reflection is absent. On the other hand, for $(e + f + g)$ even, we have $|F|^2 = (2f_s)^2$ and the reflection is present. We leave it as a problem to show that in a face-centered cubic lattice all reflections will be missing for which the numbers e, f, g are mixed odd and even, such as 100, 211, 324, etc. The results of such considerations for cubic lattices of similar atoms are represented in Fig. 1-16 in the form in which they appear as lines in

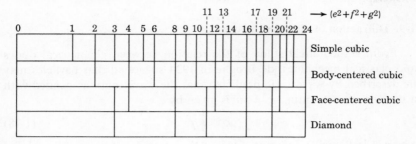

Fig. 1-16. Powder patterns for different cubic crystals, illustrating characteristic reflections and absences for each type. [By permission from C. S. Barrett, *Structure of Metals*, McGraw-Hill 2d ed., 1952, p. 136]

a powder-method experiment. Because of the characteristic line pattern produced by each of these structures, they are readily recognized.

1-8. Experimental methods of X-ray diffraction

Because of lack of space, it is not possible to discuss in any detail the experimental techniques employed in X-ray diffraction work, but a few remarks may be in order. There are essentially three methods which may be employed, as may be seen from the Bragg formula (1-8). If one uses monochromatic X-rays, equation (1-8) cannot be satisfied for an arbitrary value of θ. This has led to the rotating-crystal method, whereby reflection occurs for a discrete set of θ values. This method can of course be applied only if single crystals of reasonable size are available. If this is not the case, one can employ monochromatic X-rays when the sample is in powder form and held in a fixed position. The reason that a diffraction pattern is observed is that there are always enough crystallites of the right orientation available to satisfy the Bragg relation. By a proper analysis it is possible to identify the indices (*hkl*) of a particular reflection, and this enables one to calculate the interatomic parameters when the wavelength of the employed radiation is known. The characteristic absences, discussed in the preceding section, allow one in many cases to determine the atomic configuration of the unit cell at a glance. Finally, there is the von Laue method, in which the sample (a single crystal) is held stationary in a beam of white X-rays. Each set of planes then "chooses" its own wavelength to satisfy the Bragg relation. This method is not so useful for the determination of lattice parameters as the other two because the wavelength of a particular reflection is unknown. On the other hand, it is used in the determination of crystal symmetry. For a review of the experimental techniques we refer to the references quoted at the end of this chapter.

1-9. Diffraction of electrons by crystals

From a theoretical study of the relation between geometrical optics and classical mechanics, de Broglie in 1924 suggested that particles may be described by waves. He predicted that the wavelength associated with a particle of momentum $p = mv$ is given by

$$\lambda = h/p \qquad (1\text{-}18)$$

where h is Planck's constant. One of the most direct pieces of evidence of the wave aspect of particles was provided by the electron diffraction experiments of Davisson and Germer in 1927.[7] They concluded that if one associates a wavelength with the electrons given by (1-18), the diffraction pattern obtained can be interpreted in exactly the same way as the X-ray diffraction patterns. As long as the velocity of the electrons is small compared with the velocity of light, the wavelength of the electrons may be expressed in terms of the accelerating voltage V as follows:

$$\tfrac{1}{2}mv^2 = eV \quad \text{or} \quad \lambda = h/(2meV)^{1/2} \simeq (150/V)^{1/2} \qquad (1\text{-}19)$$

where λ is obtained in Angstroms if V is expressed in volts. Note that only 150 volts are required to produce electrons of a wavelength of 1 Å, in contrast with X-rays, which require approximately 12,000 volts for 1 Å. Although Davisson and Germer in their original experiments used electrons of 30–600 ev, modern diffraction equipment employs usually voltages of the order of 50 kilovolts, corresponding to $\lambda \simeq 0.05$ Å. In such cases, a relativistic correction must be applied to (1-19); for 50 kev electrons this correction lowers the wavelength by approximately 2.5 per cent.

The atomic scattering factor for electrons has been discussed by Born[8] and a simplified treatment has been given by Mott.[9] In contrast with X-rays, electrons are scattered by the nucleus as well as by the electrons in the atoms. For a spherical charge distribution one can show that the scattering factor is given by

$$E(\theta) = \frac{me^2}{2h^2}(Z - f_s)\frac{\lambda^2}{\sin^2\theta} \qquad (1\text{-}20)$$

Here f_s is the scattering factor for X-rays, Z is the nuclear charge, and θ is the Bragg angle. As for X-rays, the scattering factor for electrons

[7] C. Davisson and L. H. Germer, *Phys. Rev.*, **30**, 707 (1927).
[8] M. Born, *Z. Physik*, **38**, 803 (1926).
[9] N. F. Mott, *Proc. Roy. Soc.*, **127A**, 685 (1930).

decreases with increasing values of θ. However, there is a considerable difference between X-rays and electrons in that electrons are scattered much more efficiently by atoms than are X-rays. In fact, atoms scatter electrons more strongly by several powers of ten for the energies involved. At normal incidence, an electron of about 50 kev has a penetration depth for elastic scattering of only about 500 Å, while for the small angles of incidence used in reflection techniques this may be only about 50 Å measured perpendicular to the surface. It is evident, therefore, that electron diffraction is particularly useful in investigating the structure of thin surface layers such as oxide layers on metals. Such layers would not be detected by X-ray diffraction because the patterns obtained are characteristic for the bulk material. We may note that diffraction of electrons by gases requires much shorter exposure times than does X-ray diffraction, again as a result of the relatively high efficiency of scattering of electrons by atoms.

1-10. Diffraction of neutrons by crystals

We have seen above that for X-rays of 1 Å one requires energies of the order of 10^4 ev, for electrons of 1 Å about 10^2 ev. Now, the mass of a neutron is about 2000 times as large as that of an electron, so that according to the de Broglie relation (1-18) the wavelength associated with a neutron is about 1/2000 that for an electron of the same velocity. Thus the energy of a neutron required to give 1 Å is of the order of only 0.1 ev. Such neutrons can be obtained from a chain-reacting pile, and diffraction from crystals may be observed.[10] Neutrons are scattered essentially by the nuclei of the atoms, except when they are magnetic (see below). Now, the radius of an atomic nucleus is of the order of 10^{-13} cm, and as a consequence, the atomic scattering factor is nearly independent of the scattering angle, because $\lambda \gg 10^{-13}$ cm. Also, the scattering power does not vary in a regular manner with the atomic number, so that light elements such as hydrogen and carbon still produce relatively strong scattering. The scattering of X-rays by light elements is in contrast, of course, relatively weak. Thus the positions of such atoms in crystalline solids may be determined from neutron diffraction experiments.[11] Another important aspect of neutron diffraction is the fact that scattering from neighboring elements in the periodic system may differ appreciably. For example, neutron diffraction allows one to detect with relative ease ordered phases of an alloy such as FeCo, whereas their detection by X-rays is difficult.

[10] W. H. Zinn, *Phys. Rev.*, **70**, 102A (1946); **71**, 752 (1947); L. B. Borst, A. J. Ulrich, C. L. Osborne, and B. Hasbrouck, *Phys. Rev.*, **70**, 108A (1946); **70**, 557 (1946).,
[11] C. G. Shull, E. O. Wollan, G. A. Morton, and W. L. Davidson, *Phys. Rev.*, **73** 830 (1948).

A particularly important aspect of neutron diffraction is their use in investigating the magnetic structure of solids. This is a result of the interaction between the magnetic moment of the neutron and that of the atoms concerned. In a paramagnetic substance, in which the magnetic moments are randomly oriented in space, this leads to incoherent scattering, resulting in a diffuse background. This background of magnetic scattering is then superimposed on the lines produced by the nuclear scattering mentioned above. In a ferromagnetic substance in which the magnetic moments within a domain are lined up in parallel, this diffuse background is absent. It occurred to Smart that neutron diffraction

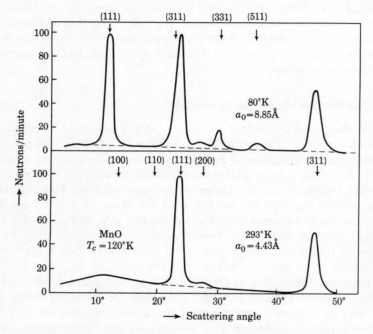

Fig. 1-17. Neutron diffraction patterns for MnO at room temperature and at 80°K. The magnetic unit cell is twice as large as the chemical one. [After Shull and Smart, ref. 12]

might provide a direct means of detecting antiferromagnetism (see Chapter 19).[12] In an antiferromagnetic solid, the magnetic moments of particular pairs of atoms are aligned antiparallel and hence, from the point of view of the neutron, such atoms would appear to be different. In Fig. 1-17 we show a neutron diffraction pattern obtained for powdered MnO at room temperature and at 80°K; the Curie temperature is 122°K and only below this temperature is MnO antiferromagnetic. The room

[12] C. G. Shull and J. S. Smart, *Phys. Rev.*, **76**, 1256 (1949).

temperature pattern shows coherent diffraction peaks as would be expected from a lattice of the NaCl structure. The diffuse background of magnetic scattering is also visible. The low-temperature pattern shows the same peaks, but in addition strong magnetic reflections at positions that one would not expect on the basis of the chemical structure of the unit cell. If, however, one introduces a magnetic unit cell twice as large as the chemical one, these reflections can be identified. Such a cell indeed corresponds to an antiferromagnetic substance.

The diffraction of particles is, of course, not confined to electrons and neutrons, but may also be observed for atoms and molecules, the corresponding wavelength being given by the de Broglie relation. Diffraction has been observed for example for H, He, H_2, and other atoms.[13]

1-11. Interatomic forces and the classification of solids

A few remarks of a qualitative nature may be made here about the forces acting between atoms or molecules in solids. We shall not enter into any detail since certain aspects of this topic will be treated in later chapters.

From the very existence of solids one may draw two general conclusions: (1) there must act attractive forces between the atoms or molecules in a solid which keep them together; (2) there must be repulsive forces acting between the atoms as well, since large external pressures are required to compress a solid to any appreciable extent. (Both conclusions also apply to liquids). In order to illustrate the importance of both types of forces, let us consider the simplest system in this respect, viz., a single pair of atoms A and B which form a stable chemical compound. Without paying attention to the physical origin of the forces between the two atoms, let us assume that the potential energy of atom B due to the presence of atom A is given by an expression of the type

$$E(r) = -\alpha/r^n + \beta/r^m \tag{1-21}$$

where r is the distance between the nuclei of the two atoms; α, β, m, and n are constants characteristic for the AB molecule. The zero of energy is chosen such that for infinite separation $E = 0$. The first term, which is negative, corresponds to the energy associated with the forces of attraction, the second (positive) term corresponds to the forces of repulsion. In fact, the force between the two atoms as function of r is given by

$$F(r) = -dE/dr = -\frac{n\alpha}{r^{n+1}} + \frac{m\beta}{r^{m+1}} \tag{1-22}$$

The energy and the force between two atoms A and B which form a

[13] For a review see, for example, I. Estermann, *Revs. Mod. Phys.*, **18**, 300 (1946).

chemical compound are represented in Fig. 1-18. The stable configuration for the system corresponds to the minimum in the $E(r)$ curve, which occurs for a particular separation $r = r_0$. The corresponding energy $E(r_0)$ is negative; thus the positive quantity $D = -E(r_0)$ is the dissociation energy of the molecule, i.e., the energy required to separate the two atoms. Dissociation may occur, for example, at high temperatures or as a result of other processes in which the molecule can absorb sufficient energy.

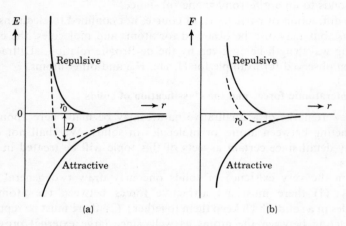

Fig. 1-18. Schematic representation of the energy (a) and force (b) between two atoms as function of their separation r. The dashed curves are the sums of the attractive and repulsive curves.

The dissociation energies are of the order of one or a few electron volts.

Assuming that the energy curve exhibits a minimum, one may express the equilibrium distance r_0 and the corresponding binding energy $E(r_0)$ in terms of the constants α, β, m, and n by making use of the condition

$$(dE/dr)_{r=r_0} = 0, \quad \text{i.e.,} \quad r_0^{m-n} = (m/n)(\beta/\alpha) \qquad (1\text{-}23)$$

According to (1-22) this condition is equivalent to the requirement that the attractive and repulsive forces balance, i.e., $F(r_0) = 0$. Substituting from (1-23) into (1-21) one obtains for the energy in the equilibrium state

$$E(r_0) = -\alpha/r_0^n + \beta/r_0^m = -(\alpha/r_0^n)(1 - n/m) \qquad (1\text{-}24)$$

Note that although the attractive and repulsive forces are equal in equilibrium, the attractive and repulsive energies are not equal since $n \neq m$. In fact, if $m \gg n$, the total binding energy is essentially determined by the energy of attraction $-\alpha/r_0^n$.

As one may expect already by looking at Fig. 1-18, a minimum in the energy curve is possible only if $m > n$; thus the formation of a chemical bond requires that the repulsive forces be of shorter range than the attractive ones. This may be shown readily by employing the condition that $(d^2E/dr^2)_{r=r_0} > 0$ if $E(r)$ must have a minimum at r_0. In fact, this condition leads to

$$-n(n+1)\alpha/r_0^{n+2} + m(m+1)\beta/r_0^{m+2} > 0$$

which upon substitution of r_0 from (1-23) immediately gives

$$m > n \qquad\qquad (1\text{-}25)$$

Although the energy can in general not be represented accurately by a power function of the type (1-21), the above treatment provides some useful qualitative conclusions which may be extended to solids. An application of this type of reasoning is given in Chapter 5 for ionic crystals.

The forces acting between the atoms in solids are electrostatic in nature; they are determined essentially by the way in which the outer electrons of the composing atoms are distributed in space. The physical properties of solids are determined to a large extent by the electron distribution, and it is thus possible on an empirical basis to divide solids into different groups corresponding to different types of electron distributions. For a discussion of the nature of chemical binding we must refer the reader to the literature.[14] One may distinguish between the following extreme types:

1. Ionic crystals (NaCl, KF)
2. Valence crystals (diamond, SiC)
3. Metals (Cu, Ag, Ma)
4. van der Waals crystals (argon, many organic crystals)

It should be said from the outset that many intermediate cases occur and in general one must be somewhat careful in employing very specific labels.

1. *Ionic crystals.* In ionic crystals one or more electrons of one type of atoms are transferred to another, leading to the formation of positive and negative ions; for example, NaCl may be considered as to be built up of Na^+ and Cl^- ions. The cohesive energy of these crystals is to a large extent determined by the Coulomb interaction between the hetero-polar ions, as discussed in Chapter 5. At elevated temperatures they exhibit ionic conductivity. Associated with the existence of positive and negative ions is a strong optical absorption coefficient in the infrared. Ionic crystals may be cleaved readily.

2. *Valence crystals.* In valence crystals neighboring atoms share their valence electrons under the formation of strong homopolar or covalent

[14] L. Pauling, *Nature of the Chemical Bond*, 2d ed., Cornell University Press, Ithaca, 1945; J. A. A. Ketelaar, *Chemical Constitution*, Elsevier, New York, 1953.

bonds. Some further remarks may be found in Sec. 13-1. Valence crystals are very hard (diamond, carborundum), are difficult to cleave, and have a poor electrical and thermal conductivity.

3. *Metals.* In metallic crystals the outer electrons of the atoms have a high degree of mobility, to which these materials owe their high electrical and thermal conductivity. In a simplified way one may say that the cohesive energy of metals is provided essentially by the Coulomb interaction between the positive ions and the negative "smeared out" charge of the conduction electrons. The cohesive energy of metals will be discussed briefly in Sec. 10-13.

4. *van der Waals crystals.* The atoms of the rare gases such as argon have little or no tendency to give up electrons or share them with others. In the liquid and solid state the forces of attraction are the so-called dispersion forces,[15] which arise in the following way: The combination of the moving negative electrons and the nucleus of an atom may be considered a system of fluctuating dipoles. The interaction between these dipoles associated with neighboring atoms then gives rise to a relatively weak binding (see Sec. 5-6). In organic crystals the cohesive energy is provided by dispersion forces as well as by the interaction between permanent dipoles (see Sec. 6-1) of neighboring molecules; the totality of such forces is referred to as van der Waals forces. Associated with the relative weakness of these forces are low boiling and melting points.

Between the extreme groups mentioned above, there are many intermediate cases. An interesting intermediate group of solids are the semiconductors. Semiconducting elements such as Ge and Si are intermediate between valence crystals and metals. The bonds are essentially homopolar and at absolute zero the elements are insulators, as diamond. However, the electrons forming the bonds between neighboring atoms are much less strongly bound than in diamond; thus already at room temperature these elements exhibit a certain amount of electrical conductivity, which increases as the temperature is raised. These elements are further discussed in Chapter 13. Ionic crystals may also become semiconducting by introducing impurities, or when the composition deviates from that represented by the chemical formula ("nonstoichiometric" compounds). These are discussed in Chapter 15.

A classification of solids given by Seitz[16] is represented in Fig. 1-19 (with some slight modifications); examples of intermediate cases are indicated. The upper row refers to elements, the lower one to solids

[15] For an elementary discussion, see, for example, M. Born, *Atomic Physics*, 5th ed., Hafner, New York, 1951.

[16] F. Seitz, *The Modern Theory of Solids*, McGraw-Hill, New York, 1940, p. 75.

containing more than one type of atom; the two groups meet in the van der Waals crystals (argon as an element and CH_4 as a compound would be examples). Between the true alloys and ionic crystals there is a group of intermetallic compounds for which the composing metallic components have different tendencies for giving up electrons (Mg_3Sb_2).

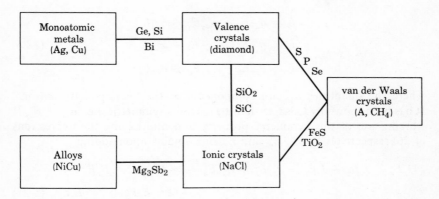

Fig. 1-19. Classification of solids, indicating intermediate cases.

1-12. Anisotropy of the physical properties of single crystals

The physical properties of single crystals in general depend on the direction along which they are measured relative to the crystal axes; this phenomenon is called anisotropy. Some examples are the following: crystals do not grow in the form of spheres, but in polyhedra; certain types of atomic planes dissolve more readily than others; the coefficient of thermal expansion of Zn is 6.39×10^{-5} along the hexagonal axis and 1.41×10^{-5} per degree C perpendicular to it; the specific resistivities of Zn parallel to the hexagonal axis and perpendicular to it are, respectively, $\rho_\parallel = 6.06 \times 10^{-6}$ and $\rho_\perp = 5.83 \times 10^{-6}$ ohm/cm. The reason for the anisotropy of the physical properties of crystals must be sought in the regular stacking of atoms. Thus as one passes through a crystalline arrangement of atoms or molecules along a given direction, one meets atoms or groups of atoms at different intervals and from different angles than one would along another direction. Single molecules are also anisotropic; however, in normal liquids or gases the orientation of the molecules is random and the physical properties become independent of the direction along which they are measured (isotropic) as long as a large number of molecules is involved or when a time average is taken for a single molecule. Polycrystalline materials with a completely random distribution of the grain orientation are also isotropic.

As an example of anisotropy in a single crystal let us consider the electrical conductivity in which an electric field E gives rise to a current I. In general, the current vector will not have the same direction as the electric vector. Thus, assuming a linear relationship between cause and effect, we may write for the current components relative to an arbitrarily chosen Cartesian coordinate system

$$I_x = \sigma_{xx}E_x + \sigma_{xy}E_y + \sigma_{xz}E_z$$
$$I_y = \sigma_{yx}E_x + \sigma_{yy}E_y + \sigma_{yz}E_z \qquad (1\text{-}26)$$
$$I_z = \sigma_{zx}E_x + \sigma_{zy}E_y + \sigma_{zz}E_z$$

where the quantities σ_{ik} are components of the "conductivity tensor." It has been shown by Onsager that the tensor is symmetric, i.e., $\sigma_{ik} = \sigma_{ki}$.[17] Making use of this symmetry property and multiplying the expressions (1-26) respectively by E_x, E_y, and E_z, one obtains upon adding

$$I_x E_x + I_y E_y + I_z E_z = \sigma_{xx}E_x^2 + \sigma_{yy}E_y^2 + \sigma_{zz}E_z^2 + 2\sigma_{xy}E_xE_y$$
$$+ 2\sigma_{yz}E_yE_z + 2\sigma_{zx}E_zE_x \quad (1\text{-}27)$$

The right-hand side represents a quadratic surface; by choosing our coordinates along the principal axes of this surface, the mixed terms disappear and one obtains in the new coordinate system

$$I_x = \sigma_1 E_x; \quad I_y = \sigma_2 E_y; \quad I_z = \sigma_3 E_z \qquad (1\text{-}28)$$

where σ_1, σ_2, and σ_3 are the principal conductivities. Thus the electrical properties of any crystal, whatever low symmetry it may possess, may be characterized by three conductivities σ_1, σ_2, σ_3 or by three specific resistivities ρ_1, ρ_2, ρ_3. Note that I and E have the same direction only when the applied field falls along any one of the three principal axes of the crystal.

In cubic crystals the three quantities are equal and the specific resistivity does not vary with direction. In hexagonal, rhombohedral (trigonal), and tetragonal crystals the resistivity depends only on the angle ϕ between the direction in which ρ is measured and the hexagonal, trigonal, or tetragonal axis, since in those crystals two of the three quantities ρ_1, ρ_2, ρ_3 are equal. One finds

$$\rho(\phi) = \rho_\perp \sin^2 \phi + \rho_\parallel \cos^2 \phi \qquad (1\text{-}29)$$

where $\perp$ and $\parallel$ refer to directions perpendicular and parallel to the axis.

The effect referred to above may be called a "vector-vector" effect

---

[17] L. Onsager, *Phys. Rev.*, **37**, 405 (1931); **38**, 2265 (1931); for the so-called "reciprocity relations" derived by Onsager on the basis of the principle of microscopic reversibility, see also C. Zwikker, *Physical Properties of Solid Materials*, Interscience, New York, 1954, Chap. 5; see also Chap. 4 for anisotropy.

since an electric current (vector) is produced by an applied electric field (vector). The relations obtained may also be applied to other vector-vector effects such as thermal conductivity, where a thermal current vector is evoked by a thermal gradient; or diffusion under influence of a concentration gradient.

When one considers scalar-tensor effects, similar relationships are obtained. For example, the deformation (tensor) of a solid resulting from a change in temperature (scalar) may be characterized by three principal expansion coefficients α_1, α_2, and α_3. Here again, in cubic crystals $\alpha_1 = \alpha_2 = \alpha_3$ and such crystals are isotropic in this respect. The angular dependence of α for hexagonal, trigonal, and tetragonal crystals is given by an expression corresponding to (1-29).

Other effects such as vector-tensor effects and tensor-tensor effects may be treated along similar general lines. An example of a vector-tensor effect is piezoelectricity,[18] in which an electric field (vector) gives rise to a deformation (tensor).[18] The elastic deformation under influence of a stress tensor is an example of a tensor-tensor effect.[19] These effects may require many more constants than appeared in the relatively simple case of a vector-vector effect outlined above.

REFERENCES

G. E. Bacon, *Neutron Diffraction*, Oxford, New York, 1955.

R. Beeching, *Electron Diffraction*, 2nd ed., Methuen, London, 1946.

M. J. Buerger, *X-ray Crystallography*, Wiley, New York, 1942.

C. W. Bunn, *Chemical Crystallography*, Oxford, New York, 1945.

A. H. Compton and S. K. Allison, *X-rays in Theory and Experiment*, Van Nostrand, New York, 1935.

International Tables for X-ray Crystallography, Kynoch Press, Birmingham, 1952.

R. W. James, *X-ray Crystallography*, 4th ed., Methuen, London, 1950.

J. A. A. Ketelaar, *Chemical Constitution*, Elsevier, New York, 1953.

K. Lonsdale, *Crystals and X-rays*, Bell and Sons, London, 1948.

L. Pauling, *Nature of the Chemical Bond*, Cornell University Press, Ithaca, 1945.

R. W. G. Wyckoff, *Crystal Structures*, Interscience, New York, 1948.

[18] See W. G. Cady, *Piezoelectricity*, McGraw-Hill, New York, 1946.
[19] See for further details Sec. 3-8.

PROBLEMS

1-1. For the packing of spheres of radius R in a simple cubic, a body-centered cubic and a face-centered cubic lattice show that the cube edge and the fraction of the volume occupied by the spheres are given by

$$\text{simple cubic:} \quad a = 2R; \ f = \pi/6$$

$$\text{b.c.c.:} \quad a = 4R/\sqrt{3}; \ f = (\pi\sqrt{3})/8$$

$$\text{f.c.c.:} \quad a = 4R/\sqrt{2}; \ f = (\pi\sqrt{2})/6$$

Calculate the density ratios for the three lattices.

1-2. Explain why in Fig. 1-6, the following structures are not included: the base-centered tetragonal, the face-centered tetragonal, and the face-centered rhombohedral.

1-3. For a b.c.c. lattice built up of spherical atoms of radius R, calculate the number of atoms per cm^2 on the planes $\{100\}$, $\{110\}$ and $\{111\}$. Do the same for a f.c.c. and a simple cubic lattice.

1-4. Explain that the diamond structure may be considered as made up of two interpenetrating f.c.c. lattices. Given that the cube edge for diamond is 3.56 Å, calculate the distance between nearest neighbors and show that there are 1.77×10^{23} atoms per cm^3. From this, calculate the density of diamond and compare the result with the observed density. Do the same for germanium (cube edge = 5.62 Å).

1-5. For a cubic lattice show that the distance between successive planes of Miller indices (h, k, l) is given by formula 1-3.

1-6. Explain qualitatively, and if possible quantitatively, why the X-ray diffraction lines observed from small crystallites become broadened; base the discussion on a one-dimensional finite array of atoms.

1-7. On the basis of the discussion of Sec. 1-7, verify the characteristic powder patterns represented in Fig. 1-16.

1-8. Discuss in some detail how the lattice constant of a cubic crystal may be obtained from a powder pattern. If possible, carry out the calculations for an actual film.

1-9. Suppose the interaction energy between two atoms is given by an expression of the type (1-21). Given that $n = 2$, $m = 10$, and that the two atoms form a stable molecule with an internuclear distance of 3 Å and a dissociation energy of 4 ev, calculate α and β. Also calculate the force required to break the molecule and the critical distance between the nuclei for which this occurs. Furthermore, calculate the force required to reduce the internuclear distance by 10 per cent relative to the equilibrium distance.

1-10. Consider a crystal which, in equilibrium, occupies a volume V_0; let the total energy of interaction between the atoms in the crystal be E_0. Assuming that the energy of interaction between the atoms may be described by an expression of the type (1-21), show that the compressibility is given by $|E_0|(mn/9V_0)$.

1-11. Discuss methods for growing single crystals (see, for example, H. E. Buckley, *Crystal Growth*, Wiley, New York, 1951).

1-12. Discuss some physical effects which are due to anisotropy (see, for example, C. Zwikker, *Physical Properties of Solid Materials*, Interscience, New York, 1954, Chapter 4).

Chapter 2

THE SPECIFIC HEAT OF SOLIDS AND
LATTICE VIBRATIONS

2-1. The specific heat at constant volume and at constant pressure

According to the first law of thermodynamics, the amount of heat dQ added to a system must be equal to the increase in energy dE of the system plus the amount of work done by the system. In case the work done by the system is of a mechanical nature only, one may thus write

$$dQ = dE + p\,dV \qquad (2\text{-}1)$$

Now, E is, except for an arbitrary constant, determined uniquely by the temperature and volume of the system. Hence

$$dE = \left(\frac{\partial E}{\partial T}\right)_V dT + \left(\frac{\partial E}{\partial V}\right)_T dV$$

and (2-1) may be rewritten in the form

$$dQ = \left(\frac{\partial E}{\partial T}\right)_V dT + \left[\left(\frac{\partial E}{\partial V}\right)_T + p\right] dV \qquad (2\text{-}2)$$

The specific heat in general is defined by dQ/dT, and unless stated otherwise, will be assumed to refer to 1 gram molecule of the solid. However, unless one specifies in which way the increase in temperature takes place, the specific heat is undetermined; in particular one must specify the corresponding change in volume, as is evident from (2-2). Thus there exist an infinite number of specific heats, but in general one is interested in only two: the specific heat at constant volume C_V and the specific heat at constant pressure C_p. According to (2-2), the former is given by

$$C_V = \left(\frac{dQ}{dT}\right)_V = \left(\frac{\partial E}{\partial T}\right)_V \qquad (2\text{-}3)$$

Theoretically speaking, this is the most interesting quantity, as it is obtained immediately from the energy of the system; most of the following discussions will therefore refer to C_V. From the experimental point of view, however, it is much more convenient to measure the specific heat of a solid at constant pressure than at constant volume. As shown in text-books on thermodynamics, the second law leads to the following relation-ship between C_p and C_V :[1]

$$C_p - C_V = -T \left(\frac{\partial V}{\partial T}\right)_p^2 \left(\frac{\partial p}{\partial V}\right)_T \qquad (2\text{-}4)$$

This may be rewritten in terms of the volume expansion coefficient α_V and the compressibility K, defined by

$$\alpha_V = (1/V)(\partial V/\partial T)_p \quad \text{and} \quad K = -(1/V)(\partial V/\partial p)_T \qquad (2\text{-}5)$$

Expression (2-4) then takes the form

$$C_p - C_V = \alpha_V^2 TV/K \qquad (2\text{-}6)$$

Thus C_V may be calculated from C_p measurements if at the same time α_V and K are known at the temperature of interest. Since both α_V and K are positive quantities, $C_p - C_V \geqslant 0$.

By way of illustration, we have given in Fig. 2-1 C_p and C_V as functions of temperature for copper; note that at low temperatures their difference becomes very small and that both go to zero at $T = 0$. It is essentially the temperature variation of the specific heat at constant volume which will be discussed in the present chapter.

It may be noted that if no direct

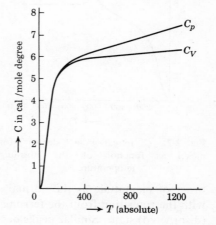

Fig. 2-1. The temperature variation of C_p and C_V for copper. [By permission from M. W. Zemansky, *Heat and Thermodynamics*, 2d ed., McGraw-Hill, New York, 1943, p. 237]

compressibility data are available for the temperature range of interest, one frequently employs the relationship

$$C_p = C_V(1 + \gamma \alpha_V T) \quad \text{with} \quad \gamma = \alpha_V V/KC_V \qquad (2\text{-}7)$$

The quantity γ is called the Grüneisen constant and is practically independent of temperature.[2] Thus by calculating γ at some arbitrary temperature from available data, one may obtain an approximation for C_V at other temperatures from a knowledge of the coefficient of volume expansion.

[1] See, for example, M. W. Zemansky, *Heat and Thermodynamics*, 2d ed., McGraw-Hill, New York, 1943, p. 227.

[2] E. Grüneisen, *Handbuch der Physik*, **10**, 1–59 (1926); see also J. C. Slater, *Phys. Rev.*, **57**, 744 (1940).

From the atomic point of view one may distinguish between various contributions to the specific heat of solids. In the first place, there is the contribution resulting from the atomic vibrations in the crystal; an increase in temperature is associated with a more vigorous motion of the atoms, which requires an input of energy. Second, in metals and in semiconductors there is an additional contribution to the specific heat from the electronic system. Usually this contribution is small relative to that of the lattice vibrations, as explained in Chapter 9. As the temperature

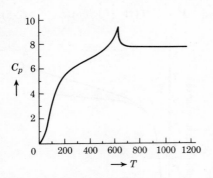

Fig. 2-2. C_p in cal mole^{-1} degree^{-1} for nickel as function of the absolute temperature.

is raised from absolute zero, the specific heat increases rather rapidly from zero and finally levels off to a nearly constant value. For elements, the value at high temperatures is about 6 cal mole^{-1} degree^{-1}. This is known as the law of Dulong and Petit. Anomalies in the specific heat curves are observed in the ferromagnetic metals; for example, in nickel, iron, and cobalt, a peak is observed in the vicinity of the ferromagnetic Curie temperature (see Fig. 2-2). The height of the peak is of the same order of magnitude as the normal specific heat. The peak is associated with the transition from the ferromagnetic (ordered) to the paramagnetic (disordered) state. Similar peaks occur in the specific heat curves of alloys which exhibit order-disorder transitions, and in ferroelectric materials. These anomalies are discussed in the relevant chapters; in the present chapter the discussion is confined to the specific heat associated with atomic vibrations.

2-2. The various theories of the lattice specific heat

In Sec. 2-10 it will be shown that the vibrational energy of a linear chain of N atoms may be expressed as the energy of N harmonic oscillators. Extending the arguments employed there to the three-dimensional case, one is led to the conclusion that:

> *The vibrational energy of a crystal containing N atoms is equivalent with the energy of a system of $3N$ harmonic oscillators.*

This feature is common to all theories of the specific heat and the distinction between the various theories is based on their differences in the proposed *frequency spectrum* of the oscillators. The central problem in the theory of the specific heat is therefore the calculation of the wavelengths and frequencies of the possible modes of vibration of the crystal under consideration. The different approaches to this problem will be outlined below.

With regard to the harmonic oscillator representation referred to above, the following qualitative remarks may provide some clarification. Suppose it were possible to fix the position of all the nuclei in a crystal such that they are all in their equilibrium position. If one of the nuclei were now displaced over a distance small compared with the shortest interatomic distances, and then set free again, the displaced atom would carry out harmonic vibrations about its equilibrium position, and its energy of vibration would be the same as that of three one-dimensional harmonic oscillators, one for each direction of motion. Applying the same reasoning to the other atoms in the crystal, one arrives at a system of $3N$ harmonic oscillators representing the vibrations of the crystal as a whole.

2-3. The breakdown of the classical theory

The energy of a harmonic oscillator of natural angular frequency ω may be written

$$\epsilon = p^2/2m + m\omega^2 q^2/2 \qquad (2\text{-}8)$$

where the first term on the right represents the kinetic energy (p is the momentum) and the second term represents the potential energy (q is the deflection from the equilibrium position). It is well known that the average energy of a harmonic oscillator according to classical statistical mechanics is given by

$$\langle \epsilon \rangle = \int_0^\infty \epsilon e^{-\epsilon/kT} \, d\epsilon \Big/ \int_0^\infty e^{-\epsilon/kT} \, d\epsilon = kT \qquad (2\text{-}9)$$

where T is the absolute temperature and k is Boltzmann's constant. It is important to note that the frequency does not enter in this result. In other words, the vibrational energy of a crystal of N atoms is classically always equal to

$$E = 3NkT \qquad (2\text{-}10)$$

independent of the assumed frequency distribution of the oscillators used in the model. Now, as long as the volume of the solid is kept constant, (2-10) is the only temperature-dependent contribution to the total energy of the system. Thus, for a solid containing one type of atoms and putting N equal to the number of Avogadro, one obtains for the specific heat per gram atom,

$$C_V = 3Nk = 3R = 5.96 \text{ cal degree}^{-1} \text{ mole}^{-1} \qquad (2\text{-}11)$$

where R is the gas constant. Similarly, if the solid consists of N atoms A and N atoms B, the specific heat per mole would be $6R$, etc. The result obtained is in quantitative agreement with experiment (if sources of the specific heat other than lattice vibrations are subtracted) at high temperatures only. In other words, it does not explain the decrease of the specific heat at low temperatures, as observed for all solids. This discrepancy is essentially removed when quantum theory is used, as will be seen below. It may be noted that the classical theory led to similar difficulties in the specific heat of molecules.

2-4. Einstein's theory of the specific heat

A great step forward toward an understanding of the specific heat curves at low temperatures was made by Einstein in 1906.[3] Although the physical model employed by Einstein was oversimplified, his results definitely indicated that quantum theory contained the answer to the difficulty encountered in the classical theory. He assumed that a solid element, containing N atoms, could be represented by $3N$ harmonic oscillators of the same frequency v. This model implies that the atoms vibrate independently of each other, their frequencies being the same because of their assumed identical surroundings. For the average energy of an oscillator Einstein made use of a result obtained by Planck in 1900, in connection with the theory of black-body radiation. According to Planck, a harmonic oscillator does not have a continuous energy spectrum, as assumed in the classical theory, but can accept only energy values equal to an integer times hv, where h is Planck's constant. The possible energy levels of an oscillator may thus be represented by[4]

$$\epsilon_n = nhv \qquad n = 0, 1, 2, 3, \dots \tag{2-12}$$

By replacing the integrals appearing in (2-9) by summations, one thus obtains for the average energy the expression

$$\langle \epsilon \rangle = \sum_{n=0}^{\infty} nhv e^{-nhv/kT} \bigg/ \sum_{n=0}^{\infty} e^{-nhv/kT} \tag{2-13}$$

To evaluate this expression, first consider the denominator

$$S = \sum_{n=0}^{\infty} e^{-nhv/kT} = (1 - e^{-hv/kT})^{-1}$$

Differentiating with respect to $1/kT$, one obtains

$$\frac{\partial S}{\partial(1/kT)} = -\sum_{n=0}^{\infty} nhv e^{-nhv/kT} = -\frac{hv e^{-hv/kT}}{(1 - e^{-hv/kT})^2}$$

It is observed that the expression in the center is identical with the

---

[3] A. Einstein, *Ann. Physik*, **22**, 180, 800 (1906); **34**, 170 (1911).
[4] See any *Introduction to Modern Physics*.

numerator in (2-13). Substitution into (2-13) thus leads to the well-known Planck formula for the average energy of an oscillator at a temperature T:

$$\langle \epsilon \rangle = \frac{h\nu}{e^{h\nu/kT} - 1} \qquad (2\text{-}14)$$

We emphasize that in contrast with (2-9), this expression contains the frequency of the oscillator. The temperature dependence of $\langle \epsilon \rangle$ is illustrated in Fig. 2-3, showing $\langle \epsilon \rangle/kT$ as function of $h\nu/kT$. Note that at high temperatures $\langle \epsilon \rangle \simeq kT$, in agreement with the classical theory. However, at low temperatures, $\langle \epsilon \rangle$ decreases exponentially

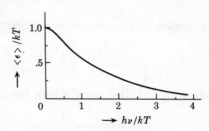

Fig. 2-3. The average energy in units of kT of a harmonic oscillator of frequency ν as a function of $h\nu/kT$, according to Planck.

to zero. In the Einstein model, the vibrational energy of a solid element containing N atoms is thus equal to

$$E = 3N\langle \epsilon \rangle = 3N \frac{h\nu}{e^{h\nu/kT} - 1} \qquad (2\text{-}15)$$

The specific heat at constant volume is therefore per mole

$$C_V = \frac{\partial}{\partial T} E = 3R \left(\frac{h\nu}{kT} \right)^2 \frac{e^{h\nu/kT}}{(e^{h\nu/kT} - 1)^2} \qquad (2\text{-}16)$$

Before discussing this result, it may be remarked that according to quantummechanics, the possible energy levels of a harmonic oscillator are given by

$$\epsilon_n = (n + \tfrac{1}{2})h\nu \qquad n = 0, 1, 2, \ldots \qquad (2\text{-}17)$$

rather than by (2-12).[5] This has the effect of shifting all energy levels by the constant amount of $h\nu/2$, and instead of (2-14), one obtains

$$\langle \epsilon \rangle = \frac{h\nu}{2} + \frac{h\nu}{e^{h\nu/kT} - 1} \qquad (2\text{-}18)$$

The first term is called the zero-point energy of the oscillator because $\langle \epsilon \rangle = h\nu/2$ for $T = 0$. Thus, according to quantum mechanics, the atoms have vibrational energy even at absolute zero. The expression for the specific heat is not altered by this result, because C_V is determined by the derivative of $\langle \epsilon \rangle$ with respect to T.

With regard to (2-16) it is observed that for $kT \gg h\nu$, this expression reduces in first approximation to the classical result (2-11). At low temperatures, however, the specific heat decreases. To discuss this

[5] For a proof see any introduction to wave mechanics.

behavior, it is convenient to introduce the Einstein temperature θ_E, defined by

$$h\nu = k\theta_E \tag{2-19}$$

Expression (2-16) may then be written in the form

$$\frac{C_V}{3R} = \left(\frac{\theta_E}{T}\right)^2 \frac{e^{\theta_E/T}}{(e^{\theta_E/T} - 1)^2} = F_E\left(\frac{\theta_E}{T}\right) \tag{2-20}$$

where F_E is called the Einstein function; it determines the ratio of the

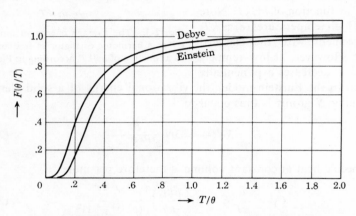

Fig. 2-4.   The Debye and Einstein functions as function of T/θ.

specific heat at a temperature T and the classical (high-temperature) value $3R$. The Einstein function is represented in Fig. 2-4, together with the Debye function, which will be discussed in Sec. 2-6. We see that the curve obtained has the same appearance as the observed specific heat curves. On the other hand, the Einstein curve deviates from the experimentally observed ones in the region of low temperatures. Experimentally, it is found that for most solids the lattice specific heat at very low temperatures (liquid helium) is proportional to T^3. However, for $T \ll \theta_E$, equation (2-20) leads to a specific heat proportional to $\exp\,(-\theta_E/T)$. In other words, the Einstein function falls off more rapidly at low temperatures than it should. The reason for this discrepancy must be sought in the oversimplified model employed by Einstein. In fact, we shall see in the next sections that rather than a single frequency ν, the vibrational spectrum of a solid covers a wide range of frequencies. This, in turn, is a result of the fact that the atomic vibrations in a crystal are strongly coupled and cannot be considered independent. On the other hand, because of its simplicity, the Einstein model is frequently used in problems in which lattice vibrations play a role.

2-5. The vibrational modes of a continuous medium

In the preceding section it was pointed out that the discrepancy between the Einstein theory and experimental results in the low temperature region was a consequence of the oversimplified model employed by Einstein. In 1912, Debye tackled the problem from a different point of view and, as we shall see, with great success.[6] Debye realized that it is possible to propagate waves through solids covering a wavelength region extending from low frequencies (sound waves) up to short waves (infrared absorption). The essential difference between the Debye model and the Einstein model is that Debye considers the vibrational modes of a crystal as a whole, whereas Einstein's starting point was to consider the vibration of a single atom, assuming the atomic vibrations to be independent of each other.

In the present section, we shall deal with the vibrational modes of a continuous medium, because the results are basic to the "continuum theories" of the specific heat. Let us first consider for simplicity the vibrational modes of a one-dimensional continuous string of length L. Suppose $u(x,t)$ represents the deflection of the string at the point x at the instant t. The waves may then be described by the one-dimensional wave equation

$$\frac{\partial^2 u}{\partial x^2} = \frac{1}{c_s^2} \cdot \frac{\partial^2 u}{\partial t^2} \qquad (2\text{-}21)$$

where c_s is the velocity of propagation of the waves. If it is assumed that the end points of the string are fixed, the solutions of (2-21) are those corresponding to standing waves:

$$u(x,t) = A \sin (n\pi x/L) \cos 2\pi \nu_n t \qquad (2\text{-}22)$$

where n is a positive integer $\geqslant 1$. The wavelengths and frequencies of the possible vibrations represented by (2-22) are given by

$$\lambda_n = 2L/n \quad \text{and} \quad \nu_n = c_s/\lambda_n = c_s n/2L \qquad (2\text{-}23)$$

The frequency spectrum is discrete, one frequency corresponding to each integer value n. Note that for the one-dimensional string the frequency spectrum corresponds to an infinite number of equidistant lines, as illustrated in Fig. 2-5a. The number of possible modes of vibration in a frequency interval $d\nu$ is, on the average, equal to

$$dn = (2L/c_s)\, d\nu \qquad (2\text{-}24)$$

In the three-dimensional case, the wave equation reads

$$\frac{\partial^2 u}{\partial x^2} + \frac{\partial^2 u}{\partial y^2} + \frac{\partial^2 u}{\partial z^2} = \frac{1}{c_s^2} \cdot \frac{\partial^2 u}{\partial t^2} \qquad (2\text{-}25)$$

[6] P. Debye, *Ann. Physik*, **39**, 789 (1912).

Assuming a continuous medium in the shape of a cube of edge L and assuming the faces of the cube to be fixed, the possible standing wave solutions are, in analogy with (2-22),

$$u(x,y,z,t) = A \sin (n_x \pi x/L) \sin (n_y \pi y/L) \sin (n_z \pi z/L) \cos 2\pi \nu t \quad (2\text{-}26)$$

where now n_x, n_y, and n_z are positive integers $\geqslant 1$. Substituting this solution into the differential equation (2-25), one obtains the following expression for the possible modes of vibration:

$$(\pi^2/L^2)(n_x^2 + n_y^2 + n_z^2) = 4\pi^2 \nu^2/c_s^2 = 4\pi^2/\lambda^2 \quad (2\text{-}27)$$

Thus the possible wavelengths and frequencies are determined by three integers in this case. Let us now ask the question: What is the number

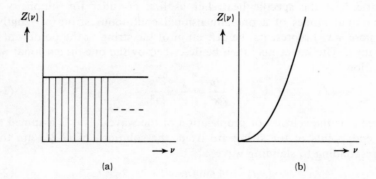

Fig. 2-5. (a) Frequency spectrum for a finite continuous string, according to (2-24). (b) Frequency spectrum for a three-dimensional continuum, according to (2-30).

of possible modes of vibrations $Z(\nu) \, d\nu$ in the frequency interval between ν and $\nu + d\nu$? To answer this, consider a network of points, each point being determined by three Cartesian positive integer coordinates n_x, n_y, and n_z. Writing

$$R^2 = n_x^2 + n_y^2 + n_z^2 = 4L^2 \nu^2/c_s^2 \quad (2\text{-}28)$$

it is evident that the number of points in a shell between R and $R + dR$ is equal to[7]

$$\tfrac{1}{8} 4\pi R^2 \, dR \quad (2\text{-}29)$$

---

[7] Each point occupies on the average a unit volume in the integer space.

Now, each point corresponds to a set of three integers n_x, n_y, n_z, and each set of integers determines, according to (2-26), a possible mode of vibration; hence (2-29) immediately gives the number of possible modes of vibration in a given range. Expressing R in terms of ν in (2-29) one thus finds

$$Z(\nu)\, d\nu = (4\pi V / c_s^3)\nu^2\, d\nu \qquad (2\text{-}30)$$

where V is the volume of the solid. For a perfect continuum, the possible frequencies vary between 0 and ∞, the number of such possible vibrations increasing with the square of the frequency (see Fig. 2-5b). This situation holds, for example, in the case of electromagnetic waves in a box of volume V. Expression (2-30) is therefore basic in the theory of black-body radiation.

In the case of elastic waves, we may distinguish between transverse and longitudinal waves. In general, the velocities of propagation, say c_t and c_l, respectively, will not be equal. To set up an expression for $Z(\nu)\, d\nu$ in this case one should keep in mind that for each frequency or wavelength there are two transverse modes and one longitudinal mode.[8] Thus, instead of (2-30) one obtains

$$Z(\nu)\, d\nu = 4\pi V \left(\frac{2}{c_t^3} + \frac{1}{c_l^3} \right) \nu^2\, d\nu \qquad (2\text{-}31)$$

How this expression has been used in the theory of the specific heat of solids will be discussed in the following two sections.

2-6. The Debye approximation

One may wonder what the discussion of the preceding section could have to do with the specific heat of crystals, which are by no means continuous but are built up of atoms, i.e., of discrete "mass points." The reason is the following: Consider an elastic wave propagated in a crystal of volume V. As long as the wavelength of the wave is large compared with the interatomic distances, the crystal "looks like" a continuum from the point of view of the wave. The essential assumption of Debye is now that this continuum model may be employed for all possible vibrational modes of the crystal. Furthermore, the fact that the crystal actually consists of atoms is taken into account by limiting the total number of vibrational modes to $3N$ (see Sec. 2-2), N being the total number of atoms. In other words, the frequency spectrum corresponding to a perfect continuum is cut off so as to comply with a total of $3N$ modes (see Fig. 2-6a). The Debye cut-off procedure leads to a maximum

[8] In the longitudinal modes, the deflection is along the direction of propagation; in the transverse modes the deflection is perpendicular to the direction of propagation, which gives two independent components.

frequency ν_D (the Debye frequency) common to the transverse and longitudinal modes; it is defined by

$$\int_0^{\nu_D} Z(\nu)\,d\nu = 4\pi V \left(\frac{2}{c_t^3} + \frac{1}{c_l^3}\right)\int_0^{\nu_D} \nu^2\,d\nu = 3N \qquad (2\text{-}32)$$

or

$$\nu_D^3 = \frac{9N}{4\pi V}\left(\frac{2}{c_t^3} + \frac{1}{c_l^3}\right) \qquad (2\text{-}33)$$

where $Z(\nu)$ as given by (2-31) has been used. It should be noted that this procedure assumes that the velocities c_t and c_l are independent of the

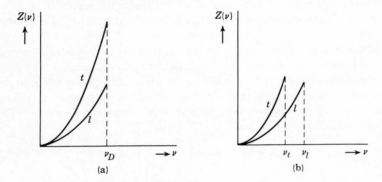

Fig. 2-6. The Debye cut-off takes place at the Debye frequency ν_D, common to the transverse and longitudinal modes (a). In Born's procedure, the cut-off takes place at a common minimum wavelength, corresponding to the maximum frequencies ν_t and ν_l for the transverse and longitudinal modes respectively (b). Note that $c_t < c_l$.

wavelength, as in the continuum. It will be seen in Sec. 2-9 that this is not correct for actual crystals. The order of magnitude of ν_D may be obtained by taking $N/V \simeq 10^{22}$ per cm^3 and using for the velocity of sound $\sim 10^5$ cm sec^{-1}. This gives $\nu_D \simeq 10^{13}$ per second. This corresponds to a minimum wavelength of the order of one Angstrom, indicating that the continuum theory may be at fault, especially in the high-frequency region.

Associating with each vibrational mode a harmonic oscillator of the same frequency, one finds from (2-31) and Planck's formula (2-14) for the vibrational energy of the crystal,

$$E = \int_0^{\nu_D} Z(\nu)\frac{h\nu}{e^{h\nu/kT}-1}\,d\nu = 9N\left(\frac{kT}{h\nu_D}\right)^3 kT\int_0^{x_m}\frac{x^3\,dx}{e^x-1} \qquad (2\text{-}34)$$

where $x = h\nu/kT$ and $x_m = h\nu_D/kT$. Here, as in the Einstein theory, it is convenient to introduce a characteristic temperature; thus one defines the Debye temperature as

$$\theta_D = h\nu_D/k \qquad (2\text{-}35)$$

The upper limit of integration is then equal to $x_m = \theta_D/T$. It is observed that for high temperatures $(T \gg \theta_D)$, x is small compared with unity for the whole range of integration. In that case, the denominator of the integrand in (2-34) may be replaced in first approximation by x. This yields for the specific heat,

$$C_V = \partial E/\partial T = 3Nk \quad \text{for} \quad T \gg \theta_D$$

a result identical with the classical theory.

In the case of very low temperatures, such that $T \ll \theta_D$, the upper limit of integration in (2-34) may be replaced by infinity. Now,[9]

$$\int_0^\infty \frac{x^3 \, dx}{e^x - 1} = 6 \sum_1^\infty \frac{1}{n^4} = \frac{\pi^4}{15}$$

so that

$$E = \tfrac{3}{5}\pi^4 NkT(T/\theta_D)^3 \qquad \text{for} \quad T \ll \theta_D \qquad (2\text{-}36)$$

Thus the energy of vibration is proportional to T^4 at low temperatures (for the theory of black-body radiation, which may be treated in a completely analogous way, this is the case at any temperature, because there the upper limit to the frequency does not exist). The specific heat at low temperatures according to Debye is thus given by

$$C_V = \tfrac{12}{5}\pi^4 Nk(T/\theta_D)^3 \qquad \text{for} \quad T \ll \theta_D \qquad (2\text{-}37)$$

This is the famous Debye T^3 law, which should hold for $T \leqslant \theta_D/10$. The general expression for the specific heat as function of temperature may be obtained by differentiating (2-34) with respect to T. For 1 mole of substance one obtains in this way

$$C_V = 3R \cdot 3 \left(\frac{T}{\theta_D}\right)^3 \int_0^{\theta_D/T} \frac{e^x x^4}{(e^x - 1)^2} \, dx = 3RF_D\left(\frac{\theta_D}{T}\right) \qquad (2\text{-}38)$$

where F_D is the Debye function. It has been represented in Fig. 2-4 together with the Einstein function. The reason that the Debye curve lies above the Einstein curve is a result of the fact that in the Debye model, the low-frequency modes are taken into account; at low temperatures these have a higher average energy and temperature derivative than the relatively high-frequency Einstein oscillators, as is evident from the Planck formula (2-14).

To illustrate the agreement between the Debye theory and experimentally observed specific heat curves, we reproduce in Fig. 2-7 measurements on silver fitted to a Debye curve. From such curves it is possible

[9] E. T. Whittaker and G. N. Watson, *Modern Analysis*, 4th ed., Cambridge, London, 1935, p. 265.

to calculate the Debye temperature of the solid involved. Some typical examples are given in Table 2-1.

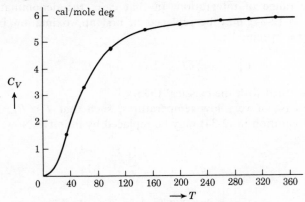

Fig. 2-7. Comparison of the Debye specific heat curve and observed values (dots) for silver; the ordinate is in cal mole^{-1} degree^{-1}.

Table 2-1. Debye Temperature in Degrees Absolute for a Number of Solids

Solid	θ_D	Solid	θ_D	Solid	θ_D
Na	150	Fe	420	C (diam.)	1860
K	100	Co	385	NaCl	281
Cu	315	Ni	375	KCl	230
Ag	215	Al	390	KBr	177
Au	170	Ge	290	AgCl	183
Be	1000	Sn	260	AgBr	144
Mg	290	Pb	88	CaF$_2$	474
Zn	250	Pt	225		
Cd	172				

Notwithstanding the great success of the Debye approximation, accurate measurements in the low-temperature region show deviations from the theoretical predictions. According to the Debye theory, the T^3 law should hold in the temperature region $T \leqslant 0.1\theta_D$. That this is not always the case may be seen from some examples given in Table 2-2, reproduced from Blackman's paper.[10]

The θ_D values given in the table are calculated from (2-37) and should be constant if the T^3 law was satisfied. Similar deviations have been found in other materials. There seems little doubt that these deviations

[10] M. Blackman, *Repts. Progr. Phys.*, **8**, 11 (1941).

Table 2-2. Deviations from the T^3 Law

NaCl			KCl			Li		
T	θ_D	$10^4 C_V/T^3$	T	θ_D	$10^4 C_V/T^3$	T	θ_D	$10^4 C_V/T^3$
20	288	0.388	14	213	0.960	30	356	0.101
15	297	0.356	8	222	0.832	20	340	0.118
10	308	0.334	4	236	0.708	15	328	0.131
			3	227	0.798			

are a result of the deficiencies of the continuum approximation, a conclusion which is supported by the work of Blackman and Kellermann,[11] the results of which will be briefly discussed in Sec. 2-13. According to Blackman one may expect the T^3 law to hold for the temperature region

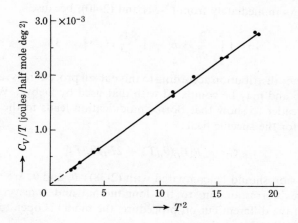

Fig. 2-8.   Comparison of the T^3 law and observed values for KCl.
[After P. H. Keesom and N. Pearlman, ref. 12]

$T \leqslant \theta_D/50$, i.e., at considerably lower temperatures than predicted by the Debye approximation. The T^3 law is illustrated in Fig. 2-8 for KCl, representing results obtained by Keesom and Pearlman.[12]

2-7. The Born cut-off procedure

A modification of the Debye theory was introduced by Born, who proposed a different cut-off procedure. In the preceding section it was

[11] E. W. Kellermann, *Phil. Trans.*, **A238**, 513 (1940); *Proc. Roy. Soc.*, **A178**, 17 (1941).
[12] P. H. Keesom and N. Pearlman, *Phys. Rev.*, **91**, 1354 (1953).

noted that in the Debye theory, the maximum frequency ν_D was common to both the longitudinal and the transverse modes. Born proposed to cut off the spectrum in such a manner that the longitudinal and transverse modes have a *common minimum wavelength*. This, as will become evident from the discussion in the following sections, is actually more sound theoretically speaking and in line with the theory of lattice vibrations developed by Born and von Karman.[13] Thus if one takes the common minimum wavelength equal to

$$\lambda_{\min} = (4\pi V/3N)^{1/3} \tag{2-39}$$

one obtains two Debye frequencies, one for the longitudinal modes and one for the transverse modes, viz.,

$$\nu_l = c_l(3N/4\pi V)^{1/3} \quad \text{and} \quad \nu_t = c_t(3N/4\pi V)^{1/3} \tag{2-40}$$

That this procedure leaves the total number of vibrational modes equal to $3N$ follows immediately from (2-31) and (2-40), because

$$4\pi V \left(\int_0^{\nu_t} \frac{2}{c_t^3} \nu^2 \, d\nu + \int_0^{\nu_l} \frac{1}{c_l^3} \nu^2 \, d\nu \right) = 3N$$

The frequency distribution according to this cut-off procedure is represented in Fig. 2-6b and may be compared with that used by Debye. We leave it up to the reader to show that Born's modification leads to the following expression for the specific heat:

$$C_V = R[F_D(\theta_l/T) + 2F_D(\theta_t/T)] \tag{2-41}$$

This expression should be compared with (2-38); θ_l and θ_t are the Debye temperatures corresponding to the longitudinal and transverse modes. Apart from the different cut-off procedure, the model is open to the same objections as the Debye theory.

2-8. Elastic waves in an infinite one-dimensional array of identical atoms

The weakest point in the model employed in the Debye theory is the assumption that the continuum representation of a crystal holds for all possible elastic waves. In fact, we have seen that the minimum wavelength is of the same order of magnitude as the interatomic distances and we may thus expect that a more rigorous treatment might give different results, especially in the high-frequency region. In the present and the following sections we shall therefore discuss the principles of finding the possible modes of vibration of atomic lattices. The original work is due

[13] M. Born, *Atomtheorie des festen Zustandes*, Leipzig (1923); M. Born and Th. von Karman, *Phys. Z.*, **13**, 297 (1912); **14**, 15 (1913).

to Born and von Karman[13] and to Blackman.[10] To begin with, consider an array of equidistant mass points as represented in Fig. 2-9; the particles all have a mass m, and for the moment the array will be considered infinitely long. It will be assumed that there exists interaction only between nearest neighbors and that Hooke's law is obeyed.[14] In equilibrium let the distance between neighboring particles be a; the deflections from the equilibrium position will be denoted by $x_0, x_1, x_2, \ldots, x_{n-1}$, $x_n, x_{n+1}, \ldots$. The equation of motion of particle n is then

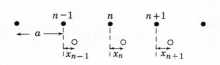

Fig. 2-9. Linear chain of identical mass points. The black dots represent the equilibrium positions, the open circles the displaced particles.

$$m\ddot{x}_n = -f(x_n - x_{n-1}) - f(x_n - x_{n+1}) = f(x_{n-1} + x_{n+1} - 2x_n) \quad (2\text{-}42)$$

where f is the force constant describing the nearest neighbor interaction. We may try to solve this equation by a running wave of the type

$$x_n(t) = e^{-i\omega(t - na/c_s)} = e^{-i(\omega t - qna)} \quad (2\text{-}43)$$

where c_s is the velocity of propagation of the wave, $q = \omega/c = 2\pi/\lambda$ is the wave vector and na the equilibrium position of particle n relative to the origin. Substituting this solution into the differential equation (2-42), one obtains after dividing through by x_n,

$$m\omega^2 = -f(e^{-iqa} + e^{iqa} - 2) = 4f \sin^2 (qa/2) \quad (2\text{-}44)$$

or

$$\omega = \omega_{\max} \sin (qa/2) \quad \text{with} \quad \omega_{\max}^2 = 4f/m$$

We have thus obtained an expression for the frequency of the waves in terms of the wave vector q, i.e., in terms of the wavelength. To each wave vector q corresponds a frequency ω_q. The relationship has been represented in Fig. 2-10, curve a. It is important to note that for a continuous string, the frequency ν would be equal to $qc_s/2\pi$, i.e., ν would be proportional to the wave vector q as illustrated by curve b in Fig. 2-10. We are thus led to the conclusion that a continuous string and an array of mass points give identical results only if $qa \ll 1$, i.e., when the wavelength is large compared with the interatomic distance. This we had expected. The difference between a continuous string and an array of mass points may also be expressed in this way: the velocity of propagation in a continuous string is independent of the wavelength, whereas in an array of mass points the velocity of propagation becomes smaller as the

[14] For a more general treatment, see L. Brillouin, *Wave Propagation in Periodic Structures*, Dover, New York, 1953.

wavelength decreases. It is evident that this result must have a bearing on the theory of the specific heat, because in the continuum models it was assumed that c_s is a constant.

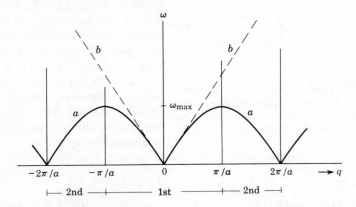

Fig. 2-10. Frequency of elastic waves in a mono-atomic linear lattice as function of the wave vector q. The dashed lines correspond to a continuous string. The first and second Brillouin zones are indicated.

Another important result which follows from the above discussion may be obtained by comparing the solution (2-43) with another in which q has been replaced by

$$q_m = q + 2\pi m/a \quad \text{with} \quad m = \pm 1, \pm 2, \ldots \tag{2-45}$$

First of all, it follows from (2-44) that the frequencies corresponding to the modes q and q_m are identical. From this, and from the fact that $\exp(2\pi im) = 1$, it then follows that the solutions (2-43) with q and q_m are identical. In other words, the state of vibration of the array of mass points corresponding to a wave vector q is the same as that for any of the wave vectors $q + 2\pi m/a$. In order to obtain a unique relationship between the state of vibration of the lattice and the wave vector q, the latter must be confined to a range of values $2\pi/a$. Usually one chooses the range such that

$$-\pi/a \leqslant q \leqslant \pi/a \tag{2-46}$$

The positive q values correspond to waves propagated in one direction, the negative q values represent waves going in the opposite direction (see 2-43). It also follows from the above discussion that the frequency is a periodic function of q, as illustrated in Fig. 2-10. The region of q values defined by (2-46) is referred to as the first Brillouin zone. The second zone consists of two intervals of half a period each, one on each side of the first zone as indicated in Fig. 2-10. Higher-order zones are defined in a similar manner.

It is interesting to note that according to (2-44) there exists a maximum frequency ν_{max} which can be propagated through the chain, viz.,

$$\nu_{max} = \frac{1}{\pi} \left(\frac{f}{m} \right)^{1/2} \tag{2-47}$$

The chain may thus be considered a low-pass filter which transmits only in the frequency range between zero and ν_{max}. In contrast with this, the continuous string has no frequency limit. The maximum frequency of the chain of atoms occurs when the wave vector is equal to π/a, i.e., for a wavelength $\lambda_{min} = 2a$. Now $a \simeq 10^{-8}$ cm and the velocity of sound in solids is of the order of 10^5–10^6 cm sec^{-1}; this gives $\nu_{max} \simeq 10^{13}$ sec^{-1}.

2-9. Vibrational modes of a finite one-dimensional lattice of identical atoms

In the preceding section the discussion referred to an infinite lattice; in the present section we shall see how the boundary conditions required for a finite lattice lead in a natural manner to an enumeration of the possible modes of vibration. The boundary conditions may be introduced in either of two ways, which will now be discussed:

1. *Boundary conditions leading to standing waves.* Consider an array of $(N + 1)$ similar atoms, numbered from zero to N. Suppose the two end atoms are fixed, so that $(N - 1)$ atoms are mobile. The general solution of the equation of motion (2-42) for a single wavelength may be written as the sum of two running waves, one propagating to the right, the other to the left:

$$x_n(t) = (A_1 e^{iqna + i\beta_1} + A_2 e^{-iqna + i\beta_2}) e^{-i\omega t} \tag{2-48}$$

Here A_1 and A_2 are amplitudes, and β_1, β_2 are phase angles. The boundary conditions are

$$x_0(t) = 0 \quad \text{and} \quad x_N(t) = 0 \quad \text{for all } t$$

The first of these, when substituted in (2-48), requires $A_1 = -A_2$ and $\beta_1 = \beta_2$. Since the phase angles are equal, we shall choose $\beta_1 = \beta_2 = 0$. Taking the real part of the remaining solution, one obtains

$$x_n(t) = 2A_1 \sin qna \sin \omega t \tag{2-49}$$

which represents a standing wave. These solutions lead to the same relationship between ω and q as the running wave solutions, viz., to (2-44). Furthermore, q is now limited to positive values ranging from 0 to π/a. The second boundary condition imposed on (2-49) selects a discrete set of q values, viz., those which satisfy the condition

$$\sin qNa = 0 \quad \text{or} \quad q = (\pi/Na)j \tag{2-50}$$

where j is an integer. Note that $j = 0$ must be excluded, since this corresponds to $q = 0$, i.e., all particles are at rest. The maximum value of q, viz., π/a gives $j_{max} = N$; however, this value must be excluded for the same reason as $j = 0$. We thus conclude that

$$j = 1, 2, 3, \ldots, (N - 1) \qquad (2\text{-}51)$$

In other words, *there are just as many modes of vibration (q-values) as there are mobile atoms.*

To each value of q there corresponds a value of the frequency ω_q. Hence the frequency spectrum consists of $(N - 1)$ discrete lines. For macroscopic chain lengths the spacing of the lines is so close that we may speak of a quasi-continuous spectrum.

2. Another way of introducing the boundary conditions has been proposed by Born and von Karman; they are called *cyclic* or *periodic boundary conditions* and they are very convenient in the running-wave representation of the vibrational modes. Suppose for a moment we had a circularly shaped chain of atoms, the interatomic separation being a. Let the length of the chain be $L = Na$, where the number of atoms $N \gg 1$. If the atoms are numbered $1, 2, 3, \ldots, N$ going around the circle, the boundary condition that applies here is

$$x_n(t) = x_{n+N}(t) \qquad (2\text{-}52)$$

because the subscripts n and $n + N$ refer to the same particle. Applying this to the running wave (2-43), this condition may be written

$$e^{iqna} = e^{iq(n+N)a} \quad \text{or} \quad q = (2\pi/Na)g = (2\pi/L)g \qquad (2\text{-}53)$$

where g is an integer. Now, in accordance with (2-46), q is confined to the region between $-\pi/a$ and π/a. In other words, the possible values for g are

$$g = \pm 1, \pm 2, \pm 3, \ldots, \pm N/2 \qquad (2\text{-}54)$$

(the value $g = 0$ gives $q = 0$, corresponding to all particles at rest; this value must therefore be omitted). The total number of different g values (or q values) is thus equal to N. We are thus led to the same conclusion as arrived at under (1), viz., that the number of possible vibrational modes of a chain of atoms is equal to the number of atoms which are free to move. In the running-wave picture, however, q can accept positive as well as negative values; in the standing-wave representation q is always positive. Here again, the frequency spectrum forms a discrete set of lines. The number of possible modes in a wave vector interval dq in the case of the running wave representation is, according to (2-53) equal to

$$dg = (L/2\pi)\, dq \qquad (2\text{-}55)$$

In the standing wave representation the corresponding number is, according to (2-50),

$$dj = (L/\pi) \, dq \qquad\qquad (2\text{-}56)$$

In (2-55), q ranges from $-\pi/a$ to π/a, in (2-56), from 0 to π/a. This accounts for the difference of a factor 2 in the two expressions, the total number of vibrational modes being the same for the two representations.

Actually, one is, of course, not particularly interested in circular chains of atoms. However, as long as $N \gg 1$, one can employ the boundary condition (2-52) also in the case of a linear chain. Imagine, for example, an infinite one-dimensional lattice divided into macroscopic sections of length $L = Na$. From the physical point of view, each section should have the same properties as a circular chain of length L, because as long as $N \gg 1$, each atom would "see" the same atomic configuration, the interaction between the atoms being confined to very small distances.

2-10. The equivalence of a vibrational mode and a harmonic oscillator

In Sec. 2-2 it was pointed out that the central problem of the specific heat of solids is the determination of the possible modes of vibration of the lattice under consideration. Once the answer to this question has been obtained, the vibrational energy of the solid is calculated on the assumption that the energy corresponding to a particular mode is the same as that of a harmonic oscillator of the same frequency. In the present section we shall show for the simple one-dimensional lattice of identical atoms that this identification is justified. For a general treatment of the three-dimensional case we refer to the literature.[15]

It is well known that the energy of a harmonic oscillator of mass M and angular frequency ω may be written

$$E = p^2/2M + M\omega^2 y^2/2$$

where y is the deflection and $p = M \, dy/dt$ is the momentum. In terms of y alone, we may write

$$E = \tfrac{1}{2}M(dy/dt)^2 + M\omega^2 y^2/2 \qquad\qquad (2\text{-}57)$$

We shall now show that the energy associated with a vibrational mode can indeed be written in the form (2-57). Let us consider a mode corresponding to a standing wave $\sin qna \cos \omega t$. The kinetic energy of the particles in the lattice resulting from this vibrational mode is equal to

$$E_{\text{kin}} = \tfrac{1}{2}m \sum_n \left(\frac{dx_n}{dt}\right)^2 = \tfrac{1}{2}m\omega^2 \sin^2 \omega t \sum_n \sin^2 qna \qquad (2\text{-}58)$$

---

[15] M. Born and M. Goppert-Mayer, *Handbuch der Physik*, Vol. 24/2; see also F. Seitz, *Modern Theory of Solids*, McGraw-Hill, New York, 1940, p. 125.

where m is the mass per atom and the summation extends over all particles in the chain. The potential energy of the system due to the vibrational mode q is a function of all coordinates x_n; let it be denoted by $V(x_0, x_1, \ldots, x_n, \ldots)$. The force exerted on particle n is then, in accordance with (2-42),

$$-\frac{\partial V}{dx_n} = m \frac{d^2 x_n}{dt^2} = f(x_{n-1} + x_{n+1} - 2x_n) \qquad (2\text{-}59)$$

from this one may arrive at the following expression for the potential energy

$$V(x_0, x_1, \ldots, x_n, \ldots) = \tfrac{1}{2} f \sum_n (2x_n^2 - x_n x_{n+1} - x_n x_{n-1}) \qquad (2\text{-}60)$$

(Note that each of the mixed terms appears twice in the summation, providing agreement between the last two equations; this may readily be verified by writing out the sum explicitly.) Substituting the standing wave solution into (2-60), one obtains after some manipulation,

$$V = 2f \sin^2 (qa/2) \cos^2 \omega t \sum_n \sin^2 qna \qquad (2\text{-}61)$$

Making use of the relation between ω and q as given by (2-44), one may write

$$V = \tfrac{1}{2} m \omega^2 \cos^2 \omega t \sum_n \sin^2 qna \qquad (2\text{-}62)$$

The total vibrational energy resulting from mode q is obtained by adding (2-58) and (2-62), leading to

$$E = \tfrac{1}{2} m \omega^2 S \quad \text{with} \quad S = \sum_n \sin^2 qna \qquad (2\text{-}63)$$

Note that this expression is independent of time. Suppose now we identify (2-62) with the potential energy of a harmonic oscillator, i.e., with the last term in (2-57). This requires evidently

$$y = (mS/M)^{1/2} \cos \omega t \qquad (2\text{-}64)$$

If the vibrational mode were indeed equivalent with a harmonic oscillator, the kinetic energy should be, according to (2-57) and (2-64),

$$E_{\text{kin}} = \tfrac{1}{2} M (dy/dt)^2 = \tfrac{1}{2} m \omega^2 S \sin^2 \omega t$$

This expression is identical with (2-58), which proves the sought equivalence. The average energy associated with a particular mode of vibration of angular frequency ω_q is thus given by Planck's formula (2-14), i.e.,

$$\langle \epsilon \rangle = \frac{\hbar \omega_q}{e^{\hbar \omega_q / kT} - 1} \qquad (2\text{-}65)$$

The number of quanta n_q associated with the vibrational mode of wave vector q at a temperature T is

$$n_q = \langle \epsilon \rangle / \hbar \omega_q = (e^{\hbar \omega_q / kT} - 1)^{-1} \tag{2-66}$$

The quanta are commonly referred to as phonons of frequency ω_q, in analogy with photons in the case of electromagnetic radiation. The concept of a phonon is convenient in the discussion of interaction of electrons with lattice vibrations in the theory of electrical conductivity. A phonon, like a photon, has particle aspects in the sense that one can associate with it a certain energy $h\nu_q = \hbar \omega_q$ as well as a momentum $p = h\nu_q / c_s$, where c_s is the velocity of propagation of the vibrational mode. Thus the "collision" between a phonon and an electron may be treated as a collision between two particles for which the conservation laws of energy and momentum hold.

2-11. The specific heat of a one-dimensional lattice of identical atoms

From the results obtained in the preceding sections it is a simple matter to derive an expression for the specific heat of a one-dimensional lattice of identical atoms. In the standing-wave representation the number of modes in the wave vector interval dq is, according to (2-56), equal to $L\,dq/\pi$ where L is the length of the chain. The wave vector is confined between 0 and π/a. The vibrational energy of the lattice at a temperature T is thus given by

$$E = \frac{L}{\pi} \int_0^{\pi/a} \frac{\hbar \omega_q}{\exp(\hbar \omega_q / kT) - 1}\, dq \tag{2-67}$$

where the summation over the possible wave vectors defined by (2-50) has been approximated by an integral. Employing the relation between ω_q and q as given by (2-44), one may replace dq by

$$\frac{dq}{d\omega}\, d\omega = \frac{2d\omega}{a\omega_{max} \cos(qa/2)} = \frac{2d\omega}{a(\omega_{max}^2 - \omega^2)^{1/2}} \tag{2-68}$$

Hence

$$E = \frac{2L}{\pi a} \int_0^{\omega_{max}} \frac{\hbar \omega\, d\omega}{[\exp(\hbar \omega / kT) - 1][\omega_{max}^2 - \omega^2]^{1/2}} \tag{2-69}$$

The specific heat as function of temperature may be obtained by differentiating with respect to T. The result is represented by the lower curve in Fig. 2-11 for a critical temperature $\theta = \hbar \omega_{max}/k = 200°\text{K}$. It is of interest to compare this result with the continuum theory corresponding to the Debye approximation in one dimension. According to (2-24) the number of vibrational modes in the range $d\omega$ of a continuous string of length L is equal to $L\,d\omega/\pi c_s$, where the velocity of propagation c_s is a constant. Applying this model to a string of atoms by a suitable cut-off of the frequency spectrum, one obtains for the vibrational energy

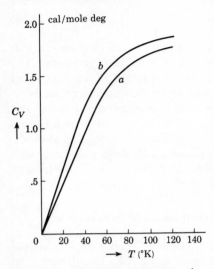

$$E = \frac{L}{\pi c_s} \int_0^{\omega'_{max}} \frac{\hbar\omega\,d\omega}{\exp(\hbar\omega/kT) - 1} \tag{2-70}$$

The upper limit ω'_{max} in this case is determined by the fact that the number of modes is equal to the number of particles N in the string, i.e.,

$$(L/\pi c_s) \int_0^{\omega'_{max}} d\omega = N$$

or $\tag{2-71}$

$$\omega'_{max} = N\pi c_s/L$$

Fig. 2-11. Curve a represents the specific heat versus T for a monoatomic linear lattice according to (2-69); curve b refers to the Debye theory, representing C_V derived from (2-70). In both cases $\theta = 200°K$. [After M. Blackman, *Proc. Roy. Soc.*, London, **A148**, 365 (1935)]

Note that this limit is different from that appearing in (2-69). The specific heat calculated on the basis of (2-70) is given by the upper curve in Fig. 2-11 again for a critical temperature $\theta = \hbar\omega'_{max}/k = 200°K$.

2-12. The vibrational modes of a diatomic linear lattice

Consider a diatomic lattice in one dimension as illustrated in Fig. 2-12; the distance between nearest neighbors will be denoted by a. The particles are numbered in such a way that the even numbers have a mass M, the odd ones m. In analogy with (2-42) we now have the following equations of motion, assuming nearest neighbor interaction only:

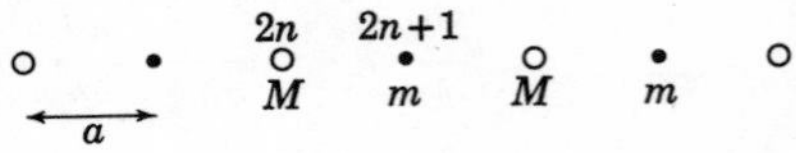

Fig. 2-12. A linear chain of equidistant masspoints M and m.

$$M\ddot{x}_{2n} = f(x_{2n-1} + x_{2n+1} - 2x_{2n})$$

$$m\ddot{x}_{2n+1} = f(x_{2n} + x_{2n+2} - 2x_{2n+1}) \tag{2-72}$$

We try to solve these equations by running waves of the type

$$x_{2n} = Ae^{-i(\omega t - 2nqa)} \quad \text{and} \quad x_{2n+1} = Be^{-i[\omega t - (2n+1)qa]} \tag{2-73}$$

where q is the wave vector of a particular mode of vibration; A and B

are the amplitudes corresponding to particles of mass M and m, respectively. Substitution of the solution into (2-72) yields the following two equations:

$$(M\omega^2 - 2f)A + 2Bf\cos qa = 0$$

$$(m\omega^2 - 2f)B + 2Af\cos qa = 0 \qquad (2\text{-}74)$$

This system has nonvanishing solutions for A and B only if the determinant of the coefficients of A and B vanishes, i.e.,

$$\begin{vmatrix} (M\omega^2 - 2f) & 2f\cos qa \\ 2f\cos qa & (m\omega^2 - 2f) \end{vmatrix} = 0 \qquad (2\text{-}75)$$

This gives for the square of the frequency the following two possibilities:

$$\omega^2 = f\left(\frac{1}{m} + \frac{1}{M}\right) \pm f\left[\left(\frac{1}{m} + \frac{1}{M}\right)^2 - \frac{4\sin^2 qa}{Mm}\right]^{1/2} \qquad (2\text{-}76)$$

Since ω should be positive, each value of ω^2 leads to a single value for ω. Thus in contrast to the monoatomic lattice, there are now two angular frequencies ω_+ and ω_- corresponding to a single value of the wave vector q. In a plot of ω versus q (Fig. 2-13) this leads to two "branches"; the one corresponding to ω_- is called the acoustical branch, the one associated with ω_+ is the optical branch. These two branches will now be discussed on the assumption that $M > m$. For $q = 0$ we obtain

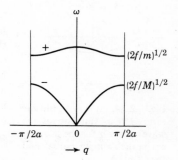

Fig. 2-13. The optical (upper curve) and acoustical (lower curve) branches corresponding to a diatomic linear lattice.

$$\omega_+ = \left[2f\left(\frac{1}{m} + \frac{1}{M}\right)\right]^{1/2} \quad \text{and} \quad \omega_- = 0 \quad \text{for} \quad q = 0 \qquad (2\text{-}77)$$

From the form of (2-76) it is observed that here, as in the monatomic case, the frequency is a periodic function of the wave vector. The first zone thus limits the values of q to the range between $-\pi/2a$ and $+\pi/2a$ as shown in Fig. 2-13. For $q = \pm\pi/2a$, the two angular frequencies are evidently

$$\omega_+ = (2f/m)^{1/2} \quad \text{and} \quad \omega_- = (2f/M)^{1/2} \quad \text{for} \quad q = \pm\pi/2a \qquad (2\text{-}78)$$

The complete curves for ω_+ and ω_- versus q are illustrated in Fig. 2-13. The larger the mass ratio M/m, the wider the frequency gap between the two branches. The existence of a "forbidden" frequency (or energy) region will also be encountered in the electron theory of solids. Note also that the optical band becomes narrower with increasing M/m ratio.

It is of interest to investigate the physical difference between the two branches. This may be done by calculating the ratio of the amplitudes A and B in the two cases. Let us first consider the situation for $q = 0$, i.e., for infinite wavelength. From (2-77) and (2-74) it follows that

for the acoustical branch: $\qquad A = B$

$\qquad\qquad\qquad\qquad\qquad\qquad\qquad$ for $q = 0$ $\qquad$ (2-79)

for the optical branch: $\qquad -MA = mB$

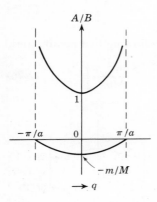

Fig. 2-14. The amplitude ratio A/B as function of the wave vector q for the acoustical branch (upper curve) and the optical branch (lower curve). A corresponds to m, B to M and $M > m$.

In other words, in the acoustical branch all particles move in the same direction. In the optical branch, on the other hand, the two types of particles move in opposite directions in such a manner that the center of gravity in each cell remains at rest. For other values of q the ratio A/B may be calculated from (2-76) and (2-74). The results are shown in Fig. 2-14. It is observed that at the edge of the zone, i.e., for $q = \pm \pi/2a$, the following conclusion can be drawn: in the acoustical branch the light particles of mass m are all at rest $(B = 0)$, whereas in the optical branch the heavy particles of mass M are at rest $(A = 0)$. For a more detailed discussion we refer to Brillouin, *op. cit.*, Sec. 15.

A few remarks may be made here in connection with the absorption of electro-magnetic radiation by ionic crystals. It is well known that these crystals absorb strongly in the infrared region of the spectrum, corresponding to a frequency $\nu \simeq 10^{13}$ sec^{-1} and a wavelength $\lambda \simeq 3 \times 10^{-3}$ cm. Evidently the wave vector of these waves is of the order $q = 2\pi/\lambda \simeq 10^3$ cm^{-1}. Now the limit of the zone of the lattice vibrations corresponds to $\pi/2a \simeq 10^8$ cm^{-1}. In other words, in the ω versus q plot, these vibrations are practically those corresponding to the maximum of the upper branch. The infrared absorption frequency should thus be approximately given by

$$\omega_{\text{optical}} \simeq \left[2f \left(\frac{1}{m} + \frac{1}{M} \right) \right]^{1/2}$$

in accordance with (2-77). It is for this reason that the upper branch is called the optical branch. The infrared absorption thus corresponds to a vibration of the positive ion lattice relative to the negative ion lattice such that the center of gravity in each cell remains at rest.

2-13. Vibrational spectra and specific heat of three-dimensional lattices

The calculations of the vibrational modes of a one-dimensional lattice may be extended to two and three dimensions. For the general theory we refer to the literature, and it may suffice here to mention some of the results obtained.[16] The vibrational spectrum of a two-dimensional lattice was first calculated by Blackman, who also computed the spectrum for a

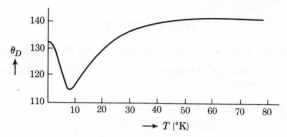

Fig. 2-15.   The Debye temperature as function of T for a simple cubic lattice. [After Blackman, ref. 17]

simple cubic lattice.[17] From these results he was able to calculate the specific heat in the manner outlined for the one-dimensional case in Sec. 2-11. In the low temperature region the specific heat thus obtained may be equated to the Debye formula (2-37) and the Debye temperature θ_D can be computed for different temperatures. The results obtained by

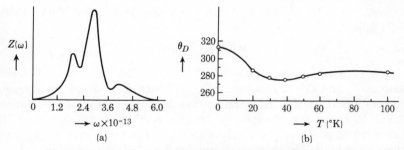

Fig. 2-16.   The vibrational spectrum of NaCl is given in (a). The circles in (b) represent θ_D calculated on the basis of (a); the curve in (b) is obtained from experiment. [After Kellerman, ref. 18]

Blackman for the simple cubic lattice are represented in Fig. 2-15. It is observed that θ_D is by no means constant, indicating the possibility of appreciable deviations from the Debye theory in actual crystals.

[16] See M. Born and M. Goppert-Mayer, *op. cit.*; F. Seitz, *op. cit.*; L. Brillouin, *op. cit.*

[17] M. Blackman, *Proc. Roy. Soc.* (London), **A148**, 384 (1935); **A159**, 416 (1937); *Proc. Cambridge Phil. Soc.*, **33**, 94 (1937).

An investigation of NaCl has been made by Kellermann,[18] using ionic and repulsive forces between the particles. Figure 2-16a gives the vibrational spectrum of NaCl obtained by Kellermann, and the difference with a continuum spectrum as used in the Debye theory is obvious. The Debye temperature θ_D as function of T calculated by Kellermann is given by the circles in Fig. 2-16b. It is observed that the theory is in remarkably good agreement with the curve obtained experimentally.

REFERENCES

M. Born and M. Goppert-Mayer, *Handbuch der Physik*, **24** (2) (1933).

M. Born and K. Huang, *Dynamical Theory of Crystal Lattices*, Oxford, New York, 1954.

M. Blackman, *Reports on Progress in Physics*, **8**, 11 (1941).

L. Brillouin, *Wave Propagation in Periodic Structures*, Dover, New York, 1953.

A. Eucken, *Handbuch der Experimental Physik*, **8** (1) (1929).

P. H. Keesom and N. Pearlman, *Encyclopedia of Physics*, **14**, Springer, Berlin, 1956.

J. de Launay, in F. Seitz and D. Turnbull (eds.), *Solid State Physics*, Vol. 2, Academic Press, New York, 1956.

E. Schrödinger, *Handbuch der Physik*, **10** (1933).

F. Seitz, *Modern Theory of Solids*, McGraw Hill, New York, 1940, Chap. 3.

PROBLEMS

2-1. (a) Give a derivation of expression (2-4) for the difference between C_p and C_V. (b) Calculate $C_p - C_V$ per mole of sodium at room temperature if at this temperature the compressibility of sodium is 12.3×10^{-12} cm^2 dyne^{-1} and the linear coefficient of expansion is 6.22×10^{-5}; compare the result with $C_p - C_V$ for a monatomic gas. Also calculate the Grüneisen constant for Na.

2-2. The possible energy levels of a rigid rotator according to quantum mechanics are given by $E_n = (\hbar^2/2J)n(n+1)$ where J is the moment of inertia and $n = 0, 1, 2, \ldots$. For the molecules H_2 and Cl_2 calculate the energy difference between the ground state and the first excited state for rotation about an axis perpendicular to the line joining the nuclei. (Answers. Resp., 14.7×10^{-3} and 0.06×10^{-3} ev.) Also estimate the value of $E_1 - E_0$ for rotation about the line joining the nuclei and show

[18] E. W. Kellermann, *Phil. Trans.*, **A238**, 513 (1940); *Proc. Roy. Soc.* (London), **A178**, 17 (1941).

that this rotation does not in general contribute to the rotational specific heat. At which temperatures for H_2 and Cl_2 do quantum effects enter in the rotational specific heat? If it is given that the number of possible states corresponding to an energy level E_n for a rotator is equal to $2n(n + 1)$, show on the basis of statistical mechanics that the rotational specific heat for a molecule such as Cl_2 at room temperature is R cal per mole. (*Hint*: According to statistical mechanics the average energy at T is given by

$$\langle E \rangle = [\sum_n E_n Z_n \exp (-E_n/kT)]/[\sum_n Z_n \exp (-E_n/kT)]$$

where Z_n is the number of possible states associated with E_n. For the problem under consideration one can replace the summations by integrals.)

2-3. Discuss in some detail the specific heat of a diatomic molecule (including translation, rotation, and vibration). What is the value of C_p/C_V in various temperature regions?

2-4. Consider an array of N similar atoms, the separation between nearest neighbors being a. Discuss the specific heat of the system on the basis of the Debye approximation and show that at low temperatures the specific heat is proportional to T.

2-5. Discuss the specific heat of a two-dimensional square lattice with a nearest neighbor separation a on the basis of the Debye approximation. Show that at low temperatures the specific heat is proportional to T^2.

2-6. Consider a cavity filled with black-body radiation in equilibrium with a temperature bath T. As is well known, the energy of radiation per unit volume u is a function only of T; also, the radiation pressure $p = u/3$. In a p-V diagram, carry out a Carnot cycle with this "gas": first expand isothermally from V_1 to V_2, then expand adiabatically such that the temperature drops slightly from $T - \Delta T$; finally, return to the starting point by isothermal and adiabatic compression. By making use of a well-known theorem about the efficiency of transforming heat into work, show that the energy density u is proportional to T^4. Explain why the specific heat of the radiation gas is always proportional to T^3, whereas for a solid in the Debye approximation this is true only at low temperatures.

2-7. Discuss in some detail the analogy between the mechanical properties of an array of equidistant similar atoms and a low-pass electric filter. (See, for example, Brillouin, *op. cit.*)

2-8. Discuss the specific heat of a solid on the basis of the cut-off procedure suggested by Born (Sec. 2-7) and show that one arrives at an expression of the type (2-41).

Chapter 3

SOME PROPERTIES OF METALLIC LATTICES

3-1. The structure of metals

Most metals crystallize in one of the following three structures: the body-centered cubic lattice (b.c.c.) in which each atom is surrounded by eight nearest neighbors, the face-centered cubic lattice (f.c.c.) in which a given atom has twelve nearest neighbors, and the hexagonal close packed lattice (h.c.p.), also with a coordination number of twelve.

From the dimensions of the elementary cell, as obtained from X-ray diffraction or otherwise, one may define a radius for the atoms on the assumption that they are spherical in shape; the radius so defined is then given by half the distance between nearest neighbors. That this procedure has a physical meaning follows from the fact that for those metals which crystallize in more than one structure, each structure being stable over a certain range of temperatures, the radii so obtained are very nearly the same. Table 3-1 gives the distances of closest approach (twice the atomic

Table 3-1. Structure and Distance of Closest Approach (at 20 °C) for Metals which Crystallize in Any of the Three Simple Metallic Structures. The asterisks indicate the normal form.

Body-centered cubic		Face-centered cubic		Hexagonal close packed	
Metal	d (Å)	Metal	d (Å)	Metal	d (Å)
Li	3.039	Cu	2.556	α Be*	2.225
Na	3.715	Ag	2.888	Mg	3.196
K	4.627	Au	2.884	Zn	2.664
V	2.632	Al	2.862	Cd	2.979
Ta	2.860	Th	3.60	α Tl*	3.407
Cr	2.498	Pb	3.499	α Ti*	2.89
Mo	2.725	γ Fe (extra-			
		polated)	2.525	α Zr*	3.17
α W*	2.739	β Co	2.511	Hf	3.15
α Fe*	2.481	Ni	2.491	α Co*	2.506
δ Fe (1425 °C)	2.54	β Rh*	2.689	Ru	2.649
		Pd	2.750	Os	2.675
		Ir	2.714		
		Pt	2.775		

radii) for metals which crystallize in one of the three structures mentioned above.[1]

The b.c.c. and f.c.c. lattices have been represented in Fig. 1-4. The h.c.p. structure represented in Fig. 3-1 is closely related to the f.c.c. structure, as may be illustrated with reference to Fig. 3-2. Let the dots in Fig. 3-2 represent a layer of spheres in close packing. On top of this we place another layer, represented by the crosses. The atoms of a third layer may now be placed on top of the second one in either of two ways: (1) they can be placed in positions corresponding to the open circles in Fig. 3-2, or (2) they can be placed in positions identical in projection with

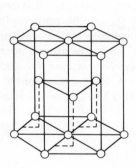

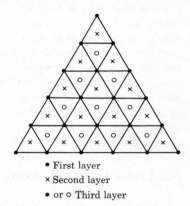

• First layer
× Second layer
• or ○ Third layer

Fig. 3-1. The hexagonal close packed structure.

Fig. 3-2. Illustrating the relationship between the h.c.p. (●×●× etc.) and the f.c.c. (●×○●×○●, etc.) structures.

those of layer 1 (dots). Thus the two possible arrangements may be represented symbolically by the sequences 1, 2, 1, 2, ... and 1, 2, 3, 1, 2, 3, ... The former corresponds to the h.c.p. structure; the latter is equivalent to the f.c.c. structure as may readily be seen by identifying the layers of Fig. 3-2 with atomic planes perpendicular to a body diagonal in the f.c.c. structure. Hence, both the h.c.p. and f.c.c. structures correspond to a close packing of spheres; the b.c.c. structure does not. The fraction of volume occupied by spheres in closest packing is $2^{1/2}(\pi/6) \simeq 0.74$, as shown in Problem 1-1. The density ratio for a f.c.c. (or h.c.p.) lattice and a b.c.c. lattice built up of spheres of the same radii is 1.09 (see Problem 1-1)·

The reason for a particular metal to crystallize in a particular structure must be sought in the fact that the free energy $E - TS$ of the system for this structure is lower than that for any other structure.[2] The same remark

---

[1] For a complete list of lattice parameters, see, for example, C. S. Barrett, *Structure of Metals*, 2d ed., McGraw-Hill, New York, 1952, p. 646.

[2] For the thermodynamic conditions for equilibrium, see Appendix A.

may be made with reference to those metals which have different structures in different temperature regions (allotropy). This phenomenon is exhibited especially by the three- and four-valent metals and by the transition metals.[3] For example, α Fe (b.c.c.) is stable up to 910°C; between 910°C and 1400°C the stable structure is γ Fe (f.c.c.); between 1400°C and the melting point (1530°C) the structure is again b.c.c. (δ Fe). Here again, the transformation from one structure to another is dictated by the requirement of minimum free energy. This does not mean that such transformations take place as soon as the existing structure becomes unstable. In fact, a transformation of structure involves a rearrangement of atoms, and such a process may take a long time. The reason is that even though the free energy after the transformation is lower than in the initial state, the two states are usually separated by an energy barrier or activation energy (see Sec. 3-5). Thermodynamics specifies only the equilibrium condition but does not give any information about the velocity of the reaction or processes involved in establishing equilibrium. From the atomic point of view, the stability of crystal structures is a problem of cohesive energy, involving the interaction between the atoms. A brief discussion of the cohesive energy of metals is presented in Sec. 10-13 based on the electron theory of metals.

3-2. Lattice defects and configurational entropy

According to thermodynamics, the equilibrium of a solid (under low external pressure) at a temperature T is determined by the minimum value of the free energy $F = E - TS$ (see Appendix A). We shall see below that this condition leads necessarily to the existence of a certain amount of disorder in the lattice at all temperatures $T > 0°K$. We emphasize from the beginning that the lattice disorder or lattice defects discussed in this section do not include accidental faults in the crystal resulting from non-ideal growing conditions; the defects under consideration are present as a result of the thermodynamic equilibrium conditions. Frenkel[4] was the first to recognize that lattice defects play an important role in a number of physical properties of solids, and Schottky[5] has contributed a great deal by expanding these ideas. The simplest examples of lattice disorder are vacant lattice sites and interstitial atoms (see Fig. 3-3); the latter are

[3] Elements with incompletely filled inner electron shells are called transition elements. For example, Fe, Ni, and Co have an incompletely filled 3d shell, while the 4s shell is occupied; these metals thus belong to the transition metals. For the notation of s, p, d, f, g, ... electrons, see textbooks on atomic theory; see also Sec. 18-2.

[4] J. Frenkel, *Z. Physik*, **35**, 652 (1926); also J. Frenkel, *Kinetic Theory of Liquids*, Oxford, New York, 1946, an extremely clear book, which, notwithstanding its title, contains a great deal of information about solids.

[5] See, for example, C. Wagner and W. Schottky, *Z. physik. Chem.*, **B11** 163 (1931); W. Schottky, *Z. physik. Chem.*, **B29**, 353 (1935).

atoms occupying positions in the lattice which in the perfect lattice would be unoccupied. In discussions of this kind it is necessary to point out the distinction between what we shall refer to as *thermal* and *configurational* (or mixing) *entropy*; these quantities will be denoted, respectively, by S_{th} and S_{cf}. The thermal entropy S_{th} is determined by the number of different ways W_{th} in which the total vibrational energy of the crystal may be distributed over the possible vibrational modes; according to the well-known Boltzmann relation (see Appendix E),[6]

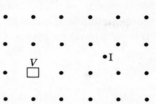

Fig. 3-3. A vacancy (V) and an interstitial atom (I) in a two-dimensional square lattice.

$$S_{th} = k \log W_{th} \tag{3-1}$$

For example, in the Einstein model of a solid (see Sec. 2-4), W_{th} stands for the number of different ways in which the energy of vibration may be distributed over the $3N$ harmonic oscillators representing the solid consisting of N atoms. When ν is the Einstein frequency, and $h\nu \ll kT$, we have, according to Problem 3-3,

$$S_{th} = 3Nk[1 + \log (kT/h\nu)] \tag{3-2}$$

The configurational entropy of a crystal has nothing to do with the distribution of energy; it is determined solely by the number of different ways W_{cf} in which the atoms may be arranged over the available number of lattice sites. Consider for example a lattice containing N_a atoms of type A and N_b atoms of type B and assume that the lattice sites are all equivalent in the sense that a given lattice site may be occupied by A or B. It is left to the reader to show in Problem 3-2 that

$$W_{cf} = \frac{(N_a + N_b)!}{N_a! \, N_b!} \tag{3-3}$$

represents the number of different arrangements of N_a A atoms and N_b B atoms over a total of $(N_a + N_b)$ lattice points. The configurational entropy associated with W_{cf} is again given by the Boltzmann relation,

$$S_{cf} = k \log W_{cf} = k \log \left[\frac{(N_a + N_b)!}{N_a! \, N_b!} \right] \tag{3-4}$$

[6] For an elementary treatment of statistical thermodynamics and a number of applications to solid state physics, see R. W. Gurney, *Introduction to Statistical Mechanics*, McGraw-Hill, New York, 1949; also M. Born, *Atomic Physics*, 5th ed., Hafner, New York, 1951.

For a perfect crystal containing identical atoms and in the absence of any lattice defects, $W_{cf} = 1$ and $S_{cf} = 0$ because there is only one possible arrangement of the atoms. The total entropy occurring in the usual thermodynamic formulas is equal to the sum of the thermal and configurational entropies, i.e.,

$$S = S_{th} + S_{cf} \qquad (3\text{-}5)$$

The results obtained above may be used to explain qualitatively the reason for the existence of lattice defects at any temperature $T > 0$. Suppose, for example, that in a perfect metallic crystal we produce a certain number of vacant lattice sites by transferring atoms from the interior of the crystal to the surface. This will require a certain amount of energy, i.e., E increases. Consequently F increases and this by itself is thus unfavorable in the thermodynamic sense. On the other hand, the creation of the vacancies increases the disorder in the crystal and thus increases the configurational entropy from zero to a certain value determined by the number of vacancies n produced. In fact, according to (3-4) the configurational entropy associated with the possible arrangements of N atoms and n vacancies over a total of $(N + n)$ lattice sites is

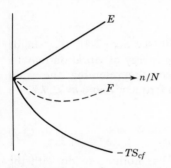

Fig. 3-4. Schematic representation of the energy and the configurational entropy term as function of the fraction of vacant lattice sites n/N. The minimum of the free energy F determines the equilibrium value of n/N.

$$S_{cf} = k \log \left[\frac{(N + n)!}{N!\, n!} \right] \qquad (3\text{-}6)$$

Now, because the entropy enters in the free energy expression in the form $-TS$, an increase in entropy reduces F and is thus favorable thermodynamically. As a result of the above described competition between energy on the one hand and entropy on the other, the stable configuration is one in which a certain fraction of the lattice sites is unoccupied. A schematic representation of F as function of the fraction n/N has been given in Fig. 3-4.; it has been assumed for simplicity that the thermal entropy is independent of n/N. The equilibrium corresponds to the minimum value of F at the temperature T. Any further increase in the disorder of the lattice would require an energy larger than the associated reduction due to the increase in entropy. Similar arguments may be applied to other types of lattice defects. In the next section we shall discuss the number of lattice defects as function of temperature quantitatively.

3-3. The number of vacancies and interstitials as function of temperature

Consider a perfect lattice containing N similar atoms at a temperature T; the free energy of this (unstable) crystal will be denoted by $F_{\text{perfect}}(T)$. Suppose we create n vacant lattice sites; let the energy required to create one vacancy be ϕ_v. We shall assume that ϕ_v is independent of n, which is justified as long as $n \ll N$; also, we assume that no two vacancies are nearest neighbors of each other. The energy of the imperfect crystal is then increased by $n\phi_v$ relative to that of the perfect crystal. Also there is associated with the imperfect crystal a configurational entropy S_{cf} given by (3-6). Furthermore, let us assume that the thermal entropy increases per vacancy by an amount ΔS_{th}; the physical reason for this change will be discussed below. We may then write for the free energy of the imperfect crystal

$$F(n, T) = F_{\text{perfect}}(T) + n\phi_v - nT\Delta S_{\text{th}} - kT \log \frac{(N + n)!}{N! \, n!} \qquad (3\text{-}7)$$

In order to find the equilibrium value of n, we make use of the fact that in equilibrium $(\partial F/\partial n)_T = 0$. Employing Stirling's formula in the form $\log x! \simeq x \log x$ for $x \gg 1$, we find from (3-7),

$$n/(N + n) \simeq n/N = e^{\Delta S_{\text{th}}/k} e^{-\phi_v/kT} \qquad (3\text{-}8)$$

Thus, apart from a constant determined by ΔS_{th}, the probability for a given lattice site to be unoccupied is given by a Boltzmann factor containing the energy of formation of a vacancy ϕ_v. We shall see in Sec. 3-4 that for metals ϕ_v is of the order of one electron volt. The type of disorder discussed above is usually called Schottky disorder; vacancies are frequently referred to as Schottky defects.

So far, our treatment has been essentially a thermodynamic one. In order to get an insight into the physical meaning of the thermal entropy change ΔS_{th} per vacancy, we shall consider a simple Einstein model of a solid. The thermal entropy of the perfect crystal is then equivalent to the thermal entropy of a system of $3N$ harmonic oscillators with the Einstein frequency ν and is given by (3-2) as long as $kT \gg h\nu$.

In the imperfect crystal, the atoms neighboring a vacancy will have a vibrational frequency smaller than ν because the restoring forces are reduced, particularly along the direction of the line joining the atom and the vacancy. In order to simplify the discussion, we shall assume that in the imperfect crystal each atom neighboring a vacancy is, in the Einstein model, equivalent to 3 harmonic oscillators of a frequency $\nu' < \nu$. Thus when x is the number of atoms surrounding a vacancy, the Einstein model as used here leads to

$3nx$ oscillators of frequency ν'

$(3N - 3nx)$ oscillators of frequency ν

The thermal entropy of the imperfect crystal is then, in analogy with (3-2)

$$S_{\text{th}} = 3nxk \left[1 + \log (kT/h\nu')\right] + (3N - 3nx)k \left[1 + \log (kT/h\nu)\right] \quad (3\text{-}9)$$

Subtracting (3-2) from (3-9) and dividing the result by n, one finds for the increase in thermal entropy per produced vacancy,

$$\Delta S_{\text{th}} = 3xk \log (\nu/\nu') \quad (3\text{-}10)$$

Although the model employed here is a simple one, it clearly demonstrates the fact that ΔS_{th} is a consequence of the change in the frequency spectrum of the lattice vibrations. For this model, substitution of (3-10) into (3-8) leads to

$$n/N = (\nu/\nu')^{3x} e^{-\phi_v/kT} \quad (3\text{-}11)$$

Because $\nu > \nu'$, we see that the change in thermal entropy favors the formation of vacancies, because the pre-exponential factor is >1. This factor may be large because $3x$ is a rather large number (24 for b.c.c. and 36 for f.c.c.).

A remark may be made here about the temperature dependence of ϕ_v. It is evident that as T increases, the lattice expands, the binding forces are reduced, and thus ϕ_v decreases with temperature. In first approximation one may write a linear relationship between ϕ_v and T, i.e.,

$$\phi_v = \phi_{v0} (1 - \alpha T) \quad (3\text{-}12)$$

where α is a temperature coefficient and ϕ_{v0} the energy of formation of a vacancy at $T = 0$. In the literature[7] one frequently encounters the following argument in connection with expressions of the type (3-8) or (3-11): when one substitutes (3-12) into (3-8), one obtains

$$n/N = e^{\Delta S_{\text{th}}/k} e^{\alpha \phi_{v0}/k} e^{-\phi_{v0}/kT}$$

and one argues that if it were possible to measure n/N, a plot of $\log (n/N)$ versus $1/kT$ would give ϕ_{v0} rather than ϕ_v; furthermore, it is argued that the pre-exponential factor is multiplied by $\exp [\alpha \phi_{v0}/k]$. These arguments are, however, incorrect since they neglect the temperature variation of ΔS accompanying the change in ϕ_v.[8] In fact, for zero pressure we have

$$d(\Delta S)/dT = (1/T) \, d\phi_v/dT$$

and measurements of n/N as function of T actually measure ϕ_v. (See also Sec. 7-1.)

[7] See, for example, N. F. Mott and R. W. Gurney, *Electronic Processes in Ionic Crystals*, Oxford, New York, 1946, p. 30; W. Jost, *Diffusion in Solids, Liquids, Gases*, Academic Press, New York, 1952, p. 116.

[8] This has been pointed out by C. Zener in W. Shockley (ed.), *Imperfections in Nearly Perfect Crystals*, Wiley, New York, 1952, p. 296. Similar objections in connection with the theory of diffusion in ionic crystals have been raised by Y. Haven and J. H. van Santen, *Philips Research Repts.*, **7**, 474 (1952).

Other types of lattice defects may be treated in a similar way as vacancies. Consider, for example, Frenkel defects, which are formed when atoms which initially occupy a normal lattice position migrate into interstitial lattice positions. A Frenkel defect thus consists of two components: a vacancy plus an interstitial atom. We leave it up to the reader to show in Problem 3-7 that the number of Frenkel defects in equilibrium at a temperature T is given by

$$n = (NN_i)^{1/2} \, e^{\Delta S_{th}/2k} e^{-\phi_F/2kT} \qquad \text{for} \quad n \ll N \qquad (3\text{-}13)$$

where N is the number of atoms, N_i is the number of possible interstitial positions, ΔS_{th} is the change in thermal entropy per Frenkel defect, and ϕ_F is the energy of formation of a Frenkel defect. The factors 2 appear in the exponentials because a Frenkel defect has two components. In chemical language the formation of a Frenkel defect may be written in the form of an equilibrium reaction:

$$\left.\begin{array}{l}\text{occupied lattice site} \\ + \text{ unoccupied interstitial site}\end{array}\right\} \rightleftharpoons \text{vacancy} + \text{interstitial} \qquad (3\text{-}14)$$

From this, readers familiar with the law of mass action will readily recognize that n should be proportional to $(NN_i)^{1/2}$ and that the exponentials in (3-13) are correct.

3-4. The formation of lattice defects in metals

There are a large number of different types of lattice disorder in metals. However, usually only a few of these will predominate, viz., those for which the energy of formation is smallest; this is evident from the results obtained in the preceding section. A few words may be said here about the processes and the energy involved in the creation of simple lattice defects such as vacancies and interstitials. A vacant lattice site may be formed, for example, by a process such as indicated in Fig. 3-5a. Suppose an atom such as B jumps into position A on the surface; the vacant site it leaves behind may then become occupied by an atom such as C when the latter jumps into the vacancy. Successive jumps of this kind thus lead to the diffusion of a vacant lattice site from the surface into the interior of the crystal. The external surface is not necessarily the only source of supply of vacancies; internal cracks, pores, and dislocations (see Sec. 3-12) serve a similar purpose in this respect. The sources mentioned may also act as sinks for the disposal of vacancies; for example, when the temperature of a crystal is lowered and the density of vacancies must be reduced.

The energy of formation of a vacancy by a process of the kind described above is determined essentially by the energy expended during the first few jumps. Once the vacancy is separated from the source by several lattice distances, the energy of the crystal becomes essentially independent of the lattice site "occupied" by the vacancy (at least as long as it does not become a nearest neighbor of another vacancy or lattice defect). This is represented schematically in Fig. 3-5b. It should be kept in mind, however, that although the energy before and after a jump may be the same, a certain "activation energy" is always required to make the jump. In other words, two possible neighboring lattice sites for a vacancy are separated by a barrier, as indicated by ϵ_j in Fig. 3-5b. It is for this reason that the

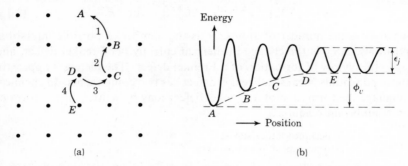

(a)   (b)

Fig. 3-5. Sequence of jumps producing a vacancy which migrates into the interior of the crystal (a). In (b) the potential energy of the vacancy is shown schematically as it diffuses in; the limiting value ϕ_v is the energy of formation, ε_j is the jump activation energy of the vacancy.

establishment of thermal equilibrium may require a long time, especially at low temperatures where the mobility of the vacancies, or rather of the atoms neighboring a vacancy, becomes small. It is thus possible, by quenching a crystal from a relatively high to a low temperature, to "freeze in" a high-temperature configuration of the atoms.

A Frenkel defect may arise as a result of the migration of a "normal" atom into a nearby interstitial position. When the interstitial does not fall back into the vacancy so produced, either the interstitial or the vacancy, or both, may migrate further away from the point of creation and ultimately one is left with a free interstitial and a free vacancy. Thus there are various degrees of dissociation before the two components of the Frenkel defect are free from each others' influence. The schematic representation of Fig. 3-5b is therefore also valid for the formation of a Frenkel defect.

A theoretical calculation of the energy ϕ_v required to create a vacancy is quite complicated. This may be appreciated from the following arguments: Consider a macroscopic piece of metal containing N atoms. Suppose that it requires a total energy E to separate all atoms from each other. When ϵ_s is the average energy required to take an atom from the surface of the metal to infinity, then $\epsilon_s = E/N$; ϵ_s is the sublimation energy. For copper, for example, $\epsilon_s = 3.52$ ev. Consider now an atom in the interior of the crystal; let the potential energy of this atom due to the presence of all other atoms in the crystal be $-\epsilon_i$. The total dissociation energy of the crystal E is then equal to $N\epsilon_i/2$, the factor 2 arising from the fact that the interaction energy between any two atoms should be counted only once; thus, $\epsilon_i = 2\epsilon_s$, which means that an atom at the surface is, on the average, bound half as strongly as an atom in the interior. The physical meaning of ϵ_i may also be expressed in this way: it represents the energy required to remove an interior atom to infinity *if the position and the charge distribution of the other atoms remain unchanged.* The energy required to form a vacancy, i.e., the energy required to transfer an atom from the interior to the surface, may then be written in the form

$$\phi_v = \epsilon_i - \epsilon_r - \epsilon_s = \epsilon_s - \epsilon_r \qquad (3\text{-}15)$$

where ϵ_r is the energy gained as a result of the rearrangement of the electrons and atoms after the vacancy is formed. Huntington and Seitz have calculated ϕ_v for copper and find $\phi_v = 1.4$ ev.[9] This is in good agreement with an experimental value of 1.39 ev derived by Overhauser from annealing experiments of copper samples bombarded with 12 Mev deuterons.[10] With the value of $\epsilon_s = 3.52$ ev quoted above, it follows from (3-15) that $\epsilon_r = 1.7$ ev. Note that the rearrangement of the atoms and electrons around the vacancy contributes an energy term of the same order as ϕ_v itself; if ϵ_r were zero, ϕ_v would be equal to the sublimation energy.

In connection with the fact that establishment of thermal equilibrium of vacancies requires the migration of vacant lattice sites, we may mention that the activation energy for jumping (ϵ_j in Fig. 3-5b) of a single vacancy in copper is approximately 0.68 ev according to Overhauser.[10]

Vacancies may also occur in pairs, i.e., in the form of two neighboring vacant lattice sites. According to an estimate by Bartlett and Dienes it requires an energy between 0.23 and 0.59 ev to dissociate a pair of vacancies in copper; the actual value is probably closer to 0.59 ev than to the lower limit.[11]   A pair of vacancies probably has a much higher mobility in the lattice than a single vacancy, since one expects smaller repulsive interactions for a pair. Experimental evidence for the presence of pairs of vacancies in copper has been obtained by studying the annealing out of lattice imperfections produced by cold working and high-energy particle bombardment. It turns out that at rather low temperatures, the annealing proceeds at a much faster rate than can be explained by the diffusion of single vacancies. Larger aggregates of vacancies may also be present.

[9] H. B. Huntington and F. Seitz, *Phys. Rev.*, **61**, 315 (1942); **76**, 1728 (1949); H. B. Huntington, *Phys. Rev.*, **61**, 325 (1942).

[10] A. W. Overhauser, *Phys. Rev.*, **90**, 393 (1953).

[11] J. H. Bartlett and G. J. Dienes, *Phys. Rev.*, **89**, 848 (1953). For further information about vacancies in metals and alloys, see F. Seitz, *Acta Cryst.*, **3**, 335 (1950); C. Zener, *Acta Cryst.*, **3**, 346 (1950); J. Bardeen, *Phys. Rev.*, **76**, 1403 (1949); R. Smoluchowski and H. Burgess, *Phys. Rev.*, **76**, 309 (1949); H. R. Paneth, *Phys. Rev.*, **80**, 708 (1950).

3-5. Interstitial diffusion in metals

The simplest mathematical formulation of the diffusion of atoms in solids is based on the assumption that the net flow of atoms is proportional to the gradient of the concentration, i.e.,

$$I = -D \text{ grad } n \qquad (3\text{-}16)$$

where I is the flux of atoms in $\text{cm}^{-2} \text{ sec}^{-1}$, n is the number of atoms per cm^3, and D is the diffusion coefficient. In general, D is itself a function of the concentration n.[12] Expression (3-16) is known as Fick's first law; the minus sign indicates that the current flows from regions of high concentration to regions of low concentration. Applying the continuity equation, one obtains Fick's second law:

$$\partial n/\partial t = -\text{div } I = \text{div } (D \text{ grad } n) = D\nabla^2 n \qquad (3\text{-}17)$$

where the last equality is correct only if D is independent of the spatial coordinates, which implies in general that D is also independent of n.

We should mention that (3-16) may be generalized in a number of ways. For example, D is a scalar quantity only in cubic crystals or in an isotropic medium; in general, D is a tensor. A discussion of the properties of this tensor has been given by Onsager (see Sec. 1-12).[13] Also, the actual driving force of the diffusion process is not the concentration gradient but the gradient of the chemical potential. For a discussion of these and other generalizations we refer the reader to a review by le Claire.[14]

From measurements of diffusion coefficients at various temperatures it has been found that the temperature dependence of D is well described by the formula

$$D(T) = D_0 e^{-\epsilon/kT} \qquad (3\text{-}18)$$

where D_0 is a constant and ϵ is the activation energy of diffusion. An analysis of the experimental data by Dienes indicates that D_0 is mainly determined by the quantity ϵ/T_m, where T_m is the melting point of the solid; in fact, he concludes that D_0 is proportional to exp (ϵ/T_m).[15] A theoretical interpretation of this proportionality has been proposed by Zener.[16]

[12] See for example D. E. Thomas and C. E. Birchenall, *J. Metals*, August 1952, p. 867.

[13] L. Onsager, *Ann. N. Y. Acad. Sci.*, **46**, 241 (1945).

[14] A. D. le Claire, *Progress in Metal Physics*, Interscience, New York, Vol. 1 (1949), Vol. 5 (1954).

[15] G. J. Dienes, *J. Appl. Phys.*, **21**, 1189 (1950).

[16] C. Zener in W. Shockley (ed.), *Imperfections in Nearly Perfect Crystals*, Wiley, New York, p. 299.

From the atomic point of view, the simplest type of diffusion in solids is the diffusion of *interstitial atoms*. The reason is that in this case there exists no doubt as to the actual atomic mechanism involved; the interstitial atoms presumably jump from one interstitial position to a neighboring one. The diffusion of hydrogen, oxygen, nitrogen, and carbon in iron and other metals are examples of this mechanism. In order to discuss this type of diffusion from an atomic point of view, consider a set of parallel atomic planes of interplanar distance λ. We shall assume that there exists a concentration gradient of the diffusing particles along the x-axis which is perpendicular to the atomic planes. An atom in an interstitial position may jump in the positive x-direction (forward) in the negative x-direction (backward) or it may jump in a direction perpendicular to the x-axis. We shall denote the probability for a given interstitial atom to make any jump per second by p. Actually, the probability for a jump depends on the probability that the neighboring interstitial site will be empty. We shall assume, however, that the fraction of interstitial positions which is occupied is $\ll 1$, so that p may be considered independent of the concentration of interstitials.[17] The probability for a jump per second in the forward direction will be denoted by fp; furthermore, we shall assume that the probabilities for a forward and backward jump are equal. The diffusion problem is then reduced to a simple random-walk problem.

Denoting the number of diffusing particles per cm² on the plane located at x at the instant t by $n(x)$ we have

$$n(x + \lambda) = n(x) + (\partial n/\partial x)\lambda + \tfrac{1}{2}(\partial^2 n/\partial x^2)\lambda^2 + \ldots$$
$$n(x - \lambda) = n(x) - (\partial n/\partial x)\lambda + \tfrac{1}{2}(\partial^2 n/\partial x^2)\lambda^2 + \ldots \tag{3-19}$$

Thus, when we consider the situation at the instant $t + \delta t$ where $\delta t \ll 1/p$, the increase δn of the number of particles on the plane located at x is given by the number of particles jumping from $(x - \lambda)$ into x, plus the number of particles jumping from $(x + \lambda)$ into x, minus the number of particles jumping away from plane x. Since we have assumed $\delta t \ll 1/p$, it is not necessary to consider other planes besides the three employed. Hence

$$\delta n(x) = fp \, \delta t \, \frac{\partial^2 n}{\partial x^2} \, \lambda^2 \quad \text{or} \quad \frac{\partial n}{\partial t} = fp\lambda^2 \, \frac{\partial^2 n}{\partial x^2} \tag{3-20}$$

It is observed that this result is identical with the "macroscopic" equation (3-17) with

$$D = fp\lambda^2 \tag{3-21}$$

Since f is determined solely by the geometry of the lattice and since λ is nearly independent of T, the temperature dependence of the diffusion

[17] This assumption is equivalent to the assumption of a diffusion constant independent of concentration in the "macroscopic" theory.

coefficient must enter via the jump probability p. The simplest model that can be set up to determine the temperature dependence of p is to consider a particle moving in a fixed potential energy curve of the type illustrated in Fig. 3-6. Let the potential minimum A correspond to the interstitial position in which the particle finds itself, and let B correspond to a neighboring interstitial position. The barrier of height ϵ_i is a result of the fact that as the particle moves from one interstitial position to another it is squeezed between the atoms constituting the host lattice. Assuming the potential to be parabolic, the atom will vibrate as a harmonic oscillator.

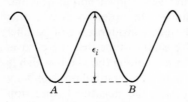

Fig. 3-6. The energy barrier between two interstitial positions.

The frequency of vibration ν_i may be considered as the number of attempts per second made by the particle to cross the barrier. However, any attempt can succeed only if the energy of the particle is $\geqslant \epsilon_i$. As shown in Problem 3-6, the fraction of time spent by the particle in energy states $\geqslant \epsilon_i$ is simply given by $\exp(-\epsilon_i/kT)$. Hence, for the probability of a jump from A to B we find per second,

$$p_i = \nu_i e^{-\epsilon_i/kT} \tag{3.22}$$

When the jumping problem is considered more rigorously than has been done above, one obtains a formula of the same form[18] as (3-22), but ϵ_i is then replaced by a free energy $\Delta F_i = \epsilon_i - T\Delta S_i$, i.e.,

$$p_i = \nu_i e^{\Delta S_i/k} e^{-\epsilon_i/kT} \tag{3.23}$$

where ΔS_i is the entropy difference between the state in which the particle is halfway between A and B, and the state in which the particle is in A. Since an interstitial atom may jump into more than one neighboring position, p is obtained by summation of (3-23) over all p_i. From (3-21) and (3-23) we thus obtain

$$D = f \sum_i \nu_i e^{\Delta S_i/k} e^{-\epsilon_i/kT} \lambda_i^2 \tag{3.24}$$

Let us now apply the results obtained above to a specific case. In Fig. 3-7 we have represented the diffusion coefficient of carbon in α iron (b.c.c.) as function of temperature according to Wert.[18] Note that equation (3-18) is satisfied for D-values covering 14 cycles of 10, with

$$\epsilon = 0.874 \text{ ev} \quad \text{and} \quad D_0 = 0.020 \text{ cm}^2 \text{ sec}^{-1} \tag{3.25}$$

The interstitial positions in a b.c.c. lattice are indicated in Fig. 3-8; they correspond to the centers of the faces and edges of the elementary cube.

[18] For details, see C. Wert and C. Zener, *Phys. Rev.*, **76**, 1169 (1949); C. Wert, *Phys. Rev.*, **79**, 601 (1950).

It is observed that only from two-thirds of these positions is it possible to jump forward or backward; from positions in which this is possible, the relative probability for a forward jump is $\frac{1}{4}$. Hence, in this case

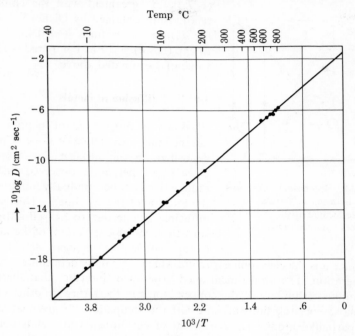

Fig. 3-7. The diffusion coefficient of carbon in α iron (b.c.c.).
[After C. Wert, *Phys. Rev.*, **79**, 601 (1950)]

$f = \frac{2}{3} \times \frac{1}{4} = \frac{1}{6}$. Since the four possible jumps from any interstitial position are equivalent, we obtain from (3-24) with $\lambda = a/2$, where a is the cube edge,

$$D = a^2 p/24 = (a^2 \nu/6)e^{\Delta S/k}e^{-\epsilon_i/kT} \qquad (3\text{-}26)$$

Comparison of (3-18) and (3-26) shows that for interstitial diffusion of the type under consideration, the activation energy for diffusion is identical with the activation energy for the atomic jumps. The value of $\exp(\Delta S/k)$ may be estimated as follows: for α iron $a = 2.86$ Å; putting $\nu \simeq k\theta/h$ where $\theta = 420°$K is the Debye temperature of iron, one obtains $\nu \simeq 10^{13}$ sec^{-1}. From the known value $D_0 = 0.020$ cm^2 sec^{-1} one then obtains $\exp(\Delta S/k) \simeq 7$.

We may mention here that Zener has derived the following approximate relationship:[19]

$$\Delta S \simeq \beta(\epsilon_i/T_m) \qquad (3\text{-}27)$$

[19] C. Zener, *J. Appl. Phys.*, **22**, 372 (1951).

where T_m is the melting point, ϵ_i is the activation energy employed above, and β is a constant which for most metals lies between 0.25 and 0.45. According to (3-27) and (3-26), D_0 should depend exponentially on (ϵ_i/T_m), in agreement with the empirical relationship obtained by Dienes.[15]   Also, for α iron Zener finds $\beta = 0.43$, leading to $\exp(\Delta S/k) \simeq 12$ as compared with the value of 7 estimated above.

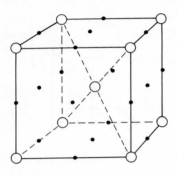

Fig. 3-8. Interstitial positions (dots) in a b.c.c. lattice; these sites are located at the centers of the faces and the edges of the cube.

3-6. Self-diffusion in metals

When a thin layer of copper containing the radioactive isotope Cu^{64} is deposited on the surface of a "normal" piece of copper, it is observed that the radioactive isotopes gradually migrate into the interior of the specimen. This type of diffusion is referred to as self-diffusion, since the electronic structures of the various isotopes of a given element are identical and since it is the electronic structure which essentially determines the rate of migration. The above-mentioned experiment indicates that there is a continuous reshuffling of the copper atoms in the lattice. In other words, one may associate a finite lifetime with the occupation of a given lattice site by a particular atom. The coefficient of self-diffusion in metals depends exponentially on the temperature in accordance with equation (3-18). For example, for the self-diffusion of copper one finds (3-18) satisfied with[20]

$$D = 0.20 \text{ cm}^2 \text{ sec}^{-1}, \qquad \epsilon = 2.05 \text{ ev} \quad (Cu)$$

Similarly, for the self-diffusion coefficient of sodium it has been found that[21]

$$D_0 = 0.242 \text{ cm}^2 \text{ sec}^{-1}, \qquad \epsilon = 0.454 \text{ ev} \quad (Na)$$

Several mechanisms have been proposed for the self-diffusion process: (1) *the vacancy mechanism*, (2) the *direct interchange* between neighboring atoms, (3) *interstitial diffusion*. In a particular case, the mechanism requiring the smallest activation energy will dominate; it is therefore well possible that in different types of metals different diffusion mechanisms occur.

[20] A. Kuper, H. Letaw, L. Slifkin, E. Sonder, and C. T. Tomizuka, *Phys. Rev.*, **96**, 1224 (1954); according to a private communication of Dr. Slifkin, the numerical values in the original paper were in error; the correct ones have been given above.

[21] N. H. Nachtrieb, E. Catalano, and J. A. Weil, *J. Chem. Phys.*, **20**, 1185 (1952); see also **20**, 1189 (1952) for a discussion of the pressure dependence of the self-diffusion coefficient of Na.

In the vacancy mechanism it is assumed that the self-diffusion is essentially determined by the diffusion of vacancies. Thus it is assumed that a given atom can jump to a neighboring site only when the latter is vacant. It is evident that the self-diffusion coefficient in this case will be proportional to the fraction of lattice sites which is vacant and to the jump probability for a vacancy per second. For a metal in thermal equilibrium, the probability for a given site to be vacant is given by (3-8).

$$n/N = e^{\Delta S_v/k} e^{-\phi_v/kT}$$

where ΔS_v refers to the thermal entropy change associated with the creation of a vacancy. The probability for a jump of a vacancy to a nearest neighbor site is given by a formula of the form (3-23). Hence the self-diffusion coefficient for the vacancy mechanism may be written as (compare 3-26):

$$D = \gamma v a^2 e^{(\Delta S_v + \Delta S_j)/k} e^{-(\phi_v + \epsilon_j)/kT} \qquad (3\text{-}28)$$

where the subscripts j refer to jumps; γ is a numerical factor determined by the geometry of the lattice. Note that the activation energy for diffusion is in this case given by the sum of the energy of formation of a vacancy and the jump activation energy, i.e.,

$$\epsilon = \phi_v + \epsilon_j \qquad (3\text{-}29)$$

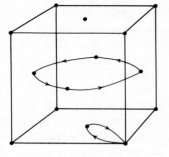

We may recall that Overhauser[10] found for copper $\phi_v = 1.39$ ev and $\epsilon_j = 0.68$ ev, the sum of which is 2.07 ev. This is in good agreement with the experimental value of ϵ quoted above. Huntington and Seitz[9] calculated the activation energy for the direct interchange (see Fig. 3-9) between two neighboring atoms in copper and found a value four times larger than the observed value. These authors

Fig. 3-9. Illustrating the two-ring (direct interchange between two atoms) and the four-ring diffusion mechanisms.

also found that the energy required to transfer a surface atom to an interstitial position requires an energy of nearly 13 ev. It thus seems that the interstitial and direct exchange mechanism are very unlikely in Cu; the vacancy mechanism is evidently operating in this case. Nachtrieb[21] et al. believe that the vacancy mechanism is also responsible for the self-diffusion in sodium.

We should mention that besides the two-ring direct interchange referred to above, there are other possibilities of direct interchange involving more than two atoms. In Fig. 3-9, for example, we have indicated a four-ring mechanism investigated by Zener.[22] Zener has shown that the activation

[22] C. Zener, *Acta Cryst.*, **3**, 346 (1950).

energy associated with the four-ring mechanism in copper requires only 40 per cent of that associated with the simple interchange of two neighbors. He concludes from his analysis that the ring mechanism might operate in b.c.c. metals and that the vacancy mechanism dominates in the f.c.c. metals, such as copper.

3-7. Chemical diffusion in metals; the Kirkendall effect

The diffusion of foreign atoms in a lattice is usually referred to as chemical or impurity diffusion. An example of this type of diffusion has already been discussed in Sec. 3-5, in which the impurities were assumed to move interstitially. Presently we shall be concerned with the diffusion of impurities which occupy normal lattice sites, i.e., the impurities have simply replaced a certain number of atoms of the host lattice. For the discussion of this type of diffusion it is convenient to distinguish between very low and high impurity concentrations.

Very low solute concentration. This is the simplest case since the interaction between the impurity atoms may be neglected; furthermore, complications arising from lattice defects associated with high-impurity densities are avoided (see below). In order to illustrate the type of problems encountered in this case, consider a certain metal A which is known to have a self-diffusion governed by the vacancy mechanism. Suppose a very small fraction of A atoms is replaced by B atoms and let us inquire about the diffusion coefficient D_{BA} of the B atoms in the A lattice. When p_{Bv} represents the probability for a B atom to have a vacant lattice site as a nearest neighbor and p_{Bj} represents the probability per second for a B atom neighboring a vacancy to jump into the vacancy, then D_{BA} will be proportional to the product $p_{Bv}p_{Bj}$. In a similar notation, the coefficient of self-diffusion D_{AA} of the A lattice is proportional to $p_{Av}p_{Aj}$. Hence

$$D_{BA}/D_{AA} = (p_{Bv}/p_{Av})(p_{Bj}/p_{Aj}) \qquad (3\text{-}30)$$

It is of interest to point out that if the vacancies were distributed at random, $p_{Bv} = p_{Av}$; when $p_{Av} \neq p_{Bv}$ the vacancies evidently have a preference for A or B neighbors.

Experimentally one finds that in general the activation energies and the D_0 values associated with D_{BA} and D_{AA} may differ appreciably. This indicates that $p_{Av} \neq p_{Bv}$ and (or) that $p_{Aj} \neq p_{Bj}$. A very accurate and systematic study in this respect has in recent years been carried out by Slifkin, Tomizuka, *et al.*[23] They measured, besides the self-diffusion of

[23] For Sb in Ag, see E. Sonder, L. Slifkin, and C. T. Tomizuka, *Phys. Rev.*, **93**, 970 (1954); for Cd, In, and Sn in Ag, see C. T. Tomizuka and L. Slifkin, *Phys. Rev.*, **96**, 610 (1954); for self-diffusion of Ag, see L. Slifkin, D. Lazarus, and C. T. Tomizuka, *J. Appl. Phys.*, **23**, 1032 (1952); R. E. Hoffman and D. Turnbull, *J. Appl. Phys.*, **22**, 634 (1951); E. S. Wadja, *Acta Metallurgica*, **2**, 184 (1954).

silver, the diffusion in silver of elements following it in the periodic table, viz., Cd, In, Sn, and Sb. Since radioactive tracer techniques were employed, the concentration of the diffusing impurities could be kept very low (10^{-4}–10^{-5}). The activation energies and the D_0 values are given below.

	Ag	Cd	In	Sn	Pb
ϵ	45.50	41.70	40.63	39.30	38.32 kcal/mole
D_0	0.724	0.454	0.416	0.255	0.179 cm²/sec

It is interesting to note that both ϵ and D_0 vary in a systematic manner as the number of extra valence electrons relative to silver increases from one (Cd) to four (Pb). A theory of impurity diffusion for low concentrations in which the excess nuclear charge and excess number of valence electrons of the impurity atoms relative to the host atoms play an essential role has been developed by Lazarus.[24] The results mentioned above have been discussed in the light of Lazarus' and Zener's[25] theories by Tomizuka and Slifkin.

High solute concentrations. The analysis and interpretation of chemical diffusion data for high concentrations of the diffusing impurities is much more complicated than for very low concentrations. First of all, the diffusion coefficient is itself a function of concentration, which makes the analysis more difficult; methods of analysis and a compilation of diffusion data may be found in Jost, *op. cit.* Furthermore, the high concentration gradients induce large gradients of the lattice parameters, and consequently, imperfections which may act as short-circuiting paths for the diffusion. It is suspected that in many of the chemical diffusion data nonhomogeneous diffusion of this kind, or along grain boundaries, is involved. For an extensive analysis of this subject we refer the reader to Nowick.[26]

The Kirkendall effect. An interesting effect associated with the diffusion of zinc and copper in brass (CuZn) was discovered by Kirkendall[27]. He observed a mass flow relative to the initial interface of a copper-brass diffusion couple which indicated that the zinc diffuses out of the brass more rapidly than copper diffuses in. Confirmation of this observation was obtained from an experiment by Smigelskas and Kirkendall in which inert wires (markers) were embedded at the two interfaces of a Cu-brass-Cu

[24] D. Lazarus, *Phys. Rev.*, **93**, 373 (1954).
[25] C. Zener. *J. Appl. Phys.*, **22**, 372 (1951).
[26] A. S. Nowick, *J. Appl. Phys.*, **22**, 1185 (1951).
[27] E. O. Kirkendall, *Trans. AIME*, **147**, 104 (1942).

system.[28] They found that as the diffusion progressed, the markers moved towards each other. The fact that the displacement of the markers was proportional to the square root of the time indicated strongly that the marker movements were related to the diffusion process itself.[29] The Kirkendall effect has since been found in many other systems; for example, da Silva and Mehl have observed the effect in Cu-Zn, Cu-Sn, Cu-Ni, Cu-Au, Ag-Au.[30]

Assuming that the markers are fixed relative to the system of lattice sites, and assuming that the diffusion is governed by a vacancy mechanism, a mass flow of atoms in a given direction must be compensated by a flow of vacancies in the opposite direction. Thus in the copper-brass system, the net flow of atoms out of the brass is balanced by a flow of vacancies from the copper into the brass. For an excellent treatment of the theory of the Kirkendall effect, the reader is referred to a paper by Bardeen and Herring in W. Shockley (ed.), *Imperfections in Nearly Perfect Crystals*, Wiley, New York, 1952. Dislocations play an essential role in the atomic theory of the effect as sources and sinks for vacancies (see Sec. 3-12).

3-8. The elastic constants of metals

For further reference and as an introduction to the following sections of this chapter we may review very briefly some of the fundamental principles of elastic stress-strain relations in crystals.[31] Let us first consider an isotropic elastic medium under uniform stress along an arbitrarily chosen x-direction. Let x' represent the distance of a given atom in the material under stress relative to a fixed plane perpendicular to the x-axis. When x represents the distance of the same atom in the unstressed material, the strain ϵ_x is defined by

$$\epsilon_x = (x' - x)/x \qquad (3\text{-}31)$$

Thus ϵ_x is a dimensionless quantity which may be positive or negative depending on whether the stress is tensional or compressional. For small values of the strain, Hooke's law is satisfied, i.e., the strain ϵ_x is then proportional to the stress along the x-direction σ_x (a force per unit area)

$$\epsilon_x = \sigma_x/E \qquad (3\text{-}32)$$

---

[28] A. D. Smigelskas and E. O. Kirkendall, *Trans. AIME*, **171**, 130 (1947).

[29] For a simple random-walk diffusion, the mean square displacement of the particles is given by $\langle x^2 \rangle = 2Dt$, so that the root mean square displacement is proportional to $t^{1/2}$. See, for example, Jost, *op. cit.*, pp. 25 ff.

[30] da Silva, *Atomic Flow in Diffusion Phenomena*, Thesis, Carnegie Institute of Technology, 1951.

[31] See for a detailed treatment, A. E. H. Love, *A Treatise on the Mathematical Theory of Elasticity*, Dover, New York, 1944; or S. Timoshenko, *Theory of Elasticity*, McGraw-Hill, New York, 1934.

The proportionality factor E is called Young's modulus. When σ_x represents a tensile stress, there will be a contraction of the material perpendicular to the x-axis such that

$$\epsilon_y = \epsilon_z = -\nu\epsilon_x = -\nu\sigma_x/E \qquad (3\text{-}33)$$

where ν is called the Poisson ratio.

Besides the compressional and tensile strains mentioned above, there are shear strains, as illustrated in Fig. 3-10; shear strains are represented by the symbol γ. Consider two parallel planes separated by a distance d and let the planes be displaced relative to each other in some direction parallel to the planes by the amount Δx; the shear strain is then defined by

$$\gamma = \Delta x/d = \tan \alpha \qquad (3\text{-}34)$$

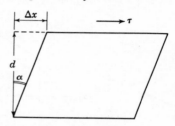

For small shear strain γ is approximately equal to the angle α. The shear strain is produced by a shear stress τ, which is a force per cm²; for small strains Hooke's law may be applied and

$$\gamma = \tau/G \qquad (3\text{-}35)$$

Fig. 3-10. The shear stress τ produces a displacement Δx of the upper plane as indicated; the shear strain is defined as $\gamma = \Delta x/d = \tan \alpha$.

where G is called the elastic shear modulus. It can be shown that, for isotropic bodies, the three quantities E, ν, and G satisfy the relation

$$G = E/2(\nu + 1) \qquad (3\text{-}36)$$

Isotropic bodies therefore are characterized by two independent elastic constants. Crystals, on the other hand, require more than two elastic constants, the number increasing with decreasing symmetry. Cubic crystals (b.c.c., f.c.c.), for example, require 3 elastic constants, hexagonal crystals require 5, and materials without symmetry elements require 21.

In discussing the stress-strain relations in crystals it is convenient to start by considering the forces acting on a small cube $dx\,dy\,dz$ which forms part of a strained crystal. The force exerted on the cube by the surrounding material may be represented by three components on each of the six faces of the cube. However, when the cube is in equilibrium, the forces on opposite faces must be equal in magnitude and of opposite sign. Thus the stress condition of the cube may be described by nine couples. Three such couples have been indicated in Fig. 3-11, viz., those for which the forces are parallel to the x-axis. One of these corresponds to a compressional or tensile stress σ_{xx} (force per cm²); the other two are the shearing stresses τ_{xz} and τ_{xy} which respectively tend to rotate the cube about the y- and

z-direction. Extending this reasoning to the forces parallel to the y- and z-axis one thus ends up with the stress tensor

$$\begin{array}{ccc} \sigma_{xx} & \tau_{xy} & \tau_{xz} \\ \tau_{yx} & \sigma_{yy} & \tau_{yz} \\ \tau_{zx} & \tau_{zy} & \sigma_{zz} \end{array}$$

However, the reader will readily convince himself that if rotation is absent,

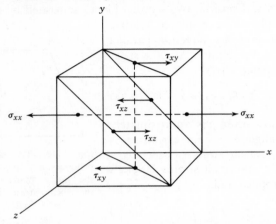

Fig. 3-11. Illustrating the three couples of forces acting along the x-direction; σ_{xx} is a tensile stress, τ_{xy} and τ_{xz} are shear stresses; τ_{xy} represents a force acting along the x-axis in a plane perpendicular to the y-axis, etc. Similar forces act along the y- and z-directions.

the tensor must be symmetrical, i.e., $\tau_{yx} = \tau_{xy}$ etc. The stress condition may thus be specified by six independent stresses,

$$\sigma_{xx}, \quad \sigma_{yy}, \quad \sigma_{zz}, \quad \tau_{yz}, \quad \tau_{zx}, \quad \tau_{xy} \tag{3-37}$$

As a result of the stresses, the crystal is strained, i.e., an atom which in the unstrained crystal occupied the position x, y, z will in the strained crystal occupy the position x', y', z'. When the distortion is homogeneous, the displacements are proportional to x, y, z and we have in analogy with (3-31) the more general expressions

$$\begin{aligned} x' - x &= \epsilon_{xx}x + \gamma_{xy}y + \gamma_{xz}z \\ y' - y &= \gamma_{yx}x + \epsilon_{yy}y + \gamma_{yz}z \\ z' - z &= \gamma_{zx}x + \gamma_{zy}y + \epsilon_{zz}z \end{aligned} \tag{3-38}$$

where the ϵ's and γ's refer to normal strains and shearing strains, respectively. The strain tensor is again symmetrical if rotation is absent and the strain condition of the cube may be specified by the six strain components

$$\epsilon_{xx}, \quad \epsilon_{yy}, \quad \epsilon_{zz}, \quad \gamma_{yz}, \quad \gamma_{zx}, \quad \gamma_{xy} \qquad (3\text{-}39)$$

When Hooke's law is satisfied the strain and stress components (3-39) and (3-37) are linearly related. Thus in analogy with (3-32) we have, for example,

$$\sigma_{xx} = c_{11}\epsilon_{xx} + c_{12}\epsilon_{yy} + c_{13}\epsilon_{zz} + c_{14}\gamma_{yz} + c_{15}\gamma_{zx} + c_{16}\gamma_{xy} \quad (3\text{-}40)$$

There are six such equations, and hence 36 moduli of elasticity or elastic stiffness constants c_{ij}.[32] The relations, which are the inverse of type (3-40), express the strains in terms of the stresses; for example,

$$\epsilon_{xx} = s_{11}\sigma_{xx} + s_{12}\sigma_{yy} + s_{13}\sigma_{zz} + s_{14}\tau_{yz} + s_{15}\tau_{zx} + s_{16}\tau_{xy} \qquad (3\text{-}41)$$

The six equations of this type define 36 constants s_{ij} which are called the elastic constants. It can be shown that the matrices c_{ij} and s_{ij} are symmetrical; hence a material without symmetry elements has 21 independent elastic constants or moduli. Due to the symmetry of crystals, several of these may vanish. In cubic crystals, as mentioned above already, there are three independent elastic moduli which are usually chosen as c_{11}, c_{12}, and c_{44}. Some representative values for cubic metals are given in Table 3-2. The atomic theory of elasticity is based on the forces acting between the atoms; we refer the reader to the books quoted at the end of this chapter for a discussion of this subject.

Table 3-2. Elastic Moduli for Some Cubic Metals
in 10^{12} dyne/cm^2

Metal	Structure	c_{11}	c_{12}	c_{44}
Al	f.c.c.	1.08	0.62	0.28
Cu	f.c.c.	1.70	1.23	0.75
Pb	f.c.c.	0.48	0.41	0.14
K	b.c.c.	0.046	0.037	0.026
Fe	b.c.c.	2.37	1.41	1.16

3-9. Plastic deformation of metals

When a crystal is deformed elastically under influence of applied stresses, it returns to its original state upon removal of the stresses. However, if the applied stresses are sufficiently large, a certain amount of deformation remains after removal of the stresses: the crystal has been

[32] Other names for these quantities are in use.

plastically deformed. We shall see below that the atomic interpretation of plastic flow of crystals requires the introduction of a new type of lattice defects, viz., dislocations. The remainder of this chapter will be devoted to a discussion of the most essential properties of such defects; the approach to the problem given here follows rather closely the exposition found in Cottrell's book *Dislocations and Plastic Flow in Crystals* cited at the end of this chapter. To begin with, a few pertinent experimental facts concerning the plastic flow of single crystals will be reviewed.

In many crystals plastic flow results from the sliding of one part of a crystal relative to another. In Fig. 3-12 we have illustrated schematically how such a process may lead to an increase in the length of a crystal under influence of tension. The sliding process is referred to as slip; the plane and direction in which the slip occurs define, respectively, the slip plane and the slip direction. This type of mechanism evidently deforms the outer surface of the crystal and leads to so-called slip bands, as indicated in Fig. 3-12. The amount of slip associated with a slip band may be several thousand Ang-

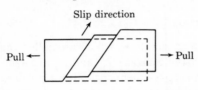

Fig. 3-12. Illustrating the slip process due to a tensile stress. The dashed line shows the original cross section of the material; note the increase in length resulting from the slip.

stroms. From what has been said so far, one can draw an important conclusion: plastic deformation is inhomogeneous in the sense that only a relatively small number of atoms actually take part in the slip process, viz., only those atoms which form layers on either side of a slip plane. Elastic deformation, on the other hand, affects all atoms in a crystal. This difference between plastic and elastic deformation indicates that the atomic interpretation of plastic flow must be based on an entirely different model than that of elastic deformation. In fact, the elastic properties of solids can be understood quite well in terms of interatomic forces acting in a perfect lattice; plastic deformation, however, cannot be discussed properly on the basis of a perfect lattice, i.e., it cannot be discussed by simply extending the theory of elasticity to the case of large stresses and strains. It will be shown below that if plastic flow were to occur in a perfectly periodic lattice, much larger shear stresses would be required than those for which plastic flow is observed.

Besides being characterized by inhomogeneity, plastic flow is also anisotropic. Slip usually takes place preferentially in planes of high atomic density, e.g. along $\{111\}$ planes in a f.c.c. lattice. Also, the direction of slip commonly coincides with a direction along which the number of atoms per unit length is high.

We shall now mention another important result obtained from experiment, viz., the existence of a critical resolved shear stress τ_c. In Fig. 3-13 consider a cylindrical crystal of cross section A under influence of a tensile force F. Let the normal to the active slip plane make an angle α with F, and let the angle between the slip direction and F be β. The resolved shear stress, i.e., the force acting per unit area of the slip plane in the slip direction, is then given by

$$\tau = (F/A) \cos \alpha \cos \beta \quad (3\text{-}42)$$

since the area of the slip plane is $A/\cos \alpha$. Similarly, the tensile stress per unit area normal to the slip plane is

$$\sigma = (F/A) \cos^2 \alpha \quad (3\text{-}43)$$

Suppose now that for given values of α and β the force F is gradually increased from zero. Even for relatively small stresses a certain amount of

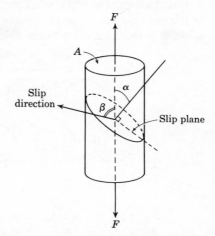

Fig. 3-13. Geometry of slip plane, slip direction, and tensile force F.

plastic flow occurs, but the rate of flow is small and one speaks of creep. It turns out, however, that the rate of flow increases very rapidly whenever the resolved shear stress τ reaches a critical value τ_c. At the same time, the results indicate that the tensile stress normal to the slip plane is of little or no influence on the mechanism of slip. For pure crystals, the critical shear stress lies in the range between 10^6–10^7 dynes per cm^2. In general, τ_c decreases with increasing temperature. Also, τ_c increases as a result of alloying or cold working.

3-10. The interpretation of slip; dislocations

One of the central facts which a theory of slip must explain is that in a pure crystal certain atomic planes start gliding across each other under influence of a shear stress of the order of 10^6–10^7 dynes per cm^2. We shall first show that the theoretical critical shear stress based on a perfect lattice is much larger than the observed values for pure crystals. For this purpose, we resort to a simplified model suggested by Frenkel.[33] With reference to Fig. 3-14a, consider a cross section through two neighboring atomic planes separated by a distance d. Without external forces, let the fully drawn circles represent the equilibrium positions of the atoms. Suppose now that a shear stress τ is applied, and that as a result, all atoms in the upper plane are displaced by an amount x relative to their original position.

[33] J. Frenkel, *Z. Physik*, **37**, 572 (1926).

Interchanging the role of dependent and independent variables, we may also say that for a displacement x, a shear stress $\tau(x)$ is required. Suppose now that we want to plot τ as a function of x. First we note that as a result of the periodic nature of the system, τ will vanish for $x = 0$, $a/2$, a, etc., where a is the distance between neighboring atoms within the planes (see

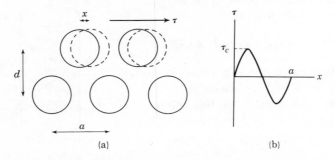

(a)   (b)

Fig. 3-14.   Under influence of the shear stress τ the upper plane of atoms in (a) is displaced over a distance x (dashed circles). The periodic behaviour of τ, according to Frenkel, is indicated in (b).

Fig. 3-14b). Oversimplifying the problem, we shall assume with Frenkel that this periodic function is given by

$$\tau(x) = \tau_c \sin (2\pi x/a) \qquad (3\text{-}44)$$

The "amplitude" τ_c is evidently the critical shear stress in this model and it is this quantity that we wish to estimate. This may be done by realizing that for $x \ll a$ the usual theory of elasticity should apply; under these circumstances

$$\tau(x) \simeq (2\pi x/a)\tau_c \qquad \text{for} \quad x \ll a$$

On the other hand, the elastic strain, in accordance with (3-34) and (3-35) is given by

$$\gamma = x/d = \tau/G \qquad (3\text{-}45)$$

where G is the shear modulus. From the last two equations it follows that in this model

$$\tau_c \simeq (G/2\pi)(a/d) \simeq G/2\pi \qquad (3\text{-}46)$$

where the last approximation is justified because $a \simeq d$. Since $G \simeq 10^{11}$ dynes per cm^2 (see c_{44} in Table 3-2), one obtains in this model a theoretical shear stress $\tau_c \simeq 10^{10}$ dynes per cm^2, which is several orders of magnitude larger than the observed ones. Although it must be admitted that Frenkel's model is open to objections, more refined calculations confirm the conclusion that it is impossible to obtain agreement between theory and experiment on the basis of a model where atomic planes glide past each other in the manner assumed above (see also Problem 3-12). In Fig. 3-14 it was assumed that the atoms of the upper atomic plane move simultaneously relative to the lower plane; this assumption is tied up with the assumption of a perfect lattice and here we are at the root of the difficulty.

In an attempt to remove this difficulty, let us assume that the crystal contains an imperfection of such a nature that the slip process is governed, not by the simultaneous motion of the atoms of one plane relative to another, but by the consecutive motion of these atoms. Before specifying this model further, it may be useful to remind the reader of the fact that a worm moves forward by displacing its segments one after the other rather than by a simultaneous displacement of all the segments. The atomic model for the progression of slip, based on the dislocation model, is analogous to a wormlike motion.

The dislocation model for slip may be introduced with reference to the crystal of Fig. 3-15a; let the plane PQR be a slip plane. This plane has been redrawn in Fig. 3-15b. In the slip plane consider an arbitrary closed curve ABC; the region inside this curve is hatched in Fig. 3-15b. Suppose now that in some way or other the material located over the hatched area in the upper half of the crystal is displaced by an amount b relative to the lower half of the crystal; at the same time, the material in the upper half lying over the area outside ABC is left undisplaced. In this manner we have obtained a situation in which only a fraction of the upper half of the crystal has slipped relative to the lower half. The ratio f of the area ABC and the total area of the slip plane will be referred to as the fraction of slip that has occurred in this plane. Thus, if in some way or other the area ABC could be made to grow, f would increase and for $f = 1$ the whole upper half of the crystal would be displaced by an amount b relative to the lower half. For $f < 1$, the average displacement of the upper half relative to the lower half is fb.

The line ABC introduced above marks the boundary in the slip plane between slipped and unslipped material; this line is called a dislocation line. The vector b which defines the magnitude and direction of the slip is called the Burgers vector.[34] Since the atoms always seek positions of minimum energy, it will be evident that b must connect two atomic equilibrium positions, i.e., the possible vectors b are determined by the crystal structure. When the displacement equals one lattice spacing, the dislocation is said to have unit strength. From calculations of the strain energy associated with dislocations, Frank has shown that dislocations of strength larger than unity are in general unstable; they dissociate into dislocations of unit strength.[35]

So far, we have only given a definition of a dislocation. In order to see

[34] J. M. Burgers, *Proc. Koninkl. Ned. Akad. Wetenschap.*, **42**, 293, 378 (1939).

[35] F. C. Frank, *Physica*, **15**, 131 (1949).

how this model may account for a number of observations on plastic flow, various questions must be raised; for example:

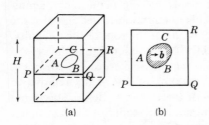

(a)   (b)

Fig. 3-15. Schematic representation of a ring dislocation *ABC* in a slip plane *PQR*. Slip has occurred only across the hatched area.

1. Assuming that a slip plane such as *PQR* in Fig. 3-15 contains a dislocation as indicated, one should be able to show that under influence of a shear stress, applied in the proper direction to the crystal, the dislocation tends to grow; under these circumstances the slipped region would increase in size and slip would proceed. Moreover, the calculated critical shear stress should agree quantitatively with the observed values.

2. We have seen above that slip in a single slip plane may correspond to displacements of the order of 1000 Å; on the other hand, once a dislocation such as *ABC* in Fig. 3-15 has swept through the whole slip plane, the slip produced is only $b \simeq 2$ Å, and moreover, the dislocation has then disappeared. It will thus be necessary to account for large numbers of dislocations taking part in the slip process and for sources which supply such dislocations.

3. Are other physical properties, besides plastic flow, determined to at least a measurable degree by the presence of dislocations so that independent information regarding the properties of dislocations can be obtained? Some of these questions will be discussed below; of course, many more can be asked.

3-11. Motion of dislocations under influence of a uniform shear stress; dislocation density

With reference to Fig. 3-15, suppose a uniform shear stress τ is applied to the crystal along the direction of the Burgers vector. Mott and Nabarro have shown that this leads to a force on the dislocation line such that the slipped area tends to grow.[36] Consider an element *ds* of the dislocation line; suppose this element is displaced outwardly (Fig. 3-15b) by an amount *dl* along a direction perpendicular to *ds*. The area swept out by the line element is then *ds dl*. According to what has been said in the preceding section, this corresponds to an average displacement of the upper part of the crystal relative to the lower part by an amount *ds dl b/A*, where *A* is the area of the slip plane. The work done by the shear stress is equal

[36] N. F. Mott and F. R. N. Nabarro, "Report on Strength of Solids," *Phys. Soc. (London)*, 1948, p. 1.

to the total shear force τA times the average shear displacement, i.e., equal to $\tau b \, ds \, dl = dW$. This corresponds to a force $-dW/dl$ acting on the element ds in the direction of the normal. Hence the force per unit length is equal to

$$F = \tau b \qquad (3\text{-}47)$$

Thus the applied shear stress produces a force per unit length everywhere along the dislocation line equal to τb and perpendicular to the line element. If the force is large enough to make the dislocation line move in the direction of F, the slipped area in Fig. 3-15 will grow and slip will occur under influence of the shear stress.

On very general grounds one can show that the critical shear stress for slip should be very small for the dislocation model. In order to see this, let us consider the regions near the dislocation line somewhat more closely. Because of the nature of interatomic forces, the boundary between the slipped and unslipped regions is not sharp, but rather vague, extending over several atomic distances. The atoms near the dislocation line of Fig. 3-15, at the inside, have nearly completed the slip process; those near the dislocation line on the outside are just beginning to slip. As a result of the periodic nature of the potential for the atoms, those at the outside of the dislocation line and close to it tend to push the dislocation line inward, since this would allow them to occupy their initial equilibrium positions. On the other hand, the atoms inside the dislocation line and situated close to it tend to push the line outward, since this would make it possible for them to occupy their new equilibrium positions associated with completed slip. Far away on either side of the dislocation line, the atoms occupy normal lattice positions and are not affected by the dislocation. Thus to a first approximation, the forces on the dislocation line balance and it should start moving under the smallest of shear forces. It thus looks as if this model is too successful in explaining the relatively low observed critical shear stress; however, when one goes to a second approximation, one finds that the critical shear stress calculated for this model is not zero, but in fact of the same order of magnitude as observed values.[37]

Density of dislocations. It was mentioned above that a single dislocation line sweeping across a slip plane gives rise to a displacement of the order of a few Angstroms; thus any appreciable plastic deformation must be the result of a large number of dislocations sweeping across many slip planes. It will be evident that the rate of plastic flow will be determined by the rate at which dislocation lines sweep through the slip planes, i.e., the rate of flow may be expected to be proportional to the total length of all active dislocation lines and the average velocity with which the elements of these lines move. One has therefore introduced the concept of "dislocation

[37] See Cottrell, *op. cit.*, p. 62.

density," $\rho = S/V$, where S is the total length of the dislocation lines and V is the volume of the crystal. Note that ρ has the dimension length^{-2}. More specifically, one arrives at this concept by the following reasoning: Consider an element ds of a dislocation line such as ABC in Fig. 3-15. Let v be the velocity of the element along the direction of the normal to ds in the slip plane. When H is the height of the crystal and A is the area of the slip plane, the increase in strain per second due to the motion of the element ds is equal to

$$dy/dt = v \, ds \, b/AH \qquad (3\text{-}48)$$

Considering the rate of flow resulting from all dislocations in planes parallel to the plane PQR in Fig. 3-15, we have to sum expression (3-48) in a suitable fashion, i.e., we must replace ds by the total length S of all these dislocations and v by some average velocity $\langle v \rangle$. Hence

$$dy/dt = \langle v \rangle \, Sb/V = \rho b \langle v \rangle \qquad (3\text{-}49)$$

where ρ is the dislocation density. Methods to determine the dislocation density in crystals will be mentioned in Sec. 3-15.

3-12. Edge and screw dislocations

The elements of a ring dislocation such as ABC in Fig. 3-15 may be considered as composed of two basic types of dislocations: edge dislocations and screw dislocations. A pure edge or Taylor-Orowan dislocation is defined as a dislocation for which the Burgers vector b is everywhere perpendicular to the dislocation line.[38] A screw or Burgers dislocation is defined as a dislocation for which the Burgers vector b is everywhere parallel to the dislocation line. Thus in Fig. 3-15b the vertical elements are of the edge type, the horizontal elements are of the screw type; the remainder is mixed edge and screw. We shall now consider the physical structure of these basic dislocations.

Edge dislocations. The simplest edge dislocation is one for which the dislocation line is straight. Its formation may be vizualized in terms of a slip process with reference to Fig. 3-16a. Suppose the block of material is cut across the area $ABEF$ so that across this area the upper and lower parts are disconnected.

The upper half is then pushed sideways such that the line $A'B'$ which initially coincided with AB is shifted by an amount b as indicated. If in this position the two halves were glued together, we would have produced an edge dislocation. The upper half of the block will clearly be under

    [38] G. I. Taylor, *Proc. Roy. Soc.*, **A145**, 362 (1934); E. Orowan, *Z. Physik*, **89**, 605, 614, 634 (1934).

compression, the lower half under tension. A square network of lines drawn on the front face *BCD* before the operation, would, after the operation, look as indicated in Fig. 3-16b. This strain pattern suggests immediately an alternative method by which an edge dislocation may be produced. Consider the intersections of the network of lines of Fig. 3-16b as representing rows of atoms perpendicular to the plane of the paper.

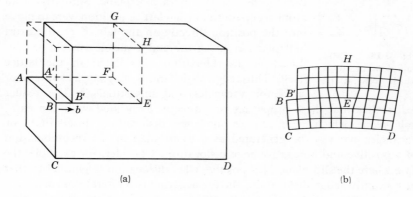

(a)   (b)

Fig. 3-16. In (a), *EF* represents an edge dislocation line; (b) gives the strain pattern. [After A. H. Cottrell, *Dislocations and Plastic Flow in Crystals*, Oxford, New York, 1953, p. 22]

The edge dislocation may then be obtained by cutting the block along the plane *EFGH*, and putting the half plane of atoms initially above *AB*, inside the cut. This gives rise to the "extra" half plane of atoms corresponding to *HE* in Fig. 3-16b, which is typical of an edge dislocation. Note that if the extra half plane *HE* were displaced to the right, slip would progress, and when *HE* has finally reached the right-hand side of the block, the upper half of the block has completed slip by the amount **b**.

The slip process resulting from a moving edge dislocation has been illustrated in Fig. 3-17. Edge dislocations for which the extra half plane lies above the slip plane are called positive. If the extra half plane lies below the slip plane, one speaks of a negative edge dislocation. We leave it to the reader to show

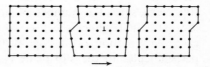

Fig. 3-17. Motion of a positive edge dislocation to the right, leading to slip. [After Taylor]

for himself that the slip process of Fig. 3-17 resulting from a positive edge dislocation moving to the right can also be achieved by motion of a negative edge dislocation of the same strength to the left.

The definition of an edge dislocation does not necessarily imply that the dislocation line is straight. In fact, any curved line will do as long as it is perpendicular to the Burgers vector **b**. Thus by inserting in a block of material an extra half plane with an irregular boundary, we can produce what is known as an irregular edge dislocation. An edge dislocation may

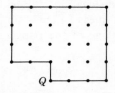

therefore contain jogs as indicated in Fig. 3-18. If an atom such as Q diffuses into the lattice, interstitial atoms may be produced or vacancies annihilated at the expense of the extra half plane. Similarly, if an atom occupying a normal lattice position were to move into the position directly on the left of Q, the extra half plane would grow and a vacancy would be pro-

Fig. 3-18. Extra half-plane of atoms which jogs at Q.

duced or an interstitial annihilated in the lattice itself. Thus edge dislocations may act as sources or sinks for vacancies and interstitials.[39] The reader will realize that these properties are directly associated with the extra half plane which characterizes an edge dislocation. Interstitials or vacancies may also be generated as a by-product of the recombination of a positive and a negative edge dislocation. Consider, for example, the case where the slip plane of a positive edge dislocation is parallel to that of a negative edge dislocation, the former lying two interatomic distances above the latter. When these dislocations meet, one arrives at a situation represented in Fig. 3-19 in which a row of vacancies is left after recombination; similarly, if the half planes overlap, one or more rows of interstitials become available.

The presence of an extra half plane of atoms in an edge dislocation restricts the motion of an edge dislocation mainly to the slip plane. The reason is that any motion perpendicular to the slip plane requires either a growth or a reduction of the half plane. Thus the easy direction of motion of an edge dislocation is in the slip plane since the number of atoms in the extra half plane is conserved in this case. Any motion of an edge dislocation perpendicular to the slip plane is termed nonconservative because it involves either rejecting or accepting "extra" atoms. Nonconservative motion is, of course, not

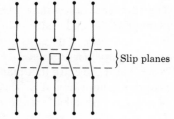

Fig. 3-19. Indicating the formation of a row of vacancies (represented by square) upon recombination of a positive and a negative edge dislocation; the dislocation lines are perpendicular to the plane of the paper.

excluded, but its occurrence depends on whether the diffusion of atoms is rapid enough to sustain it.

Screw dislocations. In Fig. 3-20 we have represented the atomic configuration in the vicinity of a screw dislocation piercing the surface of a

[39] See, for example, F. Seitz, *Advances in Physics*, **1**, 43 (1952).

simple cubic lattice. This configuration may be obtained by cutting the block across the area $BFHM$ and then pushing the upper part backward in the direction of the Burgers vector b, as indicated. The dislocation line BM is parallel to b; note that a screw dislocation line is necessarily straight, in contrast with an edge dislocation line. As one moves around the dislocation line along a circuit such as $AKLCDE$, one advances in the direction of BM by an amount equal to b for every turn; hence the term "screw" dislocation. Since no extra half plane is involved in a screw dislocation, one cannot speak in this case of nonconservative motion. Thus the motion of a screw dislocation is less restricted than that for an edge; the screw dislocation can in fact move along any cylindrical surface with the Burgers vector as its axis. If in Fig. 3-20 the dislocation line moves to the left, slip proceeds; thus screw dislocations, like edge dislocations, can produce plastic flow.

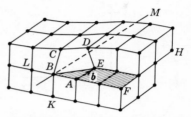

Fig. 3-20. Schematic representation of a screw dislocation in a simple cubic lattice; the dislocation line BM is parallel to the Burgers vector b.

An interesting feature of screw dislocations in connection with crystals grown from vapors or solutions may be mentioned here.[40] In these cases the crystal growth is a result of supersaturation and of the conditions on the surface of the growing crystals. In order for the atoms deposited on the surface to be firmly bound, the surface must contain steps, since at the corners of these steps they can be bound by two or more atoms. Suppose now that a crystal without dislocations has such steps on its faces. Gradually these steps become filled up and ultimately the surface becomes flat and unsuitable for further growth. However, if the crystal has a screw dislocation, such as in Fig. 3-20, continuous growth becomes possible, since as new material is deposited at the step, the step simply rotates but never disappears. Experimental evidence strongly supports these considerations.

3-13. Stress fields around dislocations

Many of the properties of dislocations are determined by the stress fields they produce in the surrounding material. Calculations of the stress fields are usually carried out on the assumption that the medium is isotropic and characterized by a shear modulus G and a Poisson ratio v. We shall not give the details of such calculations here, but only mention the results

---

[40] W. K. Burton, N. Cabrera, and F. C. Frank, *Nature*, **163**, 398 (1949); see also, on crystal growth, *Discussions Faraday Soc.*, **5** (1949); L. J. Griffin, *Phil. Mag.*, **41**, 196 (1950).

for edge and screw dislocations.[41] In Fig 3-21 consider the cross section of a cylindrical piece of material; the axis of the cylinder will be taken as the z-axis of a Cartesian coordinate system. Suppose we produce a cut in the plane $y = 0$, which extends between the axis and the outer surface as indicated. We now let the material above the cut slip to the left by an amount **b**, leading to the configuration indicated by the dotted line. We have then produced a positive edge dislocation along the z-axis with a Burgers vector along the x-axis; the plane $y = 0$ is the slip plane. In terms of the coordinates r and θ, the stress field of the dislocation line may then be shown to be given by the following tensile and shear stresses:

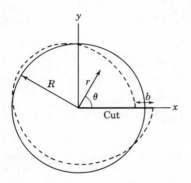

Fig. 3-21. An edge dislocation along the z-axis in a cylindrical piece of material.

$$\sigma_{rr} = \sigma_{\theta\theta} = -\frac{Gb}{2\pi r(1 - \nu)} \sin \theta \quad (3\text{-}50)$$

$$\tau_{r\theta} = \tau_{\theta r} = \frac{Gb}{2\pi r(1 - \nu)} \cos \theta \quad (3\text{-}51)$$

Here positive values of σ refer to tension, negative values of σ refer to compression; σ_{rr} is a radical compression or tension, while $\sigma_{\theta\theta}$ is a compression or tension acting in a plane perpendicular to **r**. The shear stress $\tau_{r\theta}$ acts in a radial direction. It is observed that the stresses vary as $1/r$. In the region above the slip plane σ_{rr} is negative, corresponding to a compression, in agreement with our previous qualitative discussion; below the slip plane σ_{rr} corresponds to a tensile stress. It must be emphasized that the stresses become infinite for $r = 0$ and therefore a small cylindrical region of radius r_0 around the dislocation must be excluded. In an actual crystal this difficulty does not arise, since the material consists of atoms; on the other hand, the stresses in the immediate vicinity of an actual dislocation will also be large, and Hooke's law is probably not valid in that region. For example, for $r = b$ the strains are of the order of $\frac{1}{2}\pi(1 - \nu) \simeq 25$ per cent.

On the basis of these results, let us now estimate the energy of formation of an edge dislocation of unit length. The final shear stress in the plane of the cut is given by (3-51) with $\theta = 0$. For a cut extending over unit length along the z-direction, the energy required to form the dislocation is evidently equal to the integral over the cut surface of half the product of

---

[41] For further details and references, see A. H. Cottrell, *Dislocations and Plastic Flow in Crystals*, Oxford, New York, 1953; W. T. Read, *Dislocations in Crystals*, McGraw-Hill, New York, 1953.

stress and strain, i.e., equal to

$$\frac{1}{2} \int_{r_0}^{R} \frac{Gb^2}{2\pi r(1 - \nu)} \, dr = \frac{Gb^2}{4\pi(1 - \nu)} \log (R/r_0) \qquad (3\text{-}52)$$

where R is the radius of the piece of material. Note that as R becomes infinite the energy of formation goes to infinity. By way of an estimate, let us take $R = 1$ cm, $r_0 = 10^{-7}$ cm, $G = 5 \times 10^{11}$ dynes cm^{-2}, $b = 2.5 \times 10^{-8}$ cm, and $\nu = \frac{1}{3}$. One then obtains an energy of 6×10^{-4} erg cm^{-1}, which corresponds to approximately 10 ev per atom along the dislocation line.

The configurational entropy of an edge dislocation is very small indeed; in fact, according to Problem 3-14, the configurational entropy per atom along the dislocation line for the dimensions assumed above contributes to the free energy a term of the order of $10^{-6} \, kT$. This result, combined with the energy of formation estimated above, leads to the important conclusion that the density of dislocations in thermal equilibrium with a crystal essentially vanishes. In this respect dislocations behave altogether differently from "atomic" lattice defects such as vacancies and interstitials. The configurational entropy associated with the latter is so large that the density of such defects in thermal equilibrium may be appreciable. The essential reason for this difference is the fact that a dislocation is a "line" defect rather than a collection of independent "point" defects; since the dislocated atoms must keep in line with each other, the number of possible configurations is strongly limited. The reason why relatively high dislocation densities are preserved in a crystal will be explained in Sec. 3-14.

For a screw dislocation along the z-axis in a cylindrical piece of material, the stress field is completely given by a shear stress:

$$\tau_{z\theta} = \tau_{\theta z} = Gb/2\pi r \qquad (3\text{-}53)$$

The absence of tensile and compressional stresses in this case is associated with the absence of an extra half plane of atoms. Note that the stresses do not contain θ, i.e., the stress field is cylindrically symmetric as one might have expected. The energy of formation of a screw dislocation is approximately two-thirds that of an edge dislocation of the same length in the same material, as shown in Problem 3-15.

3-14. Interaction between dislocations

Since any dislocation is surrounded by a stress field, the energy required to form a dislocation in a piece of material which contains already another dislocation will be different from that required to form the dislocation in the absence of the other. In other words, there will be an energy of interaction between two dislocations; the gradient of the interaction energy determines the force between them. This can most easily be demonstrated for two parallel screw dislocations; in this case the stress fields have cylindrical symmetry and one expects the force between them to depend only on their distance apart, i.e., the force should be a central force. To illustrate this, suppose a piece of material contains a screw dislocation along the z-axis (Fig. 3-22) and let us produce a second screw

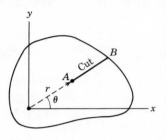

dislocation parallel to the first one, at a distance r. As before, we produce a cut extending from A to B in Fig. 3-22 and displace the material on one side of the cut relative to that on the other side over a distance b along the z-direction. Since at the moment we are interested only in the interaction energy of the two dislocations, we shall calculate only the work required to produce the second dislocation in so far as this work is determined by the presence of the first dislocation. Thus, if E_i represents the interaction energy per unit length of dislocation, we may write

Fig. 3-22. Referring to the calculation of the interaction energy of two screw dislocations running along the z-axis; one is located at the origin, the other in A. [After Cottrell, op. cit., p. 50]

$$E_i = \int_r^{r_R} (Gb/2\pi r)b \ dr \qquad (3\text{-}54)$$

where $Gb/2\pi r$ is the shear stress produced along the z-direction in the cut by the dislocation at the origin. The force between the two dislocations is then

$$F(r) = -dE_i/dr = Gb^2/2\pi r \qquad (3\text{-}55)$$

Note that the force varies as $1/r$. For dislocations of opposite sign the force is attractive; for equal signs the force is repulsive.

Similar considerations may be held for the interaction between edge dislocations. In this case the force has a radial as well as a tangential component. Thus for two-edge dislocations of equal sign, along the z-axis and with a Burgers vector along the x-axis, one obtains[42]

$$F_r = \frac{Gb^2}{2\pi(1-\nu)r}, \qquad F_\theta = \frac{Gb^2}{2\pi(1-\nu)r} \sin 2\theta \qquad (3\text{-}56)$$

where θ is the angle between r and the x-axis (see Fig. 3-23). Here again, the radial force is repulsive or attractive depending on whether the dislocations have equal or unequal signs. In the latter case the signs of both F_r and F_θ must be reversed in (3-22). We have mentioned earlier that the motion of an edge dislocation is mainly confined to the slip plane (conservative motion). For this reason, the force component along the

[42] See Cottrell, *op. cit.*, p. 47.

x-direction is the most important; for two-edge dislocation of the same sign this component may be obtained from the relation (see Fig. 3-23)

$$F_x = F_r \cos \theta - F_\theta \sin \theta \qquad (3\text{-}57)$$

Substituting F_r and F_θ from (3-56), one finds readily

$$F_x = \frac{Gb^2 x(x^2 - y^2)}{2\pi(1 - v)r^4} \qquad (3\text{-}58)$$

It is observed that this component vanishes for $x = 0$ and for $x = y$. Furthermore, when $x > y$, or $\theta < 45°$, two parallel edge dislocations of the same sign repel each other in the direction of the slip plane; for $x < y$, or $\theta > 45°$, they attract each other along the *x*-axis. The stable configuration for the two dislocations occurs when they lie vertically above each other. This conclusion is also true when a large number of edge dislocations of the same sign are involved. In fact, such an array of dislocations has been suggested by Burgers as a model for a grain boundary between two crystallites of different orientation.[43]

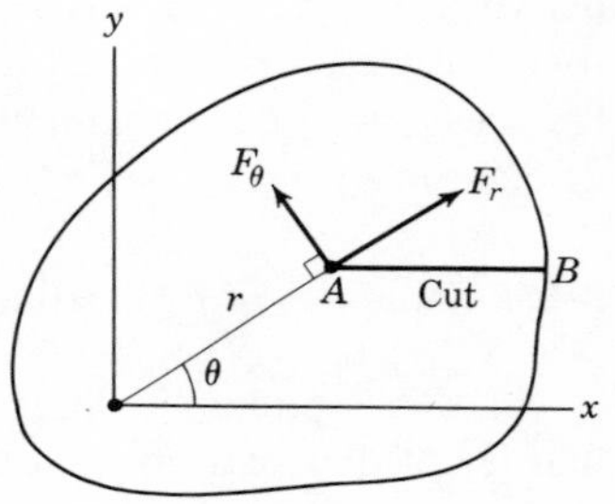

Fig. 3-23. Radial and tangential components of the force exerted by an edge dislocation at the origin on an edge dislocation at *A*. Both dislocations lie along the *z*-axis and have a Burgers vector along the *x*-axis. The calculation in this case involves a cut along *AB*.

Dislocations also interact with a free surface. In fact, any dislocation will be attracted by a free surface, since a motion towards the surface would reduce the strain energy. According to Koehler the force of attraction is approximately given by an image force, i.e., approximately equal to the force of attraction produced by a dislocation of opposite sign located at the image position of the first one relative to the surface.[44]

While on the subject of stress fields around dislocations, we may mention that impurities are in general attracted by edge dislocations. If the impurity atoms are "larger" than those of the host lattice, they will tend to move toward the region of tension, since in this way the tension will be somewhat released in this region. On the other hand, if the impurity atoms are "smaller" than the host atoms, they tend to be deposited in the region of compression.

In the preceding section we mentioned that dislocations are not in thermal equilibrium with the lattice and the question was raised as to why

[43] J. M. Burgers, *Proc. Koninkl. Ned. Akad. Wetenschap.*, **42**, 293 (1939); *Proc. Phys. Soc. (London)*, **52**, 23 (1940). For experimental evidence, see next section.

[44] J. S. Koehler, *Phys. Rev.*, **60**, 397 (1941).

it is not possible to remove almost all dislocations in a solid by annealing. The reason for this is the following: The density of dislocations in a solid is determined essentially by its history, i.e., by conditions under which the crystal was grown, cold working, etc. Certain parts of the dislocations may be mobile; for other parts the motion may be hindered or completely inhibited by interaction with impurities or other dislocations. Consider, for example, a point at which three dislocation lines meet. In general, such a point is essentially immobile, since it involves nonconservative motion of one or two of the dislocations involved. Ultimately, therefore, the dislocations probably arrange themselves in a sort of three-dimensional network or superstructure in the solid.[45] Although such a situation is not thermodynamically stable, it may be very stable in the mechanical sense for reasons just explained. We shall return to this point in the discussion of mosaic structures in Sec. 3-15.

3-15. Estimates of dislocation densities

In this section we shall discuss briefly some methods by which the density of dislocations in solids may be estimated.

1. *Plastically bent crystals.* Plastic bending of crystals takes place in a manner similar to the bending of a deck of playing cards. As illustrated in Fig. 3-24a, this process can be understood in terms of a slip process of thin layers of the crystal, the slip direction at one end being opposite to that at the other end. Since the bent state is stable, it seems reasonable to

(a)   (b)

Fig. 3-24. Plastically bent crystal (a) and the corresponding dislocation model (b). [After Cottrell, *op. cit.*, p. 29]

assume that the crystal in this state contains a number of edge dislocations in a pattern such as the one illustrated in Fig. 3-24b. In order to calculate the density of dislocations required to bend a certain specimen to a certain radius of curvature, consider a single glide packet. When L is the length of the outer arc and t is the thickness of the packet, the length of the inner arc is evidently $L(1 - t/R)$ where R is the radius of curvature. Suppose now that the packet contains n positive edge dislocations; we must then have $nb = tL/R$, where b is the absolute value of the Burgers vector. Since the density of dislocations in this case is simply given by the number of

[45] F. C. Frank, *Report of Pittsburgh Conference on Plastic Deformation of Crystals*, 1950, p. 100.

dislocation lines piercing through a unit area of the plane of the paper, we obtain

$$\rho = n/Lt = 1/Rb \tag{3-59}$$

For example, to bend a crystal to a radius of 3 cm one requires, with $b \simeq 3 \times 10^{-8}$ cm, a dislocation density $\rho \simeq 10^7$ cm^{-2}.

2. *Estimates from X-ray diffraction measurements.* In Chapter 1 we discussed the conditions for X-ray diffraction from crystals and found that reflection occurs only if the Bragg condition is fulfilled. Now, if a crystal had perfect periodicity, the angular spread about the Bragg angle should be not more than about 5 seconds. However, most crystals show an angular spread of the order of several minutes. In order to explain discrepancies of this kind, Darwin[46] and Ewald[47] introduced, many years ago, the notion of a mosaic crystal, i.e., they assumed that an actual crystal is made up of a number of small blocks which themselves are perfect but which are slightly misoriented relative to each other. It is presently believed that this mosaic structure may be the result of the three-dimensional network of dislocations mentioned in the preceding section. Assuming that this is the case,[48] an estimate of the dislocation density in terms of the observed total angular spread θ of the X-ray pattern may be made in the following manner: Suppose the surface area of the crystal involved in the X-ray measurements has a side L. Let the density of dislocations in the crystal be ρ, so that ρ dislocation lines pierce through a unit area of the surface of the crystal. Let us now define the edge λ of each block in the mosaic structure in such a way that $\lambda^2 = 1/\rho$, i.e., we associate one block with each dislocation line coming out of the surface. The average angular misfit between blocks is then $\alpha = b/\lambda$ radians; these misfits may be positive or negative. Thus as we pass across the crystal over a distance L, we pass L/λ blocks, and the probable angle of misfit between the first and the last block is $\alpha (L/\lambda)^{1/2}$. Identifying this angle with the total observed spread of θ radians, we find

$$\theta = \alpha(L/\lambda)^{1/2} \quad \text{or} \quad \theta = bL^{1/2}\rho^{3/4} \tag{3-60}$$

For a typical case of a pure crystal let us take $L = 0.1$ cm, $\theta = 10^{-2}$ radian, and $b = 3 \times 10^{-8}$ cm. We then obtain $\rho \simeq 10^8$ cm^{-2}. Note that in this case $\lambda \simeq 10^{-4}$ cm, in agreement with other estimates.

3. In heavily cold-worked metals the density of dislocations is sufficiently high to produce an increase of a few per cent in the electrical resistivity. According to calculations by Dexter, densities of dislocations of the order of 10^{12} cm^{-2} are required to explain measurements made on cold-worked copper.[49] Similar estimates have been obtained from

[46] C. G. Darwin, *Phil. Mag.*, **27**, 325, 675 (1914).

[47] P. P. Ewald, *Ann. Physik*, **54**, 519, 577 (1917).

[48] R. D. Heidenreich and W. Shockley, "Report on Strength of Solids," *Phys. Soc.* (*London*), 1948, p. 57.

[49] D. L. Dexter, *Phys. Rev.*, **86**, 770 (1952).

measurements of other physical properties, such as the magnetic saturation of cold-worked ferromagnetic materials.[50]

4. In the preceding section we mentioned that Burgers suggested that the boundary between two crystals differing in orientation by a small rotation α may consist of a set of edge dislocations as indicated in Fig. 3-25. If D

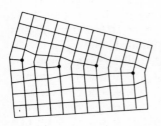

Fig. 3-25. Burgers disloca-tion model of a symmetrical grain boundary.

is the average distance between the dis-locations, the angle should presumably be equal to $\alpha = b/D$, where b is the magnitude of the Burgers vector. This model has been verified for germanium single crystals in the following manner:[51] A germanium crystal was grown from a seeded melt along the $\langle 100 \rangle$ direction. Grain boundaries were then re-vealed by etching with an acid. When the boundaries were examined under high mag-nification, they were found to consist of regularly spaced conical pits, as shown in the micrograph of Fig. 3-26. It is believed that each etch pit corresponds to a single dislocation piercing through the surface. Because of the strain in the vicinity of a dislocation line, the

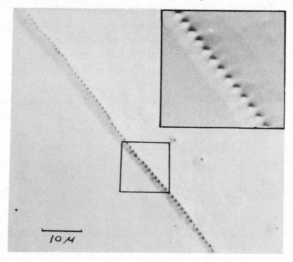

Fig. 3-26. Optical micrograph of lineage boundary in germanium single crystal, viewed in face transverse to growth direction. Lighting oblique. [Reproduced with permission from F. L. Vogel, W. G. Pfann, H. E. Corey, and E. E. Thomas, *Phys. Rev.*, **90**, 489 (1953)]

[50] W. F. Brown, *Phys. Rev.*, **60**, 139 (1941).

[51] F. L. Vogel, W. G. Pfann, H. E. Corey, and E. E. Thomas, *Phys. Rev.*, **90**, 489 (1953).

material around it presumably dissolves preferentially. The distance between the pits may be obtained by counting, and the angle α may be determined from X-ray diffraction experiments. For three specimens, the calculated distance between dislocations and the observed distance between etch pits are given below.

α (seconds)	$D_{\text{calc.}}$ (cm)	$D_{\text{obs.}}$ (cm)
17.5 ± 2.5	$(4.7 \pm 0.7) \times 10^{-4}$	$(5.3 \pm 0.3) \times 10^{-4}$
65.0 ± 2.5	$(1.3 \pm 0.1) \times 10^{-4}$	$(1.3 \pm 0.1) \times 10^{-4}$
85.0 ± 2.5	$(0.97 \pm 0.2) \times 10^{-4}$	$(0.99 \pm 0.2) \times 10^{-4}$

It is observed that the agreement is remarkably good. One might probably conclude that the etch pit method is presently the most direct method for determining the dislocation density.

3-16. The Frank-Read mechanism of dislocation multiplication

We have mentioned before that the amount of slip occurring in a slip plane requires a large number of dislocation lines sweeping across it in succession. One possible mechanism by which dislocations may multiply has been suggested by Frank and Read;[52] this mechanism is illustrated schematically in Fig. 3-27 with the slip plane coinciding with the plane of the paper. Suppose the line AB is part of the three-dimensional dislocation network in a crystal and that points A and B themselves are immobile. Under influence of a suitably applied shear stress the line will be deformed successively to the stages 1, 2, 3, 4, and 5. The latter stage results when finally the two points P and Q meet; when this happens the bent structure breaks up into a new straight part AB and a ring dislocation. In this manner, the line AB may produce an unlimited amount of slip. It can be shown that the stress required for this process is of the order of Gb/L, where L is the length of the line. For further details concerning this subject we refer the reader to the literature.

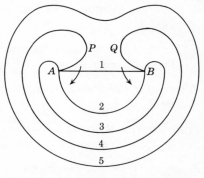

Fig. 3-27. Illustrating the Frank-Read mechanism of dislocation multiplication.

---

[52] F. C. Frank and W. T. Read, *Phys. Rev.*, **79**, 722 (1950).

REFERENCES

C. S. Barrett, *Structure of Metals*, 2d ed., McGraw-Hill, New York, 1952.

A. H. Cottrell, *Theoretical and Structural Metallurgy*, Arnold, London, 1953.

A. H. Cottrell, *Dislocations and Plastic Flow in Crystals*, Oxford, New York, 1953.

W. Hume-Rothery, *The Structure of Metals and Alloys*, Institute of Metals, London, 1936.

W. Hume-Rothery, *Electrons, Atoms, Metals and Alloys*, Institute of Metals, London, 1948.

W. Jost, *Diffusion in Solids, Liquids, Gases*, Academic Press, New York, 1952.

N. F. Mott and H. Jones, *Theory of the Properties of Metals and Alloys*, Oxford, New York, 1936.

W. T. Read, *Dislocations in Crystals*, McGraw-Hill, New York, 1953.

F. Seitz, *The Physics of Metals*, McGraw-Hill, New York, 1943.

W. Shockley (ed.), *Imperfections in Nearly Perfect Crystals*, Wiley, New York, 1952.

A. R. Verma, *Crystal Growth and Dislocations*, Academic Press, New York, 1953.

C. Zener, *Elasticity and Anelasticity of Metals*, University of Chicago Press, Chicago, 1948.

Report of a Conference on Strength of Solids, Physical Society, London, 1948.

Symposium on Plastic Deformation of Crystalline Solids, Carnegie Institute of Technology and Office of Naval Research, 1950.

Report of the Bristol Conference on Defects in Crystalline Solids, Physical Society, London, 1954.

For review papers see also:

Progress in Metal Physics, Interscience, New York, beginning with Vol. 1, 1949.

Advances in Physics, Quarterly Supplement to the *Philosophical Magazine*, beginning with Vol. 1, 1952.

PROBLEMS

3-1. When N is an integer $\gg 1$, one may approximate the expression

$$\log (N!) = \log 1 + \log 2 + \dots + \log N$$

by an integral. From this, prove Stirling's formula $\log (N!) \simeq N \log N$.

3-2. Suppose one has N boxes and n balls; the balls are all of the same color and indistinguishable.

(a) If there is no restriction on the total number of balls in any given box, show that the number of ways in which the balls can be distributed over the boxes is equal to $(N + n)!/N!n!$

(b) Suppose each box can contain either one ball or no ball; with this restriction, show that the number of ways in which the balls can be distributed over the boxes is equal to $N!/(N - n)!n!$

3-3. Consider a system of N one-dimensional harmonic oscillators, all of the same frequency ν. According to Sec. 2-4 the vibrational energy of this system for a temperature $T \gg h\nu/k$ is approximately equal to $NkT = nkT/h\nu$, where n is the total number of vibrational quanta associated with the N oscillators. Making use of the answer of Problem 3-2a, show that the thermal entropy of the system is equal to

$$S_{\text{th}} \simeq Nk \left[1 + \log (kT/h\nu) \right] \quad \text{for} \quad h\nu \ll kT$$

This proves expression (3-2). Also find an expression for S_{th} for temperatures which are not high compared with $h\nu/k$. Furthermore, derive an expression for the free energy F of the system for both temperature ranges.

3-4. Consider a system of N one-dimensional harmonic oscillators in contact with a temperature bath T; all oscillators have the same frequency ν. Assume that in equilibrium the oscillators have a total of n vibrational quanta $h\nu$; consider n for the moment as a variable and find an expression for the free energy F. From the equilibrium condition $(\partial F/\partial n)_T = 0$, derive Planck's formula for the average energy of an oscillator at a temperature T. (*Note:* In the preceding problem one makes explicit use of Planck's formula, in contrast with the present problem.)

3-5. Estimate the number of vacancies per atom in thermal equilibrium for a crystal at $T = 300°$ and $T = 600°$, assuming that the energy required to form a vacancy is 1 ev.

3-6. Show that for a quantized as well as for a classical harmonic oscillator the average fraction of time spent in energy states $\geq \epsilon$ is given by $\exp (-\epsilon/kT)$.

3-7. Show that the number of Frenkel defects in a solid element in thermal equilibrium at a temperature T is given by expression (3-13).

3-8. Consider a low-temperature modification A and a high-temperature modification B of a certain element. In order to discuss the equilibrium between these modifications, assume for simplicity that the lattice vibrations may be represented by Einstein models of frequencies ν_a and ν_b. Suppose that the binding energies per atom in the two modifications are given by $-\epsilon_a$ and $-\epsilon_b$. Explain why $\epsilon_a > \epsilon_b$. Set up an expression for the free energy per atom in each of the modifications. Then write an expression for the change in the free energy ΔF if one atom is transferred at constant T from A to B. In equilibrium, $\Delta F = 0$. Show that there is only one temperature for which the two modifications are in equilibrium, viz., $T_{eq} = (\epsilon_b - \epsilon_a)/[k \log (\nu_b/\nu_a)$. What can one conclude about the ratio ν_b/ν_a, and explain why the answer is reasonable.

3-9. Consider a b.c.c. lattice built up of atoms which may be assumed to be hard spheres of radius R. Calculate the maximum radius of a hard spherical atom that would fit in an interstitial position. Do the same for a f.c.c. lattice (in this case there are two types of interstitial positions!). How many interstitial positions are there in both types of lattices per normal lattice site?

3-10. Consider a particle restricted to motion in one dimension. Suppose the particle undergoes consecutive displacements with equal probability to the left or to the right, the absolute magnitude of the displacements being λ. Show that the mean square displacement for N steps is equal to $N\lambda^2$. Also show that the probability for the particle to be found at a distance $n\lambda$ relative to the origin, after N steps, is given by

$$P(n,\lambda) = \left(\frac{1}{2}\right)^N \frac{N!}{[(N + n)/2]![(N - n)/2]!}$$

From this, show that for $N \gg 1$ the probability to find the particle after a time interval t at a distance x relative to the origin is given by

$$P(x,t) \simeq \left(\frac{2\tau}{\pi t}\right)^{1/2} \exp\left(-x^2\tau/2\lambda^2 t\right)$$

where τ is the time required for a single step.

3-11. An infinite medium contains at $t = 0$ a quantity Q of a diffusing substance per cm^2 concentrated in the plane $x = 0$. Show that the concentration $c(x,t)$ is given by

$$c(x,t) = \frac{Q}{2(\pi Dt)^{1/2}} \exp\left(-x^2/4Dt\right)$$

From this and the results obtained in the previous problem, show that the diffusion coefficient in terms of the random walk problem is given by $D = \lambda^2/2\tau$. Also show that the mean square displacement for a time t is given by $(2Dt)^{1/2}$.

3-12. Express the theoretical shear strength of a perfect lattice in terms of the shear modulus G on the assumption that slip will start when the shear strain is 10 per cent; compare the result with that obtained in Sec. 3-10 on the basis of Frenkel's model.

3-13. Show that the elastic strain energy in a crystal under the stress at which slip begins is of the order of 10^3 ergs cm^{-3}. Assuming that the strain energy were converted into heat, what would be the rise in temperature of the material?

3-14. Consider a solid in the form of a cube of 1 cm^3 containing a dislocation line perpendicular to one of the faces. Show that the configurational entropy is $\sim 10^{-6} k$ per atom along the dislocation line. For the importance of this result see Sec. 3-13.

3-15. Show that the energy of formation for a screw dislocation per unit length is equal to $(Gb^2/4\pi) \log (R/r_0)$ where the symbols used are those of Sec. 3-13. For a Poisson ratio $\nu \simeq \frac{1}{3}$, this is about two-thirds that of an edge dislocation (see 3-52).

3-16. Show that the force between two positive edge dislocations is given by expression (3-56); follow the same procedure as that employed in the text to calculate the force between two screw dislocations. Make use of the cut indicated in Fig. 3-23.

Chapter 4

SOME PROPERTIES OF SIMPLE ALLOYS

4-1. Interstitial and substitutional solid solutions

When an element B is dissolved in a metal A and the B atoms occupy interstitial positions in the A lattice, one speaks of an interstitial solid solution. An example of this type is austenite, which is an interstitial alloy of carbon in γ iron (f.c.c.). Since the interstitial positions provide room only for relatively small atoms, interstitial solid solutions are likely to be formed with the elements H, B, C, N, and O; the approximate radii of these atoms are, respectively, 0.5, 1.0, 0.8, 0.7, and 0.6 Å.

When a metal A is alloyed with a metal B and the B atoms occupy positions which are normally occupied by A atoms, a substitutional solid solution is formed. It is only with these alloys that we shall concern ourselves. Substitutional solid solutions of two metals may occur only over limited ranges of composition, the structure varying from one range to another. A solid solution at either end of a binary phase diagram is called a terminal solid solution; the other ranges of solid solutions are referred to as intermediate solid solutions.[1]

Certain binary systems, such as the Cu-Ni and Au-Ag systems, exhibit a continuum of solid solutions for all compositions without change in structure. This requires first of all that both metals have the same structure; furthermore, the radii of the two types of atoms must be approximately the same (within about 15 per cent). Gold and silver, for example, both have an f.c.c. structure with lattice constants of, respectively, 4.0783 Å and 4.0856 Å (at room temperature). Besides these geometrical factors, other factors such as valence, chemical properties, etc. enter into the conditions for solubility. That geometrical factors and the number of valence electrons do not alone determine the formation and properties of an alloy may be illustrated by the observation that the lattice constant in the Au-Ag system exhibits a minimum, as shown in Fig. 4-1. The straight line which is dotted in the figure represents what is known as Vegard's law; negative as well as positive deviations from Vegard's law are observed in alloys.

When like atoms attract each other more strongly than unlike ones,

---

[1] For a discussion of phase diagrams, see, for example, G. Tamman, *The States of Aggregation*, Van Nostrand, New York, 1925; or J. S. Marsh, *Principles of Phase Diagrams*, McGraw-Hill, New York, 1935.

one may expect a low solubility, at least at relatively low temperatures, since there will be a tendency for a second phase to precipitate out. In the opposite case, with a dominant attraction between unlike atoms, A atoms will tend to have B atoms as nearest neighbors; in that case ordered structures or superlattices may occur (see Sec. 4-4).

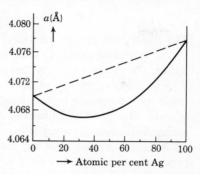

Fig. 4-1. The lattice constant (Å) for the gold-silver system as function of composition; the dashed line represents Vegard's law. [After Barrett, *Structure of Metals*, McGraw-Hill, 2d ed., p. 222, 1952]

4-2. Mutual solubility as function of temperature

In a simplified model of a metal or alloy one may describe the cohesive energy in terms of the sum of the interactions between pairs of neighboring atoms. On the basis of this model we shall consider the solubility of a metal A in a metal B as function of temperature.[2] Suppose that from a piece of metal A and from a piece of metal B we remove, respectively, an interior A and B atom; then we put the A atom in the vacancy of the B lattice and the B atom in the vacancy of the A lattice. The work required for this process, assuming the two metals have identical structures, may be written

$$z(\phi_{AA} + \phi_{BB} - 2\phi_{AB}) \equiv z\phi \qquad (4\text{-}1)$$

Here ϕ_{AA}, ϕ_{BB}, and ϕ_{AB} represent, respectively, the dissociation energy of an AA, BB, and AB pair of nearest neighbors; z is the coordination number, i.e., the number of nearest neighbors of a given atom. Whether or not the two metals will have a wide or narrow solubility range depends on the quantity ϕ defined by (4-1). When $\phi > 0$, like atoms attract each other more strongly than unlike atoms, and hence we expect a limited solubility. On the other hand, when $\phi < 0$, there is a preferential attraction between unlike atoms, and the solubility may cover the whole range of compositions, as in the Ag-Au system.

We shall consider the case $\phi > 0$ (limited solubility), inquiring about the variation of the solubility with temperature. Suppose an alloy of the substitutional type contains N_a A atoms and N_b B atoms. For convenience we shall introduce the atomic concentrations $c = N_a/N$ and $1 - c = N_b/N$, where $N = N_a + N_b$. We shall now express the free energy $F = E - TS$ of the alloy in terms of c; in order to find the equilibrium concentration

[2] See also A. H. Cottrell, *Theoretical and Structural Metallurgy*, Arnold, London, 1953.

at the temperature T we may then make use of the thermodynamic condition $(\partial F/\partial c)_T = 0$. We may write

$$F = E_{\text{binding}} + E_{\text{vibr}} - TS_{\text{th}} - TS_{\text{cf}} \qquad (4\text{-}2)$$

The terms here are, respectively, the binding energy of the alloy relative to the system of infinitely separated atoms, the vibrational energy of the lattice, the thermal entropy term, and the configurational entropy term.

The binding energy of the alloy may be found from the following arguments, assuming nearest neighbor interaction only: The total number of pairs of nearest neighbors is $Nz/2$ (the factor $\frac{1}{2}$ arises since otherwise each pair is counted twice). If we assume a completely random distribution of A and B atoms over the lattice (which is probably never exact in practice), the probability for a pair chosen at random to be

of the AA type is c^2

of the BB type is $(1 - c)^2$

of the AB type is $2c(1 - c)$

The factor 2 in the last case enters because we count AB as well as BA pairs; the sum of the probabilities equals unity, as it ought to. Employing the dissociation energies introduced above, we may write

$$E_b = -\tfrac{1}{2}Nz[c^2\phi_{\text{AA}} + (1 - c)^2\phi_{\text{BB}} + 2c(1 - c)\phi_{\text{AB}}]$$

or, in terms of ϕ defined by (4-1)

$$E_b = -\tfrac{1}{2}Nz[c\phi_{\text{AA}} + (1 - c)\phi_{\text{BB}} - c(1 - c)\phi] \qquad (4\text{-}3)$$

The minus sign arises from the fact that the mutual potential energy of two atoms equals minus the dissociation energy. In order to simplify matters we shall assume that the thermal entropy is independent of c, i.e., we assume that when an A atom is substituted for a B atom, the vibrational spectrum of the lattice does not change; this assumption does not impair the general conclusions.

The configurational entropy is determined by the number of different ways in which N_a atoms of kind A and N_b atoms of type B may be distributed over $N_a + N_b$ lattice sites (vacancies are neglected). Hence, according to the Boltzmann relation,

$$-TS_{\text{cf}} = -kT \log \frac{N!}{N_a!N_b!}$$

Applying Stirling's formula $\log N! \simeq N \log N$ and expressing the result in terms of c, we obtain

$$-TS_{\text{cf}} = NkT[c \log c + (1 - c) \log (1 - c)] \qquad (4\text{-}4)$$

Substituting (4-3) and (4-4) into (4-2) and applying $(\partial F/\partial c)_T = 0$, one arrives at the following result for the equilibrium concentration c of the A atoms:

$$kT \log \left(\frac{c}{1-c}\right) = \tfrac{1}{2}z[\phi_{AA} - \phi_{BB} - \phi(1 - 2c)] \qquad (4\text{-}5)$$

For given values of ϕ, ϕ_{AA}, and ϕ_{BB}, this equation can be solved numerically for c. If we consider the special case $\phi_{AA} = \phi_{BB}$ we obtain

$$c/(1 - c) = \exp\left[-z\phi(1 - 2c)/2kT\right] \qquad (4\text{-}6)$$

which for small concentrations reduces to the simple Boltzmann expression

$$c = \exp\left(-z\phi/2kT\right), \qquad c \ll 1 \qquad (4\text{-}7)$$

In Fig. 4-2 we have plotted $2kT/z\phi$ as function of c. The region above the curve corresponds to a homogeneous solid solution; the region below the curve corresponds to temperatures that are too low to give a true solid solution. The symmetry of the curve is, of course, due to our assumption $\phi_{AA} = \phi_{BB}$. In practical cases, a great part of the solubility curve may lie above the melting point so that in the phase diagram only those parts will enter that are close to either of the pure metals. When the reader takes a look at phase diagrams of binary alloys he will readily recognize the occurrence of the domelike shapes similar to that of Fig. 4-2. To give a numerical example, suppose that the maximum solubility of a certain metal in another is 1 per cent

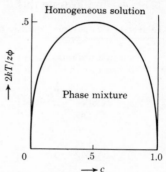

Fig. 4-2. The solubility curve for a binary alloy, according to equation (4-6).

at 300°C. In that case, $kT \simeq 0.05$ ev and from (4-7) one finds $z\phi \simeq 0.46$ ev. Treatment similar to that given here for substitutional alloys may be given for interstitial ones.

4-3. The Hume-Rothery electron compounds

When zinc is added to copper (f.c.c.) up to atomic concentrations of approximately 35 per cent, a solid solution is obtained with an f.c.c. structure in which copper atoms are replaced by zinc atoms; this phase is called the α phase. For higher zinc concentrations there is a β phase with a b.c.c. structure which is stable over a narrow concentration range in the vicinity of 50 per cent Zn; a γ phase with a complicated cubic structure containing 52 atoms per unit cell which is stable in the vicinity of 70 per cent Zn; and an ϵ phase (h.c.p.) in the neighborhood of 80 per cent Zn. These regions are separated by regions corresponding to a mixture of the two neighboring phases. If one writes the approximate concentrations for which the phases of narrow composition range occur in terms of a chemical formula, one obtains:

β phase (b.c.c.) CuZn

γ phase (complex cubic) Cu_5Zn_8

ϵ phase (h.c.p.) $CuZn_3$

Similar sequences of phases with the same structures are found in many alloys, but the compositions at which they occur may be quite different from those given for the brass system above. It is obvious that the alloy compositions corresponding to the various phases cannot be explained in terms of the usual chemical valence rules. It was pointed out by Hume-Rothery, however, that the electron to atom ratio is approximately the same for a given phase of different alloys.[3] A few examples are given in Table 4-1 to illustrate this.

Table 4-1. Compositions and Electron-to-Atom Ratio for Structurally Analogous Phases

Electron-atom ratio 3:2 β structure (b.c.c.)	Electron-atom ratio 21:13 γ structure (compl. cub.)	Electron-atom ratio 7:4 ϵ structure (h.c.p.)
CuZn	Cu_5Zn_8	$CuZn_3$
CuBe	Cu_9Al_4	$CuCd_3$
Cu_3Al	Cu_5Cd_8	Cu_3Ge
Cu_5Sn	Au_5Cd_8	$AgZn_3$
AgCd	Ag_5Cd_8	Ag_3Sn
AgMg	$Cu_{31}Si_8$	$AuZn_3$

Since the phases have a certain range of compositions over which they are stable, the chemical formulas and the electron-to-atom ratios given in the table are approximate. However, there is a striking regularity when these "compounds" are considered from this point of view. For the alloys given in the table the electron-to-atom ratios are calculated on the basis of the normal number of valence electrons associated with the atoms involved. In order to fit alloys containing transition metals such as Fe, Co, Ni into this scheme, one must assume that these atoms contribute zero valence electrons. For example, FeAl has the β structure corresponding to an electron-to-atom ratio 3 : 2.

An interpretation of the change in structure associated with an increase in the electron-to-atom ratio has been given by Jones in terms of the band theory of metals.[4] Essentially, the picture is the following: In the expression for the total energy of an alloy there occurs a term associated

[3] W. Hume-Rothery, *J. Inst. Metals*, **35**, 295, 307 (1926); see also by the same author *Atomic Theory for Students of Metallurgy*, Institute of Metals, London, 1946.

[4] H. Jones, *Proc. Roy. Soc.* (*London*), **A144**, 225 (1934); **A147**, 396 (1934). See also N. F. Mott and H. Jones, *Theory of the Properties of Metals and Alloys*, Oxford, New York, 1936; and C. Zener, *Phys. Rev.*, **71**, 846 (1947); also references in footnote 3.

with the kinetic energy of the conduction electrons; since this is a positive term, it is unfavorable for the cohesive energy. As one increases the electron-to-atom ratio it may be advantageous for the lattice to change its structure if this permits a reduction of the total energy of the system. We may give here the results obtained by Jones from calculations of the band structure for the electron-to-atom ratios for which a new phase should appear in the alloys.

Phase	β	γ	ε
Hume-Rothery ratio	1.5	1.615	1.75
Jones ratio	1.480	1.538	1.7

The agreement between theory and experiment is quite good in view of the approximate nature of the calculations.

4-4. Superlattices

In the discussion of lattice defects in metals in the preceding chapter we saw that the number of defects increases with increasing temperature. Thus the crystals are in a state of higher order at lower temperature. We shall now discuss briefly another type of order, viz., that occurring in many alloys. Although in some of our previous discussions we assumed that the various types of atoms in a solid solution are distributed at

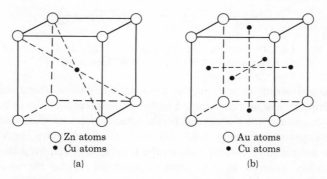

○ Zn atoms	○ Au atoms
• Cu atoms	• Cu atoms
(a)	(b)

Fig. 4-3. Ordered structures of CuZn (β brass) (a), and of AuCu₃ (b).

random over the available lattice sites, there is a great deal of experimental evidence which shows that this is frequently not the case. For example, the structure of β brass (CuZn) at low temperatures approaches an ordered structure in which corner points of a cubic unit cell are occupied by Zn atoms and the center by Cu atoms (see Fig. 4-3a). Thus, in the completely ordered state, brass may be vizualized as two interpenetrating simple cubic lattices of Cu and Zn. As the temperature is raised the degree of order decreases, as will be further discussed below; at a critical temperature T_c the degree of order drops rapidly. Another example of an ordered structure or superlattice is given in Fig. 4-3b for $AuCu_3$; the corners of the cubic cell are occupied by Au atoms, the centers of the faces by Cu atoms. This distribution is in agreement with the ratio of the numbers of Cu and Au atoms given by the formula $AuCu_3$. The same structure has been observed for $PtCu_3$, $FeNi_3$, and $MnNi_3$.

Part of the experimental evidence for the existence of ordered structures in alloys is provided by the observation of "extra" X-ray diffraction lines which gradually disappear as the temperature is increased.[5] The reason for the extra lines lies in the fact that in the ordered structures, certain planes of atoms may have a different scattering power than parallel planes

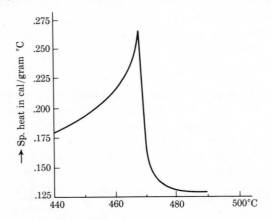

Fig. 4-4. The specific heat of β brass (CuZn) as function of temperature. [After Sykes and Wilkinson, ref. 6]

containing different atoms; in the random distribution these differences in scattering power do not occur. Further experimental evidence is derived from anomalous peaks observed in the specific heat of these alloys; an example is presented in Fig. 4-4.[6] The integral of the "extra" specific heat over the temperature corresponds to the total energy required to go from a completely ordered to a random distribution. Note the sharp drop which defines a critical temperature. The electrical resistivity of these alloys also drops quite sharply at T_c as one goes from high to low temperatures.[7] Since the resistivity decreases as the periodicity of the potential seen by the electrons becomes more perfect, this again indicates a transition from a disordered to an ordered state (see Chapter 11).

In attempting to introduce a quantity which describes the degree of order associated with a given distribution of atoms in an alloy, one may

[5] See, for example, C. Sykes and H. Evans, *J. Inst. Metals*, **58**, 255 (1936) for powder diffraction patterns of $AuCu_3$.

[6] C. Sykes and H. Wilkinson, *J. Inst. Metals*, **61**, 223 (1937).

[7] See, for example, N. S. Kurnakow and N. W. Ageew, *J. Inst. Metals*, **46**, 481 (1931).

take different points of view. In one of these one is concerned about the degree of long-distance order; in another one is interested in the degree of short-distance order. These two viewpoints will be discussed briefly below.

4-5. The long-distance order theory of Bragg and Williams[8]

We shall consider an alloy of the simple composition AB which in the completely ordered structure may be represented by two interpenetrating lattices of A and B atoms. If these lattices run through the whole crystal without discontinuities, one may define the sites corresponding to one lattice as α sites and those of the other lattice as β sites. In the completely ordered structure all α sites are occupied by A atoms, and all β sites by B atoms. In an incompletely ordered alloy one may then define right (A on α, B on β) and wrong atoms (A on β, B on α). When R and W represent, respectively, the number of right and wrong atoms, the long-distance order parameter is defined by

$$\mathscr{S} = (R - W)/N = (2R - N)/N \qquad (4\text{-}8)$$

where $N = R + W$ is the total number of atoms. When $R = N$ there is complete order and $\mathscr{S} = 1$. When $W = N, \mathscr{S} = -1$; this situation also describes a state of complete order, since by interchanging the α and β sites, this case becomes physically identical with $R = N$. Complete disorder exists when $R = N/2$, corresponding to $\mathscr{S} = 0$; therefore only the range between 0 and 1 for the order parameter is of physical interest.

Let us now investigate on the basis of a simple model how $\mathscr{S}$ should vary with temperature. First of all it will be evident that disorder in the alloy may be produced only by interchanging the positions of a right A and a right B atom; thus, if in a certain alloy there are R right atoms in all, $R/2$ of these occur on the α sites and an equal number occur on β sites. Since the alloy at absolute zero tends to be completely ordered, the energy required to produce disorder must be positive. Now suppose that the alloy in thermal equilibrium contains R right atoms and W wrong atoms. If in this state we were to interchange the positions of a right A and a right B atom, the change in W would be $\Delta W = -\Delta R = 2$. Since in thermal equilibrium the change ΔF in the free energy associated with ΔW must vanish ($\Delta W \ll W$), one can readily find the equilibrium values for R and W in the following manner: Suppose that the energy required to produce a pair of wrong atoms in the state R,W is $\phi(R,W)$. The configurational entropy associated with the state R,W is

$$S_{cf} = k(N \log N - R \log R - W \log W) \qquad (4\text{-}9)$$

[8] W. L. Bragg and E. J. Williams, *Proc. Roy. Soc.* (*London*), **A145**, 699 (1934).

Thus the change ΔS_{cf} associated with ΔW is

$$\Delta S_{cf} = -k(\Delta R \log R + \Delta W \log W) = 2k \log (R/W) \qquad (4\text{-}10)$$

Neglecting thermal entropy changes for simplicity, we may write

$$\Delta F = 0 = \phi(R,W) - 2kT \log (R/W)$$

or $\qquad\qquad\qquad R/W = \exp [\phi(R,W)/2kT] \qquad\qquad (4\text{-}11)$

Let us now inquire about the nature of the function $\phi(R,W)$. Consider a given right A atom; the probability for an arbitrarily chosen nearest neighbor of this atom to be a B atom (right) is R/N; the probability that a nearest neighbor atom is an A atom is W/N. The potential energy of the A atom in the field of its nearest neighbors is then

$$-z(\phi_{AB}R/N + \phi_{AA}W/N)$$

where we use the same symbols as in Sec. 4-2. Similarly, the potential energy of a right B atom in the field of its nearest neighbors is

$$-z(\phi_{AB}R/N + \phi_{BB}W/N)$$

We leave it as Problem 4-6 for the reader to show that this model of nearest neighbor interactions leads, for the energy required to interchange the positions of the right A and B atoms, to the expression

$$\phi(R,W) = \phi_0(R - W)/N = \phi_0 \mathscr{S} \qquad (4\text{-}12)$$

where $\phi_0 = z(2\phi_{AB} - \phi_{AA} - \phi_{BB})$ is a positive quantity since the dissociation energy ϕ_{AB} for an unlike pair is larger than that for a pair of similar atoms. The physical meaning of ϕ_0 is that it represents the energy required to produce 2 wrong atoms in the completely ordered lattice ($\mathscr{S} = 1$). It is observed that according to (4-12) the energy required to produce 2 wrong atoms decreases as the amount of order decreases. Qualitatively, this can readily be understood; for example, if two atoms in the completely disordered state ($\mathscr{S} = 0$) are interchanged, the energy is, on the average, zero because in the long-distance theory the distribution of A and B atoms around a given A or B atom is then random. Actually the simple linear relationship (4-12) between $\phi(R,W)$ and $\mathscr{S}$ was introduced by Bragg and Williams as an assumption; we see that this assumption is equivalent to the model employed above in which the interaction between the atoms is simplified to nearest neighbor interactions with constant ϕ_{AA}, ϕ_{AB}, and ϕ_{BB} values.

When (4-11) and (4-12) are substituted into (4-8) we obtain the following implicit equation for the long-distance order parameter.

$$\mathscr{S} = \tanh (\phi_0 \mathscr{S}/4kT) \qquad (4\text{-}13)$$

This equation may be solved graphically by introducing the variable

$$x = \phi_0 \mathscr{S}/4kT \quad \text{or} \quad \mathscr{S} = 4kTx/\phi_0 \qquad (4\text{-}14)$$

where $\mathscr{S}$ must satisfy the equation $\mathscr{S} = \tanh x$ as well as (4-14). The function $\tanh x$ is represented in Fig. 4-5. The $\mathscr{S}(x)$ curves corresponding

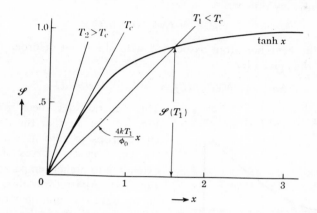

Fig. 4-5.   Graphical solution of equation (4-13) as explained in text.

to (4-14) produce a set of straight lines, of slope equal to $4kT/\phi_0$, i.e., proportional to T. The intersection of the $\tanh x$ curve with one of the straight lines then gives the value of $\mathscr{S}$ for the corresponding temperature. Since the slope of the $\tanh x$ curve for very small values of x is equal to unity, there exists a critical temperature T_c above which $\mathscr{S} = 0$, viz.,

$$T_c = \phi_0/4k \qquad (4\text{-}15)$$

Thus in this theory the order disappears altogether at T_c. The temperature dependence of $\mathscr{S}$ according to the Bragg-Williams theory is given in Fig. 4-6. Note the rapid drop in the vicinity of T_c. The reason for this lies in the fact that once a certain amount of disorder is present, it becomes easier for the thermal motions to produce more disorder (see 4-12). One therefore speaks of a cooperative phenomenon. Other

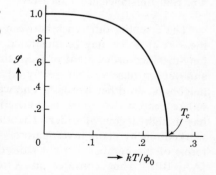

Fig. 4-6. The long distance order parameter as function of temperature, according to the Bragg-Williams theory.

cooperative phenomena are ferromagnetism and ferroelectricity; it is instructive to compare the theoretical treatment of those phenomena with the order-disorder treatment given above.

For β brass, $T_c \simeq 740°$K, so that according to (4-15) the quantity ϕ_0 is approximately 0.25 ev in this case.

A few words may be said here about the "extra" specific heat associated with the order-disorder transition. The energy required to increase R by dR is, according to the definition of ϕ, equal to $-\phi_0 \mathscr{S} dR/2$. Making use of (4-8) one may thus write

$$dE = -(N\phi_0/4)\mathscr{S} \, d\mathscr{S} \qquad (4\text{-}16)$$

The specific heat per atom associated with the order-disorder transformation if thus given by

$$\Delta c_v = (1/N)(dE/dT) = -(\phi_0 \mathscr{S}/4)(d\mathscr{S}/dT) \qquad (4\text{-}17)$$

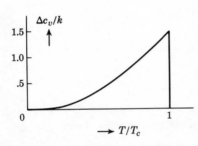

Fig. 4-7. The specific heat associated with the order-disorder transition, according to Bragg and Williams.

This function has been plotted in Fig. 4-7; we see that the theoretical curve drops to zero at T_c, whereas the experimental curves show tails extending to higher temperatures (see Fig. 4-4). Apart from this, the two curves have the same general shape. When one calculates the area under the extra specific heat curve, one obtains from (4-17),

$$\int_0^\infty c_v \, dT = kT_c/2 \qquad (4\text{-}18)$$

in fair agreement with experiment.

4-6. Short-distance order theories

The essential difference between the long-distance and short-distance theories of order may be illustrated with reference to Fig. 4-8. From the long-distance order point of view, this lattice would be highly disordered and yet we observe that nearly all atoms have unlike atoms as nearest neighbors. In other words, if one were to employ the relative number of unlike nearest neighbors as a criterion for order, the lattice of Fig. 4-8 has a high degree of order. Theories based on this concept have been worked out by many investigators.[9] Short-range order may be defined in terms of the number of right pairs (AB) and the number of wrong pairs (AA, BB). Thus consider an A atom and let the probability for a given nearest neighbor to be a B atom be $(1 + \sigma)/2$ and to be an A atom

[9] H. A. Bethe, *Proc. Roy. Soc. (London)*, **A150**, 552 (1935); E. J. Williams, *Proc. Roy. Soc. (London)*, **A152**, 231 (1935); R. Peierls, *Proc. Roy. Soc. (London)*, **A154**, 207 (1936); J. G. Kirkwood, *J. Chem. Phys.*, **6**, 70 (1938); C. N. Yang, *J. Chem. Phys.*, **13**, 66 (1949); Y. Y. Li, *J. Chem. Phys.*, **17**, 447 (1949); H. A. Kramers and G. H. Wannier, *Phys. Rev.*, **60**, 252, 263 (1941); L. Onsager, *Phys. Rev.*, **65**, 117 (1944); F. Zernicke *Physica*, **7**, 565 (1940).

$(1 - \sigma)/2$; σ is then the short-distance order parameter. For complete order, $\sigma = 1$, for a random distribution of atoms, $\sigma = 0$. Suppose that the dissociation energies ϕ_{AA} and ϕ_{BB} are equal, and, of course, smaller than ϕ_{AB}. In that case we should have, according to the Boltzmann distribution,

$$(1 + \sigma)/(1 - \sigma) = \exp\left[(\phi_{AB} - \phi_{AA})/kT\right] = \exp\left(\phi/kT\right) \quad (4\text{-}19)$$

Thus if ϕ were a constant independent of the degree of order, σ would decrease slowly to zero at high temperatures and there would be no critical temperature. In Bethe's theory ϕ is calculated in terms of the long-range order which exists in the crystal; since ϕ decreases with decreasing long-range order, σ decreases more rapidly to zero in the

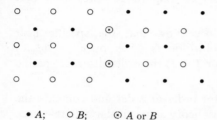

• A;   ○ B;   ⊙ A or B

Fig. 4-8. Illustrating the difference between long distance and short distance order; from the former point of view the lattice is very disordered, from the latter point of view it is well ordered.

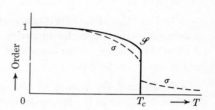

Fig. 4-9. The temperature dependence of the long-range and short-range order parameters for an AB_3 super-lattice. [According to Bethe, ref. 9]

vicinity of the critical point than for constant ϕ. As an example we give in Fig. 4-9 the long-range and short-range order parameters $\mathscr{S}$ and σ for a superlattice of the AB_3 structure. For the details of short-distance order theory we refer the reader to the literature. We may mention here an approximate theory developed by Cowley in which the order parameter is expressed in terms of the coefficients of the Fourier series, which determines the intensity of X-ray scattering.[10] This makes a direct comparison between theory and experiment possible; the agreement is very good.

REFERENCES

Besides the references given at the end of Chapter 3, see also:

J. Lumsden, *Thermodynamics of Alloys*, Institute of Metals, London, 1952.

J. S. Marsh, *Principles of Phase Diagrams*, McGraw-Hill, New York, 1935.

For reviews of the theory of order-disorder, see:

F. C. Nix, *J. Appl. Phys.*, **8**, 783 (1937).

[10] J. M. Cowley, *Phys. Rev.*, **77**, 669 (1950); *J. Appl. Phys.*, **21**, 25 (1950).

F. C. Nix and W. Shockley, *Revs. Mod. Phys.*, **10,** 1 (1938).

T. Muto and Y. Takagi, "The Theory of Order-Disorder Transitions in Alloys," in *Solid State Physics*, Vol. 1, edited by F. Seitz and D. Turnbull, Academic Press, New York, 1955.

PROBLEMS

4-1. Write an essay on the phase diagrams of binary alloys, showing that you are familiar with the meaning of such diagrams. (See, for example, J. S. Marsh, *Principles of Phase Diagrams*, McGraw-Hill, New York, 1935).

4-2. For the Bragg-Williams theory of long range order show that $-(d\mathscr{S}/dT)$ for $T = T_c$ is infinite.

4-3. For the Bragg-Williams theory show that the specific heat associated with the order-disorder transition is given by $c = -(\phi_0/8)$ $(d\mathscr{S}^2/dT)$ per atom. Also show that for $T = T_c$ the order-disorder specific heat is equal to $3k/2$ per atom.

4-4. Discuss the theory of Bethe for order-disorder and compare the results with those of the Bragg-Williams theory, in particular with reference to the value of the critical temperature and the specific heat versus temperature curve. (See H. A. Bethe, *Proc. Roy. Soc. (London)*, **A150,** 552 (1935), or N. F. Mott and H. Jones, *Theory of Metals and Alloys*, Oxford, New York, 1936).

4-5. Discuss the work of Cowley on the order-disorder problem (see footnote 10).

4-6. Consider an alloy AB with R right atoms and W wrong atoms in the sense of the Bragg-Williams theory. Assuming only nearest neighbor interaction, show that the energy required to produce two more wrong atoms is given by $\phi = \phi_0(R - W)/(R + W)$, where ϕ_0 corresponds to ϕ for $W = 0$. This proves equation (4-12).

Chapter 5

LATTICE ENERGY OF IONIC CRYSTALS

5-1. Introductory remarks

One of the fundamental problems in the theory of solids is the calculation of the binding energy of a crystal. This evidently requires a knowledge of the forces acting between the composing particles. The simplest group of crystals to deal with in this respect are the ionic crystals, for which calculations of the cohesive energy were made in 1910 by Born[1] and Madelung.[2] The basic assumption in the theory of the cohesive energy of ionic crystals is that the solid may be considered as a system of positive and negative ions. This is a good example of the simplification of a problem resulting from considering certain groups of elementary particles as units, the calculations being carried out for these units rather than for the elementary particles themselves. For example, in sodium chloride it is assumed that these units are the Na^+ ion, with an electron configuration $1s^2$, $2s^2$, $2p^6$ and the Cl^- ion, with an electron configuration $1s^2$, $2s^2$, $2p^6$, $3s^2$, $3p^6$. In the theory one works with these ions as "charged particles," forgetting to a large extent about their internal constitution. The influence of the latter may then be introduced in the form of refinements of the theory.

We shall begin with a discussion of perfect crystals, assuming that all ions occupy the proper lattice points. However, perfect crystals do not exist, and even if a crystal is "perfectly grown" and chemically pure there are always a (relatively small) number of lattice defects present, as discussed in Chapter 3. The changes in lattice energy resulting from a few simple types of lattice defects will be discussed in Chapter 7.

5-2. The fundamental assumptions of Born's theory

Born's theory of the lattice energy is based on the assumption that the crystals under consideration are built up of positive and negative ions. If we assume that the charge distribution in these ions is spherically symmetric, the force between two such ions depends only on their distance apart and is independent of direction. As an example, consider a lattice of the NaCl structure, represented in Fig. 5-1. We shall denote the

[1] See, for example, M. Born, *Atomtheorie des festen Zustandes*, Teubner, Leipzig, 1923; also, *Handbuch der Physik*, Vol. 24/2, Springer, Berlin, 1933.
[2] E. Madelung, *Physik. Z.*, **11**, 898 (1910).

shortest interionic distance by r and consider this quantity a variable for the moment. A given sodium ion is surrounded by 6 Cl⁻ ions at a distance r, 12 Na⁺ ions at a distance $r\sqrt{2}$, 8 Cl⁻ ions at a distance $r\sqrt{3}$, etc. The Coulomb energy of this ion in the field of all other ions is therefore

$$\epsilon_c = -\frac{e^2}{r}\left(\frac{6}{\sqrt{1}} - \frac{12}{\sqrt{2}} + \frac{8}{\sqrt{3}} - \frac{6}{\sqrt{4}} + \frac{24}{\sqrt{5}} - \ldots\right) \qquad (5\text{-}1)$$

where e is the charge per ion. Note that because Coulomb forces decrease relatively slowly with distance, it is not sufficient to consider only a few shells of ions around the central ion.

Evidently, the coefficient of e^2/r is a pure number, determined only by the crystal structure. Series of this type have been calculated by Madelung,[3] Ewald,[4] and Evjen.[5] For the NaCl structure the result is

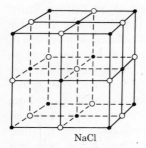

$$\epsilon_c = -Ae^2/r \quad \text{with} \quad A = 1.747558\ldots \qquad (5\text{-}2)$$

The constant A is called the Madelung constant. For other crystal structures composed of positive and negative ions of the same valency, the Madelung constants are[6]

Cesium chloride	$A = 1.762670$
Zincblende (ZnS)	$A = 1.6381$
Wurtzite (ZnS)	$A = 1.641$

Fig. 5-1. The sodium chloride structure.

NaCl

Note that e in (5-2) represents in general the electronic charge times the valence of the ions under consideration. The minus sign in (5-2) indicates that the average influence of all other ions on the one under consideration is of an attractive nature. To prevent the lattice from collapsing, there must also be repulsive forces between the ions. These repulsive forces become noticeable when the electron shells of neighboring ions begin to overlap, and they increase strongly in this region with decreasing values of r. These forces, as other overlap forces, can best be discussed on the basis of wave mechanics, because they are of a nonclassical nature. Born in his early work made the simple assumption that the repulsive energy between two ions as function of their separation could be expressed by a power law of the type B'/r^n, where B' and n are as yet undetermined constants characteristic of the ions in the solid under consideration.[7]

[3] E. Madelung, *Physik. Z.*, **19**, 524 (1918).

[4] P. P. Ewald, *Ann. Physik*, **64**, 253 (1921).

[5] H. M. Evjen, *Phys. Rev.*, **39**, 675 (1932).

[6] J. Sherman, *Chem. Revs.*, **11**, 93 (1932); for other structures containing ions of different valency, see, for example, F. Seitz, *Modern Theory of Solids*, McGraw-Hill, New York, 1940, p. 78.

[7] See also Sec. 1-11.

Focusing our attention again on one particular ion, we may thus write for the repulsive energy of this ion due to the presence of all other ions,

$$\epsilon_{rep} = B/r^n \qquad (5\text{-}3)$$

where B is related to B' by a numerical factor. In view of the fact that repulsive forces depend so strongly on the distance between the particles, the repulsive energy (5-3) is mainly determined by the nearest neighbors of the central ion. The total energy of one ion due to the presence of all others is then obtained by adding (5-2) and (5-3):

$$\epsilon = -Ae^2/r + B/r^n \qquad (5\text{-}4)$$

Assuming that the two types of forces just discussed are the only ones we have to take into account and neglecting surface effects, we thus find for the total binding energy of a crystal containing N positive and N negative ions,

$$E(r) = N\left(-A\frac{e^2}{r} + \frac{B}{r^n}\right) = N\epsilon(r) \quad (5\text{-}5)$$

We multiplied by N rather than by $2N$ because otherwise the energy between each pair of ions in the crystal would have been counted twice. The two contributions to $E(r)$ are represented schematically in Fig. 5-2. If we consider the crystal at absolute zero, the equilibrium conditions require E to be a minimum, which will be the case for the equilibrium value $r = a_0$, where a_0 represents the smallest interionic distance in the crystal at $T = 0$. For this minimum

$$(dE/dr)_{r=a_0} = 0 \qquad (5\text{-}6)$$

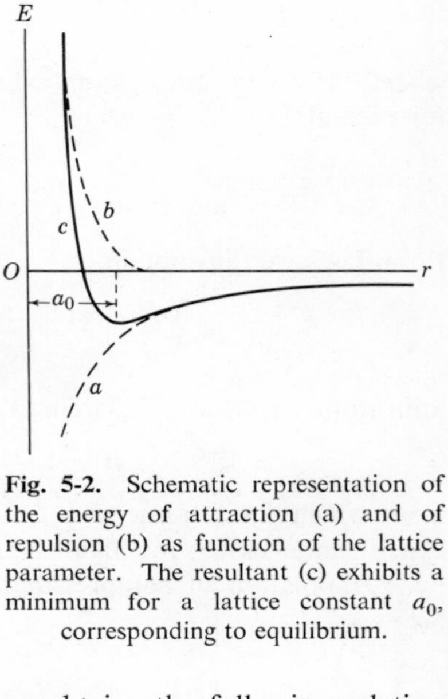

Fig. 5-2. Schematic representation of the energy of attraction (a) and of repulsion (b) as function of the lattice parameter. The resultant (c) exhibits a minimum for a lattice constant a_0, corresponding to equilibrium.

From the last two expressions one thus obtains the following relation between the two unknown parameters B and n:

$$B = (Ae^2/n)a_0^{n-1} \qquad (5\text{-}7)$$

Substitution into (5-5) yields for the lattice energy E_L,

$$E_L = E(a_0) = -NA\frac{e^2}{a_0}\left(1 - \frac{1}{n}\right) = N\epsilon_L \qquad (5\text{-}8)$$

$e = 4.8 \times 10^{-10}$ esu eV

where $\epsilon_L = \epsilon(a_0)$. The interionic distance can be obtained from X-ray diffraction data; the charge per ion is also known, and thus the lattice energy can be calculated if the repulsive exponent n is known. How information regarding n may be obtained is discussed in the next two sections.

5-3. Calculation of the repulsive exponent from compressibility data

Born obtained the unknown repulsive exponent n from measurements of the compressibility of the crystals as follows: The compressibility K_0 at absolute zero is given by

$$1/K_0 V_0 = (d^2E/dV^2)_{V=V_0} \tag{5-9}$$

where V_0 is the volume of the crystal corresponding to an interionic distance a_0; V corresponds to the variable r. The relation between volume and interionic distance must of course be of the form

$$V = cNr^3 \tag{5-10}$$

where c is a constant determined only by the type of lattice. For NaCl, for example, $c = 2$. Hence

$$\frac{dE}{dV} = \frac{1}{3cNr^2} \cdot \frac{dE}{dr} \quad \text{and} \quad \frac{d^2E}{dV^2} = \frac{1}{9c^2N^2r^2} \cdot \frac{d}{dr}\left(\frac{1}{r^2} \cdot \frac{dE}{dr}\right) \tag{5-11}$$

From (5-5) we thus obtain

$$\frac{1}{K_0 cNa_0^3} = \left(\frac{d^2E}{dV^2}\right)_{a_0} = \frac{1}{9c^2Na_0^2}\left[\frac{-4Ae^2}{a_0^5} + \frac{n(n+3)B}{a_0^{n+4}}\right] \tag{5-12}$$

Substituting B from (5-7), we find

$$n = 1 + 9ca_0^4/K_0e^2A \tag{5-13}$$

from which the parameter n can be calculated if K_0 is known. Some experimental values for alkali halides according to Slater, and obtained by extrapolation of compressibility measurements to $T = 0$, are given below.[8]

LiF	$n = 5.9$	NaCl	$n = 9.1$
LiCl	$n = 8.0$	NaBr	$n = 9.5$
LiBr	$n = 8.7$		

We note that there is a marked variation from one crystal to another. However, even an appreciable error in n leads to a relatively small error in the lattice energy, which is proportional to $(1 - 1/n)$. If we change n by unity, E_L changes by only 1 or 2 per cent. According to (5-8) and in view of the relatively large values of n, most of the lattice energy is due to

[8] J. C. Slater, *Phys. Rev.*, **23**, 488 (1924).

the Coulomb interaction, and the repulsion contributes only a relatively small fraction. On the other hand, the repulsive and attractive forces acting on any one ion just balance for $r = a_0$ and thus are equal in magnitude.

5-4. The repulsive exponent as function of electron configuration

It will be obvious that the repulsive forces acting between two ions will depend on the distribution of the electronic charges in the ions and especially on the number of electrons in the outer shells. For example, we would expect n to be larger for NaCl than for LiCl, because the Na^+ ion has eight outer electrons, the Li^+ ion has only two. From an approximate treatment of the interaction between closed-shell electronic configurations, Pauling arrived at the following values of n as a function of the occupation of electronic shells.[9]

Table 5-1. Repulsive Exponent as Function of Electron Configuration

Ion type	Electron configuration					
	K	L	M	N	O	n
He	2	......	......	......	......	5
Ne	2	8	......	......	......	7
Ar (Cu)	2	8	8(18)	......	......	9
Kr (Ag)	2	8	18	8(18)	......	10
Xe (Au)	2	8	18	18	8(18)	12

This table should be used by taking the average value of n for the two ion types occurring in the crystal. For NaCl, for example, one takes the average of 7 and 9; for NaF the average of 7 and 7, etc. Note that this table is in qualitative agreement with the experimental values of Slater referred to above.

5-5. Calculated and experimental lattice energies

The lattice energy ϵ_L may now be calculated from (5-8) by substituting the proper values for the charge of the ions, the interatomic distance and the Born exponent n. Values for ϵ_L so obtained are given in Table 5-2 for alkali halides and the alkaline earths oxides. The charge per ion in the latter group is assumed to be $2e$; it is not quite certain that these

[9] L. Pauling, *Proc. Roy. Soc.* (*London*), **114**, 181 (1927); *J. Am. Chem. Soc.*, **49**, 765 (1927); *Z. Krist.*, **67**, 377 (1928).

oxides can be considered ionic compounds. It may be remarked that CsCl, CsBr, and CsI crystallize in the cesium chloride structure (see Fig. 5-3), whereas all other compounds in the table have the NaCl structure. The expansion of the lattice, entering through the interionic distance a_0, can usually be neglected; the coefficient of expansion of ionic crystals at room temperature is of the order of 10^{-4} per degree.

Table 5-2. Lattice Energies for Alkali Halides and Alkaline Earth Oxides.
The calculated values are based on (5-8). The experimental values are obtained in a manner to be described below.

Compound	a_0 in Angstroms	n	ϵ_L in ev calc.	ϵ_L in ev exp.
LiF	2.07	6.0	10.5	. . . . . .
NaF	2.31	7.0	9.3	. . . . . .
KF	2.66	8.0	8.3	. . . . . .
RbF	2.82	8.5	7.9	. . . . . .
CsF	3.00	9.5	7.5	. . . . . .
LiCl	2.57	7.0	8.4	8.6
NaCl	2.81	8.0	8.0	7.9
KCl	3.14	9.0	7.1	7.1
RbCl	3.27	9.5	6.9	7.0
CsCl	3.56	10.5	6.5	6.7
LiBr	2.74	7.5	7.9	8.2
NaBr	2.97	8.5	7.5	7.5
KBr	3.29	9.5	6.8	6.8
RbBr	3.42	10.0	6.6	6.6
CsBr	3.71	11.0	6.2	6.4
LiI	3.03	8.5	7.4	7.8
NaI	3.23	9.5	7.0	7.2
KI	3.53	10.5	6.5	6.6
RbI	3.66	11.0	6.2	6.5
CsI	3.95	12.0	5.9	6.3
MgO	2.10	7.0	41.0	. . . . . .
CaO	2.40	8.0	36.5	. . . . . .
SrO	2.57	8.5	34.5	. . . . . .
BaO	2.75	9.5	32.5	. . . . . .

An experimental check on the calculated values of the lattice energies may be obtained from what is known as a Born-Haber cycle. Consider, for example, 1 gram atom of solid sodium reacting with $\frac{1}{2}$ gram molecule of Cl_2 gas. As a result of the reaction, solid NaCl is formed and a certain amount of heat Q (the "heat of formation") is given off. The change in energy due to such a reaction may be calculated by considering the following steps

$$Na_{solid} + S_{Na} \rightarrow Na_{vapor}$$
$$Na_{vapor} + I_{Na} \rightarrow Na^+ + electron$$
$$\tfrac{1}{2}Cl_2 + \tfrac{1}{2}D_{Cl_2} \rightarrow Cl$$
$$Cl + electron \rightarrow Cl^- + E_{Cl}$$
$$(Na^+ + Cl^-)_{gas} \rightarrow NaCl_{solid} + \epsilon_L$$

$$Na_{solid} + \tfrac{1}{2}Cl_2 + S_{Na} + I_{Na} + \tfrac{1}{2}D_{Cl_2} \rightarrow NaCl_{solid} + E_{Cl} + \epsilon_L$$

The quantities introduced all refer to the formation of one ion pair of solid NaCl. Here S_{Na} represents the sublimation energy of sodium per atom. Sublimation energies in general can be determined experimentally

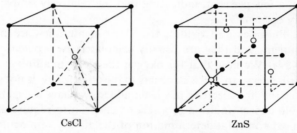

CsCl   ZnS

Fig. 5-3. The CsCl and the ZnS (sphalerite or zincblende) structures. The open circles in the ZnS structure are located at points obtained by displacements of 1/4 along three cube edges of the corresponding corner point. For one of the open circles we have indicated how it is surrounded by four black dots occupying the corner points of a regular tetrahedron, with the open circle at the center.

by direct caloric measurements or from measurements of the vapor pressure as function of temperature. The ionization energy I_{Na} represents the energy required to take away the outer electron of the sodium atom, and can be obtained experimentally either from optical measurements or by bombardment of atoms with electrons and measuring the minimum energy of the latter required to produce ions. The dissociation energy D_{Cl_2} required to separate the two Cl atoms in a Cl_2 molecule can be obtained by determining the dissociation constant as function of temperature. The electron affinity E_{Cl} is the energy gained by combining an electron and a Cl-atom. Electron affinities can be determined by measuring the ionization energy of the negative ions, or by measuring the density of halide ions in alkali halide vapor.[10] Now, we also know that

$$Na_{solid} + \tfrac{1}{2}Cl_2 \rightarrow NaCl_{solid} + q$$

[10] J. E. Mayer, *Z. Physik*, **61**, 798 (1930); L. Helmholz and J. E. Mayer, *J. Chem. Phys.*, **2**, 245 (1934); P. P. Sutton and J. E. Mayer, *J. Chem. Phys.*, **2**, 146 (1934); **3**, 20 (1935); J. E. Mayer and M. McC. Maltbie, *Z. Phys.*, **75**, 748 (1932).

where q refers again to the heat of formation per "molecule" NaCl formed. Subtracting this equation from the one obtained above, we find for the lattice energy per ion pair,

$$\epsilon_{L\ exp.} = S_{Na} + I_{Na} + \tfrac{1}{2}D_{Cl_2} - E_{Cl} + q \qquad (5\text{-}14)$$

For NaCl, all quantities on the right-hand side are known from experiments and thus we are able to give an experimental value for ϵ_L which may be compared with the one calculated with the Born theory. For NaCl we find, for example, from (5-14),

$$\epsilon_{L\ exp.} = 1.1 + 5.1 + 1.2 - 3.8 + 4.3 = 7.9\ ev$$

whereas Born's theory yields 8.0 ev. The experimental values obtained in this way are listed in Table 5-2, and we see that theory and experiment agree within a few per cent, indicating that the relatively simple approach is essentially correct.

For the fluorides and oxides, the electron affinities are not known from experiment, and they are usually calculated by replacing $\epsilon_{L\ exp.}$ by $\epsilon_{L\ calc.}$ in (5-14). We note that for oxygen the electron affinity is negative, i.e., it requires energy to add 2 electrons to the atom. This is not surprising, because after the first electron has been added, we have a negative O^- ion and we would expect addition of a second electron to require appreciable energy. An experimental determination of the affinity of a neutral oxygen atom for the first electron added gave 2.2 ev according to Lozier.[11] Now the total electron affinity for the addition of 2 electrons is -7.3 ev when calculated from the lattice energy of oxides in the manner indicated above. Thus addition of the second electron requires about 9.5 ev. The usually accepted values of the electron affinities are given in Table 5-3 together with the dissociation energies of the diatomic molecules (in electron volts).

Table 5-3. Electron Affinities and Dissociation Energies

	Electron affinity	Dissociation energy
F	4.25 ev	2.75 ev
Cl	4.0	2.50
Br	3.8	2.01
I	3.45	1.58
O	−7.3	1.52
S	−3.5	2.75
Se	−4.2	2.50

5-6. Stability of structures and ionic radii

Ionic compounds of the composition A^+B^- occur in the sodium chloride structure, the cesium chloride structure, and the zincblende

[11] W. W. Lozier, *Phys. Rev.*, **46**, 268 (1934).

structure (ZnS). The latter two are represented in Fig. 5-3. In the CsCl structure each ion is surrounded by 8 nearest neighbors of opposite sign; in NaCl by 6, and in zincblende by 4. One may thus ask why a certain compound crystallizes in a particular structure.

The answer must obviously be sought in the fact that the energy should be a minimum, and the problem is thus reduced to explaining why for a given compound its natural structure has a lower energy than any other structure. We shall see that some insight into this problem may be obtained from considerations of the size of the ions.

For metals one defines the atomic radius as half the distance between nearest neighbors, although it is recognized that the meaning of the size of an atom is necessarily vague. For ionic crystals one could try a similar approach, but one is immediately faced with the difficulty that these compounds consist of at least 2 types of ions, so that the lattice constant provides information only about the sum of two radii. A little consideration of the interionic distances as given in the preceding section shows that to a fair approximation ionic radii are additive quantities. For example, if one calculates the difference $(r_{K^+} - r_{Na^+})$ from the values given in Table 5-2 for the halides of these metals, one finds from the fluorides,

$$r_{K^+} - r_{Na^+} = a_{KF} - a_{NaF} = 0.35 \text{ Angstrom}$$

and from the chlorides, bromides, and iodides in the same manner 0.33 Å, 0.32 Å, and 0.30 Å, respectively. We see that the difference is roughly constant and that it has meaning to associate a rather definite radius with each ion. It is also obvious that a table of ionic radii can be obtained only if the radius of one ion is known. Goldschmidt in 1927 has tabulated ionic radii based on a radius of the F^- ion of 1.33 Å, a value which he decided upon on the basis of work by Wasastjerna on the relation between polarizability and ion size.[12] Pauling, in the same year, independently published ionic radii based on theoretical calculations of the radii of some ions.[12] The two sets are not equal, which is not surprising because of the inaccuracies involved. One commonly refers to the Goldschmidt and the Pauling radius of a given ion. In Table 5-4 the Goldschmidt radii (G) do not refer to the original set but include many recent X-ray diffraction data, especially those of Zachariasen.[13] Contrary to the tables by Goldschmidt, the radius for O^{2-} is 1.45 Å rather than 1.35 Å. The radii according to Pauling are also given in Table 5-4.

Returning now to the question of stability, we would expect at first sight that the CsCl structure should always be more stable than the other

[12] V. M. Goldschmidt, *Chem. Berichte*, **60**, 1263 (1927); L. Pauling, *J. Am. Chem. Soc.*, **49**, 765 (1927).

[13] W. H. Zachariasen, *Acta Crystall.*, **1**, 265 (1948); *Phys. Rev.*, **73**, 1104 (1948); *Chem. Phys.*, **16**, 254 (1948).

structures, because it has the highest coordination number. Now, although it is true that a high coordination number will lead to strong binding and thus high stability, there is another requirement to be fulfilled, viz., that ions of opposite sign should be separated by as small a distance as possible. In other words, positive and negative ions should "touch," because any increase in their separation would give a higher energy (less binding) according to equation (5-8). It is at this point that a consideration of the relative radii of the ions can provide at least a guiding principle. To illustrate this, let us consider an ionic crystal of the type A^+B^- with ionic radii r_1 and r_2, where we assume $r_1 < r_2$. Suppose we build a CsCl structure with these ions, assuming that positive and negative ions touch each other. The cube edge, corresponding to the separation of ions of equal sign, is then

$$a = (2/\sqrt{3})(r_1 + r_2)$$

Table 5-4. Goldschmidt (G) and Pauling (P) Ionic Radii in Å

Ion	G	P	Ion	G	P	Ion	G	P
H^-	1.54	2.08	Be^{2+}	0.30	0.31	B^{3+}	0.2	0.20
F^-	1.33	1.36	Mg^{2+}	0.65	0.65	Al^{3+}	0.45	0.50
Cl^-	1.81	1.81	Ca^{2+}	0.94	0.99	Sc^{3+}	0.68	0.81
Br^-	1.96	1.95	Sr^{2+}	1.10	1.13	Y^{3+}	0.90	0.93
I^-	2.19	2.16	Ba^{2+}	1.29	1.35	La^{3+}	1.04	1.15
			Zn^{2+}	0.69	0.74	Ga^{3+}	0.60	0.62
O^{2-}	1.45	1.40	Cd^{2+}	0.92	0.97	In^{3+}	0.81	0.81
S^{2-}	1.90	1.84	Hg^{2+}	0.93	1.10	Tl^{3+}	0.91	0.95
Se^{2-}	2.02	1.98	Pb^{2+}	1.17	1.21			
Te^{2-}	2.22	2.21				Fe^{3+}	0.53	......
			Mn^{2+}	0.80	0.80	Cr^{3+}	0.55	......
Li^+	0.68	0.60	Fe^{2+}	0.76	0.75			
Na^+	0.98	0.95	Co^{2+}	0.70	0.72	C^{4+}	0.15	0.15
K^+	1.33	1.33	Ni^{2+}	0.68	0.69	Si^{4+}	0.38	0.41
Rb^+	1.48	1.48	Cu^{2+}	0.92	......	Ti^{4+}	0.60	0.68
Cs^+	1.67	1.69				Zr^{4+}	0.77	0.80
Cu^+	0.95	0.96				Ce^{4+}	0.87	1.01
Ag^+	1.13	1.26				Ge^{4+}	0.54	0.53
Au^+	......	1.37				Sn^{4+}	0.71	0.71
Tl^+	1.51	1.44				Pb^{4+}	0.81	0.84

Suppose the ion of radius r_1 is the ion in the center of the cube. If we now increase the radius r_2 gradually, leaving r_1 constant, we reach a value of r_2 such that further increase makes it impossible for the central ion to touch the ones at the corners. This critical value is clearly reached when

$$a = 2r_2 = (2/\sqrt{3})(r_1 + r_2) \quad \text{or} \quad r_2 = 1.37r_1$$

Thus $r_2 > 1.37r_1$ would lead to an increase in the distance between positive and negative ions and consequently to an increase in energy. The competition between coordination number on the one hand and separation between positive and negative ions on the other will thus set in as soon as the ratio of the radii becomes larger than 1.37 and a more favorable structure may result, viz., the NaCl structure. The stability limits of the latter may be investigated in the same way. In this case the critical ratio of the radii is determined by

$$2r_2 = (r_1 + r_2)\sqrt{2} \quad \text{or} \quad r_2 = 2.44r_1$$

Again, if the ratio becomes larger than 2.44, positive and negative ions cannot touch each other, leading to an increase of the energy and consequently to the formation of the more stable zincblende structure (Fig. 5-3). For this structure, positive and negative ions cannot touch each other if $r_2 > 4.55r_1$. The stability limits as derived from the above simplified billiard ball model for the ions are therefore

cesium chloride ....$1 < r_2/r_1 < 1.37$

sodium chloride.........$1.37 < r_2/r_1 < 2.44$

zincblende ....$2.44 < r_2/r_1 < 4.55$

It must be emphasized that these results can be looked upon only as a rough rule. In general, however, one may say that the CsCl structure is found in those compounds for which the ionic radii are nearly equal, whereas the zincblende structure occurs only when the ratio of the radii is about two or more. This may be illustrated by a few examples in Table 5-5.

Table 5-5. Ratio of Negative and Positive Ion Radii for Salts with the
Cesium Chloride and Zincblende Structure

Cesium chloride structure	r_-/r_+	Zincblende structure	r_-/r_+
CsCl	1.1	ZnS	2.1
CsBr	1.2	ZnSe	2.3
CsI	1.3	BeS	5.1
TlCl	1.2	BeSe	5.6
TlBr	1.3	CuCl	1.9
TlI	1.5	CuBr	2.0
		CuI	2.3

A detailed discussion of the stability of the cesium chloride and sodium chloride structures has been given by May.[14] It is finally of interest to note that structure transformations have been observed under

[14] A. May, *Phys. Rev.*, **52**, 339 (1937).

high pressures. A review of this subject may be found in a book by Bridgman.[15]

5-7. Refinements of the Born theory

The development of wave mechanics provided a better understanding of the chemical bond and interatomic forces in general. As a result, several refinements of the Born theory have been made, in particular by Born and Mayer and their collaborators.[16] The essential refinements were the following:

1. Quantum mechanical calculations of the forces between ions indicate that a simple power law for the repulsive forces (5-3) cannot be rigorous. One therefore replaced this law by an exponential one of the form

$$\epsilon_{\text{rep}}(r) = ce^{-r/\rho} \qquad (5\text{-}15)$$

where c and ρ are constants.

2. One added an attractive term to the lattice energy corresponding to the van der Waals forces which act between ions or atoms with a rare gas electron configuration.

3. One took into account the "zero-point energy" of the crystal.

We shall not go through the calculation of the lattice energy which includes the modifications just mentioned, because the method is in principle the same as the one followed above. Also, the differences in the results obtained are slight. However, a few remarks about the modifications themselves, in particular about those mentioned under (2) and (3) may be in order.

The van der Waals forces are responsible for the cohesion in the liquid and solid states of rare gases as well as for most organic crystals. These forces have been treated by London[17] and Margenau[18] on a quantum mechanical basis. An approximate expression for the interaction energy of two atoms or ions with filled shell electron configuration is

$$\epsilon(r) = -\frac{3}{2} \cdot \frac{\alpha_1\alpha_2}{r^6} \cdot \frac{I_1 I_2}{I_1 + I_2} \qquad (5\text{-}16)$$

where I_1 and I_2 refer to the ionization energies of the particles involved and α_1, α_2 refer to the polarizabilities. The nature of these forces is essentially a quantum effect, although the fact that they vary with the sixth power of the distance may easily be shown from classical considerations.

[15] P. W. Bridgman, *Physics of High Pressure*, 2d ed., Macmillan, New York, 1950.
[16] M. Born and J. E. Mayer, *Z. Physik*, **75**, 1 (1932); J. E. Mayer, *J. Chem. Phys.*, **1**, 270 (1933); J. E. Mayer and M. G. Mayer, *Phys. Rev.*, **43**, 605 (1933).
[17] F. London, *Z. Physik*, **63**, 245 (1930).
[18] H. Margenau, *Phys. Rev.*, **38**, 747 (1931); *Revs. Mod. Phys.*, **11**, 1 (1939).

A homogeneous electric field E induces in an atom a dipole (see Sec. 6-2):

$$\mu = qx = \alpha E \qquad (5\text{-}17)$$

where q and x are, respectively, the effective charge and displacement; α is the polarizability of the atom. The energy of the atom in the field is then

$$\epsilon = -\int_0^x qE\,dx = -\int_0^E qE\frac{\alpha}{q}\,dE = -\tfrac{1}{2}\alpha E^2 \qquad (5\text{-}18)$$

For a field strength varying with time, one would have for the average energy,

$$\epsilon = -(\alpha/2)\langle E^2\rangle \qquad (5\text{-}19)$$

Now, suppose the atom is under influence of another atom at a distance r. The latter may be considered a system of oscillating dipoles formed by the nucleus and the electrons. The electric field strength of a dipole varies as r^{-3} and hence, according to (5-18), the energy of one atom in the field of another may be written

$$\epsilon = -\text{constant}/r^6 \qquad (5\text{-}20)$$

The mutual energy of two atoms would then be given by the sum of two terms of the type (5-20). From the classical point of view, therefore, these forces are a consequence of the dipole-dipole interaction between the atoms.

Actually, the energy corresponding to (5-16) is only part of the van der Waals energy and there is an infinite series of rapidly converging terms. The next one corresponds to dipole-quadrupole interaction and varies as r^{-8}.

For the alkali halides, the attractive energy corresponding to (5-16) is of the order of a few per cent of the total lattice energy. For the silver halides it is appreciably more; e.g., for AgBr it is about 14 per cent. This is a consequence of the relatively high polarizability of the silver ion. We should note that the van der Waals energy sometimes plays an important role in the discussion of the stability of different lattice structures.[19]

The zero-point energy of the crystal is also a consequence of quantum mechanics. The possible energy levels of a harmonic oscillator are given by

$$\epsilon = (n + \tfrac{1}{2})h\nu \qquad (5\text{-}21)$$

where n is an integer and ν is the frequency. Thus, even at absolute zero an oscillator has a zero point energy of $h\nu/2$. Now, in the Debye theory

[19] J. E. Mayer, *J. Chem. Phys.*, **1**, 270 (1933); **1**, 327 (1933); J. E. Mayer and R. B. Levy, *J. Chem. Phys.*, **1**, 647 (1933).

of the specific heat of solids, a crystal is represented formally by a system of harmonic oscillators with a frequency spectrum given by (see Sec. 2-6)

$$F(\nu)\, d\nu = 4\pi V \left(\frac{2}{c_t^3} + \frac{1}{c_l^3}\right)\nu^2\, d\nu \qquad (5\text{-}22)$$

where V is the volume of the crystal and c_t and c_l are, respectively, the velocities of propagation of transverse and of longitudinal elastic waves. Making use of the definition of the Debye frequency ν_D, one may write

$$F(\nu)\, d\nu = (9N/\nu_D^3)\nu^2\, d\nu \qquad (5\text{-}23)$$

where N stands for the total number of atoms or ions in the crystal. Hence, at absolute zero, the contribution of the zero-point energy is

$$\tfrac{1}{2}\int_0^{\nu_D} F(\nu)h\nu\, d\nu = \tfrac{9}{8}Nh\nu_D \qquad (5\text{-}24)$$

Per ion pair this corresponds to $9h\nu_D/4$. With a Debye frequency of the order of 10^{12}–10^{13} sec^{-1} this gives about 0.1 ev. As a correction to the lattice energy the zero point energy thus contributes about 1 per cent. Note that this correction reduces the values given in Table 5-2, whereas the van der Waals correction raises them. In general, the van der Waals correction is more important for heavy elements (large polarizabilities), and the zero-point energy for light elements (high Debye frequency). As an example, we give here the various contributions to the lattice energy for the two extreme cases LiF and CsI (all energies in ev).

	LiF	CsI
Coulomb	−12.4	−6.4
Repulsive	+ 1.9	+0.63
Dipole-dipole	− 0.17	−0.48
Dipole-quadrupole	− 0.03	−0.04
Zero-point	+ 0.17	+0.3

REFERENCES

M. Born, *Atomtheorie des festen Zustandes*, Teubner, Leipzig, 1923.

M. Born and M. Göppert-Mayer, *Handbuch der Physik*, Vol. 24/2, Springer, Berlin, 1933, pp. 723–794.

J. A. A. Ketelaar, *Chemical Constitution*, Elsevier, New York, 1953.

N. F. Mott and R. W. Gurney, *Electronic Processes in Ionic Crystals*, 2d ed., Oxford, New York, 1948, Chap. 1.

F. Seitz, *The Modern Theory of Solids*, McGraw-Hill, New York, 1940, Chap. 2.

PROBLEMS

5-1. Show that the Madelung constant for a one-dimensional array of ions of alternating sign with a distance a between successive ions is equal to 2 log 2.

5-2. Calculate the compressibilities at absolute zero from (5-13) for LiF and BaO, assuming the values of n given in Table 5-1.

5-3. A molecule of the vapor of an alkali halide is presumably built up of a positive and a negative ion. Assuming the quantities B' and n in the repulsive energy to be the same as in the solid state, show that

$$\epsilon_g/\epsilon_s = r_s/Ar_g \quad \text{and} \quad (r_s/r_g)^{n-1} = 6/A$$

where ϵ_g and ϵ_s represent, respectively, the binding energy per molecule in the gaseous and solid state; r_g and r_s are the equilibrium distances in the gaseous and solid state. Show further that for this model ϵ_g is approximately two-thirds of ϵ_s.

5-4. Set up the simple Born theory in a more general fashion than is done in the text, so as to include cases of ions of different valency, such as CaF_2, Fe_2O_3, etc.

5-5. Discuss the experimental methods by which the quantities on the right-hand side of equation (5-14) may be determined.

5-6. Derive the expression for the lattice energy, replacing the power law describing the repulsive energy by an exponential law of the type (5-15). Calculate the constants c and ρ occurring in that expression for KBr.

5-7. Verify the values for the dipole-dipole contribution and for the zero-point energy to the total lattice energy for LiF and CsI, given on page 130.

5-8. Show that the polarizability of a metal sphere of radius R is equal to R^3.

5-9. Consider two ions of charges $+e$ and $-e$. Assume that one of them has a polarizability α and that the other has zero polarizability. Show that the Coulomb interaction between the two ions as function of their separation r is given by $\phi = -(e^2/r)(1 + \alpha/2r^3)$.

5-10. Consider two ions of charges $+e$ and $-e$; the polarizabilities of the ions are α_1 and α_2. Show that the dipole moment induced in one of them is given by

$$\mu_1 = (r^4 e\alpha_1 + 2re\alpha_1\alpha_2)/(r^6 - 4\alpha_1\alpha_2)$$

with a similar expression for μ_2; r denotes the separation between the nuclei. (See, for example, P. Debye, *Polar Molecules*, Dover, New York, 1945, p. 60.)

5-11. Discuss the binding energy and dipole moment of alkali halide molecules on the basis of an ionic picture and compare the results with experiment (see E. S. Rittner, *J. Chem. Phys.*, **19**, 1030, 1951).

5-12. Give a simplified discussion of van der Waals forces (see, for example, S. Glasstone, *Theoretical Chemistry*, Van Nostrand, New York, 1944, p. 423).

Chapter 6

DIELECTRIC AND OPTICAL PROPERTIES
OF INSULATORS

In the present chapter a brief survey will be given of the atomic interpretation of the dielectric and optical properties of insulators. The theory given here is essentially classical; for the quantum theory of dielectrics we refer to the literature (see, for example, J. H. van Vleck, *Theory of Electric and Magnetic Susceptibilities,* Oxford, New York, 1932). This chapter is divided into two parts: in part A we shall essentially be concerned with the static dielectric constant, in part B, the frequency dependence of the dielectric properties, including optical absorption and dielectric losses, will be discussed. It may be emphasized that only isotropic substances, for which E, D, and P are parallel vectors, will be considered.

Part A. Static Fields

6-1. Macroscopic description of the static dielectric constant

As an introduction to the concept of the static dielectric constant of a substance, consider the following well-known experimental result: Two plane parallel plates of area A and separation d are charged with a surface charge density q, one plate being positive, the other negative. If the space between the plates is evacuated and if d is small compared with the dimensions of the plates, there will result a homogeneous electric field between the plates, the field strength being given by

$$E_{vac} = 4\pi q = D \qquad (6\text{-}1)$$

in esu; D is called the electric displacement or flux density. The potential difference between the plates is equal to

$$\phi_{vac} = E_{vac} \cdot d \qquad (6\text{-}2)$$

and the capacitance of the system is defined by

$$C_{vac} = Aq/\phi_{vac} = Q/\phi_{vac} \qquad (6\text{-}3)$$

Suppose now that the space between the plates is filled with an insulating substance, the charge on the plates being kept constant. It is then observed that the new potential difference ϕ is lower than ϕ_{vac}, and similarly, the capacitance C of the system is increased. The static dielectric constant ϵ_s is then defined by

$$\epsilon_s = \phi_{\text{vac}}/\phi = C/C_{\text{vac}} \tag{6-4}$$

Thus, as a result of introducing the substance, the field strength is reduced from the value E_{vac} to the value E, where

$$E_{\text{vac}} = D = \epsilon_s E \tag{6-5}$$

In other words, the effective surface charge density on the plates is now $q' = E/4\pi$ rather than $q = E_{\text{vac}}/4\pi$, and one may say that introducing the dielectric is equivalent to reducing the surface charge density by an amount

$$P = q - q' = (E_{\text{vac}}/4\pi)(1 - 1/\epsilon_s) = (\epsilon_s - 1)E/4\pi \tag{6-6}$$

Thus, under influence of the external field, the dielectric facing the positive plate acquires a negative induced surface charge density P and vice versa. This is illustrated in Fig. 6-1. We shall see later that this conclusion is in accord with the atomic interpretation of the dielectric constant; in fact, it will be shown that P is equal to the electric dipole moment induced in the substance per unit volume by the external field; P is called the *polarization* of the substance. From (6-5) and (6-6) it follows that one may write

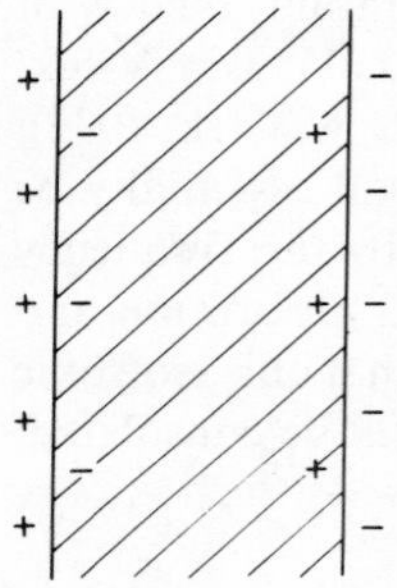

Fig. 6-1. Schematic illustration of charges induced at the surface of a dielectric.

$$D = E + 4\pi P = \epsilon_s E \tag{6-7}$$

The link between the macroscopic quantity ϵ_s and the atomic theory of the dielectric constant is provided by the relation (6-6). In fact, it will be shown below that P may be expressed in terms of the properties of the atoms and molecules composing the dielectric.

6-2. The static electronic and ionic polarizabilities of molecules

Although we are mainly interested in the dielectric properties of solids, it will be useful to consider first the much simpler problem of the behavior of free atoms and molecules in an external electric field. The term "free" refers to a system in which to a good degree of approximation the mutual interaction between the particles may be neglected, as in a gas of low density. A basic concept in the discussions to follow is that of the electric dipole moment of a system. For a system of elementary charges e_i located at the end points of a set of vectors r_i, drawn from a common origin, the dipole moment is defined as

$$M = \Sigma_i e_i r_i \tag{6-8}$$

For systems which, as a whole, are neutral, i.e., when $\Sigma_i e_i = 0$, one can show readily that M is independent of the origin chosen (see Problem 6-1); it is with such neutral systems that we shall concern ourselves. As an example, the dipole moment corresponding to two charges $+e$ and $-e$, separated by a distance d, is ed.

In a free atom, the charge distribution is such that the dipole moment in the absence of an external field vanishes; the center of gravity of the electron distribution coincides with the nucleus. Consider now an atom in a static homogeneous external field E. The force exerted on the positive nucleus will then be oppositely directed to the forces exerted on the electrons. As a result, the external field tends to draw the center of gravity of the electrons away from the nucleus. On the other hand, the attractive forces between the electrons and the nucleus tend to preserve a vanishing

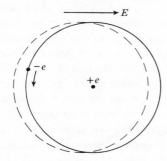

Fig. 6-2. Schematic illustration of the displacement of the electron orbit relative to the nucleus for a hydrogen atom under influence of an external field E.

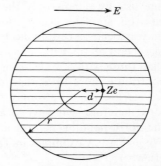

Fig. 6-3. Simplified model for estimating the magnitude of the electronic polarizability of an atom, as described in the text.

dipole moment in the atom. Consequently, an equilibrium situation is reached in which the atom bears a finite dipole moment. This has been represented schematically in Fig. 6-2. The resulting dipole moment is thus induced by the field as a result of an elastic displacement of the electronic charge distribution relative to the nucleus. The induced moment may be represented by

$$\mu_{\text{ind}} = \alpha_e E \tag{6-9}$$

where α_e is called the electronic polarizability of the atom. It should be noted that (6-9) is actually only the first term of a power series in the field strength. For the usual fields employed in dielectric measurements, however, (6-9) is a very good approximation.

To obtain an idea of the magnitude of α_e, consider the following simplified model: Suppose the atom is represented by a nucleus of charge Ze and a homogeneous negative charge distribution inside a sphere of radius r. If the nucleus is displaced over a distance d, as shown in Fig. 6-3, the restoring force is equal to the force exerted on the nucleus by a negative charge Zed^3/r^3. The equilibrium condition is then

$$ZeE = (Ze)^2 d/r^3 \qquad (6\text{-}10)$$

This gives for the induced dipole moment,

$$\mu_{\text{ind}} = \alpha_e E = Zed = r^3 E \qquad (6\text{-}11)$$

For this simple model, therefore, the polarizability α_e is equal to r^3.[1] Note that α_e has the dimensions of a volume. For $r \simeq 10^{-8}$ cm, we see that α_e is of the order of 10^{-24} cm³. Hence, for an external field of 300 volts per cm one finds $d \simeq 10^{-15}$ cm, which shows that for most practical field strengths the condition $d \ll r$ is satisfied. It is for this reason that in (6-9) one usually retains only the first term. For atoms with more than one electron, similar considerations are valid, and with each atom or ion one may associate a certain electronic polarizability α_e. It will be evident that in general atoms with many electrons tend to have a larger polarizability than those with few electrons. Electrons in the outer electronic shells will contribute more to α_e than do electrons in the inner shells, because the former are not so strongly bound to the nucleus as the latter. Positive ions therefore will have relatively small polarizabilities compared with the corresponding neutral atoms; for negative ions the reverse is true. We give a few examples in Table 6-1; more complete tables are available elsewhere.[2]

Table 6-1. Some Electronic Polarizabilities in 10^{-24} cm³. The values for the alkali and halide ions are those given by Böttcher; the others are due to Pauling

	α_e		α_e		α_e
He	0.20	Li⁺	0.02		
Ne	0.39	Na⁺	0.22	F⁻	0.85
Ar	1.62	K⁺	0.97	Cl⁻	3.00
Kr	2.46	Rb⁺	1.50	Br⁻	4.13
Xe	3.99	Cs⁺	2.42	I⁻	6.16

The polarizability as function of the frequency of the applied field will be discussed in Sec. 6-9. It will be shown there that α_e may be considered a constant up to frequencies corresponding to the ultraviolet spectrum.

[1] A wave-mechanical treatment of the polarizability of the hydrogen atom may be found in N. F. Mott and S. N. Sneddon, *Wave Mechanics and its Applications*, Oxford, New York, 1948, p. 166. See also H. R. Hassé, *Proc. Cambridge Phil. Soc.*, **26**, 542 (1930). Second-order perturbation theory gives the value $\alpha_e = 9a_0^3/2 = 0.667 \times 10^{-24}$ cm³ (a_0 is the radius of the H atom).

[2] C. J. F. Böttcher, *Rec. trav. chim.*, **62**, 325, 503 (1943); L. Pauling, *Proc. Roy. Soc.* (*London*), **A114**, 181 (1927); N. F. Mott and R. W. Gurney, *Electronic Processes in Ionic Crystals*, 2d ed., Oxford, New York, 1948, p. 14.

So far, we have considered only simple atoms and ions. For molecules one is faced with two more possible influences of an external field:

1. Molecules may have permanent dipole moments which may be aligned in an external field.

2. The distances between ions or atoms may be influenced by an external field.

For example, a molecule such as HCl may in first approximation be considered to consist of two ions; the permanent dipole moment is thus equal to the effective charge per ion times the separation of the ions. Symmetric molecules like H_2, CO_2, CCl_4, etc. evidently have no permanent dipole moment. An external electric field will tend to orient permanent dipoles along the field direction, and one speaks of orientational polarization. This contribution to the total polarizability of a molecule will be discussed in Sec. 6-3.

In molecules as well as in atoms an external field will displace the electrons with respect to the corresponding nuclei. Over and above this, however, a displacement of atoms or ions within the molecule may be caused by an external field. For example, in an HCl molecule an external field will change the interionic distance to some extent, leading to a change in the dipole moment. Similarly, in a molecule like CCl_4 (which has no permanent dipole moment) a change in the bond angles between the CCl groups will produce a dipole moment because each of these groups by itself does have a dipole moment. This kind of induced polarization is called atomic or ionic polarization because it is a consequence of the displacement of atoms within the molecule. The induced electric dipole moment resulting from elastic displacements of ions within the molecule may again be represented by an expression of the type (6-9), by replacing α_e by the atomic polarizability α_a. It should be noted that α_a refers to an average over all possible orientations of the molecule with respect to the field. In Sec. 6-9 it will be shown that α_a may be considered a constant up to frequencies in the infrared spectrum. For most molecules, α_a is of the order of 10 per cent of α_e.

Summarizing, one may conclude that the electric properties of a molecule may be characterized by the following three quantities:

(a) α_e, representing the polarizability due to electronic displacements within the composing atoms or ions.

(b) α_a, representing the polarizability due to atomic or ionic displacements within the molecule (changes in bond angles and interatomic distances).

(c) a permanent dipole moment $\boldsymbol{\mu}$.

6-3. Orientational polarization

In this section we shall consider the polarizability of a molecule in a static field, resulting from its permanent dipole moment. Consider, for example, a gas containing a large number of identical molecules, each with a permanent dipole moment μ. Without an external field, the dipoles will be oriented at random and the gas as a whole will have no resulting dipole moment. An external field E will exert a torque on each dipole and will tend to orient the dipoles in the direction of the field (see Fig. 6-4). On the other hand, this ordering influence of the external field will be counteracted by the thermal motion of the particles. The problem therefore may be stated as follows: What is the average component of the dipole moment per molecule in the direction of the applied field at a temperature T? To answer this question it will be assumed that the dipoles may rotate freely. We then have before us a simple problem in statistical mechanics.

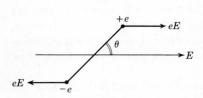

Fig. 6-4. Illustrating the torque exerted on a dipole by an external field.

Let us define the potential energy of a dipole making a 90° angle with the external field as zero. The potential energy corresponding to an angle θ between μ and E is then equal to

$$-\mu E \cos \theta = -\mu \cdot E \qquad (6\text{-}12)$$

According to statistical mechanics, the probability for a dipole to make an angle between θ and $\theta + d\theta$ with the electric field is then proportional to

$$2\pi \sin \theta \, d\theta \exp \left[(\mu E \cos \theta)/kT \right]$$

where $2\pi \sin \theta \, d\theta$ is the solid angle between θ and $\theta + d\theta$. Hence the average component of the dipole moment along the field direction is equal to

$$\mu \langle \cos \theta \rangle = \frac{\displaystyle\int_{\theta=0}^{\pi} \mu \cos \theta \sin \theta \, d\theta \exp \left[(\mu E \cos \theta)/kT \right]}{\displaystyle\int_{\theta=0}^{\pi} \sin \theta \, d\theta \exp \left[(\mu E \cos \theta)/kT \right]} \qquad (6\text{-}13)$$

To evaluate the integrals, let

$$(\mu E/kT) \cos \theta = x \quad \text{and} \quad (\mu E/kT) = a \qquad (6\text{-}14)$$

We then obtain

$$\langle \cos \theta \rangle = \frac{1}{a} \frac{\int_{-a}^{+a} x e^x \, dx}{\int_{-a}^{+a} e^x \, dx} = \frac{e^a + e^{-a}}{e^a - e^{-a}} - \frac{1}{a} = L(a) \qquad (6\text{-}15)$$

The function $L(a)$ is called the Langevin function, since this formula was first derived by Langevin in 1905 in connection with the theory of para-magnetism.[3] In Fig. 6-5, $L(a)$ has been plotted as a function of $a = \mu E/kT$. Note that for very large values of a, i.e., for high field strengths, the function approaches the saturation value unity. This situation would correspond to complete alignment of the dipoles in the field direction, because then $\mu \langle \cos \theta \rangle = \mu$.

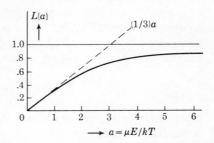

Fig. 6-5. The Langevin function $L(a)$. For $a \ll 1$, the slope is 1/3.

As long as the field strength is not too high and the temperature is not too low, the situation may be strongly simplified by making the approximation $a \ll 1$ or $\mu E \ll kT$. Under these circumstances the Langevin function $L(a) = a/3$, so that then

$$\mu \langle \cos \theta \rangle = (\mu^2/3kT)E \quad \text{for} \quad \mu E \ll kT \qquad (6\text{-}16)$$

As an example of the condition implied in (6-16), consider a field of 3000 volts per cm. The dipole moment μ of a molecule is of the order of 10^{-10} esu of charge times 10^{-8} cm, i.e., about 10^{-18} cgs units,[4] so that $\mu E \simeq 10^{-17}$ in cgs units. On the other hand, kT at room temperature is of the order of 10^{-14} erg and for this example the condition is certainly satis-fied. In this example saturation would be approached only in the vicinity of $1°K$. It may be noted that the quantum mechanical treatment of this problem leads essentially to the same results as obtained here.[5]

The existence of electric dipoles in molecules was first postulated by Debye in 1912;[6] this concept has contributed a great deal to the present understanding of dielectrics as well as to our knowledge of molecular structure. We shall now see how the molecular quantities α_e, α_a, and μ enter in the description of the macroscopic dielectric constant.

[3] P. Langevin, *J. Physique*, **4**, 678 (1905).

[4] 10^{-18} esu cm is called a "Debye unit."

[5] See, for example, P. Debye, *Polar Molecules*, Dover, New York, 1945.

[6] P. Debye, *Phys. Z.*, **13**, 97 (1912).

6-4. The static dielectric constant of gases

We are now in a position to give an atomic interpretation of the static dielectric constant of a gas. It will be assumed that the number of molecules per unit volume is small enough so that the interaction between them may be neglected. In that case, the field acting at the location of a particular molecule is to a good approximation equal to the applied field E. Suppose the gas contains N molecules per unit volume; the properties of the molecules will be characterized by an electronic polarizability α_e, an atomic polarizability α_a, and a permanent dipole moment μ. From the discussions in the preceding two sections it follows that, as a result of the external field E, there will exist a resulting dipole moment per unit volume:

$$P = N(\alpha_e + \alpha_a + \mu^2/3kT)E \qquad (6\text{-}17)$$

Note that only the permanent dipole moment gives a temperature-dependent contribution, because α_e and α_a are essentially independent of T. If the gas fills the space between two capacitor plates of area A and separation d, the total dipole moment between the plates will be equal to

$$M = PAd$$

This simple relation shows immediately that the same total dipole moment would be obtained by assuming that the dielectric acquires an induced surface charge density P at the boundaries facing the capacitor plates, as discussed in Sec. 6-1. Hence the quantity P introduced here as the dipole moment per unit volume is identical with the quantity P introduced in Sec. 6-1, where it represented the induced surface charge density at the dielectric-plate interface. Therefore, combination of (6-17) and (6-6) leads immediately to the Debye formula for the static dielectric constant of a gas.[6]

$$\epsilon_s - 1 = 4\pi P/E = 4\pi N(\alpha_e + \alpha_a + \mu^2/3kT) \qquad (6\text{-}18)$$

As an example of an application of this formula, we show in Fig. 6-6 the temperature dependence of some organic substances in the gaseous state.[7] Note that $(\epsilon_s - 1)$ has been plotted versus the reciprocal of the absolute temperature, leading to straight lines, in agreement with formula (6-18). From the slope of the lines and a knowledge of the number of molecules per unit volume, the dipole moment μ may be obtained. Also, from the extrapolated intercept of the lines with the ordinate, one can calculate $(\alpha_e + \alpha_a)$. The determination of dipole moments has contributed a great deal to our knowledge of molecular structure. For example, CCl_4 and

[7] R. Sänger, *Phys. Z.*, **27**, 556 (1926).

CH_4, according to Fig. 6-6, do not possess permanent dipole moments, in agreement with the symmetric structure of these molecules. Similarly, the fact that H_2O has a dipole moment of 1.84 Debye units, whereas CO_2 has no dipole moment, indicates that the CO_2 molecule has a linear structure, whereas in H_2O the two OH bonds must make an angle different from 180° with each other.[8]

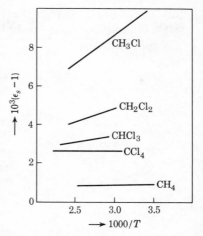

Fig. 6-6. Temperature variation of the static dielectric constant of some vapors. [After Sänger, ref. 7]

6-5. The internal field according to Lorentz

The theory of the dielectric constant of solids and liquids is much more complicated than that for gases. In gases one may, to a good approximation, assume that the field acting on the particles is equal to the externally applied field E. In solids and liquids, however, a given molecule or atom "sees" not only the external field, but the fields produced by the dipoles on other particles as well. As a result of the long range of Coulomb forces, the latter contribution can no longer be neglected. The central problem in the theory of the dielectric constant of liquids and solids is therefore the calculation of the field at the position of a given atom. This field is called the internal or local field and is different from the externally applied field E.

To calculate the internal field, the following method was suggested by Lorentz:[9] Select a small spherical region from the dielectric with the atom for which the local field must be calculated at the center (see Fig. 6-7). The radius of the sphere is chosen large enough to consider the region outside the sphere as a continuum of dielectric constant ϵ_s. For the region inside the sphere, however, the actual structure of the substance must be taken into account. The following contributions to the internal field at the location of the atom then arise:

(i) The contribution from the charge density on the plates, giving $4\pi q = D$.

---

[8] For a table of dipole moments of a large number of molecules, see, for example, the article on dielectric polarization by O. Fuchs and K. L. Wolf, *Hand- und Jahrbuch der chemischen Physik*, Vol. 6, Leipzig, 1935.

[9] H. A. Lorentz, *The Theory of Electrons*, Teubner, Leipzig, 1909, Sec. 117.

(ii) The contribution from the induced charges at the plate-dielectric interface. According to Sec. 6-1, this contributes $-4\pi P$ to the field strength.

(iii) The contribution from the charges induced at the spherical surface.

(iv) The contribution from the atomic dipoles of all atoms inside the spherical region.

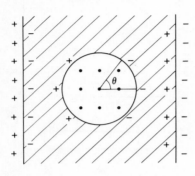

Fig. 6-7.   Illustrating the calculation of the internal field as described in the text.

To calculate the contribution (iii) we first note that as a consequence of the symmetry of the problem, only field components parallel to E have to be taken into account. Thus, consider a ring of area $2\pi R^2 \sin \theta \, d\theta$ on the inner surface of the sphere. The surface charge density depends on the angle θ and is equal to $-P \cos \theta$. Hence the charge on this ring is $-P \cos \theta \, 2\pi R^2 \sin \theta \, d\theta$, leading to a Coulomb field at the center in the direction of E equal to

$$\frac{P \cos^2 \theta \cdot 2\pi R^2 \sin \theta \, d\theta}{R^2} \qquad (6\text{-}19)$$

Thus the contribution (iii) is equal to

$$-2\pi P \int_{+1}^{-1} \cos^2 \theta \, d(\cos \theta) = (4\pi/3)P \qquad (6\text{-}20)$$

For the moment let contribution (iv) be represented by E_4. When certain conditions of symmetry are fulfilled, this contribution may vanish and in that case the internal field would be given by

$$E_i = D - 4\pi P + 4\pi P/3 = E + 4\pi P/3$$

or
$$E_i = \frac{\epsilon_s + 2}{3} E \quad \text{for} \quad E_4 = 0 \qquad (6\text{-}21)$$

This field is frequently referred to as the Lorentz field; it is always larger than the applied field E. To investigate whether or not $E_4 = 0$, we may proceed as follows. Let the atoms inside the sphere have coordinates x_k, y_k, z_k and dipole moment components μ_{kx}, μ_{ky}, μ_{kz}. One may then write for the contribution E_4 in the direction of E,

$$E_4 = \sum_k \left(\mu_{kx} \frac{3x_k^2 - r_k^2}{r_k^5} + \mu_{ky} \frac{3x_k y_k}{r_k^5} + \mu_{kz} \frac{3x_k z_k}{r_k^5} \right) \qquad (6\text{-}22)$$

As an example, consider a simple cubic lattice of like atoms, the external field direction coinciding with a cube edge. In view of the symmetry of the problem, $\mu_{ky} = \mu_{kz} = 0$, and μ_{kx} will be the same for all atoms. Furthermore, for the atoms inside a spherical region,

$$\sum_k x_k^2 = \sum_k y_k^2 = \sum_k z_k^2 = \sum_k r_k^2/3 \qquad (6\text{-}23)$$

Obviously, (6-22) vanishes for a simple cubic lattice and (6-21) should hold if the assumption of point like dipoles is accepted. We leave it up to the reader to show that (6-22) also vanishes for b.c.c. and f.c.c. lattices and for crystals such as NaCl. It must be emphasized that (6-21) does not hold for all cubic crystals. For example, in barium titanate, which has cubic symmetry, the oxygen ions are surrounded by Ti^{4+} ions in such a way that their contribution to (6-22) does not vanish.[10] One must therefore be careful in applying (6-21); one should start from (6-22) in order to evaluate E_4 for the particular problem encountered.[11] It will also be evident from the above discussion that each type of atom in a given crystal has, in general, its own internal field because the environment of the different atoms is generally different. Thus the internal field at the location of atoms of type 1, 2, etc. may be written in the form

$$E_{i1} = E + \gamma_1 P; \quad E_{i2} = E + \gamma_2 P, \quad \text{etc.} \qquad (6\text{-}24)$$

where the γ's are the internal field constants. Only if $E_4 = 0$ do we have $\gamma = 4\pi/3$. The internal field for tetragonal and simple hexagonal lattices has been calculated by Mueller.[12]

Even if the crystal symmetry is such that (6-21) applies, it does not mean that the Lorentz field gives results in agreement with experiments. This may be due to an overlapping of atoms as well as to the fact that the dipolar fields produced by atoms which are only a few Angstroms away are far from homogeneous.[13] The latter makes it doubtful whether one may employ the relation

$$\mu_{\text{induced}} = \alpha E_i \qquad (6\text{-}25)$$

to calculate the dipole moment induced in the central atom, as is done in the theory outlined in the next section.

As a side line, it may be of interest to remark that the application of (6-21) to polar liquid dielectrics has led to a great deal of confusion in the literature. It was not until 1936 that Onsager realized that the internal field cannot be used as the field which tends to orient the dipoles.[14] The

[10] For a discussion of the dielectric properties of this material, see Chapter 8.

[11] For a generalized expression for E_4 and an application to $BaTiO_3$ see J. H. van Santen and W. Opechowski, *Physica*, **14**, 545 (1948).

[12] H. Mueller, *Phys. Rev.*, **47**, 947 (1935); **50**, 547 (1936).

[13] See N. F. Mott and R. W. Gurney, *op. cit.*, p. 16.

[14] L. Onsager, *J. Am. Chem. Soc.*, **58**, 1486 (1936); see also C. J. F. Böttcher, *Physica*, **9**, 937 (1942); A. J. Dekker, *Physica*, **12**, 209 (1946); D. G. Frood and A. J. Dekker, *J. Chem. Phys.*, **20**, 1030 (1952).

reason is that part of the internal field is contributed by the "reaction field" of the dipole, which has the same direction as the dipole itself and hence is ineffective in orienting the dipole. (See Problem 6–6.)

6-6. The static dielectric constant of solids

From the discussions in the preceding sections it is evident that in general the dielectric polarization P may be considered the sum of three contributions,

$$P = P_e + P_a + P_d \qquad (6\text{-}26)$$

where the subscripts e, a, and d refer, respectively, to electronic, atomic, and dipolar polarization. This provides a basis for the classification of dielectrics into three classes:

(i) Substances for which $P_a = P_d = 0$, so that $P = P_e$

(ii) Substances for which $P_d = 0$ and $P = P_e + P_a$

(iii) Substances for which all three contributions are different from zero.

Although the calculation of the internal field is usually complicated by the fact that the Lorentz expression (6-21) does not apply, some remarks may be made about each of these classes in so far as they apply to solids.

(i) Substances for which the static polarization is entirely due to electronic displacements are necessarily elements, such as diamond. If we assume for the internal field an expression of the type (6-24), one obtains from the relation

$$P_e = N\alpha_e E_i = (\epsilon_s - 1)E/4\pi \qquad (6\text{-}27)$$

the following expression for the dielectric constant:

$$\epsilon_s - 1 = 4\pi N\alpha_e/(1 - N\gamma\alpha_e) \qquad (6\text{-}28)$$

where N represents the number of atoms per unit volume. In the particular case for which the Lorentz expression for the internal field (6-21) is valid, $\gamma = 4\pi/3$. The resulting expression is then usually written in the form of the Clausius-Mosotti formula, which may be obtained by substitution of (6-24) into (6-27):

$$(\epsilon_s - 1)/(\epsilon_s + 2) = (4\pi/3)N\alpha_e \qquad (6\text{-}29)$$

The main experimental test of the correctness of either (6-28) or (6-29) is provided by measurements of the dielectric constant as function of the number of atoms per unit volume. It has therefore been applied mainly to gases. For solid elements one would have to vary the temperature in order to vary N and the possible range of N values is of course very limited. We do not know of any such measurements on, say, diamond or other possible solids which may fall in this class of dielectrics.

It may be noted that for the class of substances under consideration, the dielectric constant is equal to the square of the index of refraction, $\epsilon_s = n^2$. The reason is, that α_e is constant even for frequencies in the visible spectrum, as will be explained in Sec. 6-9. This relationship has been confirmed experimentally for diamond by Whitehead and Hackett.[15] The dielectric constant of diamond is 5.68 ± 0.03.

(ii) In general, solids containing more than one type of atom, but no permanent dipoles, exhibit electronic as well as atomic or ionic polarization. Of particular interest in this respect are the ionic crystals, such as the alkali halides. Consider, for example, a NaCl crystal in an external static field E. Apart from the electronic displacements in the ions relative to the nuclei, the positive ion lattice will tend to move as a whole relative to the negative ion lattice. Consequently, a considerable contribution to the total polarization may be expected to arise from the ionic displacements (P_a). That this is indeed the case, becomes apparent from a comparison of the values of the static dielectric constant defined by

$$P_e + P_a = (\epsilon_s - 1)E/4\pi \qquad (6\text{-}30)$$

and the "high-frequency dielectric constant" ϵ_0, defined by

$$P_e = (\epsilon_0 - 1)E/4\pi \qquad (6\text{-}31)$$

(The high-frequency dielectric constant is equal to the square of the index of refraction for visible light; at such frequencies the ionic displacements cannot follow the field variations and consequently $\epsilon_0 = n^2$ is a measure only of P_e.) By way of illustration, we give in Table 6-2 values for ϵ_s and ϵ_0 for the alkali halides.[16]

Table 6-2. Static and High-Frequency Dielectric Constant for Alkali Halides

	ϵ_s	$\epsilon_0 = n^2$		ϵ_s	$\epsilon_0 = n^2$
LiF	9.27	1.92	KF	6.05	1.85
LiCl	11.05	2.75	KCl	4.68	2.13
LiBr	12.1	3.16	KBr	4.78	2.33
LiI	11.03	3.80	KI	4.94	2.69
NaF	6.0	1.74	RbF	5.91	1.93
NaCl	5.62	2.25	RbCl	5.0	2.19
NaBr	5.99	2.62	RbBr	5.0	2.33
NaI	6.60	2.91	RbI	5.0	2.63

Hence P_a is about two or three times P_e in these compounds. In non-ionic compounds, on the other hand, P_a is usually a relatively small fraction of P_e.

[15] S. Whitehead and W. Hackett, *Proc. Phys. Soc. (London)*, **51**, 173 (1939).

[16] For a number of other ionic solids, see for example N. F. Mott and R. W. Gurney, *op. cit.*, p. 12.

Let us now investigate if a simple theory can account for the observed difference between the static and high-frequency dielectric constants. Suppose the positive and negative ions acquire induced dipole moments of, respectively, μ_+ and μ_-, under influence of a static field E. Furthermore, suppose the positive ion lattice is displaced over a distance x relative to the negative ion lattice. The atomic polarization may then be represented by a point dipole ex at the location of each positive ion, because x is very small compared with the lattice constant. The total electric dipole moment per unit volume is then

$$P = N(\mu_+ + \mu_- + ex) = (\epsilon_s - 1)E/4\pi \qquad (6\text{-}32)$$

where N represents the number of ion pairs per unit volume. For the moment let us assume that the internal field at the location of a positive ion is the same as that at a negative ion site and let it be represented by E_i. We may then write

$$\mu_+ = \alpha_{e+}E_i \quad \text{and} \quad \mu_- = \alpha_{e-}E_i \qquad (6\text{-}33)$$

where α_{e+} and α_{e-} represent the electronic polarizabilities of the positive and negative ions. To find the ionic displacement x, it should be remembered that the equilibrium situation is determined by the equality of the force on a positive ion resulting from the field and the restoring force produced by the deformation of the lattice. Let the latter be represented by fx, where f is the restoring force constant. Then

$$eE_i = fx \quad \text{or} \quad x = eE_i/f \qquad (6\text{-}34)$$

From the last three equations it then follows that

$$(\epsilon_s - 1)E = 4\pi N(\alpha_{e+} + \alpha_{e-} + e^2/f)E_i \qquad (6\text{-}35)$$

If it were assumed that E_i is given by the Lorentz expression (6-21), the last expression could be rewritten as

$$(\epsilon_s - 1)/(\epsilon_s + 2) = (4\pi/3)N(\alpha_{e+} + \alpha_{e-} + e^2/f) \qquad (6\text{-}36)$$

This expression is analogous to the Clausius-Mosotti equation (6-29), with the additional term e^2/f associated with the elastic ionic displacements. To investigate whether or not (6-36) describes the alkali halides satisfactorily, it is convenient to set up an equation relating ϵ_s and the high-frequency dielectric constant ϵ_0, determined by (6-31). Thus, if there were only electronic polarization, which is the case if one measures the index of refraction for visible light ($\epsilon_0 = n^2$), and if again the validity of the Lorentz expression were assumed, one would have

$$P_e = \frac{\epsilon_0 - 1}{4\pi} E = N(\alpha_{e+} + \alpha_{e-}) \frac{\epsilon_0 + 2}{3} E \qquad (6\text{-}37)$$

Substitution of the factor $N(\alpha_{e+} + \alpha_{e-})$ from this equation into (6-36) yields the following relation between ϵ_s and ϵ_0:

$$(\epsilon_s - 1)/(\epsilon_s + 2) = (\epsilon_0 - 1)/(\epsilon_0 + 2) + (4\pi/3)Ne^2/f \qquad (6\text{-}38)$$

This relation may be checked by inserting the value for f as obtained from compressibility data and the Born lattice theory. It turns out, however, that the measured values of ϵ_s and ϵ_0 do not satisfy (6-38) too well. This indicates that the Lorentz expression for the internal field does not describe the situation correctly. In fact, it seems that the formula

$$\epsilon_s - \epsilon_0 = \frac{4\pi Ne^2/f}{1 - 4\pi Ne^2/3f} \qquad (6\text{-}39)$$

gives much better agreement with the experiments. This formula was first derived by Hojendahl,[17] who introduced rather special assumptions about the internal field at the location of positive and negative ion sites. From the above discussion it is evident that the theory of the static dielectric constant of simple crystals such as the alkali halides is not in a completely satisfactory state, mainly because of the difficulties involved in calculating quantitatively the internal field.

It may be noted here that the force constant f and the masses of the positive and negative ions determine the infrared frequency associated with the lattice vibrations. It is therefore possible to express the difference $(\epsilon_s - \epsilon_0)$ in terms of the infrared absorption frequency of the lattice.[18] A discussion of recent work on this topic may be found in H. Fröhlich, *Theory of Dielectrics*, Oxford, New York, 1949, Sec. 18.

(iii) In substances composed of molecules which bear permanent electric dipole moments, the total polarization is made up of three contributions,

$$P = P_e + P_a + P_d \qquad (6\text{-}40)$$

where P_d corresponds to the dipolar contribution. There exists no general quantitative theory for dipolar solids because first of all the same difficulties arise in evaluating the internal fields as in class (ii), and furthermore, the dipoles in such solids may not be able to rotate at all or only to some extent. The discussion must therefore be limited to some qualitative remarks. As an example of a dipolar solid which behaves in a relatively simple manner, we show in Fig. 6-8 the dielectric constant measured as function of temperature for $C_6H_5NO_2$ (nitrobenzene).[19] It is observed that at the melting point there is a large increase in the dielectric constant. This is interpreted as an indication that in the solid the dipoles

[17] K. Hojendahl, *Kgl. Danske Videnskab. Selskab*, **16**, No. 2 (1938).

[18] B. Szigeti, *Trans. Faraday Soc.*, **45**, 155 (1949); *Proc. Roy. Soc.* (London), **A204**, 51 (1950).

[19] C. P. Smyth and C. S. Hitchcock, *J. Am. Chem. Soc.*, **55**, 1830 (1933).

cannot rotate freely and P_d is essentially zero; in the liquid, alignment of the dipoles in the field direction is possible, so that the increase in ϵ is determined by the now freely rotating dipoles. The subsequent slow decrease in ϵ is a consequence of the thermal motion of the particles, as may be understood from equation (6-16). In other cases, the behavior may be more complicated, as illustrated by Fig. 6-9, in which ϵ versus T

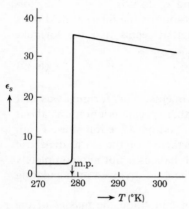

Fig. 6-8. The static dielectric constant of nitrobenzene as a function of temperature. [After Smyth and Hitchcock, ref. 20]

Fig. 6-9. Dielectric constant of hydrogen sulfide as function of temperature. [After Smyth and Hitchcock, ref. 20]

has been plotted for H_2S.[20] The melting point of H_2S is $187.7°K$. In this case, the dipoles are apparently "frozen in" at temperatures below $103.5°K$; at this temperature the structure changes in such a manner that the dipolar groups become mobile; as the temperature is further increased, the dielectric constant decreases as a result of increased thermal motion. The other changes evidently affect essentially the density of the material, i.e., N is reduced at these transition points.

Part B. Alternating Fields

6-7. The complex dielectric constant and dielectric losses

When a dielectric is subjected to an alternating field, the polarization P also varies periodically with time and so does the displacement D. In general, however, P and D may lag behind in phase relative to E, so that, for example, if

$$E = E_0 \cos \omega t \qquad (6-41)$$

[20] C. P. Smyth and C. S. Hitchcock, *J. Am. Chem. Soc.*, **55**, 1296 (1933); **56**, 1084 (1934).

we have

$$D = D_0 \cos(\omega t - \delta) = D_1 \cos \omega t + D_2 \sin \omega t \qquad (6\text{-}42)$$

where δ is the phase angle. Clearly,

$$D_1 = D_0 \cos \delta \quad \text{and} \quad D_2 = D_0 \sin \delta \qquad (6\text{-}43)$$

For most dielectrics D_0 is proportional to E_0, but the ratio D_0/E_0 is generally frequency-dependent. To describe this situation, one may thus introduce two frequency dependent dielectric constants:

$$\epsilon'(\omega) = D_1/E_0 = (D_0/E_0) \cos \delta$$
$$\epsilon''(\omega) = D_2/E_0 = (D_0/E_0) \sin \delta \qquad (6\text{-}44)$$

It is frequently convenient to lump these two constants into a single complex dielectric constant,

$$\epsilon^* = \epsilon' - i\epsilon'' \qquad (6\text{-}45)$$

because the relation between D and E, both expressed as complex quantities, is then simply

$$D = \epsilon^* E_0 e^{i\omega t} \qquad (6\text{-}46)$$

as may readily be verified.

It is noted that according to (6-44) there exists the relation

$$\tan \delta = \epsilon''(\omega)/\epsilon'(\omega) \qquad (6\text{-}47)$$

and because both ϵ' and ϵ'' are frequency-dependent, the phase angle δ is frequency-dependent. We shall now show that the energy dissipated in the dielectric in the form of heat is proportional to ϵ''. The current density in the capacitor is equal to

$$I = \frac{dq}{dt} = \frac{1}{4\pi} \cdot \frac{dD}{dt} = \frac{\omega}{4\pi} \left(-D_1 \sin \omega t + D_2 \cos \omega t \right) \qquad (6\text{-}48)$$

where use has been made of (6-1) and (6-42); q is the surface charge density on the capacitor plates. The energy dissipated per second in the dielectric per unit volume is

$$W = \frac{\omega}{2\pi} \int_0^{2\pi/\omega} IE \, dt \qquad (6\text{-}49)$$

By substitution of (6-48) and (6-41) into (6-49) one readily finds that the integral containing D_1 vanishes and one is left with

$$W = (\omega/8\pi) D_2 E_0 = (\omega/8\pi) E_0^2 \epsilon'' \qquad (6\text{-}50)$$

The energy losses are thus proportional to $\sin \delta$; for this reason $\sin \delta$ is called the loss factor and δ is the loss angle.[21]

---

[21] One frequently calls $\tan \delta$ the loss factor; this is correct only for small values of δ, because then $\tan \delta \simeq \sin \delta \simeq \delta$.

6-8. Dielectric losses and relaxation time

Let us consider a dielectric for which the total polarization P_s in a static field is determined by three contributions,

$$P_s = P_e + P_a + P_d \qquad (6\text{-}51)$$

In general, when such a substance is suddenly exposed to an external static field, a certain length of time is required for P to be built up to its final value. In the present section it will be assumed that the values of P_e and P_a are attained instantaneously, i.e., we shall be concerned with frequencies appreciably smaller than infrared frequencies. The time required for P_d to reach its static value may vary between days and 10^{-12} second, depending on temperature, chemical constitution of the material, and its physical state.

To begin with we shall give a phenomenological description of the transient effects based on the assumption that a relaxation time can be defined; we can then proceed to consider the case of an alternating field. Let P_{ds} denote the saturation value of P_d obtained after a static field E has been applied for a long time. It will be assumed that the value of P_d as function of the time after the field has been switched on is given by

$$P_d(t) = P_{ds}(1 - e^{-t/\tau}) \qquad (6\text{-}52)$$

Hence,

$$dP_d/dt = (1/\tau)[P_{ds} - P_d(t)] \qquad (6\text{-}53)$$

For the decay occurring after the field has been switched off, this leads to a well-known proportionality with $e^{-t/\tau}$. In the case of an alternating field $E = E_0 e^{i\omega t}$, equation (6-53) may be employed if we make the following change: P_{ds} must be replaced by a function of time $P_{ds}(t)$ representing the saturation value which would be obtained in a static field equal to the instantaneous value $E(t)$. Hence for alternating fields we shall employ the differential equation[22]

$$dP_d/dt = (1/\tau)[P_{ds}(t) - P_d] \qquad (6\text{-}54)$$

Now, our final goal is to express the real and imaginary parts of the dielectric constant in terms of the frequency ω and the relaxation time τ. For this purpose we shall define the "instantaneous" dielectric constant ϵ_{ea} by

$$P_e + P_a = \frac{\epsilon_{ea} - 1}{4\pi} E \qquad (6\text{-}55)$$

[22] For a proof that this procedure is correct, see, for example, M. Gevers, *Philips Research Repts.*, **1**, 279, 298 (1946); M. Gevers and F. K. Du Pré, *Trans. Faraday Soc.*, **42A**, 47 (1946).

We may then write

$$P_{ds} = P_s - (P_e + P_a) = \frac{\epsilon_s - \epsilon_{ea}}{4\pi} E \qquad (6\text{-}56)$$

where ϵ_s is the static dielectric constant. Substitution of P_{ds} into (6-54) yields

$$\frac{dP_d}{dt} = \frac{1}{\tau} \left(\frac{\epsilon_s - \epsilon_{ea}}{4\pi} E_0 e^{i\omega t} - P_d \right) \qquad (6\text{-}57)$$

Solving this equation, we obtain

$$P_d(t) = Ce^{-t/\tau} + \frac{1}{4\pi} \cdot \frac{\epsilon_s - \epsilon_{ea}}{1 + i\omega\tau} E_0 e^{i\omega t} \qquad (6\text{-}58)$$

The first term represents a transient in which we are not interested here. The total polarization is now also a function of time and is given by $P_e + P_a + P_d(t)$. Hence, for the displacement one obtains

$$D(t) = \epsilon^* E(t) = E(t) + 4\pi P(t) \qquad (6\text{-}59)$$

where ϵ^* is the complex dielectric constant. From the last two equations and from the definition $\epsilon^* = \epsilon' - i\epsilon''$ the following expressions result:

$$\epsilon'(\omega) = \epsilon_{ea} + \frac{\epsilon_s - \epsilon_{ea}}{1 + \omega^2\tau^2} \qquad (6\text{-}60)$$

$$\epsilon''(\omega) = (\epsilon_s - \epsilon_{ea}) \frac{\omega\tau}{1 + \omega^2\tau^2} \qquad (6\text{-}61)$$

These equations are frequently referred to as the Debye equations. In Fig. 6-10 the quantities ϵ' and ϵ'' are represented as functions of $\omega\tau$. It is observed that the dielectric loss, which is proportional to ϵ'' according to (6-50), exhibits a maximum for $\omega\tau = 1$, i.e., for an angular frequency equal to $1/\tau$. Also, for frequencies appreciably less than $1/\tau$, the real part of the dielectric constant ϵ' becomes equal to the static dielectric constant. In this frequency range, therefore, the losses vanish and the dipoles contribute their full share to the polarization. On the other hand, for frequencies larger than $1/\tau$, the dipoles are no longer able to follow the field variations and the dielectric constant ϵ' approaches ϵ_{ea}.

The question may now be raised as to which physical models actually satisfy the above phenomenological theory. We shall discuss here a particular one as an example, viz., the case in which certain positive ions in a solid may have two equilibrium positions separated by a distance $2a$. For simplicity it will be assumed that the line joining the two positions A and B is parallel to the external field direction, as indicated in Fig. 6-11.

As long as there is no external field, we shall assume that the energy in sites A and B are equal, so that without field there are just as many ions in A sites as in B sites. If we assume that, without field, the potential

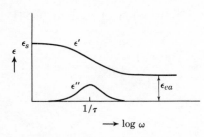

Fig. 6-10. Debye curves for ϵ' and ϵ'' as function of frequency for a dielectric with a single relaxation time.

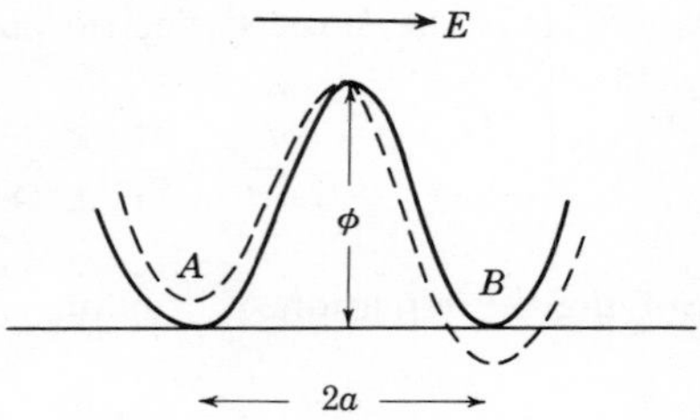

Fig. 6-11. The full curve represents the potential energy for a positive ion in the absence of an external field; with a field E, the dashed curve results.

energy barrier separating the two types of sites is ϕ, the probability per second for an ion in an A site to jump into a B site is, according to statistical mechanics, of the form

$$p_0 = \nu \exp(-\phi/kT) \qquad (6\text{-}62)$$

where ν is a frequency factor of the order of 10^{12} per second. Thus, without external field, the ions will continuously change over from A and B sites, but on the average there are per unit volume $N/2$ in A sites and $N/2$ in B sites if N is the total number of such ions per unit volume.

Suppose now that suddenly a static field E is applied in the direction as indicated in Fig. 6-11. Particles in A sites will then see a potential barrier $(\phi - eaE)$ and particles in B sites see a barrier $(\phi + eaE)$; hence the ions will prefer B sites over A sites. In equilibrium we must evidently have just as many particles making transitions $A \to B$ as $B \to A$, so that

$$N_{a\infty} p_0 \exp(eaE/kT) = N_{b\infty} p_0 \exp(-eaE/kT) \qquad (6\text{-}63)$$

or $\qquad\qquad N_{a\infty} p_{ab} = N_{b\infty} p_{ba}$

where $N_{a\infty}$ and $N_{b\infty}$ represent the equilibrium values for the number of particles in A and B sites with an external field E. Let us now consider the transient phenomenon as we go from the initial state $N_{a0} = N_{b0} = N/2$ to the final state $N_{a\infty}$ and $N_{b\infty}$. Particularly, we are interested in the time dependence of $(N_b - N_a)$ because the dipole moment per unit volume resulting from this effect is

$$P_d = (N_b - N_a)ea \qquad (6\text{-}64)$$

At a particular instant we have

$$dN_a/dt = -N_a p_{ab} + N_b p_{ba}$$
$$dN_b/dt = N_a p_{ab} - N_b p_{ba}$$
(6-65)

Subtracting these equations, keeping in mind that $N_a + N_b = N$, one may write

$$(d/dt)(N_b - N_a) = -(p_{ab} + p_{ba})(N_b - N_a) + (p_{ab} - p_{ba})N \quad (6\text{-}66)$$

Now, one may assume for not too high field strengths that $eaE \ll kT$, so that

$$p_{ab} = p_0 \exp(eaE/kT) \simeq p_0(1 + eaE/kT)$$

and similarly,

$$p_{ba} \simeq p_0(1 - eaE/kT)$$

Hence (6-66) reduces to

$$(d/dt)(N_b - N_a) = -2p_0(N_b - N_a)$$
$$+ 2p_0 NeaE/kT \quad (6\text{-}67)$$

The solution of this equation, for the initial condition specified above, is

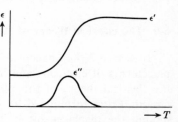

Fig. 6-12. The dielectric constant as a function of temperature at a given frequency, as predicted from the model discussed in the text.

$$N_b - N_a = \frac{NeaE}{2kT}(1 - e^{-2p_0 t}) \quad (6\text{-}68)$$

and the polarization due to this mechanism is, according to (6-64) and (6-68), given by

$$P_d(t) = \frac{Ne^2 a^2 E}{2kT}(1 - e^{-t/\tau}) \quad \text{with} \quad \tau = \frac{1}{2p_0} \quad (6\text{-}69)$$

Note that this equation has the same form as (6-52), which was the basis on which the Debye equations were derived. The relaxation time is thus equal to the reciprocal of the jumping probability per unit time in the absence of an external field. Note also, that for this type of mechanism the relaxation time decreases with increasing temperature and so does the saturation polarization. It is of interest to observe that if the quantities ϵ' and ϵ'' are measured at a constant frequency but at different temperatures, the curves as indicated in Fig. 6-12 may be expected to result.

For other possible models which lead to the Debye equations, see Fröhlich, *op. cit.*, Sec. 11. It should be pointed out that the interpretation of experimental results on dielectric losses frequently requires a distribution of relaxation times rather than a single one as assumed in the above discussions. One then employs the following equations instead of (6-60) and (6-61)

$$\epsilon' = \epsilon_{ea} + (\epsilon_s - \epsilon_{ea}) \int_0^\infty \frac{F(\tau)\, d\tau}{1 + \omega^2\tau^2}$$

$$\epsilon'' = (\epsilon_s - \epsilon_{ea}) \int_0^\infty \frac{F(\tau)\omega\tau\, d\tau}{1 + \omega^2\tau^2}$$

(6-70)

where $F(\tau)$ is the distribution function of the relaxation times, such that

$$\int_0^\infty F(\tau)\, d\tau = 1 \qquad (6\text{-}71)$$

For further details we refer to the literature.[23,24]

6-9. The classical theory of electronic polarization and optical absorption

In Sec. 6-2 the concept of the static polarizability due to elastic displacements of electrons and ions was introduced. In the present section the classical theory of this phenomenon in alternating fields will be discussed. From formula (6-10) it is evident that the restoring force determining the displacement is in first approximation proportional to the displacement itself. The discussion is therefore based on the model of an harmonic oscillator. The differential equation governing the motion of an elastically bound particle of charge e and mass m in an alternating field $E_0 e^{i\omega t}$ may be written

$$m \frac{d^2x}{dt^2} + m\gamma \frac{dx}{dt} + m\omega_0^2 x = eE_0 e^{i\omega t} \qquad (6\text{-}72)$$

where ω_0 is the natural angular frequency of the particle; $\omega_0 = (f/m)^{1/2}$ where f is the restoring force constant; the second term on the left-hand side is a damping term, which results from the fact that the particle emits radiation as a consequence of its acceleration.[25] The solution for this forced damped vibration is

$$x(t) = \frac{e}{m} \cdot \frac{E_0 e^{i\omega t}}{\omega_0^2 - \omega^2 + i\gamma\omega} \qquad (6\text{-}73)$$

We first of all note that in a static field, i.e., for $\omega = 0$, this reduces simply to

$$x = eE_0/m\omega_0^2 \quad \text{or} \quad \alpha_s = ex/E_0 = e^2/m\omega_0^2 \quad \text{for} \quad \omega = 0 \qquad (6\text{-}74)$$

[23] For a review, see M. Gevers, *Philips Research Repts.*, **1**, 279, 298 (1946); see also M. Gevers and F. K. Du Pré, *Trans. Faraday Soc.*, **42A**, 47 (1946).

[24] For dielectric losses in alkali halides resulting from Schottky defects and divalent impurities, see R. G. Breckenridge, *J. Chem. Phys.*, **16**, 959 (1948); **18**, 913 (1950); also his article in W. Shockley (ed.), *Imperfections in Nearly Perfect Crystals*, Wiley, New York, 1952.

[25] A proof that this leads to a term proportional to dx/dt may be found in R. Becker, *Theorie der Elektrizität*, 6th ed., Teubner, Leipzig, 1933.

where α_s is static polarizability associated with the elastically bound particle. If we take for e and m the electronic charge and mass, this expression would correspond to the contribution of a particlar electron to the electron polarizability. Now we have seen in Sec. 6-2 that the electronic polarizabilities are of the order of 10^{-24} cm³; this gives a natural frequency $\nu_0 = \omega_0/2\pi \simeq 10^{15}$ per second. Thus, even for frequencies corresponding to the visible spectrum, the electronic polarizability may be considered constant. If e and m refer to an ion, the natural frequencies are of the order of 10^{13} per second, corresponding to the infrared part of the spectrum.

Let us now consider the frequency dependence of the polarization resulting from the elastic displacements. It must be emphasized that the field strength appearing in equation (6-73) for the displacement $x(t)$ is the internal field and not the externally applied field; only in the case of gases of low density may these two fields be considered equal. Let us first consider the case of a gas, for which one may write

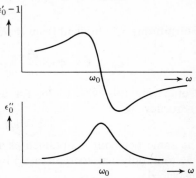

Fig. 6-13. Behaviour of ϵ_0' and ϵ_0'' as function of frequency in the vicinity of the resonance frequency ω_0.

$$P_e^* = \frac{\epsilon_0^* - 1}{4\pi} E_0 e^{iwt} = N\alpha_e^* E_0 e^{i\omega t} \quad (6\text{-}75)$$

where the asterisks indicate complex functions. The polarizability is immediately obtained from (6-73) by multiplying by e and dividing by the field strength. Hence

$$\epsilon_0^* = 1 + 4\pi N \frac{e^2}{m} \cdot \frac{1}{\omega_0^2 - \omega^2 + i\gamma\omega} \quad (6\text{-}76)$$

Now, writing again $\epsilon_0^* = \epsilon_0' - i\epsilon_0''$, one finds

$$\epsilon_0' = 1 + 4\pi N \frac{e^2}{m} \cdot \frac{\omega_0^2 - \omega^2}{(\omega_0^2 - \omega^2)^2 + \gamma^2\omega^2} \quad (6\text{-}77)$$

$$\epsilon_0'' = 4\pi N \frac{e^2}{m} \cdot \frac{\gamma\omega}{(\omega_0^2 - \omega^2)^2 + \gamma^2\omega^2} \quad (6\text{-}78)$$

The energy absorbed per unit volume is proportional to ϵ_0'', according to (6-50). In Fig. 6-13 we have represented $(\epsilon_0' - 1)$ and ϵ_0'' as functions of the frequency ω. Note that ϵ_0'' contains the damping factor γ, which has the dimensions of a frequency; if there were no damping, there would be no absorption. This type of absorption is called resonance absorption, for obvious reasons. In the absorption region, the dielectric constant ϵ_0' depends on frequency and one speaks in this connection of dispersion.

The region for which ϵ_0' decreases with increasing frequency is referred to as the region of anomalous dispersion.

For solids, assuming the internal field to be given by the Lorentz expression (6-21), we should write instead of (6-75),

$$P_e^* = \frac{\epsilon_0^* - 1}{4\pi} E_0 e^{i\omega t} = N\alpha_e^* \left(\frac{\epsilon_0^* + 2}{3} \right) E_0 e^{i\omega t} \tag{6-79}$$

which leads to

$$\frac{\epsilon_0^* - 1}{\epsilon_0^* + 2} = \frac{4\pi}{3} N\alpha_e^* \quad \text{or} \quad \epsilon_0^* = 1 + \frac{4\pi N}{1/\alpha_e^* - 4\pi N/3} \tag{6-80}$$

Substituting α_e^* obtained from (6-73) in the same way as above, this gives

$$\epsilon_0^* = 1 + 4\pi N \frac{e^2}{m} \cdot \frac{1}{\omega_0^2 - \omega^2 + i\gamma\omega - 4\pi Ne^2/3m} \tag{6-81}$$

Comparing this with (6-76) for a gas, we see that by defining a new frequency

$$\omega_1^2 = \omega_0^2 - 4\pi Ne^2/3m \tag{6-82}$$

the same behavior is obtained as above; in the formulas obtained for a gas, one only has to replace ω_0^2 by ω_1^2, i.e., the absorption frequency is displaced.

In optical work it is usual to introduce instead of the quantity ϵ_0^* the complex index of refraction. A few remarks in this connection may therefore be in order. It is well known that Maxwell's equations for a non-magnetic insulator give for the velocity of propagation of light the expression $v = c/\sqrt{\epsilon}$. On the other hand, the index of refraction is defined as $n = c/v$. This leads to the Maxwell relation $\epsilon = n^2$. Now, when there is absorption, the electric component of a light wave polarized in the y-direction and propagated in the x-direction may be represented by

$$E_y(x,t) = Ae^{-\omega kx/c} e^{i\omega(t - nx/c)} \tag{6-83}$$

where $\exp(-\omega kx/c)$ takes care of the absorption. The coefficient k is called the extinction coefficient. Its physical meaning is the following: when the wave has propagated over a distance equal to the wavelength in vacuum $\lambda_0 = 2\pi c/\omega$, the amplitude is reduced by a factor $e^{-2\pi k}$. Now instead of (6-83) we may also write

$$E_y(x,t) = Ae^{i\omega(t - n^* x/c)} \tag{6-84}$$

where n^* is the complex index of refraction and where evidently

$$n^* = n - ik \tag{6-85}$$

From this relation, together with $(n^*)^2 = \epsilon_0^* = \epsilon_0' - i\epsilon_0''$, it then follows that

$$\epsilon_0' = n^2 - k^2 \quad \text{and} \quad \epsilon_0'' = 2nk \tag{6-86}$$

and the formulas (6-77) and (6-78) are thus also valid for $(n^2 - k^2)$ and $2nk$, respectively. Note that the absorption per unit volume is proportional to nk.

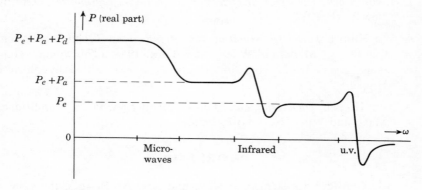

Fig. 6-14. The real part of the total polarization P as function of frequency for a dipolar substance with a single atomic and electronic resonance frequency.

The above considerations may be applied equally well to ionic displacements. To summarize the frequency-dependence of the polarization we have represented, in Fig. 6-14, $P(\omega)$ for a dipolar substance with a single atomic and electronic absorption line.

REFERENCES

R. Becker, *Theorie der Elektrizität*, 6th ed., especially volume II, Teubner, Leipzig, 1933.

C. J. F. Böttcher, *Theory of Electric Polarization*, Elsevier, Amsterdam, 1952.

W. Fuller Brown jr., *Encyclopedia of Physics*, **27,** Springer, Berlin, 1956, pp. 1–154.

P. Debye, *Polar Molecules*, Dover, New York, 1945.

Dielectrics discussion, *Trans. Faraday Soc.*, **42A,** (1946).

H. Fröhlich, *Theory of Dielectrics*, Oxford, New York, 1949.

R. J. W. LeFèvre, *Dipole Moments*, 2d ed., Methuen, London, 1948.

O. Fuchs and K. L. Wolf, "Dielektrische Polarisation," *Hand- und Jahrbuch der chemischen Physik*, Vol. 6, Leipzig, 1935.

E. J. Murphy and S. O. Morgan, "Dielectric Properties of Insulating Materials," *Bell System Tech. J.*, **16,** 493 (1937); **17,** 640 (1938); **18,** 502 (1939).

C. P. Smyth, *Dielectric Constant and Molecular Structure*, Chem. Catalog, New York, 1931.

J. H. van Vleck, *Theory of Electric and Magnetic Susceptibilities*, Oxford, New York, 1932.

A. von Hippel, *Dielectric Materials and Applications*, Technology Press, Cambridge, Mass. and Wiley, New York, 1954. (This volume contains papers by 22 contributors and has been edited by A. von Hippel.)

A. von Hippel, *Dielectrics and Waves*, Technology Press, Cambridge, Mass. and Wiley, New York, 1954.

PROBLEMS

6-1. Consider a system of positive and negative charges, the system being neutral as a whole. Show that the dipole moment of the system as defined by (6-8) is independent of the location of the origin of the coordinate system.

6-2. Show that the potential energy of a dipole μ in an external field E may be written $-\mu \cdot E$. Also show that if α is the polarizability of an atom, the energy of the atom in an electric field E is given by $-(\alpha/2)E^2$.

6-3. From the electronic polarizabilities for the alkali and halide ions given in Table 6-1 and from the lattice constants for the alkali halides as obtained from X-ray diffraction data, calculate the high-frequency dielectric constant for some of these salts on the assumption that the internal field is given by the Lorentz expression; compare the results with the experimental values given in Table 6-2.

6-4. Calculate the field strength required to reach 0.1 per cent of the saturation value of the orientational polarization of a dipolar gas at room temperature if the dipoles have a strength of 1 Debye unit.

6-5. Consider a system of noninteracting dipoles which are confined to two possible orientations relative to an applied field E: either parallel or antiparallel. Show that at a temperature T the average dipole moment along the field direction is equal to μ^2/kT (which differs by a factor 3 from formula (6-16).

6-6. (a) A sphere of dielectric constant ϵ_i and radius R is brought in a homogeneous field E; the sphere is surrounded by vacuum. Show that the field inside the sphere is homogeneous and given by $3E/(\epsilon_i + 2)$.

(b) A substance of dielectric constant ϵ_0 contains a spherical cavity of radius R. If the field at large distances from the sphere is homogeneous and equal to E, show that the field inside the cavity is homogeneous and equal to $3\epsilon_0 E/(2\epsilon_0 + 1)$. (This field is called the cavity field; note that it is independent of R.)

(c) Consider a homogeneously polarized sphere of radius R in vacuum; there is no applied field. If P is the polarization of the sphere show that the field inside the sphere (the self-field) is given by $E_s = -(4\pi/3)P = -M/R^3$, where M is the total dipole moment of the sphere.

(d) A spherical cavity of radius R inside a homogeneous dielectric ϵ contains a rigid dipole μ at its center. There is no applied field. Show that the field inside the cavity is homogeneous and given by $f\mu$, where

$$f = \left(\frac{\epsilon - 1}{2\epsilon + 1}\right) \frac{2}{R^3}$$

This field is called the reaction field of the dipole.

Hint: For all these problems the general solution of Laplace's equation $\nabla^2 V = 0$ is of the form

$$V = -(A/r^2 + Br) \cos \theta$$

The constants A and B must be found from the boundary conditions.

6-7. Discuss the theory of Böttcher of the refraction of electrolytes and explain how he arrived at the polarizabilities of the alkali and halide ions given in Table 6-1. (See C. J. F. Böttcher, *Theory of Electric Polarization*, Elsevier, New York, 1953, p. 273; also footnote 2.)

6-8. Readers familiar with the variation method in wave mechanics may show that if one employs a variation function $\psi_{1s}(1 + Az)$ for a hydrogen atom in an external field along the z-direction, one obtains for the polarizability $4a_0^3 = 0.59 \times 10^{-24}$ cm^3 (a_0 = radius of first Bohr orbit; the correct answer is $9a_0^3/2$).

6-9. Explain the shapes of the ϵ' and ϵ'' curves represented in Fig. 6-12.

6-10. Discuss the dielectric losses in alkali halide crystals resulting from pairs of vacancies and from divalent positive impurities (see footnote 24; also, Y. Haven, *Report of the Conference on Defects in Crystalline Solids*, Bristol, 1954, p. 261).

6-11. Consider the parallel arrangement of the following two circuit branches: one branch consists of a capacitor C_1, the other of a capacitor C_2 plus a series resistor R. Show that this circuit is the equivalent of a capacitor filled with a dielectric satisfying the Debye equations.

6-12. Discuss the theory of the dielectric constant of alkali halides of Roberts; this theory is based on a simplified model involving rigid and weightless ionic boundaries. See S. Roberts, *Phys. Rev.*, **77**, 258 (1950).

Chapter 7

IONIC CONDUCTIVITY AND DIFFUSION

7-1. Lattice defects in ionic crystals

We have seen in Sec. 3-3 that a metallic lattice in thermal equilibrium contains a certain number of lattice defects. Examples of such defects are vacant lattice sites, interstitial atoms, pairs of vacancies, etc. The formation of a particular type of lattice defect requires a certain energy ϕ and because the equilibrium number of defects depends on a Boltzmann factor containing ϕ, those defects with the lowest ϕ value will predominate.

Ionic crystals should, according to thermodynamics, also contain defects in thermal equilibrium with the lattice. Here again, the most common types are vacancies and interstitial ions. Other defects are, of course, possible in principle; for example, some positive ions may occupy lattice positions that are normally occupied by negative ions. It would seem, however, that the production of such disorderly arrangements would require very high energies and thus their relative numbers would be very small.[1] In other words, ionic crystals may be looked upon as completely ordered "alloys" (apart from vacant sites and possible interstitial ions) of a metal and a metalloid.

Let us consider an ionic crystal of the composition A^+B^-. Positive ion vacancies may then be produced in a similar way as in metals, viz., by a number of successive jumps of positive ions (Fig. 7-1). The result would be equivalent to taking a positive ion somewhere from the interior of the crystal and placing it at the surface.[2] Suppose now that a number of positive ion vacancies would have been produced in this manner while the negative ion lattice remained perfect. The surface of the crystal would then contain an excess of positive charge, the interior an excess of negative charge. Thus space charges would be set up. It is obvious that such space charges would counteract the formation of more positive ion vacancies. On the other hand, the field set up by the space charges would favor the formation of negative ion vacancies. We thus conclude that as a consequence of the tendency to prevent the build-up of space charges, an ionic crystal should contain nearly equal numbers of positive and negative ion vacancies.[3]

---

[1] J. H. van Santen, *Philips Research Repts.*, **5**, 282 (1950), discusses order-disorder for Coulomb forces.

[2] Vacancies may also originate at dislocation jogs inside the crystal; see Sec. 3-12.

[3] A treatment of the space charge problem may be found in J. Frenkel, *Kinetic Theory of Liquids*, Oxford, New York, 1946.

Thus even if the energy ϕ_+ required to produce a single positive ion vacancy were appreciably different from the energy ϕ_- to produce a single negative ion vacancy, they would occur in approximately equal numbers in the interior of the crystal. It is obvious from this that their number will be determined only by the sum of the formation energies

$$\phi = \phi_+ + \phi_- \tag{7-1}$$

As in Chapter 3, it will again be assumed that the external pressure may be taken as zero, so that the equilibrium condition requires the free energy $E - TS$ to be a minimum. The free energy of the fictitious perfect crystal will be represented by

$$F_p = E_p - TS_p \tag{7-2}$$

where the energy E_p incorporates the binding energy as well as the vibrational energy. The entropy is thermal entropy only, because for a perfect crystal the configurational entropy vanishes. Let the actual crystal contain n positive and n negative ion vacancies. Its configurational entropy is then

$$S_{cf} = k \log \left[(N + n)!/N!n! \right]^2 \tag{7-3}$$

The term in square brackets represents the number of ways in which N positive ions and n positive ion vacancies may be distributed over a total of $(N + n)$ sites. The same holds for the negative ion sites, hence the square. The free energy of the actual crystal may thus be represented by

$$F_a = F_p + n\phi - T(S_a - S_p) - 2kT \log \left[(N + n)!/N!n! \right] \tag{7-4}$$

where S_a is the thermal entropy of the actual crystal. Let us define the increase in thermal entropy ΔS_{th} resulting from the production of a positive plus a negative ion vacancy by

$$n\Delta S_{th} = S_a - S_p \tag{7-5}$$

Applying the equilibrium condition $(\partial F/\partial n)_T = 0$ to (7-4) we obtain for $n \ll N$,

$$n = N \exp\left(\Delta S_{th}/2k - \phi/2kT\right) \tag{7-6}$$

Note that the essential factor is the Boltzmann factor containing $\phi/2$, i.e., half the energy required to produce a positive plus a negative ion vacancy. The exponential term containing the change in thermal entropy per vacancy $\Delta S_{th}/2$ may be calculated on the basis of a particular model, for example, an Einstein model. In that case the calculation is similar to that given in Sec. 3-3 for metals. Thus let us assume that the Einstein frequency associated with the ions in the perfect lattice is ν.[4] In the actual lattice,

---

[4] It would be more realistic to introduce two Einstein frequencies, one for the positive and one for the negative ions; the essential conclusions, however, would remain the same.

let the Einstein frequency of an ion neighboring a vacancy be ν' ($< \nu$). The actual crystal then corresponds to $6zn$ linear oscillators of frequency ν' and $(6N - 6zn)$ oscillators of frequency ν', where z is the number of nearest neighbors surrounding a vacancy. The thermal entropies of the perfect and actual crystals are then given, respectively, by (see equation 3-2)

$$S_p = 6Nk \log (kT/h\nu) + 6Nk$$

$$S_a = 6znk \log (kT/h\nu') + (6N - 6zn)k \log (kT/h\nu) + 6Nk$$

where we assumed $kT \gg h\nu$. Hence

$$S_a = S_p + 6znk \log (\nu/\nu') \tag{7-7}$$

According to (7-7) and (7-5), we may then write for the increase in thermal entropy per vacancy formed,

$$\Delta S_{\text{th}}/2 = 3kz \log (\nu/\nu') \tag{7-8}$$

For this model, the expression for the density of vacancies may then be be obtained by substituting (7-8) into (7-6), giving

$$n/N = C \exp (-\phi/2kT) \quad \text{with} \quad C = (\nu/\nu')^{3z} \tag{7-9}$$

Note that the frequency ratio is larger than unity, so that the thermal entropy changes favor the formation of vacancies.

Here, as in the case of metals, one frequently finds the argument in the literature that if ϕ depends on temperature in accordance with a relation of the type

$$\phi(T) = \phi_0 + T (d\phi/dT) = \phi_0 - \gamma T \tag{7-10}$$

the actual expression for the density of vacancies should be

$$n = N(\nu/\nu')^{3z} e^{\gamma/2k} \exp (-\phi_0/2kT) \tag{7-11}$$

However, the objections raised in connection with this argument in Sec. 3-3 are also valid in this case:[5] it does not take into account the temperature variation of the thermal entropy change ΔS_{th}. In fact, for zero pressure we have

$$d\phi/dT = Td(\Delta S_{\text{th}})/dT \tag{7-12}$$

Suppose now that n/N could be measured in some way and that over a limited range of temperatures the result could be expressed by

$$n/N = A \exp (-\epsilon/kT) \quad \text{or} \quad \epsilon = -k \frac{d}{d(1/T)} \log (n/N) \tag{7-13}$$

[5] Y. Haven and J. H. van Santen, *Philips Research Repts.*, **7**, 474 (1952).

where ϵ is the "experimental" slope of log (n/N) plotted versus $1/kT$. Substituting the general expression (7-6) into (7-13) and making use of (7-12), one finds

$$\epsilon = \phi/2 \qquad (7\text{-}14)$$

Hence, one actually measures ϕ in this manner. Also, the pre-exponential factor A as determined experimentally is always equal to exp $(\Delta S/2k)$.

Approximate methods to calculate the energy ϕ required to create a positive plus a negative ion vacancy will be discussed in Sec. 7-3 and we shall therefore postpone giving numerical values for the quantities involved.

It will be evident that a positive and a negative ion vacancy will attract each other as a result of the Coulomb field between them. For large distances, the energy of attraction is equal to $-e^2/\epsilon r$, where ϵ is the dielectric constant of the medium. They may therefore combine to form pairs of vacancies (Fig. 7-1). At a given temperature there will exist a certain ratio between the number of single vacancies and the number of pairs, the ratio depending on the dissociation energy required to separate a pair into two singlets. There are evidently certain degrees of dissociation depending on whether the distance between the single vacancies is small or large; in a sense one may therefore speak of a thermally excited state of a pair if the distance between the vacancies is only a few atomic diameters. Reference to the importance of pairs of vacancies for diffusion in ionic crystal will be made later.

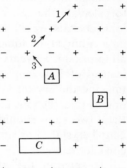

Fig. 7-1. The sequence of jumps 1, 2, 3 may lead to the formation of a positive ion vacancy A; B represents a negative ion vacancy; C an associated pair of vacancies formed as a result of Coulomb attraction.

Interstitial ions in combination with vacancies may also occur: for example, a positive ion may jump into an interstitial position, leaving a vacancy behind. If the vacancy and interstitial ion are far enough apart to prevent an immediate recombination, one speaks of Frenkel defects. In this case it is not necessary to have equal numbers of positive and negative Frenkel defects, because their formation does not require the setting up of space charges over macroscopic distances. In general, depending essentially on the energy required to form them, either the positive or negative Frenkel defects will predominate. Also, they may occur in combination with Schottky defects. The calculation of their density as function of the energy ϕ required to produce a Frenkel defect is essentially the same as that given above for Schottky defects, i.e., one finds an expression for the free energy of a crystal containing n defects and minimizes F. We leave it to the reader to show that in this case, neglecting thermal entropy changes,[6]

$$n = (NN_i)^{1/2} e^{-\phi/2kT} \tag{7-15}$$

where N is the number of ions under consideration and N_i is the number of possible interstitial positions in the crystal; ϕ represents the energy required to produce a Frenkel defect.

7-2. The hydration energy of ions

As an introduction to the next section, where we shall discuss attempts to calculate the activation energy for the formation of lattice defects in ionic crystals, we shall sidestep to another problem. It is well known that a large number of ionic crystals dissolve readily in water, but hardly at all in organic solvents. To understand this, consider the following cycle:[7] instead of following what happens when a crystal is dissolved in water, imagine the crystal taken apart into its separate ions in vacuum. Then, one by one, the ions are put into the solvent. The total energy involved in these two steps should then be equal to that required for dissolving the actual crystal. For simplicity we shall neglect all entropy changes and only consider energies.

To separate the crystal into its individual ions requires, according to the Born theory, an energy

$$E_L = NA \frac{e^2}{a_0} \cdot \left(1 - \frac{1}{n}\right) \tag{7-16}$$

where N is the number of ion pairs, A is the Madelung constant, a_0 is the shortest interionic distance, n is the Born repulsion exponent. For NaCl this is equal to about 7.9 ev per ion pair.

The next question is, What is the change in energy when an ion is taken from vacuum into the solvent? To simplify the problem let us consider the ion as a sphere of radius R and the solvent as a continuous medium of dielectric constant ϵ. If the charge of the ion is e, the energy required to charge the sphere in vacuum is equal to $e^2/2R$. This energy may be considered as the energy associated with the Coulomb field around the sphere. If the sphere were inside a homogeneous dielectric ϵ, the field energy would be $e^2/2\epsilon R$. Thus when a sphere of radius R and charge e is taken from vacuum into the dielectric, there is a gain of energy equal to

$$H = \frac{e^2}{2R} \left(1 - \frac{1}{\epsilon}\right) \tag{7-17}$$

[6] See, for example, N. F. Mott and R. W. Gurney, *Electronic Processes in Ionic Crystals*, 2d ed., Oxford, New York, 1948, p. 28.

[7] M. Born, *Z. Physik*, **1**, 45 (1920); K. Fajans, *Verhandl. deut. physik. Ges.*, **21**, 549, 709, 714 (1919).

If (7-17) refers to an ion taken from vacuum to water, H is called the hydration energy of the ion.

It is probably useful to look at this electrostatic problem from a somewhat different angle: an ion inside a dielectric material produces a polarization in the dielectric as a consequence of its Coulomb field. In turn, the polarized surroundings will produce a field at the location of the ion. To find the reaction potential at the center of the ion we proceed as follows. Referring to Fig. 7-3 the field strength in the dielectric is given by

$$E = e/\epsilon r^2 = D - 4\pi P = \epsilon E - 4\pi P \qquad (7\text{-}18)$$

all vectors having radial direction. Hence the dipole moment induced in a volume element $d\tau$ located at a distance r from the center is equal to

$$P\, d\tau = (e/4\pi r^2)(1 - 1/\epsilon)\, d\tau \qquad (7\text{-}19)$$

This dipole moment produces a potential at the center of the sphere of $P\, d\tau/r^2$, and thus the reaction potential in the center is

$$V = \int_{r=R}^{\infty} \frac{P\, d\tau}{r^2} = \int_{R}^{\infty} \frac{e}{4\pi r^2}\left(1 - \frac{1}{\epsilon}\right) \cdot \frac{1}{r^2} \cdot 4\pi r^2\, dr = \frac{e}{R}\left(1 - \frac{1}{\epsilon}\right) \qquad (7\text{-}20)$$

Thus we conclude from (7-17) and (7-20) that the energy of the ion in the reaction field is

$$\frac{1}{2}\, eV = \frac{e^2}{2R}\left(1 - \frac{1}{\epsilon}\right) \qquad (7\text{-}21)$$

We note the appearance of the factor $\frac{1}{2}$, which always occurs whenever we are concerned with the energy of a charge in a reaction potential.

Returning to our original problem, we see that according to (7-16) and (7-17) the energy required to dissolve the crystal is, per ion pair,

$$A\frac{e^2}{a_0}\left(1 - \frac{1}{n}\right) - \frac{1}{2}e^2\left(1 - \frac{1}{\epsilon}\right)\left(\frac{1}{R_+} + \frac{1}{R_-}\right) \qquad (7\text{-}22)$$

where R_+ and R_-, respectively, represent the radii of a positive and a negative ion. For the NaCl lattice $A = 1.746$, and if for simplicity we assume $R_+ + R_- = a_0$ and $R_+ = R_-$, then (7-22) becomes

$$1.746\frac{e^2}{a_0}\left(1 - \frac{1}{n}\right) - \frac{2e^2}{a_0}\left(1 - \frac{1}{\epsilon}\right) \qquad (7\text{-}23)$$

We see that, for sufficiently high values of ϵ, expression (7-23) may become negative, in which case one would expect appreciable solubility because energy is liberated by dissolving the crystal. This is frequently the case for water ($\epsilon = 81$), whereas for most organic solvents ϵ is too small to make (7-23) negative. Although the above reasoning is strongly simplified, it is obvious that the dielectric constant, and thus the hydration energy of the ions, plays a major role in the theory of solubility of ionic solids. The simple electrostatic problem mentioned above will also enter in the discussion of the next section.

7-3. The activation energy for the formation of defects in ionic crystals

In Sec. 7-1 we derived an expression for the number of vacancies in an ionic crystal in thermal equilibrium at a temperature T. According to (7-6) or (7-9) this number is essentially determined by the formation energy $\phi = \phi_+ + \phi_-$. Let us first consider the energy ϕ_+ involved in the formation

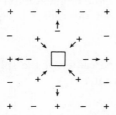

Fig. 7-2. Showing the polarizing effect of a positive ion vacancy on its surroundings. The surrounding negative ions are displaced slightly outward; the positive ions assume positions slightly displaced toward the vacancy. In addition to the ionic displacements, the effective negative charge of the vacancy induces dipoles in the surrounding ions.

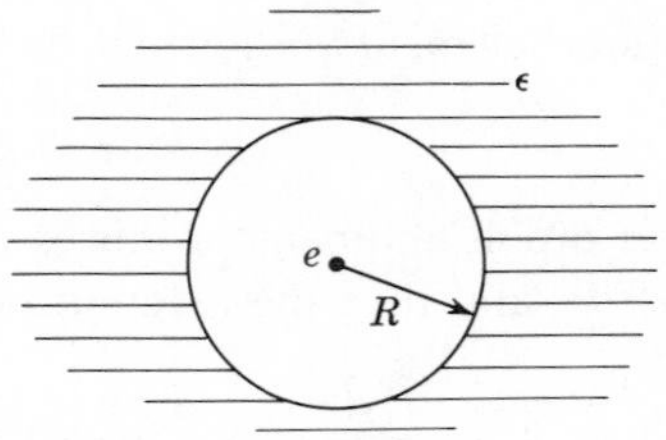

Fig. 7-3. Jost model to calculate the polarization energy resulting from the presence of a vacancy. The vacancy is represented by a spherical cavity of radius R inside a homogeneous dielectric ϵ; the charge e at the center represents the effective charge of the vacancy.

of a positive ion vacancy. Suppose a positive ion is removed from the interior of the crystal to infinity, while the charge distribution in the crystal is kept the same as it was. The energy required for this step is obviously given by

$$\epsilon_L = A \frac{e^2}{a_0} \left(1 - \frac{1}{n}\right) \tag{7-24}$$

if we use the simple Born lattice theory. Putting the ion from infinity on the surface of the crystal leads to a gain in energy of

$$\frac{1}{2}\epsilon_L = \frac{1}{2} A \frac{e^2}{a_0} \cdot \left(1 - \frac{1}{n}\right) \tag{7-25}$$

Thus if nothing else would happen, ϕ_+ would be equal to the difference of (7-24) and (7-25). However, the removal of a positive ion will affect the neighboring ions in such a way that an adjustment takes place by which energy is gained, thereby lowering ϕ_+. Referring to Fig. 7-2, we note that from the point of view of the surroundings of a positive ion vacancy, it looks as if a negative charge has been added at this lattice site. In other words, there is an excess of negative charge in the vicinity of the missing positive ion. Consequently the surrounding material will become polarized. This polarization consists first of the formation of dipoles induced in the ions by the Coulomb field of the missing ion, second of a slight ionic displacement as indicated in Fig. 7-2. Because of the long range of Coulomb forces, it is not sufficient to take into account only nearest neighbors; the effect will spread over distances many times the lattice constant. The calculation of this polarization energy P_+ is very complicated although it may be understood in principle on the basis of a simplified model, first introduced by Jost.[8] If we consider the vacancy as a spherical hole inside a homogeneous dielectric constant ϵ the hole bearing a charge e at its center, we obtain the situation given in Fig. 7-3. The charge e, due to the missing ion, polarizes the dielectric and thus in turn will create a reaction potential V at the location of the charge. We see that this problem is identical with the one treated in the preceding section. Thus the polarization energy is given by

$$P_+ = \frac{1}{2} eV = \frac{1}{2} \cdot \frac{e^2}{R_+}\left(1 - \frac{1}{\epsilon}\right) \tag{7-26}$$

From (7-24), (7-25), and (7-26), one obtains

$$\phi_+ = \frac{1}{2} A \frac{e^2}{a_0}\left(1 - \frac{1}{n}\right) - \frac{1}{2} \cdot \frac{e^2}{R_+}\left(1 - \frac{1}{\epsilon}\right) \tag{7-27}$$

For negative ion vacancies the same reasoning applies, so that the energy required to produce a positive and a negative ion vacancy is equal to

$$\phi = \phi_+ + \phi_- = A\frac{e^2}{a_0}\left(1 - \frac{1}{n}\right) - \frac{1}{2}e^2\left(1 - \frac{1}{\epsilon}\right)\left(\frac{1}{R_+} + \frac{1}{R}\right) = \epsilon_L - P_+ - P_- \tag{7-28}$$

The first term, of course, can be calculated with good accuracy, but as far as the remainder is concerned the problem arises as to what values one should assign to R_+ and R_- in this idealized model. These values can be found with good approximation only by comparison with more accurate calculations of P_+ and P_- based on an actual ionic picture rather than on a continuum. Calculations of this kind have been made by Mott and Littleton[9] and more recently to a higher approximation by Rittner, Hutner, and Du Pré.[10] As an example of the results of the former authors, we cite those for NaCl and KCl below (all energies in electron volts).

	ϵ_L	P_+	P_-	ϕ	R_+	R_-
NaCl.........	7.94	3.32	2.76	1.86	$0.58a_0$	$0.95a_0$
KCl..........	7.18	2.71	2.39	2.08	$0.61a_0$	$0.85a_0$

[8] W. Jost, *J. Chem. Phys.*, **1**, 466 (1933); *Trans. Faraday Soc.*, **34**, 860 (1938); W. Jost and G. Nehlep, *Z. Physik. Chem.*, **B32**, 1 (1936); **B34**, 348 (1938).

[9] N. F. Mott and M. J. Littleton, *Trans. Faraday Soc.*, **34**, 485 (1938).

[10] E. S. Rittner, R. A. Hutner, and F. K. Du Pré, *J. Chem. Phys.*, **17**, 198 (1949).

The values of R_+ and R_- are obtained by substituting the values of P_+ and P_- given by Mott and Littleton into (7-26). We note that the number of vacancies depends on $\phi_0/2$, according to (7-6). Also, we see how important the polarization energy is for the formation of vacancies in ionic crystals. In fact, for NaCl it reduces the value of ϕ for NaCl from 7.94 to only 1.86 ev. Because of the relatively small value of ϕ, vacancies in alkali halides close to the melting point may occur in concentrations of the order of 10^{-4} per ion.

From the results quoted above it follows that for alkali halides $R_+ \simeq 0.6a_0$ and $R_- \simeq 0.9a_0$. We shall see in Sec. 7-5 that the calculated values of ϕ are in fairly good agreement with experiments.

Similar estimates have been made of the activation energies required for the formation of Frenkel defects in ionic crystals. It turns out that in alkali halides, defects of the vacancy type are much more likely to occur than interstitial ions. However, for silver halides there is theoretical and experimental evidence for the occurrence of Frenkel defects.[11]

We have seen above that the "effective" charge of a positive ion vacancy is negative, of a negative ion vacancy is positive. Thus there will be attraction between vacancies of opposite sign and one may expect them to form pairs. The binding energy of a pair of vacancies is about 0.9 ev in the alkali halides.[12] A pair of vacancies is neutral and thus will not lead to ionic conductivity. On the other hand, they correspond to dipoles and consequently may give rise to dielectric losses at relatively low frequencies; for a review of recent work on this subject we refer to the literature.[13] Also, pairs of vacancies of opposite sign appear to be very mobile in the alkali halides and are therefore important for diffusion in these crystals.[14]

Besides single vacancies and pairs of vacancies, higher aggregates of course are possible, as triplets, quadruplets, etc.

7-4. Example of self-diffusion in alkali halides

As an example of diffusion in ionic crystals, some measurements by Mapother, Crooks, and Maurer will be discussed briefly.[15] These investigators measured the self-diffusion of radioactive sodium in NaCl and NaBr in the following manner: A thin layer of about 5×10^{-4} cm of radioactive salt containing the isotope Na^{24} was deposited on one face of a cubic crystal, approximately 1 cm on edge. The crystal was then held at a

[11] J. Tetlow, *Ann. Physik*, **5**, 63, 71 (1949); *Z. physik. Chem.*, **195**, 197, 213 (1950); for further references see the article by F. Seitz in W. Shockley (ed.), *Imperfections in Nearly Perfect Crystals*, Wiley, New York, 1952.

[12] J. R. Reitz and J. L. Gammel, *J. Chem. Phys.*, **19**, 894 (1951).

[13] See, for example, the paper by R. G. Breckenridge in W. Shockley (ed.), *Imperfections in Nearly Perfect Crystals*, Wiley, New York, 1952.

[14] J. G. Dienes, *J. Chem. Phys.*, **16**, 620 (1948); F. Seitz. *Phys. Rev.*, **79**, 529 (1950).

[15] D. Mapother, H. N. Crooks and R. Maurer, *J. Chem. Phys.*, **18**, 1231 (1950).

constant temperature for a certain length of time. After this diffusion anneal, the distribution of radioactive sodium was determined by means of a sectioning technique, employing a microtome. In a similar fashion, Schamp has investigated the diffusion of bromine in NaBr.[16]. What one measures in this way is the self-diffusion of the radioactive ions in the salt. It must be emphasized that this type of experiment is altogether different from one in which one heats the salt in the vapor of one of the constituents; in such experiments one obtains information about the diffusion of color centers in the lattice (see Sec. 15-6).

According to Fick's first law, the net flux of ions is proportional to the concentration gradient (see Sec. 3-5), i.e.,

$$J = -D \text{ grad } n^* \tag{7-29}$$

where J is the number of radioactive atoms crossing 1 cm^2 per sec., D is the diffusion coefficient, and n^* is the number of radioactive ions per cm^3. Applying the continuity condition $-\partial n^*/\partial t = \text{div } J$, (7-29) becomes

$$\frac{\partial n^*}{\partial t} = \text{div } (D \text{ grad } n^*) \tag{7-30}$$

Assuming the diffusion coefficient D to be independent of the concentration of radioactive ions, one obtains for the one-dimensional problem under consideration,

$$\frac{\partial n^*}{\partial t} = D\frac{\partial^2 n^*}{\partial x^2} \tag{7-31}$$

The solution of this equation for the boundary conditions in the experiment mentioned above is[17]

$$n^*(x,t) = \frac{n_0^*}{(\pi Dt)^{1/2}} \exp \left(\frac{-x^2}{4Dt}\right) \tag{7-32}$$

Here $n^*(x,t)$ is the density of radioactive ions at x after an annealing period t; n_0^* is the initial density at the surface. This solution is based on the assumption that the migration of radioactive sodium is a result of a single diffusion process, because only one diffusion constant D has been introduced. That this assumption is correct may be seen from Fig. 7-4 where the logarithm of the counting rate has been plotted versus the square of the distance from the surface. It may be pointed out that the situation is not always so clearcut as in these experiments. For example, results of similar measurements made by Redington[18] on the self-diffusion of Ba in BaO crystals, when plotted in analogy with Fig. 7-4, give a curve

[16] H. W. Schamp, Thesis, University of Michigan, 1951.

[17] See, for example, W. Jost, *Diffusion in Solids, Liquids, Gases*, Academic Press, New York, 1952, p. 19.

[18] R. W. Redington, *Phys. Rev.*, **87**, 1066 (1952).

consisting of two straight parts separated by a knee. Redington has interpreted his results in terms of two diffusion processes, each having its own diffusion constant.

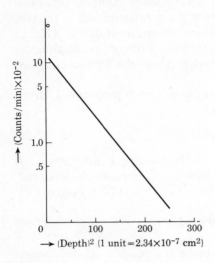

Fig. 7-4. Distribution of radioactive Na in NaCl. $T = 603°C$; $t = 5.92$ h; $D = 1.52 \times 10^{10}$ cm²/sec. [After Mapother, Crooks, and Maurer, ref. 15]

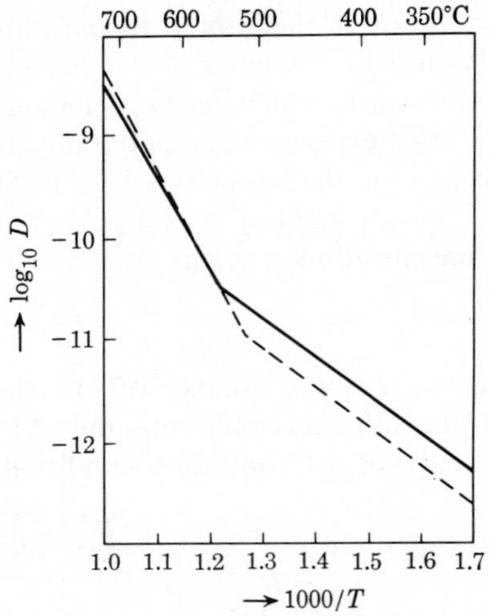

Fig. 7-5. The fully drawn curve represents the directly measured self-diffusion coefficient of Na in NaCl as function of temperature. The dashed curve is calculated from the measured conductivity by means of equation (7-45). [After Mapother, Crooks, and Maurer, ref. 15]

The diffusion constant of Na in NaCl as a function of temperature is represented by the fully drawn curve in Fig. 7-5. Evidently the diffusion constant satisfies the relation

$$D = D_0 e^{-\epsilon/kT} \tag{7-33}$$

where ϵ is an activation energy. It must be noted, however, that the high- and low-temperature regions have different activation energies of, respectively, 1.80 ev and 0.77 ev. This point will be taken up below; it is believed that the low activation energy results from the presence of divalent positive impurities. For diffusion measurements on crystals containing intentionally added divalent positive ions, see the work by Witt and Aschner.[19] In the next section, the diffusion measurements will be interpreted in terms of the migration of lattice defects.

[19] H. Witt, *Z. Physik*, **134**, 117 (1953); J. F. Aschner, Thesis, University of Illinois, 1954.

7-5. Interpretation of diffusion in alkali halides

It is evident that diffusion of ions in a perfect lattice, i.e., in a lattice in which all lattice sites are occupied by the proper ions, is impossible because a given ion has no place to go. Diffusion is therefore possible only by the migration of interstitial ions or by the migration of vacant lattice sites. We have seen before that in the alkali halides lattice vacancies are the predominant type of defects. Thus the positive ions surrounding a positive ion vacancy may jump into the latter; consequently, the vacancy moves through the crystal by virtue of positive ions jumping into it and diffusion becomes possible.

Consider then in Fig. 7-6 the sodium chloride structure, assuming for simplicity that the x-axis along which the diffusion of radioactive sodium takes place coincides with one of the cube edges. A particular positive ion vacancy, such as the one in Fig. 7-6 indicated by the square may then in time carry out a jump to any of 12 equivalent positions, assuming the latter are occupied by positive ions. Of these possible jumps, there are 4 in the positive x-direction, 4 in the negative x-direction, and the remaining 4 leave the vacancy in the original plane. Thus if p is the probability per second for the vacancy to make any jump, $p/3$ is the probability per second for

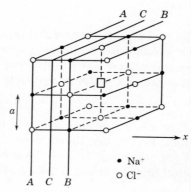

Fig. 7-6. The positive ion vacancy at the center may jump to any of the twelve surrounding positive ion sites at a distance $a\sqrt{2}$. The planes A, B, and C are perpendicular to the x-axis, along which the diffusion takes place.

a displacement $+a$, $-a$, and 0, respectively, if a is the shortest interionic distance. Let us represent the number of radioactive positive ions crossing 1 cm² of the plane C in Fig. 7-6 per second, going from plane A to B, by $N^*_{\rightarrow}$. Similarly, let $N^*_{\leftarrow}$ represent the same number crossing plane C by going from plane B to A. Then if N is the density of positive ions per cm³, n is the density of vacancies, and n^* is the density of radioactive positive ions,

$$N^*_{\rightarrow} = \frac{1}{2a^2} \cdot \frac{n}{N} \cdot \frac{p}{3} \cdot \frac{n^*}{N}$$

$$N_{\leftarrow} = \frac{1}{2a^2} \cdot \frac{n}{N} \cdot \frac{p}{3} \cdot \frac{1}{N} \left(n^* + \frac{dn^*}{dx} a \right)$$

Here $1/2a^2$ represents the total number of positive lattice sites per cm² on plane A or B; n/N represents the probability that such a site is vacant, and n^*/N represents the probability that a positive ion in plane A is radioactive. Consequently the net number of radioactive positive ions passing 1 cm² of plane C per second from left to right is

$$J = N_{\rightarrow}^* - N_{\leftarrow}^* = -\frac{np}{6N^2a} \cdot \frac{dn^*}{dx} \qquad (7\text{-}34)$$

Comparing (7-34) with (7-29) and remembering that $N = 1/2a^3$, one obtains for the diffusion constant associated with the migration of single positive ion vacancies

$$D = \frac{1}{3} a^2 \frac{n}{N} p \qquad (7\text{-}35)$$

The reader may compare this result with expression (3-21). As expected, the self-diffusion coefficient is proportional to the number of vacancies per unit volume n and to the jump probability of a vacancy per second p. As in Sec. 3-5, p may be written in the form

$$p = ve^{-\varepsilon_j/kT} \qquad (7\text{-}36)$$

where v is a frequency and ε_j is the activation energy associated with a jump. Finally then, the coefficient of self-diffusion based on the assumption of the migration of single positive ion vacancies may be obtained by substituting (7-9) and (7-36) into (7-35), yielding

$$D = \frac{1}{3} Cva^2 e^{-\phi/2kT} e^{-\varepsilon_j/kT} \qquad (7\text{-}37)$$

The constant C arises from the thermal entropy change associated with the production of vacancies, as discussed in Sec. 7-1. We note that in a plot of $\log D$ versus $1/kT$, the slope of the line according to the above interpretation is determined by the sum $(\varepsilon_j + \phi/2)$, i.e., by the energy required for the formation of vacancies plus the activation energy for jumping. Thus, from the diffusion measurements of Na in NaCl, represented in Fig. 7-5, it follows from the slope in the high-temperature region that $\varepsilon_j + \phi/2 = 1.80$ ev.

The break in the $\log D$ versus $1/T$ curve leading to a smaller slope in the low-temperature region may in principle be a result of either or both of the following two causes: (1) the presence of divalent positive impurities, (2) the freezing-in of positive ion vacancies. The explanation is as follows: Suppose that a salt like NaCl contains in solid solution a small amount of $SrCl_2$ or of the chloride of another divalent metal, the divalent positive ions occupying sites which are normally occupied by the singly charged Na^+ ions. The condition of electric neutrality then requires that for each divalent positive ion present, there must be a positive ion vacancy. Such crystals then may contain at lower temperatures more positive ion vacancies than would be expected on the basis of thermal equilibrium alone. In fact, below a critical temperature, the number of vacancies per unit volume would then remain constant, the critical temperature being higher the larger the density of divalent impurities. At high temperatures, however, the number of thermally produced vacancies would predominate over the number required by the presence of the divalent ions and the crystal would behave in a normal fashion. Now, if the number of vacancies per unit volume is independent of temperature, the temperature dependence of the diffusion coefficient is according to (7-35) and (7-36) determined by the factor exp $(-\epsilon_j/kT)$. Thus if the presence of divalent metallic ions is accepted as the cause of the break in the log D versus $1/T$ curve, the activation energy for jumping may be obtained separately from the slope of the curve in the low-temperature region. In view of the fact that $(\epsilon + \phi/2)$ is known from the high-temperature slope (the "intrinsic" region), both ϵ_j and ϕ may be obtained. Because of strong experimental evidence, to be further discussed in the next sections, the above explanation seems now generally favored over the freezing-in hypothesis. The latter hypothesis is based on the following reasoning: Suppose a crystal contains a certain number of lattice defects in thermal equilibrium at a high temperature. If the temperature is suddenly lowered, it will take a certain amount of time for the new equilibrium to be established because this requires a migration of vacancies. At lower temperatures such time intervals may be very long and consequently, the crystals may contain many more defects than would be permitted by the equilibrium conditions.

For the diffusion of positive ion vacancies in NaCl, it follows from the slope in the low-temperature region of Fig. 7-5 that $\epsilon_j = 0.77$ ev. Hence, because $(\epsilon_j + \phi/2) = 1.80$ ev, the experimental value for ϕ is 2.06 ev. This is in reasonable agreement with the theoretical value of 1.86 ev given on page 167.

For a vibrational frequency of the ions in the lattice of the order of 10^{13} per sec, one finds for the probability of a jump of a positive ion vacancy per second in the alkali halides,

$$p = \nu e^{-\epsilon_j/kT} \simeq 1 \text{ sec}^{-1} \text{ at room temp.} \tag{7-38}$$

From (7-37) it follows that the pre-exponential factor in the expression for the diffusion coefficient is equal to

$$D_0 = \tfrac{1}{3}C\nu a^2 \simeq 1 \text{ cm}^2 \text{ sec}^{-1}$$

when $\nu \simeq 10^{13}$, $a \simeq 3 \cdot 10^{-8}$ cm and $C \simeq 100$. The experimental value of D_0 for the intrinsic region in NaCl, according to the work of Mapother, Crooks, and Maurer, is 3.1 cm^2 sec^{-1}, and 0.67 cm^2 sec^{-1} for NaBr.

Diffusion of positive ions does not necessarily take place as a result of migration of single positive ion vacancies only. In fact, at least two other possible diffusion mechanisms must be considered in the alkali halides:

(i) Diffusion resulting from migration of pairs.

(ii) Diffusion resulting from migration of divalent positive impurities together with associated vacancies.

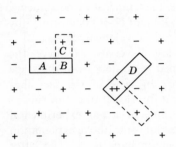

These two mechanisms are illustrated in Fig. 7-7. A pair of vacancies may diffuse as a result of positive or negative ions jumping into the corresponding vacant site of the pair. The resulting diffusion coefficient is given by an expression of the type

$$D_{\text{pair}} = \text{const. exp} \left(\frac{\phi - \epsilon_p + \epsilon_{jp}}{kT} \right) \quad (7\text{-}39)$$

Fig. 7-7. The pair AB may diffuse by the positive ion C jumping into the vacancy A, or by a negative ion jumping into B. The associated complex divalent positive ion-positive ion vacancy may migrate as a result of interchange between the divalent ion and the vacancy D, combined with singly charged positive ions jumping into the vacancy.

where ϕ is the energy required to produce a positive plus a negative ion vacancy, ϵ_p is the binding energy of a positive and negative ion vacancy and ϵ_{jp} is the activation energy for the jumping of a pair. Theoretical estimates give $\epsilon_p \simeq 1$ ev and $\epsilon_{jp} \simeq 0.4$ ev for NaCl.[20] It may be expected, therefore, that pairs diffuse much more rapidly than single vacancies, because their activation energy for jumping is only about half that for a single positive ion vacancy. That this must be so may be seen qualitatively because the jumping ions are allowed more free space in the former case.

The influence of the presence of divalent positive ions on the diffusion may be understood as follows: For each divalent positive ion, there must be a positive ion vacancy to satisfy the neutrality condition. A certain fraction of these vacancies are free and contribute to the diffusion as discussed above. However, not all these vacancies are free, because they are attracted by the divalent positive ions as a result of Coulomb interaction. Thus there will be a certain number of associated complexes, consisting of a divalent positive ion and a neighboring vacant positive ion site. This unit may migrate through the crystal as a result of other positive ions jumping into the vacancy and as a result of possible jumps of the divalent ion into the vacancy. It may be of interest at this point to give

[20] G. J. Dienes, *J. Chem. Phys.*, **16**, 620 (1948); N. F. Mott and R. W. Gurney *Electronic Processes in Ionic Crystals*, Oxford, New York, 1940, Chap. 2.

values of the binding energy between divalent positive ions and positive ion vacancies as calculated by Bassani and Fumi:[21]

	Cd^{2+}	Ca^{2+}	Sr^{2+}
NaCl.........	0.38 ev	0.38 ev	0.45 ev
KCl..........	0.32	0.32	0.39

Thus these binding energies are roughly half as large as those for pairs of vacancies in the alkali halides. The study of the influence of divalent impurities on the physical properties of alkali halides receives a good deal of attention at present.

Although we have limited ourselves to the discussion of a rather restricted area of the field of diffusion in ionic crystals, the same general ideas apply to other cases. For further study we therefore refer the reader to the literature.[22]

7-6. Ionic conductivity in "pure" alkali halides

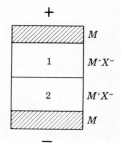

Fig. 7-8. Essential experimental arrangement for measuring transport numbers.

When a potential difference is applied between two opposite faces of an ionic crystal, an electric current may be detected. For the alkali halides these currents are too large to be explained in terms of the motion of electrons because the number of electrons in the conduction band for the temperatures involved would be much too small. Thus the currents must be a result of the migration of ions under influence of the electric field, similar to the electrolytic conduction of aqueous solutions of salts. That the currents are indeed of an ionic nature is also indicated by the fact that decomposition occurs at the electrodes.

The first problem which arises is to determine which constituent carries the current. Although the actual experiments are usually more involved, this question may be answered in principle by employing an experimental arrangement[22] such as indicated in Fig. 7-8. Two slabs of a salt M^+X^- are pressed together between two electrodes of the metal M. For the polarity as indicated, the two following extreme possibilities exist:

(i) Only positive ions move; in that case the cathode will grow at the expense of the anode, the thickness of the two salt slabs remaining the same.

(ii) Only the negative ions move; the X^- ions are then neutralized at the anode and form new layers of salt. Hence the anode decreases

[21] F. Bassani and F. G. Fumi, quoted by F. Seitz, *Revs. Mod. Phys.*, **26**, 7 (1954).

[22] See W. Jost, *Diffusion in Solids, Liquids, Gases*, Academic Press, New York, 1952, Chap. 4.

in thickness, the cathode increases. Furthermore, slab 1 will grow at the expense of slab 2.

If both types of ions contribute to the current, the result will be intermediate between (i) and (ii). By weighing, the relative contributions to the ionic current by the positive and negative ions may be determined.

The ionic conductivity of an isotropic crystal is defined by the scalar equation

$$I = \sigma E$$

where I is the current density, E is the field strength, and σ is the conductivity. If the conductivity of the positive ions alone is σ_+, the transport number of these ions is defined by

$$t_+ = \sigma_+/\sigma \qquad (7\text{-}40)$$

Similarly, $t_- = \sigma_-/\sigma$, and of course $t_+ + t_- = 1$.

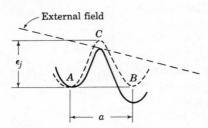

Fig. 7-9. The fully drawn curve represents the resultant of the field-free potential curve (dashed) and the linear potential (dashed) resulting from the external field E. A, B, and C may be associated with positions of a positive ion in the planes A, B, C of Fig. 7-6.

In the alkali halides the experiments show that the positive ions are much more mobile than the negative ones. In the older literature one will find for KCl, for example, values for t_+ of about 0.9 over a wide temperature range. Recent measurements on crystals of high purity indicate, however, that the presence of small amounts of divalent positive ions has a marked influence on the measured transport numbers. For very pure KCl, Kerkhoff finds $t_+ = 0.88$ at 525°C and $t_+ = 0.70$ at 600°C.[23] We shall return to this point in Sec. 7-7 and first discuss the interpretation of ionic conductivity in terms of lattice defects.

In the alkali halides ionic conductivity, like diffusion, is explained in terms of the motion of vacant lattice sites. The positive ion vacancies have an effective negative charge and will therefore move toward the anode; similarly, the negative ion vacancies will move towards the cathode. As mentioned above, the mobility of the positive ion vacancies is appreciably larger than that of the negative ones, and for the moment it will therefore be assumed that the conductivity is entirely due to the motion of the former. For simplicity we shall use the geometry of Fig. 7-6, assuming an electric field along the x-axis. Let us denote the number of

[23] F. Kerkhoff, *Z. Physik*, **130**, 449 (1950).

positive ion sites per cm³ by N, the number of positive ion vacancies per cm³ by n. If the electric field in Fig. 7-6 is directed to the right, a positive ion vacancy will jump with a higher probability to the left than to the right, because it is negatively charged. The potential energy along the line of motion may therefore be represented by the full curve in Fig. 7-9 which is the resultant of the dashed field-free curve and the linear potential due to the external potential difference. Clearly then, the probabilities per second for a jump to the left and to the right are, respectively,

$$p_\leftarrow = \tfrac{1}{3}\nu \exp\left[-(\epsilon_j - \tfrac{1}{2}\,aeE)/kT\right]$$

$$p_\rightarrow = \tfrac{1}{3}\nu \exp\left[-(\epsilon_j + \tfrac{1}{2}\,aeE)/kT\right]$$

(7-41)

where the notation used is identical with that of Sec. 7-5; E represents the field strength. The current density, i.e., the net flux of charge passing per second through 1 cm², is then equal to

$$I = \frac{1}{2a^2}\cdot\frac{n}{N}\,(p_\leftarrow - p_\rightarrow)e \tag{7-42}$$

because $1/2a^2$ is the number of positive ion sites in a plane perpendicular to the x-axis of an area of 1 cm² and n/N is the probability for such a site to be vacant. Now, for nearly all practical cases, $aeE \ll kT$, so that in first approximation

$$I = \frac{n}{N}\cdot\frac{e^2\nu E e^{-\epsilon_j/kT}}{6akT} = \sigma E \tag{7-43}$$

Now the number of vacancies n is given by (7-9), so that the conductivity is equal to

$$\sigma = \frac{Ce^2\nu}{6akT}\exp\left[-(\epsilon_j + \tfrac{1}{2}\phi)/kT\right] \tag{7-44}$$

We note that the current density is proportional to E only as long as $aeE \ll kT$, i.e., Ohms law is valid only under this particular condition. For very high electric fields such that aeE is not small compared with kT, the current increases exponentially with the field strength. According to (7-44), the conductivity associated with the positive ion vacancies depends on the two activation energies ϵ_j and ϕ, as does the coefficient of self-diffusion. In fact, the conductivity σ is related in a simple manner to the diffusion coefficient, as was first pointed out by Einstein. From (7-37) and (7-44) it follows that

$$\sigma/D = Ne^2/kT \tag{7-45}$$

It must be emphasized that the Einstein relation is valid only if the conductivity and self-diffusion are due to the same mechanism; in the present case the assumption implicit in the derivation of (7-45) is that both phenomena are a result of the migration of single positive ion vacancies. In Fig. 7-5 the diffusion coefficient calculated from the conductivity by means of (7-45) is represented by the dashed curve. That the Einstein relation is not exactly satisfied is of interest for the interpretation of the diffusion mechanism. First of all, in the high-temperature region the slope of the diffusion coefficient curve as calculated from (7-45) appears to be slightly larger than the directly measured one. This may be explained as a result of the fact that a small fraction of the ionic current is carried by the negative ion vacancies; these, of course, do not contribute to the self-diffusion of Na. In the low-temperature region, the calculated diffusion coefficient is somewhat smaller than the directly measured one. This implies that besides the diffusion of positive ion vacancies, there is some diffusion associated with the migration of neutral carriers. For example, pairs of vacancies and positive divalent ions associated with vacancies (see Fig. 7-7) may contribute to the diffusion but will not contribute to the ionic conductivity.

We have seen above that in the alkali halides the ionic current is carried for the greater part by the positive ions. This is not always the case, however. In the halides of barium and lead, for example, the negative ions are mainly responsible for the ionic conductivity. In the silver halides, the positive ions are the mobile constituent.

7-7. Ionic conductivity in alkali halides with added divalent impurities

We have mentioned several times the influence of the presence of divalent metallic ions on the properties of alkali halides. Although the study of such solid solutions was initiated in 1938 by Koch and Wagner on silver halides, the subject has received a great deal of attention lately, and a few remarks may therefore be in order.

It is possible to grow crystals of alkali halides or silver halides with intentionally added small amounts of the halides of divalent metals, such as Sr, Ba, or Ca. The density of crystals of KCl containing small amounts of $CaCl_2$ and $SrCl_2$ has been measured by Pick and Weber.[24] The results demonstrate that the divalent ions are incorporated substitutionally, i.e., they occupy lattice sites which are normally occupied by the monovalent alkali ions.

In Fig. 7-10 we give as an example of the influence of the divalent ions on the conductivity some results obtained by Kelting and Witt.[25] The logarithm of σ has been plotted versus $1/T$ for a "pure" crystal of KCl (curves 7 and 8) and for KCl with different amounts of $SrCl_2$. We note

[24] H. Pick and H. Weber, Z. Physik, **128,** 409 (1950).
[25] H. Kelting and H. Witt, Z. Physik, **126,** 697 (1949).

that all curves come together to a single straight line, the intrinsic region. In that region, the conductivity is determined essentially by the density of vacancies produced thermally. Thus the slope of the intrinsic curve is determined by the sum of the activation energies ϵ_j and $\phi/2$ in accordance with (7-44). Now for each divalent ion there is one positive ion vacancy.

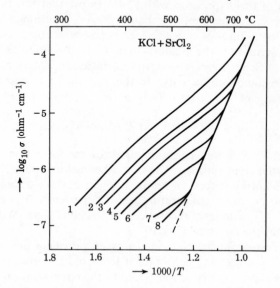

Fig. 7-10. The ionic conductivity of KCl crystals containing various amounts of $SrCl_2$. In units of 10^{-5} the numbers refer to the following mole fractions: $M_1 = 19$; $M_2 = 8.7$; $M_3 = 6.1$; $M_4 = 3.5$; $M_5 = 1.9$; $M_6 = 1.2$; $M_{7,8} = 0$. [After Kelting and Witt, ref. 25]

Consequently, at low temperatures the number of vacancies per unit volume remains constant and is equal to the density of divalent metal ions. At a given temperature, the experiments show that the "induced" conductivity is nearly proportional to the concentration of the divalent metal. This justifies the above interpretation and indicates that the vacancies are almost completely dissociated from the divalent ions. The importance of measurements of this kind lies in the fact that they permit us to determine:

(i) The mobility of the positive ion vacancies.

(ii) The density of Schottky defects in the intrinsic range.

(iii) The binding energy of a divalent impurity and a positive ion vacancy.

This follows from the following considerations: when the conductivity

σ and the concentration of charge carriers n are known, the mobility μ (i.e., the velocity per unit field) may be calculated from the relation

$$\sigma = ne\mu \qquad (7\text{-}46)$$

Comparison of this expression with (7-43) shows that this in turn allows one to calculate the jump probability. As mentioned before, the probability for a jump of a positive ion vacancy at room temperature is about 1 per second for the alkali halides. Once the mobilities are known, the density of Schottky defects in the intrinsic range may be determined from the measured conductivity. In this fashion Etzel and Maurer find for the density of Schottky defects in the intrinsic range for NaCl,[26]

$$n = 1.2 \times 10^{23} \exp\left(-\phi/2kT\right) \text{ per cm}^3 \qquad (7\text{-}47)$$

where $\phi = 2.02$ ev is the energy required for the formation of a positive and a negative ion vacancy. Close to the melting point, this gives a density of Schottky defects of about 10^{18} per cm³, i.e., about 1 vacancy per 10^4 ions. At room temperature $n \simeq 10^6$ per cm³. It is of interest to compare (7-47) with the theoretical expression (7-9). With $N \simeq 10^{22}$ it follows that the constant $C \simeq 10$.

Information about the binding energy of a divalent positive ion and a positive ion vacancy may be obtained from the fact that the "induced" conductivity is not exactly proportional to the concentration of the added divalent salt. In this way, Etzel and Maurer conclude that a fraction of the vacancies is associated with the divalent impurities, the binding energy being about 0.3 ev for NaCl containing $CaCl_2$.[26] However, this topic is still in a state of flow and will not be discussed here any further. We may refer to page 175, where calculated binding energies are given.

We mentioned in Secs. 7-5 and 7-6 that the break in the log D and log σ versus $1/T$ curves is now generally interpreted as resulting from the presence of divalent impurities rather than as a freezing-in of vacancies. As experimental evidence we reproduce in Fig. 7-11 measurements by Kerkhoff[27] of the conductivity and positive ion transport number for three KCl crystals. It is important to compare the position of the knees in the three cases; as the materials become purer, the knee shifts to lower temperatures, in agreement with the above interpretation. It is also of interest to note the influence of the divalent ions on the measured positive ion transport numbers, mentioned in Sec. 7-6. Evidently most of the transport numbers quoted in the literature are unreliable as a consequence of the presence of impurities. The recrystallization of the "analytically pure" KCl carried out by Kerkhoff corresponds to a tenfold increase in purity.

[26] H. W. Etzel and R. J. Maurer, *J. Chem. Phys.*, **18**, 1003 (1950).
[27] F. Kerkhoff, *Z. Physik*, **130**, 449 (1951).

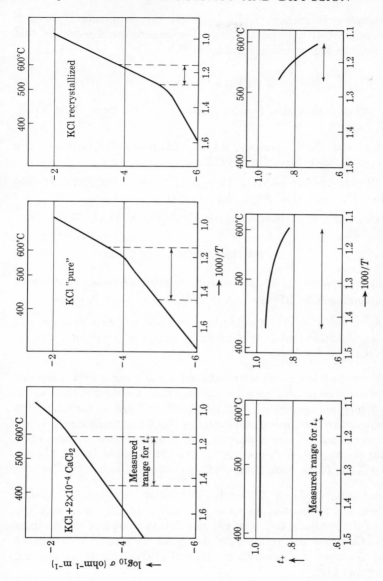

Fig. 7-11. The conductivity and positive ion transport numbers for three specimens of KCl. [After Kerkhoff, ref. 27]

We may finally mention the influence of divalent positive ions on the dielectric losses of alkali halides. The associated complex of a divalent ion and a vacancy corresponds to a dipole. The direction of this dipole may change as a result of the jumping of the vacancy as well as by the interchange of the divalent ion and the vacancy. When the dielectric losses are measured as function of frequency (or temperature), a peak at the jumping frequency (which depends on temperature through a Boltzmann factor) may be expected. For experimental work on this topic we refer to Breckenridge and Haven.[28]

REFERENCES

W. Jost, *Diffusion in Solids, Liquids, Gases*, Academic Press, New York, 1952.

N. F. Mott and R. W. Gurney, 2d ed., *Electronic Processes in Ionic Crystals*, Oxford, New York, 1950.

F. Seitz, "Color Centers in Alkali Halides I, "*Revs. Mod. Phys.*, **18**, 384 (1946); II, *Revs. Mod. Phys.*, **26**, 7 (1954).

W. Shockley (ed.), *Imperfections in Nearly Perfect Crystals*, Wiley, New York, 1952.

PROBLEMS

7-1. From equation (7-9) calculate the number of vacancies per unit volume, assuming $N = 10^{22}$ cm^{-3}, $\phi = 2$ eV, and $\nu_0 = \nu\sqrt{2}$.

7-2. Assuming a simple Coulomb interaction between positive and negative ion vacancies, estimate the binding energy of a pair of vacancies in LiF, NaCl, and KI.

7-3. Neglecting ionic displacements, set up a general expression for the energy required to produce a Frenkel defect in a crystal of the sodium chloride structure, employing the simple Born theory. Calculate the energy required to form a Frenkel defect in NaCl and compare the result with that required to form a positive and a negative ion vacancy. (To check your results, see, for example, W. Jost, *Diffusion in Solids, Liquids, Gases, Academic Press*, New York, 1952, p. 108.)

7-4. Assuming only a Coulomb interaction between a divalent positive ion and a positive ion vacancy, employing the static dielectric constant of the medium, calculate the association energy of the complex for NaCl. Compare the result with the more detailed calculations of Reitz and Gammel, *J. Chem. Phys.*, **19**, 894 (1951) and of Bassini and Fumi (footnote 21).

7-5. Neglecting thermal entropy changes, set up an expression for the free energy of a crystal with the NaCl structure containing n_1 single positive ion vacancies, n_1 single negative ion vacancies, and n_2 pairs of

[28] R. G. Breckenridge, *J. Chem. Phys.*, **16**, 959 (1948); **18**, 913 (1950); see also his article in W. Shockley (ed.), *Imperfections in Nearly Perfect Crystals*, Wiley, New York, 1952, p. 219; Y. Haven, *J. Chem. Phys.*, **21**, 171 (1953).

vacancies. From the minimum conditions $\delta F/\partial n_1 = 0$ and $\partial F/\partial n_2 = 0$, show that

$$n_2/n_1 = 6 \exp\left[(\epsilon - \tfrac{1}{2}\phi)/kT\right]$$

where ϵ represents the binding energy of a pair and ϕ is the energy required to produce a single positive and negative ion vacancy.

7-6. On the basis of the simple Born lattice theory calculate the energy required to create a positive and negative ion vacancy in MgO. Assume that in the Jost model $R_+ = 0.6a$ and $R_- = 0.9a$ and use for the dielectric constant the value 9.8 (*Answer*: The lattice energy is 41 ev per ion pair; the total polarization energy in 34 ev; $\phi = 7$ ev).

7-7. Consider a crystal of monovalent ions of the NaCl structure. Let N represent the number of positive ion sites per cm³, n_a the number of added divalent positive ions per cm³. Furthermore, let n_c be the number of associated complexes per cm³, so that $(n_a - n_c)$ equals the density of free positive ion vacancies and free divalent ions. Show that in thermal equilibrium

$$\frac{n_c n_0}{(n_a - n_c)^2} = 12 e^{\epsilon/kT}$$

where ϵ is the association energy of the complex. (See A. B. Lidiard, *Phys. Rev.*, **94**, 29 (1954).)

7-8. Consider a solution of n molecules of NaCl per cm³ of water. Suppose the concentration is small enough for the interaction between the ions to be negligible. Consider the ions as spheres of radii R_+ and R_- and show that the electrical conductivity is given by $\sigma = (ne^2/6\pi\eta)$ $(1/R_+ + 1/R_-)$ where η is the viscosity of water ($\eta \simeq 10^{-2}$ cgs units at 20°C). Find an expression for the "effective viscosity" in the case of ionic conductivity in solid NaCl. Calculate the mobilities of Na⁺ and Cl⁻ ions in solution on the assumption that R_+ and R_- are equal to the ionic radii; compare the results with the experimental values at 20°C ($\mu_+ = 4.5 \times 10^{-4}$ and $\mu_- = 6.8 \times 10^{-4}$ cm sec⁻¹ volt⁻¹ cm⁻¹).

7-9. Discuss the determination of the concentration and association of lattice defects in NaCl from measurements of the ionic conductivity and dielectric losses. (See Y. Haven, *Report of the Conference on Defects in Crystalline Solids* (Bristol 1954), Physical Society (London), 1955, p. 261.

Chapter 8

FERROELECTRICS

8-1. General properties of ferroelectric materials

The dielectrics discussed in the preceding chapter show a linear relationship between polarization and applied electric field. In the present chapter we shall deal with dielectrics for which this relationship exhibits hysteresis effects. Since the dielectric behavior of these materials is in many respects analogous to the magnetic behavior of ferromagnetic materials, they are called ferroelectric solids, or simply ferroelectrics. A ferroelectric is spontaneously polarized, i.e., it is polarized in the absence of an external field; the direction of the spontaneous polarization may be altered under influence of an applied electric field. In general, the direction of spontaneous polarization is not the same throughout a macroscopic crystal. Rather, the crystal consists of a number of domains; within each domain the polarization has a specific direction, but this direction varies from one domain to another. On the basis of the domain concept, the occurrence of hysteresis in the P versus E relationship can be explained

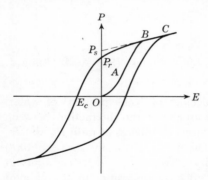

Fig. 8-1. Schematic representation of hysteresis in the polarization versus applied field relationship.

as follows: With reference to Fig. 8-1, consider a crystal which initially has an over-all polarization equal to zero, i.e., the sum of the vectors representing the dipole moments of the individual domains vanishes. When an electric field is applied to the crystal, the domains with polarization components along the applied field direction grow at the expense of the "antiparallel" domains; thus the polarization increases (OA). When all domains are aligned in the direction of the applied field (BC), the polarization saturates and the crystal has become a single domain. A further increase in the polarization with increasing applied field results from "normal" polarization effects discussed in the preceding chapter; rotation of domain vectors may also be involved if the external field does not coincide with one of the possible directions of spontaneous polarization. The extrapolation of the linear part BC to zero external field gives the *spontaneous polarization* P_s. The value of P_s so obtained is evidently the same as the polarization which existed already within each of the domains in the virgin state corresponding to O in Fig. 8-1. Thus, when we speak of "spontaneous polarization" we have in mind the polarization within a single domain and not the over-all polarization of a crystal. We note here that the spontaneous polarization and its dependence on temperature, or on other external conditions that might be imposed, can be measured by displaying the hysteresis loop on an oscilloscope screen. When the applied field for a crystal corresponding to point B in Fig. 8-1 is reduced, the polarization of the crystal decreases, but for zero applied field there remains the *remanent polarization* P_r where P_r refers to the crystal as a whole. In order to remove the remanent polarization, the polarization of approximately half the crystal must be reversed and this occurs only when a field in the opposite direction is applied. The field required to make the polarization zero again is called the *coercive field* E_c. It is evident that if the coercive field is larger than the breakdown field of the crystal, no change in the direction of spontaneous polarization can be achieved, i.e., under those circumstances we cannot speak of the solid as a ferroelectric.

In connection with the last remark a few words may be said here about the crystal structure of ferroelectrics. A necessary, but not sufficient, condition for a solid to be ferroelectric is the absence of a center of symmetry. In total there are 21 classes of crystals which lack a center of symmetry; the classes are based on the rotational symmetry of crystals. Of these 21 classes, 20 are *piezoelectric*, i.e., these crystals become polarized under influence of external stresses. As soon as the crystal structure of a particular solid falls within this group, it can be predicted to be piezoelectric; piezoelectricity is thus determined solely by the symmetry properties of a crystal. Ten out of the 20 piezoelectric classes exhibit *pyroelectric* effects. These pyroelectric crystals are spontaneously polarized. However, the polarization is usually masked by surface charges which collect on the surface from the atmosphere; when the temperature of such a crystal is altered, the polarization changes and this change can be observed, hence the name pyroelectricity. As in the case of piezoelectricity, pyroelectric properties can be predicted as soon as the crystal structure of the solid has been determined. The ferroelectric materials discussed below are part of the group of spontaneously polarized pyroelectrics. However, they have the additional property that the polarization can be reversed by an applied field. This additional feature cannot be predicted from the crystal structure; it can be established only on the basis of a dielectric experiment.

The ferroelectric properties of a ferroelectric disappear above a critical temperature T_c; this temperature is called the *ferroelectric Curie temperature*. Associated with the transition from the ferroelectric to the nonferroelectric phase are anomalies in other physical properties. Thus for a first-order transition, there will be a latent heat; for a second-order transition the specific heat will exhibit a discontinuity (see Sec. 8-7). We should also mention that the spontaneous polarization in the ferroelectric state is associated with spontaneous electrostrictive strains in the crystal; thus the ferroelectric structure has a lower symmetry than the nonpolarized state. At the transition temperature a change in crystal structure is therefore observed.

The dielectric constant of a ferroelectric is, of course, not a constant, but depends on the field strength at which it is measured; this is a consequence of the nonlinear relationship between P and E. When one speaks of "the dielectric constant," one refers to the slope of the curve OA in Fig. 8-1 at the origin, i.e., ϵ is measured for small applied fields so that no motion of domain boundaries occurs. The dielectric constant ϵ so defined is very large in the vicinity of the transition temperature, of the order of 10^4–10^5. Above the transition temperature ϵ obeys the Curie-Weiss law,

$$\epsilon = C'/(T - \theta) + \epsilon_0 \qquad (8\text{-}1)$$

where C' is a constant and θ is a characteristic temperature which is usually some degrees smaller than the transition temperature T_c; ϵ_0 is a constant contributed by the electronic polarization. In the vicinity of the transition temperature ϵ_0 may be neglected, since it is of the order of unity and $\epsilon \gg \epsilon_0$. Likewise, the susceptibility $\chi = (\epsilon - 1)/4\pi \simeq \epsilon/4\pi$ is given by $\chi = C/(T - \theta)$ in this region, where $C = C'/4\pi$ is called the *Curie constant*.

The interpretation of ferroelectric properties is based on the one hand on thermodynamic considerations, which are independent of any particular model; on the other hand, theories have been advanced on the basis of atomic models. The latter require for their verification detailed studies of the structure of the crystals as function of temperature. An excellent description of structure studies on ferroelectrics can be found in G. Shirane, F. Jona, and R. Pepinsky, "Some Aspects of Ferroelectricity," *Proc. IRE*, December 1955, p. 1738. This paper also contains a large number of references to the literature on the subject.

8-2. Classification and properties of representative ferroelectrics

We shall now give some experimental data concerning the properties of representative ferroelectrics. The presently known ferroelectrics can be conveniently classified into four groups, the classification being based on their chemistry and structure.

1. The first solid which was recognized to exhibit ferroelectric properties is Rochelle salt, the sodium-potassium salt of tartaric acid; it has the

chemical formula $NaKC_4H_4O_6 \cdot 4H_2O$.[1] The salt was first prepared in 1672 by a pharmacist Seignette, living in Rochelle; it is therefore also known under the name Seignette salt. It is representative of the "tartrate group." Other members of this group are those in which a fraction of the potassium in Rochelle salt is replaced by NH_4, Rb, or Tl. Lithium ammonium tartrate and lithium tantalum tartrate also belong to this group.

Rochelle salt has the peculiar property of being ferroelectric only in the temperature region between $-18°C$ and $23°C$, i.e., it has two transition temperatures. In the region above $23°C$ and below $-18°C$ it crystallizes in the orthorhombic structure (three mutually perpendicular axes a, b, c). In the ferroelectric phase the crystal is monoclinic and the angle between the a- and c- axes differs from $90°$. The spontaneous polarization occurs along the direction of the original orthorhombic a-axis. Thus Rochelle salt has only one polar axis and two possible polarization directions ($+$ and $-$ along the a-axis). The domain pattern of this salt is therefore rather simple.

The dielectric constants for Rochelle salt along the three axes are given in Fig. 8-2, according to Halblützel.[2] Note that ϵ_a reaches values as high as 4000 near the transition temperatures. In the region above $23°C$ the susceptibility along the a-axis can be represented by the Curie-Weiss law,

$$\chi_a \simeq \epsilon_a/4\pi = C_1/(T - \theta_1) \quad \text{with} \quad C_1 = 178°K; \quad \theta_1 \simeq 296°K$$

In the region below $-18°C$ the susceptibility is described by

$$\chi_a = C_2/(\theta_2 - T) \quad \text{with} \quad C_2 = 93.8°K; \quad \theta_2 \simeq 255°K$$

The spontaneous polarization of Rochelle salt as function of temperature is represented by the lower curve in Fig. 8-3; the upper curve corresponds to the deuterated salt. Note that the replacement of hydrogen by deuterium has a marked influence on the magnitude of the spontaneous polarization and on the temperature range over which the material is ferroelectric. In this connection we may mention that some theories of the ferroelectric properties of Rochelle salt have been based on the idea that certain hydrogen bonds are essential in the polarization mechanism;[3] the effect associated with the replacement of H by D would seem to support this idea. Recent investigations of the structure of Rochelle salt with X-ray and neutron diffraction techniques are believed to show, however, that the hydrogen bonds may not at all be involved in the mechanism of the transition.[4]

[1] J. Valasek, *Phys. Rev.*, **17**, 475 (1921); **19**, 478 (1922); **20**, 644 (1922); **24**, 560 (1924).

[2] J. Halblützel, *Helv. Phys. Acta*, **12**, 489 (1939).

[3] W. P. Mason, *Phys. Rev.*, **72**, 854 (1947).

[4] B. C. Frazer, M. McKeown, and R. Pepinsky, *Phys. Rev.*, **94**, 1435 (1954).

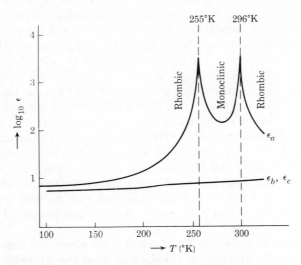

Fig. 8-2. The logarithm of the dielectric constants of Rochelle salt along the a, b and c axes as function of the absolute temperature. [After Halblützel, ref. 2]

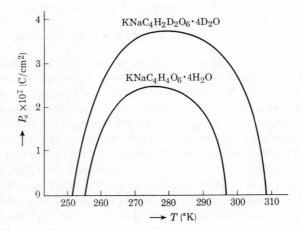

Fig. 8-3. The lower curve represents the spontaneous polarization for Rochelle salt as function of temperature. The upper curve corresponds to the deuterated salt. [After Halblützel, ref. 2]

2. In 1935 Busch and Scherrer discovered ferroelectric properties in potassium dihydrophosphate, KH_2PO_4.[5] This is a typical example of the second group of ferroelectrics, consisting of dihydrogen phosphates and arsenates of the alkalimetals.

In contrast with Rochelle salt, KH_2PO_4 has one Curie temperature, $T_c = 123°K$. Above the transition temperature it has a tetragonal structure (3 mutually perpendicular axes a, a, c); below T_c it is ortho-rhombic (3 mutually perpendicular axes a, b, c). The c-axis is the direction

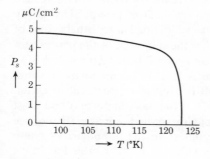

Fig. 8-4. The spontaneous polarization of KH_2PO_4 as function of temperature. [After A. von Arx and W. Bantle, *Helv. Phys. Acta*, **16**, 211 (1943)]

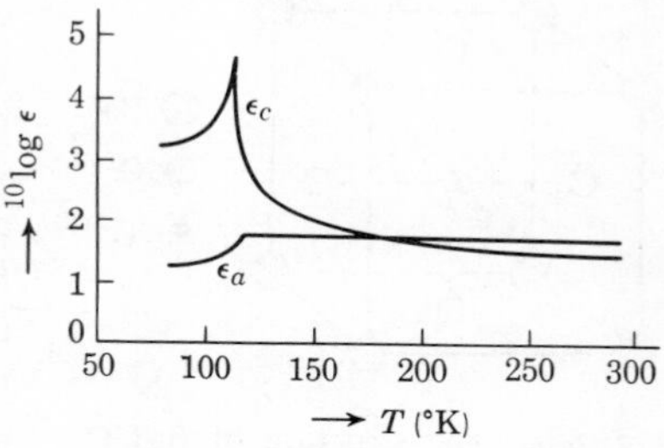

Fig. 8-5. The logarithm of the dielectric constants of KH_2PO_4 along the c- and a-axes. [After Busch, ref. 5]

along which the spontaneous polarization occurs and here, as in Rochelle salt, there is only one polar axis. The spontaneous polarization and the dielectric constant as function of temperature are given in Fig. 8-4 and Fig. 8-5. The dielectric constant above the Curie temperature follows the Curie-Weiss law (8-1) with the numerical values

$$\epsilon = 4.5 + 3100/(T - 121)$$

From an analysis of the structure of KH_2PO_4 it appears that the PO_4 groups form tetrahedrons with the four oxygens at the corners and the phosphorus at the center.[6] These phosphate groups are bound together by what is known as a hydrogen bond.[7] In these bonds, the proton may occupy a number of possible positions, each of which corresponds to a certain polarization of the unit cell. Recent experiments employing neutron diffraction confirm the important role played by these ions.

[5] G. Busch and P. Scherrer, *Naturwiss.*, **23**, 737 (1935); G. Busch, *Helv. Phys. Acta*, **11**, 269 (1938).

[6] B. C. Frazer and R. Pepinsky, *Acta Cryst.*, **6**, 273 (1953); S. W. Peterson, H. A. Levy, and S. H. Simonsen, *J. Chem. Phys.*, **21**, 2084 (1953); *Phys. Rev.*, **93**, 1120 (1954); G. E. Bacon and R. S. Pease, *Proc. Roy. Soc.* (*London*), **A220**, 397 (1953).

[7] See L. Pauling, *Nature of the Chemical Bond*, Cornell University Press, Ithaca, 1945.

Replacement of hydrogen by deuterium in KH_2PO_4 raises its Curie temperature from $123°$ to $213°K$, an increase of $90°C$.[8] It thus seems fairly certain that the hydrogen bonds are essential in the polarization of this group of ferroelectrics.

3. Wainer and Salomon in 1942 observed a number of anomalous dielectric properties of barium titanate ($BaTiO_3$). It was recognized in this country as a ferroelectric material by von Hippel and coworkers[9] and independently, by investigators in England, Holland, and Switzerland. This brings us to the third group of ferroelectrics, viz., the so-called oxygen octahedron group. This group can be subdivided into others, one of which is the subgroup of the perovskites with the general chemical formula ABO_3, where A is a di- or monovalent metal and B is a tetra- or pentavalent metal. $BaTiO_3$ is the most important and most thoroughly studied representative of the perovskites. In the nonpolarized phase it has cubic symmetry; the Ba^{2+} ions occupy the corners of a cube, the oxygen ions are located at the centers

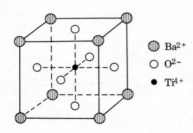

Fig. 8-6. The structure of $BaTiO_3$ in the cubic phase.

○○○ Ba^{2+}
○ O^{2-}
● Ti^{4+}

of the faces, and the Ti^{4+} ion is at the center (see Fig. 8-6). Typical for the $BaTiO_3$ structure and for the other members of this group is the arrangement of the highly polarizable oxygen ions in the form of an octahedron with a small metallic ion at the center.

Barium titanate has an upper transition temperature of $120°C$; above this temperature it is nonferroelectric and has the cubic structure of Fig. 8-6. In this region the dielectric constant is well described by the Curie-Weiss law,

$$\epsilon = 1.7 \times 10^5/(T - 393)$$

Below the Curie temperature, the direction of the spontaneous polarization and the crystal structure vary in the following fashion:

Temp. region (°K)	Dir. of pol.	Structure
278–393	[001]	tetragonal
193–278	[011]	orthorhombic
<193	[111]	rhombohedral

The transition points are evident from Fig. 8-7 and Fig. 8-8, representing, respectively, the dielectric constant and spontaneous polarization as

[8] B. T. Matthias, *Science*, **113**, 591 (1951); see also *Phase Transformations in Solids*, National Research Council, Wiley, New York, 1951.

[9] For a review, see A. von Hippel, *Revs. Mod. Phys.*, **22**, 221 (1950).

function of temperature.[10] Thus $BaTiO_3$ has three ferroelectric phases. As the spontaneous polarization sets in at 393°K, the crystal expands in the direction of polarization (c-axis) and contracts perpendicular to it (a-axis).

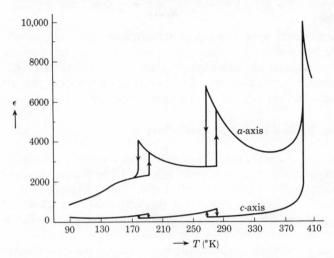

Fig. 8-7. The dielectric constant of $BaTiO_3$ as function of temperature. [After Merz, ref. 10]

In connection with Fig. 8-8 it should be mentioned that the spontaneous polarization was measured along the [001] direction, so that actually the values obtained in the regions $193° < T < 278°$ and $T < 193°K$ should

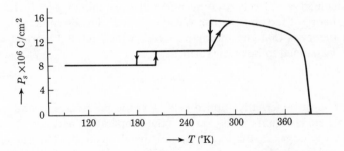

Fig. 8-8. The spontaneous polarization of $BaTiO_3$. [After Merz, ref. 10]

be multiplied, respectively, by $\sqrt{2}$ and $\sqrt{3}$. Thus the spontaneous polarization is nearly constant in the region below say 300°K.

It is interesting to note that the Curie temperature of barium-strontium titanate mixtures varies linearly with the lattice constant of the mixed

[10] W. J. Merz, *Phys. Rev.*, **76**, 1221 (1949).

crystals.[11] In this way Curie temperatures between 83°K and 393°K can be obtained.

Other compounds of the perovskite structure which are known to be ferroelectric are $KTaO_3$, $NaTaO_3$, $KNbO_3$ ($T_c = 708°K$) and $NaNbO_3$ ($T_c = 913°K$).

4. Recently a fourth group of ferroelectrics has been found which is unrelated to the groups mentioned above. This group is exemplified by guanidine aluminium sulfate hexahydrate, $NHC(NH_2)_2AlH(SO_4)_2 \cdot 6H_2O$.[12] The structure of these compounds is presently unknown; they apparently decompose before a Curie temperature is reached.

8-3. The dipole theory of ferroelectricity

In order to obtain some appreciation of the problems encountered in the interpretation of ferroelectricity, we shall first discuss the dipole theory of ferroelectricity in its simplest form. The existence of spontaneous polarization in general requires a physical model in which the dipole moments of the different unit cells are oriented along a common direction. This brings ferroelectrics in the class of cooperative phenomena, the cooperation between the different unit cells in this case consisting of a tendency for a given unit cell to have its dipole direction parallel to that of its neighbors. The dipole moment per unit cell may result partly from electronic and ionic displacements and partly from permanent dipoles. The early theories aimed at explaining the properties of Rochelle salt were based on the assumption that the permanent dipole moments of the H_2O groups were responsible for the spontaneous polarization.[13] These dipoles were assumed to be freely rotating, and a theory analogous to the Langevin-Weiss theory of ferromagnetism was developed. The essential point in the dipole theory is that the internal field E_i which tends to orient a given dipole is assumed to be of the form,

$$E_i = E + \gamma P \qquad (8-2)$$

where E is the externally applied field, P is the polarization, and γ is the internal field constant. This expresses the cooperation between the dipoles, because the larger P, the larger E_i and the stronger the tendency for the dipole under consideration to align itself in the direction of the polarization of its surroundings. For the high temperature region, an internal field of the form (8-2) indeed leads to the Curie-Weiss law (8-1), as may be seen in

---

[11] D. F. Rushman and M. A. Strivens, *Trans. Faraday Soc.*, **42A**, 231 (1946).

[12] G. Shirane, F. Jona, and R. Pepinsky, *loc. cit.*

[13] P. Kobeko and I. Kurchatov, *Z. Physik*, **66**, 192 (1930); R. H. Fowler, *Proc. Roy. Soc. (London)*, **149**, 1 (1935). It is illustrative to compare the dipole theory of ferro-electricity with the Bragg-Williams theory for order-disorder transitions in alloys (see Chapter 4).

the following manner. As long as one is far away from saturation of the polarization, one may write in accordance with (6-16)

$$P = N\mu \langle \cos \theta \rangle = N (\mu^2/3kT)E_i \qquad (8\text{-}3)$$

where N is the number of dipoles μ per unit volume.[14] From (8-2) and (8-3) it then follows that

$$\chi = P/E = \frac{N\mu^2/3kT}{1 - N\gamma\mu^2/3kT} = \frac{\theta/\gamma}{T - \theta} \qquad (8\text{-}4)$$

where the "extrapolated" Curie temperature $\theta = \gamma N\mu^2/3k$ and the Curie constant is θ/γ.

To show that (8-2) also leads to spontaneous polarization, we make use of the Langevin expression (6-15), which allows for saturation effects. Applied to the case under consideration, this gives

$$P = N\mu \langle \cos \theta \rangle = N\mu L \left(\frac{\mu E_i}{kT} \right)$$

$$= N\mu L \left[\frac{\mu}{kT} (E + \gamma P) \right] \qquad (8\text{-}5)$$

where $L(x)$ is the Langevin function. We may now ask, Does this equation provide a nonvanishing solution for P in the absence of an external field?

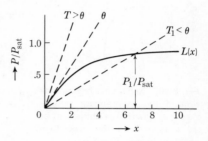

Fig. 8-9. The fully drawn curve represents the Langevin function; the dashed lines are those given by expression (8-7) for various temperatures. The slope of $L(x)$ at the origin is 1/3.

We shall see that the answer is positive, so that (8-2) indeed leads to the possibility of spontaneous polarization. Putting $E = 0$ in (8-5), we may write

$$P/N\mu = P/P_{\text{sat}} = L(x) \qquad (8\text{-}6)$$

where

$$x = \mu\gamma P/kT \quad \text{or} \quad P/N\mu = (kT/N\mu^2\gamma)x \qquad (8\text{-}7)$$

$N\mu = P_{\text{sat}}$ represents evidently the saturation polarization corresponding to complete alignment of the dipoles. In Fig. 8-9 we have represented P/P_{sat} as function of x according to (8-6), leading to $L(x)$. However, P/P_{sat} should also satisfy (8-7), which corresponds to a set of straight lines passing through the origin, the slope of the lines being given by $kT/N\mu^2\gamma$. A few of these lines have been represented in Fig. 8-9. Thus the solution for P/P_{sat} corresponding to the temperature T_1 is determined by the intersection of $L(x)$ and the line of slope $kT_1/N\mu^2\gamma$.[15] It is observed that as T

[14] For simplicity, the contributions to P resulting from electronic and ionic displacements will be neglected in this section, because it does not impair the essential arguments.

[15] It can be shown that the origin, which is also a common point of the straight line and the Langevin function, corresponds to an unstable physical state; P_1, however, corresponds to a stable physical state.

decreases, the slope of the straight line (8-7) decreases and the solution P/P_{sat} approaches unity. Also, when the temperature is higher than a critical value determined by

$$kT_c/N\mu^2\gamma = \tfrac{1}{3} \quad \text{or} \quad T_c = N\mu^2\gamma/3k = \theta \qquad (8\text{-}8)$$

it is observed that (8-6) and (8-7) intersect only at the origin. (Note that in this model $T_c = \theta$.) In other words, there is no spontaneous polarization for $T > \theta$. By means of the method outlined above, it is thus possible, to find P/P_{sat} as function of T/θ and the result is represented in Fig. 8-10. It is observed that just below the Curie temperature, the spontaneous polarization increases rapidly, in agreement with experiment. (Compare, for example, Fig. 8-4.)

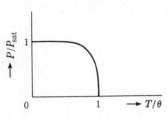

Fig. 8-10. Schematic representation of the spontaneous polarization as function of temperature, as derived from the procedure given in Fig. 8-9.

One may thus conclude that the assumption (8-2) for a model of freely rotating dipoles accounts for: (a) the Curie-Weiss law above the Curie temperature; (b) the possibility of spontaneous polarization below the Curie temperature; (c) qualitatively the correct temperature behavior of P/P_{sat} versus temperature in the ferroelectric region. It does not explain the existence of two Curie temperatures, observed in the case of Rochelle salt.

It may be of interest to point out the relation between the internal field constant γ appearing in the above theory and the anomalous peak in the specific heat as function of temperature observed for ferroelectrics in the vicinity of the Curie temperature. In the completely ordered state, when all dipoles are aligned in parallel, the energy of a given dipole in the field of all others is equal to $-\mu\gamma P_{sat}$ because in general the energy of a dipole $\boldsymbol{\mu}$ in a field E is given by $-\boldsymbol{\mu} \cdot E$. Thus the energy of polarization in the ordered state is per unit volume equal to $-N\mu\gamma P_{sat}/2$, where the factor of $\tfrac{1}{2}$ is introduced because otherwise the energy of each pair of dipoles would be counted twice. Now, as the temperature is increased to above the Curie temperature, the spontaneous polarization decreases to zero. It is evident that an "extra" amount of heat must be supplied to the crystal to bring about the transition from the completely ordered to the completely disordered state. Let C_e represent the extra specific heat per unit volume; we may then write

$$\int C_e (T)\, dT = N\mu\gamma P_{sat}/2 = \gamma P_{sat}^2/2 \qquad (8\text{-}9)$$

Thus, if $C_e(T)$ and P_{sat} are known from experiment, (8-9) allows one to calculate the internal field constant γ. However, γ may also be obtained from (8-4) if the Curie constant and the Curie temperature are known. According to Blattner and Merz one obtains the following results:[16]

	γ from (8-9)	γ from (8-4)
Rochelle salt.........	2.1	2.2
$BaTiO_3$	0.044	0.049
KH_2PO_4	0.37	0.48

It is observed that the agreement is rather good, especially because γ differs appreciably for the three substances. Blattner and Merz take this as an argument in favor of the internal field theory outlined above. It seems, however, that the agreement between (8-4) and (8-9) follows from much more general considerations than given here and the conclusion drawn is probably unjustified.[17]

8-4. Objections against the dipole theory

In connection with Rochelle salt, the following objections may be raised against the theory outlined in the preceding section: in the vapor, H_2O has a dipole moment of 1.85 Debye units; if we assume this to be the same in Rochelle salt, one calculates for the maximum spontaneous polarization

$$P_{\text{sat}} = N\mu = 1.52 \times 10^{22} \times 1.85 \times 10^{-18} = 28120 \text{ esu}$$

The experimental value is about 750 esu which is smaller by a factor of nearly 40. Furthermore, the dipole theory does not predict the existence of two Curie points, as observed for Rochelle salt.

A much more serious objection against the dipole theory is of a theoretical nature and refers to the use of the internal field given by equation (8-2). In fact, if the dipole theory based on (8-2) were correct, a large number of polar liquids should also be ferroelectric; we know, on the other hand, that ferroelectric materials are rare. The incorrectness of (8-2) was first pointed out by Onsager in 1936 and may be understood in the following way:[18] Consider a spherical cavity of molecular radius inside a dielectric in the absence of an external field. Suppose a dipole μ is located at the center of the cavity. The dipole will polarize the surrounding material and this in turn will produce a "reaction field" inside the cavity. If the dielectric is homogeneous, it can be shown that the reaction field E_r is homogeneous and parallel to the dipole μ.[19] It is evident

[16] H. Blattner and W. Merz, *Helv. Phys. Acta*, **21**, 210 (1948).
[17] For a discussion of this point see E. T. Jaynes, *Ferroelectricity*, Princeton University Press, Princeton, 1953, Chaps. 1, 3.
[18] L. Onsager, *J. Am. Chem. Soc.*, **58**, 1486 (1936); see also C. J. F. Böttcher, *Theory of Electric Polarization*, Elsevier, New York, 1952, pp. 63 ff.
[19] See, for example, C. J. F. Böttcher, *op. cit.*, Chap. 3; see also Problem 6-6.

that the reaction field does not exert a torque on the dipole. If one now applies to this system a homogeneous external field E and calculates the internal field by the Lorentz method, a part of the internal field is contributed by the timeaverage of the reaction field; this part is equal to $E_r\langle\cos\theta\rangle$ where θ is the angle between μ and E and, as emphasized above, does not produce a torque on the dipole. To find the actual field strength tending to orient the dipole, one must subtract the reaction field component in the external field direction. This may be done simply by first taking away the dipole and calculating the field inside the cavity. The field so obtained is called the cavity field and is equal to

$$E_c = [3\epsilon/(2\epsilon + 1)]E \qquad (8\text{-}10)$$

(Note that this is always smaller than the Lorentz field.) Making use of the formula $P/E = (\epsilon - 1)/4\pi$, we may write (8-10) in the form

$$E_c = E + 4\pi P/(2\epsilon + 1) = E + \gamma(\epsilon)P \qquad (8\text{-}11)$$

Comparing this expression with (8-2), one sees that γ is not a constant but that it depends on the dielectric constant in such a manner that as ϵ increases, γ decreases. Now, if instead of (8-2) one were to employ (8-10) as the field producing the torque on the dipoles, the possibility for spontaneous polarization disappears (see Problem 8-5). Although the above model is admittedly over-

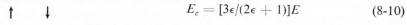

Fig. 8-11. Antiferroelectric arrangement of dipoles.

simplified and needs refinement, the arguments shed doubt on the validity of the dipole theory based on the internal field (8-2). In fact, calculations by Luttinger and Tisza on a model consisting of dipoles occupying the lattice points in a simple cubic structure indicate that the stable configuration for such a system contains alternate arrays of dipoles oriented in opposite directions (see Fig. 8-11).[20] Such arrangements of course, have no resultant polarization; they correspond to a so-called antiferroelectric arrangement.[21] Substances which appear to be antiferroelectrics are tungsten trioxide (WO_3) and lead zirconate ($PbZrO_3$).[22]

8-5. Ionic displacements and the behavior of BaTiO₃ above the Curie temperature

In Sec. 8-3 we have seen that the dipole theory, with an expression of the type (8-2) for the internal field, led to a Curie-Weiss law for the susceptibility above the Curie temperature. However, in Sec. 8-4 it was pointed

[20] J. M. Luttinger and L. Tisza, *Phys. Rev.*, **70**, 954 (1946); **72**, 257 (1947).

[21] C. Kittel, *Phys. Rev.*, **82**, 313, 729 (1951).

[22] S. Roberts, *Phys. Rev.*, **83**, 1078 (1951); E. Sawaguchi, H. Mariwa, and S. Hoshino, *Phys. Rev.*, **83**, 1078 (1951).

out that the internal field (8-2) could not be considered the field producing a torque on the dipoles. On the other hand, the objection of Onsager raised there does not refer to electronic and ionic displacements, and for these an internal field of type (8-2) may still be applied. In this section it will be shown that in case the dielectric constant of a material is large compared with unity, a Curie-Weiss law may be obtained which is solely due to electronic and ionic displacements.[23] At first sight this may seem somewhat surprising because one generally connects a strong temperature dependence of ϵ with the existence of permanent dipoles.

For the sake of argument, let us assume that for a particular nondipolar solid the Clausius-Mosotti expression holds (which is based on the Lorentz internal field formula):

$$(\epsilon - 1)/(\epsilon + 2) = (4\pi/3)\, N\alpha = \beta N \quad (8\text{-}12)$$

Here N represents the number of unit cells per cm³ and α represents the total polarizability per unit cell; it will be assumed that α is independent of temperature. As long as ϵ is of the order of 10 or smaller, any changes in N resulting from thermal expansion do not affect the value of ϵ to any great extent. On the other hand, if $\epsilon \gg 1$, the left-hand side

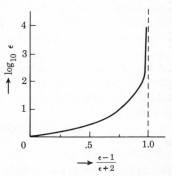

Fig. 8-12. The logarithm of the dielectric constant ε as function of the quantity $(\varepsilon - 1)/(\varepsilon + 2)$.

of (8-12) approaches unity and it is observed from Fig. 8-12 that small variations in βN may lead to large changes in the dielectric constant. In order to determine the temperature coefficient of ϵ, differentiate (8-12) with respect to T; this yields, after dividing through by N,

$$\frac{3}{(\epsilon + 2)(\epsilon - 1)}\frac{d\epsilon}{dT} = \frac{1}{N}\cdot\frac{dN}{dT} = -3\lambda \quad (8\text{-}13)$$

where λ is the linear coefficient of expansion of the solid. Making use of the fact that $\epsilon \gg 1$, so that $(\epsilon + 2)(\epsilon - 1) \simeq \epsilon^2$, one obtains

$$\int \frac{d\epsilon}{\epsilon^2} = -\int \lambda\, dT \quad \text{or} \quad \epsilon = \frac{1/\lambda}{T - \theta} \quad (8\text{-}14)$$

The last expression has indeed the form of the Curie-Weiss law; the Curie temperature θ enters as a constant of integration. It is of interest to note that the Curie constant is equal to the reciprocal of the linear coefficient of expansion. For $BaTiO_3$, $\lambda \simeq 10^{-5}$ per degree, which gives fair agreement with the experimental value for the Curie constant quoted in

[23] G. H. Jonker and J. H. van Santen, *Science*, **109**, 632 (1949).

Sec. 8-2. Although the assumption of the validity of the Clausius-Mosotti relation (8-12) for $BaTiO_3$ is doubtful, the simple arguments given here definitely indicate the importance of lattice expansion for the temperature dependence of the dielectric constant in case $\epsilon \gg 1$.

8-6. The theory of spontaneous polarization of $BaTiO_3$

Since ferroelectricity occurs in relatively few substances, it seems that the crystal structure of ferroelectrics is of paramount importance in any explanation of this phenomenon. It was first pointed out by Megaw that if one employs the Goldschmidt radii for the different ions in $BaTiO_3$ it is found that the space available for the Ti^{4+} ion inside the oxygen octahedron is somewhat larger than the size of this ion requires.[24] This observation has induced a number of theoretical attempts to explain the ferroelectricity of $BaTiO_3$ on the assumption that the Ti^{4+} ion plays an essential role. If one were to explain the spontaneous polarization of 50,000 esu solely on the basis of a displacement of Ti^{4+} ion, one would require a displacement d such that

$$4\ Ned = 50,000 \quad \text{or} \quad d \simeq 0.15 \times 10^{-8}\ cm$$

which seems not unreasonable. Actually, the required displacement would be less than this, because $BaTiO_3$ has a large index of refraction ($n = 2.4$ or $\epsilon_0 = 5.76$). In fact, if one assumes the Lorentz-Lorenz relation one obtains

$$(\epsilon - 1)/(\epsilon + 2) = (4\pi/3)\sum_i(N_i\alpha_{ei} + N_i\alpha_{ai}) = 0.62 + (4\pi/3)\sum_i N_i\alpha_{ai} \quad (8\text{-}15)$$

where α_{ei} and α_{ai} are the polarizabilities of the ions associated with electronic and ionic displacements, respectively.[23] Now, if the right-hand side of this expression becomes unity, ϵ becomes infinite, and spontaneous polarization will occur. Thus the Ti^{4+} displacement would have to account for less than 38 per cent of the total polarization.

One theory based on the assumption that the Ti^{4+} ions are mainly responsible for the ferroelectric properties of $BaTiO_3$ has been developed by Mason and Matthias.[25] These authors assume that the stable position for the Ti^{4+} is not in the center of the unit cell (Fig. 8-6) but that there exist six stable positions corresponding to slight displacements from the center toward the six surrounding oxygen ions. In each of these positions, the unit cell would thus bear a dipole moment. They furthermore assumed an internal field of the type (8-2) and essentially their theory is similar to the dipole theory discussed in Sec. 8-3. With this theory it is not

[24] H. D. Megaw, *Trans. Faraday Soc.*, **42A**, 224, 244 (1946).

[25] P. Mason and B. T. Matthias, *Phys. Rev.*, **74**, 1622 (1948); also W. P. Mason, *Piezoelectric Crystals and Their Applications in Ultrasonics*, Van Nostrand, New York, 1950.

possible, however, to obtain consistent agreement with experiment.[26] That a dipole theory for $BaTiO_3$ is hardly acceptable follows from the fact that the observed Curie constant is about 10^4 degrees absolute, whereas (8-4) gives $393/\gamma$, where γ is certainly larger than unity. Besides, the same objections as in Sec. 8-4 may be brought to bear.

Another type of theory that has been suggested does away with the assumption of permanent dipoles and is based solely on electronic and ionic displacements. The essential point of these theories consists of the calculation of the internal field at the positions of the different ions. We have seen already in the preceding chapter that the Lorentz field $E + (4\pi/3)P$ holds only when all atoms are surrounded cubically by others. This is the case for the Ba^{2+} and Ti^{4+} ions, but not for the oxygen ions in $BaTiO_3$. The interesting feature of this type of theory is that it brings in explicitly the peculiarities of the perovskite structure. Calculations of the internal field, which will not be given here, indicate that in the perovskite structure there exists a strong coupling between the Ti^{4+} and O^{2-} ions, leading to internal field constants about eight times as large as the usual $4\pi/3$ factor.[27] Thus the internal field at the position of the Ti^{4+} ion is very strong, and this, combined with the high charge and small restoring force of the Ti^{4+} ion, would lead to the conclusion that the perovskite structure is particularly favorable for ferroelectricity to occur. It must be emphasized, however, that in the calculations referred to above, the internal field is calculated at the position of the undisplaced ions. Actually, one is interested in the internal field at the position of the displaced ions. That this is a serious objection has been pointed out by Cohen, who showed that this may lead to an appreciable overestimation of the internal fields.[28] Also, the theories under consideration leave unexplained the pertinent experimental fact that as the temperature of $BaTiO_3$ is lowered, the direction of spontaneous polarization changes in the order [001], [011], [111].

A model which explains in a natural fashion the existence of the three transitions just mentioned is based on the assumption that the displacement of oxygen ions is essential in the understanding of $BaTiO_3$.[29] It was first pointed out by Devonshire that the restoring force for small oxygen displacements in a direction perpendicular to the plane of the four surrounding Ba^{2+} ions is probably very small.[30] This is a consequence of the fact that the O^{2-} ions are tightly squeezed between the Ba^{2+} ions. Now, with each unit cell one can associate three oxygen ions (because each of the

[26] For a discussion see for example E. T. Jaynes, *op. cit.*, Chap. 2.

[27] J. H. van Santen and W. Opechowski, *Physica*, **14**, 545 (1948); J. C. Slater, *Phys. Rev.*, **78**, 748 (1950).

[28] M. A. Cohen, *Phys. Rev.*, **84**, 368 (1951).

[29] E. T. Jaynes, *Phys. Rev.*, **79**, 1008 (1950).

[30] A. F. Devonshire, *Phil. Mag.*, **40**, 1040 (1949).

six ions belongs to two unit cells), which may be denoted by O_x, O_y and O_z. As the crystal is cooled from above the Curie point, the cubic lattice contracts and at the Curie point one of the three oxygen ions is squeezed out of the plane of the barium ions, let us say the ion O_z. This produces a dipole moment per unit cell along the z-axis, part of which is equal to $2ed_z$, where d_z is the displacement of the ion O_z relative to the plane of Ba^{2+} ions. At the same time, this allows for a possible contraction of the lattice in the plane of the barium ions. The direction of polarization corresponds to the c-axis of the tetragonal structure and sets in along one of the cube edges at the Curie temperature. As the temperature is lowered further, the O_y and O_x ions are successively squeezed out of their normal positions, leading to a polarization along a face diagonal [011] and a body diagonal [111], respectively, (by combination of their own effect with the polarization already existing). This model is in agreement with the changes of structure associated with the changes in polarization direction mentioned in Sec. 8-2. Also, X-ray diffraction studies have shown that the oxygen ions are indeed displaced by 0.08–0.1 Å relative to the Ba^{2+} ions; the displacement of the Ti^{4+} is about 0.06 Å according to these measurements (the cube edge of $BaTiO_3$ is 4.00 Å).[31] The essential feature of this model is that it combines the mechanical forces with the electric forces.

On the quantitative side, the following simple argument may be put forward: Experimentally it is found that in the tetragonal region the contraction of the lattice is proportional to the square of the polarization and satisfies the relation

$$\Delta a/a = 1.2 \times 10^{-12} P^2 \qquad (8\text{-}16)$$

where a is the cube edge just above the Curie point and Δa is the contraction in the tetragonal phase. Now, in the cubic phase, the sum of the radii of the Ba^{2+} and O^{2-} ions is equal to $a/\sqrt{2}$. Suppose now that the oxygen ion is displaced out of the plane of Ba^{2+} ions by an amount z and let it be assumed that the radii of the ions remain constant and that the oxygen and barium ions remain in contact. With reference to Fig. 8-13 it then follows that if $(a - \Delta a)$ is the new edge of the square of Ba^{2+} ions, we must have

$$(a - \Delta a)^2/2 = a^2/2 - z^2$$

As long as $\Delta a/a \ll 1$, this yields

$$\Delta a/a = (z/a)^2 \qquad (8\text{-}17)$$

The dipole moment per unit volume resulting only from the displaced oxygen ions is equal to $P_{O_z} = 2ez/a^3$ and it thus follows from (8-17) that

$$\Delta a/a = (a^4/4e^2)P_{O_z}^2 = 2.8 \times 10^{-12} P_{O_z}^2 \qquad (8\text{-}18)$$

[31] H. T. Evans, *Acta Cryst.*, **4**, 377 (1951); W. Känzig, *Helv. Phys. Acta*, **24**, 175 (1951).

Comparison of (8-16), and (8-18) shows that both expressions are of the same form, and that if P_{O_z} represents two thirds of the total polarization, the agreement is quantitative. Although the oxygen displacement theory has attractive features, recent neutron diffraction studies suggest that the oxygen octahedra suffer little distortion in passing through the transition, in contradiction with the theory. One must therefore conclude that the problem is still not solved satisfactorily.[32]

8-7. Thermodynamics of ferroelectric transitions

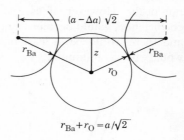

It is of interest to investigate the behavior of a ferroelectric in the vicinity of its transition temperature T_c on the basis of thermodynamic arguments. A thermodynamic theory has the advantage of being independent of any particular atomic model and thus leads to quite general conclusions. Although such a theory does not provide the physical

Fig. 8-13. Relative position of barium ions and displaced oxygen ions in a (110) plane.

mechanism responsible for the ferroelectric properties of a given material, it does point to certain features one should look for in atomic models. We shall now discuss the elements of the thermodynamic theory of ferroelectricity developed by Devonshire.[33]

Consider a solid which is ferroelectric for temperatures $T < T_c$; let the external pressure be zero and let there be no applied electric field. If the crystal is in equilibrium at a given temperature, the free energy of the crystal F should be a minimum. For simplicity we shall assume that in the ferroelectric region the spontaneous polarization occurs along a single axis; this would be the case for the Rochelle salt, KH_2PO_4, and for the upper transition of $BaTiO_3$. Let F_0 represent the free energy of the unpolarized crystal; the free energy F of the polarized crystal may then be expanded as a power series in the polarization

$$F - F_0 = \tfrac{1}{2}c_1 P^2 + \tfrac{1}{4}c_2 P^4 + \tfrac{1}{6}c_3 P^6 + \dots \qquad (8\text{-}19)$$

The coefficients c are functions of temperature; the numerical factors are introduced for later convience. Note that since we want the free energy to be the same for "positive" and "negative" polarization along the polar axis, only even powers of P are included. In thermal

[32] G. Shirane, F. Jona, and R. Pepinsky, *op. cit.*

[33] For a review of this work see A. F. Devonshire, "Theory of Ferroelectrics," *Advances in Physics* (quarterly suppl. of *Phil. Mag.*), **3**, April 1954, p. 85.

equilibrium $(\partial F/\partial P)_T = 0$ so that the spontaneous polarization satisfies the equation

$$0 = c_1 P_s + c_2 P_s^3 + c_3 P_s^5 + \ldots \qquad (8\text{-}20)$$

It is observed that $P_s = 0$ is always a root of this equation and that this will correspond to a minimum of the free energy if c_1 is positive. If c_1, c_2 and c_3 are all positive, the root $P_s = 0$ will correspond to the only minimum of the free energy and thus spontaneous polarization would not occur. However, if as a result of the temperature dependence the coefficient c_1 would become negative, F would have a maximum for $P_s = 0$ and there would be at least one nonvanishing value for P_s for which F would be a minimum, i.e., spontaneous polarization would occur.

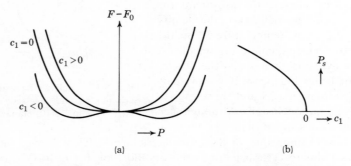

Fig. 8-14. Second-order transition. In (a) the free energy is given schematically as function of polarization for various values of c_1; in (b) the spontaneous polarization is represented as function of c_1. The critical temperature corresponds to $c_1 = 0$. [After Devonshire, ref. 33]

Consequently, if c_1 changes continuously with temperature from a positive to a negative value, the equilibrium of the crystal changes from an unpolarized to a spontaneously polarized state. In order to discuss the properties in the vicinity of the transition temperature, we shall consider two cases of particular interest.

(i) *Second-order transitions.* If the coefficients c_2, c_3, ... are all positive and the value of c_1 varies from positive to negative as the temperature is lowered, one obtains free energy curves as illustrated in Fig. 8-14a. The corresponding spontaneous polarization as function of temperature is indicated in Fig. 8-14b. The transition temperature corresponds to $c_1 = 0$. Assuming in (8-20) that the term with c_3 is negligible, one obtains for the spontaneous polarization,

$$P_s^2 = -c_1/c_2 \qquad . \qquad (8\text{-}21)$$

Note that P_s is a continuous function of temperature; a transition of this type is not associated with a latent heat but with a discontinuity in the specific heat and is called a *second-order transition*. We shall return to this point below.

Let us now consider the susceptibility of the crystal above and below the transition temperature. For this purpose it is necessary to apply a small electric field to the crystal. Now, for a crystal under zero pressure in an applied field E, we may write according to thermodynamics,

$$dF = -S \, dT + E \, dP \qquad (8\text{-}22)$$

Hence the applied field may be written $E = (\partial F/\partial P)_T$. Above the transition temperature the polarization will be small for small applied fields, and in this region we may neglect all terms on the right-hand side of (8-19) except the first. We thus obtain for $T > T_c$,

$$E = \partial F/\partial P = c_1 P \quad \text{and} \quad 1/\chi_a = dE/dP = c_1 \qquad (8\text{-}23)$$

where χ_a is the susceptibility above the critical temperature; the coefficient c_1 is evidently equal to the reciprocal of the susceptibility χ_a. However, we know that in this temperature range the susceptibility is given by the Curie-Weiss law $\chi_a = C/(T - \theta)$, so that $c_1 = (T - \theta)/C$, where C is the Curie constant. However, since the transition at T_c corresponds to $c_1 = 0$, we have $\theta = T_c$ and thus

$$c_1 = (T - T_c)/C = 1/\chi_a \qquad (8\text{-}24)$$

In the ferroelectric region we obtain likewise from (8-19) and (8-23),

$$E = c_1 P + c_2 P^3 \quad \text{or} \quad 1/\chi_b = dE/dP = c_1 + 3c_2 P^2 \qquad (8\text{-}25)$$

where χ_b is the susceptibility below the transition temperature; the terms with powers $\geqslant 6$ have been neglected in (8-19). For small applied fields, $P \simeq P_s$ in this region, so that according to (8-25) and (8-21) we have

$$1/\chi_b = -2c_1 \qquad (8\text{-}26)$$

If we assume that the temperature dependence of c_1 on the ferroelectric side of T_c is still given by (8-24), we obtain

$$1/\chi_b = 2(T_c - T)/C \qquad (8\text{-}27)$$

The temperature dependence of the reciprocal of the susceptibility on both sides of the transition temperature as given by (8-24) and (8-27) is illustrated in Fig. 8-15a. Note that the slope in the ferroelectric region is twice that above the transition temperature.

In connection with the remark made above that the transition under discussion is of the second order, let us consider the entropy associated with the spontaneous polarization. According to (8-22) and (8-19), the entropy is given by

$$S = -(\partial F/\partial T)_P = S_0 - \tfrac{1}{2}P^2(\partial c_1/\partial T) - \tfrac{1}{4}P^4(\partial c_2/\partial T) + \cdots$$

where S_0 is the entropy of the unpolarized crystal. To a first approximation we may then write

$$S - S_0 \simeq -\tfrac{1}{2}P^2(\partial c_1/\partial T) \qquad (8\text{-}28)$$

Since P is a continuous function of temperature for the case under consideration and since the slope of P^2 has a discontinuity at $T = T_c$, there

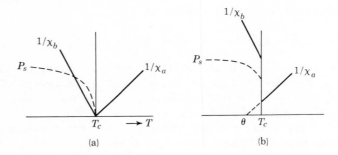

Fig. 8-15. Reciprocal susceptibility near the critical temperature. (a) For a second-order transition; (b) for a first-order transition. The corresponding spontaneous polarizations are indicated by the dashed curves; in (a) P_s is continuous, in (b) discontinuous at T_c.

should be a discontinuity in the specific heat, but no latent heat, i.e., the transition is of the second order. This type of transition is observed in Rochelle salt and in KH_2PO_4.

(ii) *First-order transitions*. We have seen that spontaneous polarization requires the coefficient c_1 to be negative. Furthermore, we have seen that if at the same time c_2 is positive, a second-order transition results. We shall now consider the case for which c_2 is negative and c_3 is positive. Under these circumstances it is possible for the free energy curves to have a minimum value for a nonzero value of the polarization to coexist with a minimum for $P_s = 0$. Assuming that c_1 varies from positive to negative values as the temperature is lowered, one obtains free energy curves of the type indicated in Fig. 8-16a. A transition from the nonpolarized state to a spontaneously polarized state will now occur when the minimum of the free energy corresponding to $P_s = 0$ becomes equal to the minimum associated with a nonzero value for P_s. It will be evident that in this case the polarization jumps at the critical temperature from zero to some nonzero value, i.e., the polarization as function of temperature exhibits a discontinuity at $T = T_c$ as shown in Fig. 8-16b. According to (8-28), the entropy will also be discontinuous at $T = T_c$ and there will be a latent heat, i.e., the transition is of the first order.

In the absence of an external field we obtain from the equilibrium condition $(\partial F/\partial P)_T = 0$ and from (8-19) for the nonvanishing value of the spontaneous polarization the equation

$$0 = c_1 + c_2 P_s^2 + c_3 P_s^4 + \cdots \qquad (8\text{-}29)$$

At the critical temperature T_c the quantity $P_s(T_c)$ should satisfy (8-29)

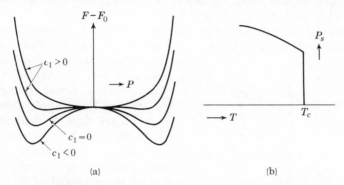

Fig. 8-16. First-order transition. In (a) the free energy is represented as function of P for different values of c_1. In (b) the spontaneous polarization is given as function of T; note the discontinuity at T_c. [After Devonshire, ref. 33]

as well as the condition mentioned above that $F(T_c) = F_0(T)$. According to (8-19) we thus have also

$$0 = \tfrac{1}{2}c_1 P_s^2(T_c) + \tfrac{1}{4}c_2 P_s^4(T_c) + \tfrac{1}{6}c_3 P_s^6(T_c) + \cdots \qquad (8\text{-}30)$$

From this equation and (8-29) as applied to the critical temperature we then find the relations

$$P_s^2(T_c) = -\tfrac{3}{4}(c_2/c_3); \quad c_1 = \tfrac{3}{16}(c_2^2/c_3); \quad P_s^4(T_c) = 3c_1/c_3 \qquad (8\text{-}31)$$

The first of these results shows that the polarization is discontinuous at the critical temperature (Fig. 8-16b).

We shall now consider the susceptibility on both sides of the critical temperature. As in case (i), the coefficient c_1 in the region above the temperature T_c is again equal to $1/\chi_a$. In this region the susceptibility follows the Curie-Weiss law, so that

$$\chi_a = C/(T - \theta) \quad \text{and} \quad c_1 = (T - \theta)/C \qquad (8\text{-}32)$$

where θ is somewhat smaller than T_c, as mentioned in Sec. 8-1. We leave it to the reader to show that by similar arguments as used under (i) and by making use of the relations (8-31) we find for the susceptibility below the critical temperature,

$$1/\chi_b = 4c_1 \qquad (8\text{-}33)$$

At the critical temperature c_1 is, according to (8-32), equal to $(T_c - \theta)/C$ and the susceptibilities just above and just below T_c are given by

$$1/\chi_a = (T_c - \theta)/C \quad \text{and} \quad 1/\chi_b = 4(T_c - \theta)/C \quad \text{for} \quad T = T_c \quad (8\text{-}34)$$

The reciprocal susceptibility as one passes through the transition temperature is illustrated in Fig. 8-15b.

We should mention here that decisive evidence as to whether a particular ferroelectric transition is of the first order may be obtained from a so-called "double loop" experiment in which the transition is induced slightly above the critical temperature T_c by application of a strong electric field. Such an induced transition was first produced by Roberts in ceramic material and has more recently been demonstrated for a good single crystal of $BaTiO_3$ by Merz.[34] A strong a-c field is applied to the crystal a few degrees above its normal transition temperature. At zero applied field the crystal is nonferroelectric but at a critical value of the applied field the polarization increases rapidly and upon reversal of the field hysteresis is observed. The hysteresis loop is not complete, however, and for low applied fields the behavior is normal again (see Fig. 8-17). A double hysteresis loop obtained in this manner can only occur if the transition is of the first order, as may be understood in the following manner: In the absence of an applied field the transition occurs when in Fig. 8-16a the minimum of the free energy for $P_s = 0$ is equal to the minimum associated with nonvanishing value of the spontaneous polarization. For a crystal subjected to a field E, however, the induced transition occurs when $F - EP$ rather than F has the same value as the minimum at the origin. Such induced transitions can evidently occur only if the free energy curves are of the type illustrated in Fig. 8-16a and not if they are of the type corresponding to Fig. 8-14a. Hence the double loop experiment distinguishes between first- and second-order transitions. Since a

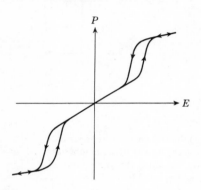

Fig. 8-17. Schematic representation of a double hysteresis loop, of the type observed for $BaTiO_3$, slightly above the transition temperature.

[34] S. Roberts, *Phys. Rev.*, **85**, 925 (1952); W. J. Merz, *Phys. Rev.*, **91**, 513 (1953).

double loop has been observed for $BaTiO_3$, the upper transition of this material is evidently of the first order. We should note that it is usually not possible to obtain a clear-cut distinction between a first- or second-order transition from measurement of the spontaneous polarization as function of temperature, since P_s rises rapidly just below T_c even for a second-order transition. For further details on the thermodynamic theory of ferroelectricity and for a treatment of antiferroelectric transitions we refer the reader to A. F. Devonshire, *op. cit.*

8-8. Ferroelectric domains

It was mentioned in Sec. 8-2 that when a Rochelle salt crystal is cooled to below the Curie temperature, spontaneous polarization along the *a*-axis of the orthorhombic structure sets in. In general, however, the direction of spontaneous polarization is not the same throughout the crystal; certain regions are polarized in the $+a$ direction, others in the $-a$ direction. These regions are referred to as domains. The boundaries between domains are called domain walls. In a Rochelle salt crystal the domains are polarized in opposite directions. For KH_2PO_4 there is also only one axis along which spontaneous polarization takes place, viz., the *c*-axis of the tetragonal structure. The domain structure is thus similar to that of Rochelle salt. In the case of $BaTiO_3$, spontaneous polarization may occur along any one of the three edges, leading to six possible directions for the spontaneous polarization. The domain structure for $BaTiO_3$ is therefore more complicated than in the other two groups of ferroelectrics.

The ferroelectric domains are the electrical analogues of the Weiss domains in ferromagnetic materials, although there are certain interesting differences in their formation and growth, as we shall see below. The existence of domains, which has been confirmed by X-ray investigations and optical studies[35], explains the possibility for a crystal below the Curie temperature to have a zero or very small total polarization. By applying an electric field to such a crystal, the number and size of domains polarized in the external field direction may be increased. This process leads, upon reversal of the field direction, to hysteresis in the P versus E curves, and gives rise to dielectric losses. These losses are proportional to the area of the hysteresis loop and to the frequency of the applied a-c field.

Optical observation of ferroelectric domains is possible since ferroelectrics are birefringent. In $BaTiO_3$ for example, the optical axis coincides with the direction of spontaneous polarization. Thus a domain polarized in a direction perpendicular to the surface of a crystal plate looks dark

[35] B. T. Matthias and A. von Hippel, *Phys. Rev.*, **73**, 1378 (1948); P. W. Forsbergh, *Phys. Rev.*, **76**, 1187 (1949); Blattner, Känzig, Merz, and Sutter, *Helv. Phys. Acta*, **21**, 207 (1948); W. J. Merz, *Phys. Rev.*, **95**, 690 (1954).

through a microscope between crossed nicols. On the other hand, a domain polarized in a direction parallel to the surface appears bright between crossed nicols, except when the direction of polarization of the light is parallel or perpendicular to the domain polarization. It is thus possible to see the domains and to study changes in the domain structure. In barium titanate the direction of polarization of neighboring domains differs either by 90° or by 180°; this is a consequence of the three mutually perpendicular axes along which spontaneous polarization may occur. In this connection one speaks of 90° and 180° walls. The latter can be observed only when the crystals are strained, by an external electric field or by mechanical stresses.

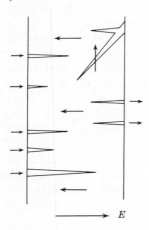

Fig. 8-18. Schematic representation of new antiparallel domains resulting from application of an external field E.

A number of interesting experiments on the formation of domains and the motion of domain walls in $BaTiO_3$ have been carried out by Merz.[36] His work shows that when an electric field is applied in a direction opposite to that of the spontaneous polarization, a large number of new needle shaped domains of about 10^{-4} cm width are created (Fig. 8-18). These new domains grow essentially in the forward direction rather than sideways. This behavior is quite different from that of ferromagnetic materials, where the change in direction of magnetization is accomplished by the growth of domains which have the right direction of magnetization, the growth resulting from a sidewise motion of the domain walls. This indicates that the forward coupling of the electric dipoles is much stronger than the sidewise coupling. At this point the reader may be reminded of the remarks made at the end of Sec. 8-4, with reference to the calculations of Tisza and Luttinger.[20] Merz has given some semiquantitative arguments which confirm this behavior: when one estimates the energy per cm² of a domain wall between antiparallel domains and minimizes this with respect to the thickness of the wall, it is found that the wall thickness is of the order of a few lattice distances. In contrast with this, the wall thickness in a ferromagnetic material is of the order of 300 lattice constants. Thus to move a domain wall in $BaTiO_3$ sidewise over one lattice distance requires an energy which is about equal to the energy of the wall itself. In a ferromagnetic material, it takes roughly 1/300 of the total wall energy to displace the wall over one lattice distance.

For Rochelle salt and for KH_2PO_4 it has also been found that

[36] W. J. Merz, *Phys. Rev.*, **95**, 690 (1954).

the wall thickness is considerably smaller than for ferromagnetic materials.[37]

In view of the absence, or at least infrequent occurrence, of a sidewise motion of the domain walls in ferroelectric materials, the problem of nucleation of the needle shaped new domains becomes of primary importance for the understanding of the reversal of polarization in an external field.

REFERENCES

W. G. Cady, *Piezoelectricity*, McGraw-Hill, New York, 1946.

A. F. Devonshire, "Theory of Ferroelectrics," *Advances in Physics* (quarterly supplement of *Phil. Mag.*). Vol. 3, April 1954. p. 85.

P. W. Forsbergh jr., "Piezoelectricity, Electrostriction and Ferro-electricity," *Encyclopedia of Physics*, Springer, Berlin, 1956, vol. 17, pp. 264–391.

E. T. Jaynes, *Ferroelectricity*, Princeton University Press, Princeton, 1953.

W. P. Mason, *Piezoelectric Crystals and their Application to Ultrasonics*, Van Nostrand, New York, 1950.

G. Shirane, F. Jona, and R. Pepinsky, "Some Aspects of Ferroelectricity," *Proc. IRE*, December, 1955. p. 1738.

PROBLEMS

8-1. Let P be the spontaneous polarization of a ferroelectric solid and let γP be the internal field. Show that the "extra specific heat" of the material is given by $C = -(\gamma/2)(dP^2/dT)$. For the dipole theory, draw the curve for specific heat versus temperature and show that at the critical temperature the specific heat is equal to $3k/2$ per dipole.

8-2. In the theory of Mason and Matthias[25] of ferroelectricity of barium titanate it is assumed that the Ti^{4+} ion has six stable positions corresponding to small displacements from the center of the unit cell toward the six surrounding oxygen ions. If the absolute value of the dipole moment due to this displacement is μ, show that in a field applied parallel to a cube edge, the polarization due to these dipoles is given by

$$P_d = N\mu \, \frac{\sinh{(\mu E_i/kT)}}{\cosh{(\mu E_i/kT)} + 2}$$

where N is the number of unit cells per unit volume and E_i is the internal field. Introduce the approximation $\mu E_i \ll kT$ and compare the result with

[37] T. Mitsui and J. Furuichi, *Phys. Rev.*, **90**, 193 (1953); W. Känzig and R. Sommerhalder, *Helv. Phys. Acta*, **26**, 603 (1953).

that for freely rotating dipoles. Assume further that the internal field is given by $E_i = E + \gamma(P_d + \alpha E_i)$ where α represents the polarizability per unit volume with the exclusion of the Ti^{4+} displacements. Show that spontaneous polarization can occur only below a critical temperature $T_c = (\gamma N \mu^2/3k)/(1 - \gamma\alpha)$. Show further that the dielectric constant of the material is given by

$$\epsilon = 1 + \frac{4\pi}{1 - \gamma\alpha}\left(\alpha + \frac{1}{\gamma}\cdot\frac{T_c}{T - T_c}\right)$$

8-3. Discuss an experimental method for growing large platelike single crystals of $BaTiO_3$. (See J. P. Remeika, *J. Am. Chem. Soc.*, **76**, 940 (1954).)

8-4. Discuss the results of X-ray and neutron diffraction studies of ferro- and antiferroelectric materials. See, for example, G. Shirane, F. Jona, and R. Pepinsky, *op. cit.*

8-5. Consider a system of dipoles and assume that the field acting on a given dipole is equal to the cavity field (8-11). If there are N dipoles per cm³, show that the dielectric constant of the system is

$$\epsilon = 1 + \tfrac{3}{4}[4\pi N\alpha - 1 + (1 + 8\pi N\alpha/3 + 16\pi^2 N^2\alpha^2)^{1/2}]$$

where $\alpha = \mu^2/3\,kT$. This shows that ϵ remains finite for any finite temperature, i.e., the system is nonferroelectric.

Chapter 9

FREE ELECTRON THEORY OF METALS

In this chapter the free electron theory of metals as developed by Sommerfeld and others will be discussed. Conductivity, Hall effect and other transport phenomena will be treated separately in Chapter 11. The discussions assume the reader's familiarity with the material pertaining to Appendixes B, C, D, and E. A reference such as D-7 stands for formula 7, Appendix D, etc.

It must be emphasized that in the model employed below, the existence of free electrons is assumed. The question dealing with the reasons for the occurrence of conduction electrons in certain materials and not in others is deferred until the next chapter.

9-1. Difficulties of the classical theory

The outstanding properties of metals are their high electrical and thermal conductivities. Thus, soon after the discovery of the electron, a number of investigators, in particular Drude and Lorentz, attempted an explanation of these properties on the basis of the assumption that a metal contains a certain number of "free" electrons. The free electrons were supposed to be able to move through the lattice, thereby suffering collisions with the atoms (see Chapter 11). These theories were developed at the turn of the century and, of course, employed Boltzmann statistics. One of the greatest achievements of these theories was that they led to semiquantitative agreement with the Wiedemann-Franz law, discussed in Chapter 11.

There existed, however, a number of serious difficulties in the classical electron theory, one of which was the following: According to classical statistical mechanics, the average kinetic energy of a free electron is $3kT/2$. Thus if a metal contains N free electrons per gram atom, the total kinetic energy of the electrons should be $3NkT/2$. Associated with this is a specific heat of $3Nk/2$ per gram atom. Now, from measured values of the optical reflection coefficient of metals, one had to assume that the number of free electrons is of the order of one per atom. This corresponds to an electronic specific heat of $3R/2 \simeq 3$ cal per gram atom per degree. On the other hand, the specific heat (at high temperatures) associated with the lattice vibrations is $3R$ per gram atom. One therefore concludes that the specific heat of metals should be about 50 per cent higher than for insulators. However, experiments show that any specific heat associated with the electron gas is very small. Another difficulty encountered in the classical theory, and intimately related to the one just mentioned, pertains to the magnetic properties of the free electrons. Each electron has a magnetic moment associated with its spin, and classically, should therefore give rise to a paramagnetic susceptibility inversely proportional to the temperature. Experimental results, on the other hand, show that the paramagnetism of metals is nearly independent of temperature.

We shall see below that both difficulties are removed when quantum statistics is used.

9-2. The free electron model

An electron in a metal, or for that matter in any solid, finds itself in the field of all nuclei and all other electrons. The potential energy for

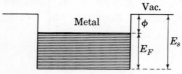

such an electron may therefore be expected to be periodic, the periodicity being that of the lattice. In the model employed by Sommerfeld, however, it is assumed that the "free" electrons, i.e., those giving rise to the conductivity, find themselves in a potential which is constant everywhere inside the metal.[1] Since one does not observe electron emission from metals at room temperature, it seems evident that the potential energy of an electron at rest inside the metal must be lower than that

Fig. 9-1. The Sommerfeld model. E_s is the energy difference between an electron at rest inside the metal and one at rest in vacuum. At $T = 0$, all energy levels up to E_F are filled, all higher ones are empty (see Sec. 9-3); the work function $\phi = E_s - E_F$.

of an electron at rest outside the metal. This is confirmed by relatively simple theoretical arguments.[2] The change in potential energy of an electron E_s as one crosses the metal-vacuum boundary may, for a number of problems, be considered abrupt (see Fig. 9-1). For some problems, however, it is necessary to consider the variation of potential at the surface in some more detail (see Sec. 9-8). One thus arrives at a physical model in which the interior of the metal is represented by a potential energy box of depth E_s as indicated in Fig. 9-1; the energy of an electron at rest outside the metal is used as a reference and is commonly referred to as the vacuum level.

It may be of interest to note that E_s may be determined experimentally from electron diffraction experiments with slow electrons (a few hundred ev). An electron impinging on the metal from the outside with an initial

---

[1] A. Sommerfeld, *Z. Physik*, **47**, 1 (1928); see also the article by A. Sommerfeld and H. Bethe, *Handbuch der Physik*, Vol. 24/2.

[2] See, for example, H. Fröhlich, *Elektronen Theorie der Metalle*, Springer, Berlin, 1936, p. 11.

energy E_0 gains an amount E_s upon entering the metal. It may be shown (see Problem 9-1) that the position of the diffraction maxima is determined by the quantity $[(E_0 + E_s)/E_0]^{1/2}$. Thus from a knowledge of the lattice structure and E_0, it is possible to determine E_s. For nickel one has found in this way $E_s = 14.8$ ev.[3] In general, E_s is of the order of 10 ev.

In the Sommerfeld model, the free electrons are assumed to be the valence electrons of the composing atoms. Thus the alkali metals are assumed to contain one free electron per atom; aluminum supposedly has three free electrons per atom.

The first problem to be discussed now is the energy distribution of a "free electron gas" with a density of the order of 10^{22} per cm³.

9-3. The Fermi-Dirac distribution

For convenience let us define the energy of a free electron at rest inside the metal as zero, i.e., we choose the bottom of the potential energy box as a reference. According to Appendix B the possible energy levels for an electron are then given by

$$E = p^2/2m = (\hbar^2\pi^2/2mV^{2/3})(n_x^2 + n_y^2 + n_z^2) \tag{9-1}$$

where V is the volume of the metal and n_x, n_y, n_z are integers $\geqslant 1$. Each

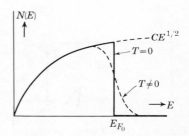

Fig. 9-2. The curve $CE^{1/2}$ represents $Z(E)$ in accordance with (9-3); the energy distribution $N(E)$ is obtained by multiplying $Z(E)$ by $F(E)$.

set of integers n_x, n_y, n_z defines an allowed wave function of the spatial coordinates x, y, z. From this, it can be shown that the number of allowed wave functions corresponding to a momentum range between p and $p + dp$ is equal to $4\pi p^2\,dp\,V/h^3$ (see Appendix B). Taking into account the fact that the electron has a spin which can accept two possible values, one concludes that the number of possible states (i.e., wave functions including the spin) corresponding to a momentum range dp is equal to

$$Z(p)\,dp = 8\pi p^2\,dp\,V/h^3 \tag{9-2}$$

It is frequently convenient to have an expression for the number of allowed states in an energy range between E and $E + dE$. This may readily be obtained from (9-2) by replacing $p^2/2m$ by E, yielding

$$Z(E)\,dE = CE^{1/2}\,dE \quad \text{with} \quad C = 4\pi V(2m)^{3/2}/h^3 \tag{9-3}$$

The function $Z(E)$ is represented schematically in Fig. 9-2. To find the states actually occupied by the free electrons at a temperature T, we must

[3] C. Davisson and L. H. Germer, *Phys. Rev.*, **30**, 705 (1927); H. Bethe, *Ann. Physik*, **87**, 60 (1928).

make use of Fermi-Dirac statistics because electrons obey the Pauli exclusion principle. Denoting the number of electrons occupying states between E and $E + dE$ by $N(E)\,dE$, we find from (D-10),

$$N(E)\,dE = Z(E)F(E)\,dE \quad \text{with} \quad F(E) = \frac{1}{e^{\alpha + E/kT} + 1} \qquad (9\text{-}4)$$

where α is a parameter and $F(E)$ is called the Fermi function. Note that $F(E)$ simply represents the fraction of possible states which is occupied. When there is about one free electron per atom in the metal, the electron gas may be expected to be highly degenerate at room temperature. This implies that $e^{\alpha} < 1$ and we shall therefore write (see Appendix D)

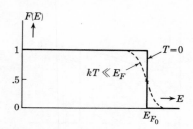

$$e^{\alpha} = e^{-E_F/kT} \qquad (9\text{-}5)$$

where E_F is called the Fermi energy; its physical meaning will become clear below. With this notation we may write

$$F(E) = \frac{1}{e^{(E - E_F)/kT} + 1} \qquad (9\text{-}6)$$

Fig. 9-3. The Fermi distribution function $F(E)$ at absolute zero and at a temperature $T \ll E_F/k$.

In discussing the energy distribution it is convenient to distinguish between different temperature ranges:

1. $T = 0$. At absolute zero, the Fermi function has the property

$$F(E) = 1 \quad \text{for} \quad E < E_{F_0}$$

$$F(E) = 0 \quad \text{for} \quad E > E_{F_0} \qquad (9\text{-}7)$$

Thus at absolute zero, all possible states below E_{F_0} are occupied, all those above E_{F_0} are empty. The physical meaning of E_{F_0} is, therefore, that it represents the highest occupied energy level at $T = 0$ (see Figs. 9-2 and 9-3). It is of interest to calculate E_{F_0} in terms of the number of free electrons per unit volume. In general, one must satisfy the condition

$$\int_0^{\infty} N(E)\,dE = \int_0^{\infty} Z(E)F(E)\,dE = N \qquad (9\text{-}8)$$

In view of (9-7) and (9-3) this gives

$$N = C \int_0^{E_{F_0}} E^{1/2}\,dE \quad \text{or} \quad E_{F_0} = \frac{h^2}{2m}\left(\frac{3n}{8\pi}\right)^{2/3} \qquad (9\text{-}9)$$

Note that E_{F_0} is determined essentially by the number n of electrons per unit volume. Values for E_{F_0} calculated from (9-9) for a number of metals are given in Table 9-1. It is observed that E_{F_0} is of the order of several electron volts. This brings out the very significant difference between classical statistics and Fermi statistics. In the former case, all electrons would have zero energy. For "classical electrons" to have an energy of 1 ev, a temperature of about 5000°K would be required.

Table 9-1. Fermi Energy Calculated from (9-9) and Work Function
φ (Exp.) for Some Metals

Metal	Valence	E_{F_0} (ev)	ϕ (ev)
Na	1	3.1	2.28
K	1	2.1	2.22
Cu	1	7.0	4.45
Ag	1	5.5	4.46
Ba	2	3.8	2.51
Al	3	11.7	4.20

The average kinetic energy of the electrons at absolute zero may be calculated from

$$\langle E_0 \rangle = \frac{1}{N} \int_0^{E_{F_0}} E Z(E)\, dE = \tfrac{2}{5} C E_{F_0}^{5/2} / N \qquad (9\text{-}10)$$

From this and (9-9) one readily finds by eliminating C that

$$\langle E_0 \rangle = \tfrac{3}{5} E_{F_0} \qquad (9\text{-}11)$$

2. $kT \ll E_F$. For all temperatures below the melting point of metals kT is small compared with E_F (kT at room temperature is only 0.025 ev). It follows from the definition of the Fermi function (9-6) that for $E = E_F$, $F = \frac{1}{2}$. Hence the physical meaning of E_F may be stated: at the Fermi level, the probability for occupation is $\frac{1}{2}$. An example of the Fermi function at $T > 0$ is given by the dashed curve in Fig. 9-3. For energies below E_F such that $(E_F - E) \gg kT$, the value of $F(E)$ is still practically unity, i.e., the energy distribution in that region is the same as that for $T = 0$. It is only in the vicinity of E_F minus a few kT that $F(E)$ begins to drop below the value at $T = 0$.

For energies above E_F, such that $(E - E_F) \gg kT$, one may neglect the term 1 in the denominator of (9-6) and one obtains

$$F(E) \simeq e^{-(E - E_F)/kT} \quad \text{for} \quad E - E_F \gg kT \qquad (9\text{-}12)$$

Thus, in this region, the Fermi distribution becomes identical with a Boltzmann distribution; one speaks in this connection of the "Boltzmann tail."

The Fermi level and the average kinetic energy of the electrons in this case are determined by the integrals

$$N = \int_0^\infty Z(E) \frac{dE}{e^{(E - E_F)/kT} + 1} \qquad (9\text{-}13)$$

$$\langle E \rangle = \frac{1}{N} \int_0^\infty Z(E) \frac{E\, dE}{e^{(E - E_F)/kT} + 1} \qquad (9\text{-}14)$$

The evaluation of these integrals may be found elsewhere and it may suffice here to give the results:[4]

$$E_F \simeq E_{F_0} \left[1 - \frac{\pi^2}{12} \left(\frac{kT}{E_{F_0}} \right)^2 \right] \tag{9-15}$$

$$\langle E \rangle \simeq \langle E_0 \rangle \left[1 + \frac{5\pi^2}{12} \left(\frac{kT}{E_{F_0}} \right)^2 \right] \tag{9-16}$$

where the subscripts 0 refer to the quantities at $T = 0$. It is observed that as T increases E_F decreases and $\langle E \rangle$ increases slightly. The smallness of the changes follows immediately from the occurrence of the factor $(kT/E_{F_0})^2$. For example, with $E_{F_0} \simeq 5$ ev, this factor is $\sim 2 \times 10^{-5}$ at room temperature. For many practical purposes, therefore, the Fermi level may be considered a constant.

9-4. The electronic specific heat

The expression for the average energy of an electron (9-16) has an important consequence for the specific heat problem mentioned in Sec. 9-1. In fact, it follows immediately from (9-16) that the specific heat at constant volume per electron is given by

$$c_V = d\langle E \rangle / dT \simeq 5\pi^2 k^2 T \langle E_0 \rangle / 6E_{F_0}^2$$

Making use of (9-11) this may be written

$$c_V = \pi^2 (kT/2E_{F_0}) k = \pi^2 (T/2T_F) k \tag{9-17}$$

where T_F is the Fermi temperature defined by $kT_F = E_F$. Thus for $E_{F_0} \simeq 5$ ev one finds at room temperature an electronic specific heat of about $k/40$, which may be compared with the classical value of $3k/2$. The use of Fermi-Dirac statistics thus removes the specific heat difficulty encountered in the classical theory. It is of interest to note that the electronic specific heat rises linearly with T. Now, at low temperatures, the specific heat associated with the lattice vibrations is proportional to T^3, so that the total specific heat of a metal may be represented by

$$C_V = AT + BT^3 \tag{9-18}$$

This expression is, at least qualitatively, in agreement with experiment. At sufficiently low temperatures the linear term predominates and this allows one to determine the electronic specific heat term from experiment. For copper, for example, Kok and Keesom find $A = 1.78$ cal/mole/deg².[5]

[4] See, for example, F. Seitz, *Modern Theory of Solids*, McGraw-Hill, New York, 1940, pp. 146ff. For numerical tables involving integrals of the type (9–13) see J.McDougall and E. C. Stoner, *Phil. Trans.*, **A237**, 67 (1929).

[5] J. A. Kok and W. H. Keesom, *Physica*, **3**, 1035 (1936); **4**, 835 (1937).

When one calculates the coefficient A on the basis of (9-17) and uses $E_{F_0} = 7.04$ ev, calculated from (9-9), one obtains $A = 1.24$, which is appreciably smaller than the observed value. This is a difficulty which one encounters also for other metals and is a consequence of the over-simplifying assumptions made in the free electron model. From the discussion to be given in Chapter 10 it may be concluded that the discrepancy is in part a result of the fact that the effective mass of the electrons may be larger than that of a free electron.

Qualitatively, the results obtained may be summarized as follows: As a consequence of the Pauli principle, even at low temperatures most electrons have appreciable kinetic energy. Thermal excitation of electrons is possible only if they can be excited into unoccupied states. This is essentially possible only for electrons in the vicinity of the Fermi level; the electrons in the low-energy region require too large an excitation energy. Thus only a relatively small number of electrons contribute to the specific heat.

9-5. Paramagnetism of free electrons

It is well known that when a certain charge distribution rotates about an axis, a magnetic dipole moment results. Thus, as a consequence of the angular momentum, or spin, each electron bears a magnetic dipole moment. An important property of the electronic magnetic moment is that in an external field H its component along the field direction is either $+eh/2mc$ or $-eh/2mc$ (see Sec. 18-2). In other words, the component is either parallel or antiparallel to the external field direction. The magnitude of the component

$$\mu_B = eh/2mc = 0.917 \times 10^{-20} \text{ erg/oersted} \qquad (9\text{-}18)$$

is called a Bohr magneton. The energy of a dipole in an external field is equal to $-\boldsymbol{\mu} \cdot \boldsymbol{H}$, so that in the parallel orientation the energy is $-\mu_B H$, and in the antiparallel orientation is $+\mu_B H$.

In a metal, let there be n free electrons per unit volume. In the presence of a magnetic field H let there be n_p with an orientation parallel to H and n_a antiparallel to H. The magnetic moment per unit volume (the magnetization) is then equal to

$$M = (n_p - n_a)\mu_B \qquad (9\text{-}19)$$

If we assume classical statistics M may be calculated in the same way as the orientation polarization of electric dipoles in the Debye-Langevin theory. We leave it to the reader (Problem 9-4) to show that in that case,

$$M = \chi_p H = (n\mu_B^2/kT)H \qquad (9\text{-}20)$$

as long as $\mu H \ll kT$. The quantity χ_p is called the paramagnetic susceptibility. Note that for freely rotating dipoles the average component in
the field direction is $(\mu_B^2/3kT)H$. The fact that the factor 3 is missing in
(9-20) is a consequence of the fact that the dipoles can accept only two
possible orientations relative to H. If (9-20) were correct, one would find for
the susceptibility of metals at room temperature with $n \simeq 10^{22}$ per cm³,
$\chi_p \simeq 10^{-4}$ per cm³. Also, χ_p should vary as $1/T$. Experimentally, however,
one finds $\chi_p \simeq 10^{-6}$ per cm³ and practically no temperature dependence.

The disagreement with experiment disappears when one applies Fermi-
Dirac statistics, as was first shown by Pauli.[6] For simplicity let us first
consider the situation at $T = 0$. Without external magnetic field all energy

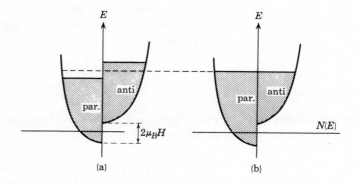

Fig. 9-4. The number of occupied states $N(E)$ as function of the
energy at $T = 0$. In (a) an external field H is applied while keeping
the electrons in their original states; as a result of the shift in
energy, this situation is unstable. In (b) equilibrium is established,
corresponding to an excess of parallel spins.

levels below E_{F_0} are occupied and all those above E_{F_0} are empty. Leaving
for a moment all electrons in their original state and applying an external
field H, all electrons with a magnetic moment parallel to H would suffer
a shift in energy of $-\mu_B H$, all antiparallel ones of $+\mu_B H$. This is indicated
in Fig. 9-4a. It must be noted that $\mu_B H \ll E_{F_0}$; in fact, even for a field
strength of 10^5 gauss, $\mu_B H \simeq 10^{-3}$ ev as compared with $E_{F_0} \simeq 5$ ev.
The situation as depicted in Fig. 9-4a is, of course, unstable and a number
of antiparallel spins will enter the group of parallel ones. In equilibrium
both halves are filled to the same level, as in Fig. 9-4b. Now, according
to (9-3), the number of allowed states in each of the halves is per cm³
equal to

$$z(E)\, dE = 2\pi(2m)^{3/2}E^{1/2}\, dE/h^3 \qquad (9\text{-}21)$$

[6] W. Pauli, *Z. Physik*, **41**, 81 (1927).

The number of antiparallel spins entering the group of parallel spins is therefore

$$2\pi(2m/h^2)^{3/2}\mu_B H E_{F_0}^{1/2}$$

because $\mu_B H \ll E_{F_0}$. The total excess of electrons with parallel orientation is twice this, so that one finds by making use of expression (9-9) for E_{F_0},

$$M = \frac{4\pi m}{h^2}\left(\frac{3n}{\pi}\right)^{1/3}\mu_B^2 H = \chi_p H \tag{9-22}$$

This may be written in a more convenient form for purposes of comparing the quantum result with the classical result (9-20) by multiplying top and bottom by E_{F_0}. This gives

$$\chi_p = 3n\mu_B^2/2kT_F \tag{9-23}$$

where T_F is the Fermi temperature defined by $kT_F = E_{F_0}$. Substituting numerical values, one finds for the volume susceptibility,

$$\chi_p = 2.21 \times 10^{-14}n^{1/3} \tag{9-24}$$

For temperatures different from zero, the theory must be extended. However, because the influence of temperature on the Fermi distribution is slight, one expects χ_p to be nearly temperature-independent. It has been shown by Stoner[7] that for $kT \ll E_F$,

$$\chi_p = \frac{3}{2}\cdot\frac{n\mu_B^2}{E_{F_0}}\left[1 - \frac{\pi^2}{12}\left(\frac{kT}{E_{F_0}}\right)^2\right] \tag{9-25}$$

The factor in brackets is identical with that occurring in (9-15) for the temperature-dependence of E_F. For $T = 0$, (9-25) reduces to (9-23). With $n \simeq 10^{22}$ it thus follows from (9-23) that the paramagnetic susceptibility of the free electron gas is of the order of 10^{-6} per cm^3, in agreement with experiment.

A quantitative comparison between the results obtained above and experiment is rather difficult. First of all, the magnetic susceptibility of a metal consists of three contributions:

(i) The paramagnetic contribution of the free electrons

(ii) A diamagnetic contribution of the free electrons, first calculated by Landau[8]

(iii) The diamagnetic contribution of the ionic cores

Thus, in order to obtain χ_p, the last two contributions must be subtracted from the total susceptibility measured. For completely free electrons, contribution (ii) is equal to $-\chi_p/3$. Contribution (iii) is usually calculated from susceptibility data on ionic solutions; this involves the

[7] E. C. Stoner, *Proc. Roy. Soc. (London)*, **A152**, 672 (1935).
[8] L. Landau, *Z. Physik*, **64**, 629 (1930).

assumption that the susceptibility per ion is the same in the solution and in the metal. Furthermore, the experimental data are sometimes impaired by the presence of ferromagnetic impurities. Finally, the free electron model can be expected to hold in good approximation only for the alkali metals, as we shall see in Chapter 10.

For further details, we refer to the literature.[9]

9-6. Thermionic emission from metals

With reference to Fig. 9-1, let us define the energy of a free electron at rest inside the metal as zero. In order to escape from the metal an electron must have an energy perpendicular to the surface of at least E_s. Thus if x is the coordinate perpendicular to the surface, an electron must have a momentum $p_x \geqslant p_{x_0}$ in order to escape, where

$$p_{x_0}^2/2m = E_s \qquad (9\text{-}26)$$

However, even if an electron at the surface has a momentum $p_x \geqslant p_{x_0}$, it does not necessarily escape, but may be reflected by the potential barrier. This is a phenomenon which follows readily from wave mechanics.[10] Thus the probability of escape for an electron satisfying the condition $p_x \geqslant p_{x_0}$ is equal to $1 - r(p_x)$, where $r(p_x)$ is the reflection coefficient as function of p_x. The reflection coefficient also depends on the shape of the potential barrier. Suppose now that the number of electrons per unit volume with a momentum between p_x and $p_x + dp_x$ inside the metal is equal to $n(p_x)\, dp_x$. The number of such electrons arriving at the surface per second per unit area is equal to $v_x n(p_x)\, dp_x$. From this it follows that the emission current density is equal to

$$I = (e/m) \int_{p_{x_0}}^{\infty} p_x n(p_x)[1 - r(p_x)]\, dp_x \qquad (9\text{-}27)$$

The term in brackets is usually replaced by a factor $(1 - r)$ in front of the integral, where r represents a suitable average of the reflection coefficient.[11] One is thus left with the problem of calculating $n(p_x)$; this quantity may be obtained in the following manner: From (9-2) it follows that for an isotropic momentum distribution, as presumably exists inside the metal, the number of allowed states corresponding to an element $dp_x\, dp_y\, dp_z$ in the momentum space is equal to

$$2\, dp_x\, dp_y\, dp_z/h^3$$

[9] N. F. Mott and H. Jones, *The Theory of the Properties of Metals and Alloys*, Oxford, New York, 1936, p. 184; A. H. Wilson, *The Theory of Metals*, 2d ed., Cambridge, London, 1953, Chap. 6.

[10] See, for example, N. F. Mott and I. N. Sneddon, *Wave Mechanics and its Applications*, Oxford, New York, 1948, pp. 13ff.

[11] For a calculation, see, for example, L. W. Nordheim, *Proc. Roy. Soc.* (*London*), **121**, 626 (1928); L. A. MacColl, *Phys. Rev.*, **56**, 699 (1939).

per unit volume. The number of electrons occupying states with momenta between $p_x, p_x + dp_x$; $p_y, p_y + dp_y$; $p_z, p_z + dp_z$ is therefore

$$n(p_x, p_y, p_z)\, dp_x\, dp_y\, dp_z = \frac{2}{h^3} \cdot \frac{dp_x\, dp_y\, dp_z}{e^{(E\,-\,E_F)/kT} + 1} \qquad (9\text{-}28)$$

where $E = (p_x^2 + p_y^2 + p_z^2)/2m$. Hence

$$n(p_x)\, dp_x = \frac{2}{h^3}\, dp_x \int_{-\infty}^{+\infty} \int_{-\infty}^{+\infty} \frac{dp_y\, dp_z}{e^{(E\,-\,E_F)/kT} + 1} \qquad (9\text{-}29)$$

Now we are interested only in those electrons for which $p_x \geqslant p_{x_0}$, i.e., the total energy of the electrons of interest is at least equal to E_s. On the other hand, $E_s - E_F = \phi \gg kT$ for all metals at temperatures below the melting point (see Fig. 9-1). Hence the term of unity in the distribution function may be neglected; we are interested only in the Boltzmann tail of the Fermi distribution. The quantity ϕ is called the work function of the metal; it represents the energy difference between an electron at the Fermi level and the vacuum level.

One thus obtains from (9-29),

$$n(p_x)\, dp_x = (4\pi m k T/h^3)e^{E_F/kT}\, e^{-p_x^2/2mkT} dp_x \qquad (9\text{-}30)$$

Substituting this expression into (9-27) one finds upon integration for the emission current density,

$$I = A(1 - r)T^2 e^{-\phi/kT} \qquad (9\text{-}31)$$

where $A = 4\pi e m k^2/h^3 = 120$ amp/cm²/deg². This is the Dushman-Richardson equation.

From the form of (9-31) one may be inclined to conclude that by simply plotting $\log (I/T^2)$ versus $1/T$ one obtains ϕ from the slope of the resulting straight line and $A(1 - r)$ from the intercept at $1/T = 0$ (see Fig. 9-5). A number of complicating factors in the thermionic emission of an actual metal must, however, be considered.[12]

(i) The apparent work function increases if a negative space charge exists in the vicinity of the emitter; the anode potential should therefore be sufficiently positive to prevent space charge build-up, i.e., one should work in the region of saturation-current density.

(ii) The apparent work function decreases with increasing external field strength, as explained in Sec. 9-8. Thus $I(T)$ should be measured for different external fields and then extrapolated by means of a so-called Schottky line to zero field strength (see Fig. 9-7).

[12] For an evaluation of thermionic emission data and a thorough discussion of the theory, see C. Herring and M. H. Nichols, "Evaluation of Thermionic Data," *Revs. Mod. Phys.*, **21**, 185 (1949).

(iii) As a result of thermal expansion, ϕ itself is a function of temperature, and so is $(1 - r)$.

(iv) In the derivation of (9-31) it has been assumed that the work function is the same over the whole area of the emitter; this assumption is valid only if the emitter is a single crystal, because ϕ varies from one crystallographic plane to another.[13]

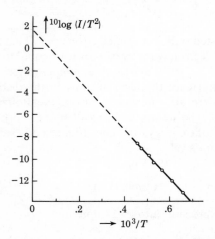

Fig. 9-5.   Richardson plot for tungsten. [After Herrmann and Wagener, l.c., vol. 2, page 74]

(v) Small amounts of adsorbed gases may influence ϕ strongly, as explained in Sec. 9-9; thus the surface should be atomically clean.

(vi) The macroscopic area of the emitter is in general not equal to the actual surface area.

From these remarks it is evident that reliable conclusions regarding ϕ and $A(1 - r)$ can be drawn only from extremely carefully controlled experiments. Many of the older experimental results in the literature are worthless because of poor vacuum techniques.[14]

A few remarks may be made in connection with (iii) above. Let us assume that r is temperature-independent and that ϕ varies linearly with T according to

$$\phi = \phi_0 + (d\phi/dT)T \qquad (9\text{-}32)$$

where ϕ_0 is the work function at absolute zero. (This assumption is

[13] For an extensive study of this and other aspects of the thermionic emission of tungsten, see G. F. Smith, *Phys. Rev.*, **94**, 295 (1954).

[14] Illustrative in this respect is a table of values for ϕ and $A(1 - r)$ for platinum in chronological order in G. Herrmann and S. Wagener, *The Oxide Coated Cathode*, Chapman and Hall, London, 1951, Vol. 2, p. 78.

probably inaccurate because the coefficient of expansion goes to zero as $T \to 0$.) Substituting (9-32) into (9-31), one obtains

$$\log (I/T^2) = \log A + \log (1 - r) - (d\phi/dT)/k - \phi_0/kT \qquad (9\text{-}33)$$

On the basis of this expression one thus determines from the slope of a Richardson plot, such as represented for tungsten in Fig. 9-5, a value for ϕ_0 rather than for ϕ. Also, it is evident that the constant obtained from the intercept at $1/T = 0$ may differ appreciably from $A = 120$ amp/cm²/deg². A number of experimental results obtained by various methods[15] indicate that for metals $d\phi/dT \simeq 10^{-4}$ ev per degree. Work functions for a number of metals are given in Table 9-2.

Table 9-2. Average Values of the Work Function of Metals in ev.

For references to the original literature, see footnote 15

Al	4.20	Cs	1.93	Na	2.28
Ag	4.46	Cu	4.45	Ni	4.96
Au	4.89	Fe	4.44	Pd	4.98
Ba	2.51	K	2.22	Pt	5.36
Cd	4.10	Li	2.48	Ta	4.13
Co	4.41	Mg	3.67	W	4.54
Cr	4.60	Mo	4.24	Zn	4.29

9-7. The energy distribution of the emitted electrons

The energy distribution of the emitted electrons may be derived from the results obtained in the preceding section as follows: According to the Dushman equation (9-31) the total number of electrons emitted per cm² per second is equal to

$$N = (4\pi m k^2/h^3)T^2 e^{-\phi/kT} \qquad (9\text{-}34)$$

if we assume for the moment that the reflection coefficient $r = 0$. Also, the number of electrons arriving at the surface per cm² per second with $p_x \geqslant p_{x_0}$ and velocities normal to the surface in the range dv_x may be obtained from (9-30):

$$n(v_x)v_x \, dv_x = (4\pi m^2 kT/h^3)e^{E_F/kT} e^{-mv_x^2/2kT} v_x \, dv_x \qquad (9\text{-}35)$$

When v_{ex} represents the velocity of an electron in the x-direction after emission, we have

$$\tfrac{1}{2}mv_{ex}^2 = \tfrac{1}{2}mv_x^2 - E_F - \phi$$
$$v_{ex} \, dv_{ex} = v_x \, dv_x \qquad (9\text{-}36)$$

[15] For a review of methods to determine ϕ, see Herrmann and Wagener, l.c. Chap. 2.

As each of the electrons of the group represented by (9-35) contributes an external electron as described by (9-36), the velocity distribution $F(v_{ex})\,dv_{ex}$ of the emitted electrons is obtained by dividing (9-35) by (9-34) and substituting (9-36); this gives

$$F(v_{ex})\,dv_{ex}/N = (mv_{ex}/kT)e^{-mv_{ex}^2/2kT}\,dv_{ex} \qquad (9\text{-}37)$$

Thus the velocity distribution perpendicular to the surface exhibits a Maxwellian form. It is left to the reader (Problem 9-6) to show that the average energy of the emitted electrons perpendicular to the surface is equal to

$$\langle E_x \rangle = (m/2)\langle v_{ex}^2 \rangle = kT \qquad (9\text{-}38)$$

Clearly, the velocities of the electrons in the y- and z-directions (parallel to the surface) do not change upon crossing the surface potential barrier; it can be shown (Problem 9-6) that $\langle E_y \rangle = \langle E_z \rangle = kT/2$. One thus concludes that the total average energy of the escaping electrons is equal to

$$\langle E \rangle = 2kT \qquad (9\text{-}38a)$$

This result is basic to the so called "cooling method" employed to determine the work function ϕ at any operating temperature.[16] To explain this method, we have to refer to a result of the thermodynamics of a gas, in this case the electron gas. The change in entropy dS resulting from a small change in the number of particles dN and a small change in the total energy dE is given by (see D-8 and E-5)

$$dS = \alpha k\,dN + dE/T + p\,dV/T \qquad (9\text{-}39)$$

where α is an undetermined multiplier, related to the Fermi energy in accordance with (9-5) by

$$\alpha = -E_F/kT \qquad (9\text{-}40)$$

Let us now apply this to the electron gas at constant volume, assuming that one electron leaves the metal with an average kinetic energy of $2kT$.

$$dN = -1, \qquad dE = -(E_F + \phi + 2kT) \qquad (9\text{-}41)$$

From the last three equations one obtains for the heat lost by the metal per emitted electron,[17]

$$dQ = T\,dS = \phi + 2kT \qquad (9\text{-}42)$$

Note the important physical meaning of the work function in this result

[16] C. Davisson and L. H. Germer, *Phys. Rev.*, **20**, 300 (1922); **30**, 634 (1927); G. M. Fleming and J. E. Henderson, *Phys. Rev.*, **58**, 887 (1940).

[17] A detailed thermodynamical study shows that an additional term must be added to the right-hand side of (9-42), containing the Thomson coefficient; this term is of the order of 10^{-2} ev. See C. Herring, *Phys. Rev.*, **59**, 889 (1941).

for the latent heat of evaporation per electron. The power consumed by the emitter per cm² due to this process is thus

$$P = (I/e)(\phi + 2kT) \tag{9-43}$$

From the power input and correcting for losses due to thermal radiation and heat conduction, it is possible to determine ϕ at a given temperature. This method has been used to determine $d\phi/dT$.[18]

9-8. Field-enhanced electron emission from metals

In the preceding sections the metal-vacuum boundary has been represented by a discontinuity in the potential. Actually, the potential

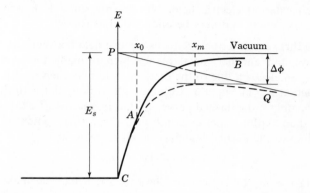

Fig. 9-6. Surface potential barrier and Schottky effect (greatly exaggerated).

changes smoothly, and this has some interesting consequences, as we shall see. Let us define the potential energy of an electron far away from the metal surface as zero. As we approach the metal with the electron, the metal will become polarized and will exert an attractive force on the electron. For distances x large compared with the interatomic distances, the metal surface may be considered homogeneous, and the attractive force is given by the well-known image force $e^2/4x^2$. This leads to a potential energy of the electron equal to

$$V_{\text{image}} = -e^2/4x \tag{9-44}$$

The image potential is represented by curve AB in Fig. 9-6. It will be evident that (9-44) is not valid for distances smaller than several Angstroms; in fact, this would lead to a potential energy of $-\infty$ for an electron at rest inside the metal. Schottky suggested that the image potential holds

---

[18] See, for example, F. Krueger and G. Stabenow, *Ann. Physik*, **22**, 713 (1935).

for $x > x_0$, where x_0 is a critical distance; for the region $0 < x < x_0$ he assumed a constant force, i.e., the potential energy in that region would be a linear function of x (see CA, Fig. 9-6).[19] Wave-mechanical calculations indicate that this model is rather good.[20] To obtain the order of magnitude of x_0, let us assume the total potential energy barrier to be $E_s = 10$ ev. For $x = x_0$ the image force is $e^2/4x_0^2$, so that the increase in potential energy along CA is $e^2/4x_0$. Also, the energy rise between A and B in Fig. 9-6 is $e^2/4x_0$, leading to $E_s = e^2/2x_0$ or $x_0 \simeq 1$ A.

The existence of the image potential has some important consequences:

(i) It reduces the reflection of escaping electrons considerably relative to that by an abrupt potential change.

(ii) It leads to a reduction in the apparent work function in the presence of an external electric field; this phenomenon is known as the Schottky effect and may be understood as follows:[19]

Suppose there exists a homogeneous electric field between the emitting metal surface and another metal plate which is made the anode. The potential for an electron due to the external field may then be represented by a line such as PQ in Fig. 9-6. Combining this potential with the image potential, we obtain the dashed curve, so that it is now easier for electrons to escape than without an external field. The total potential energy corresponding to the dashed line may be represented by

$$V(x) = -e^2/4x - eEx \qquad (9\text{-}45)$$

where the last term corresponds to the external field. The maximum of this curve occurs for $x = x_m$ and from (9-45) one finds $x_m = \frac{1}{2}(e/E)^{1/2}$. Substituting, one finds for the change in work function

$$\Delta\phi = V(x_m) = -e(eE)^{1/2} \qquad (9\text{-}46)$$

Instead of the Dushman equation, we thus obtain

$$\log(I/T^2) = \log A + \log(1 - r) - \phi/kT + e(eE)^{1/2}/kT \qquad (9\text{-}47)$$

Thus, if one plots the logarithm of the saturation current for a given temperature as function of the square root of the anode voltage, one expects a straight line (the Schottky line). A comparison of theory and experiment for tungsten is given in Fig. 9-7; the agreement is good for anode voltages above 100 volts; the deviations below 100 volts are ascribed to variations of the work function over the surface.[21]

It should be noted that the actual change in the work function is relatively small. For example, for $E = 10^3$ volts per cm, one obtains $x_m \simeq 10^{-5}$ cm and $\Delta\phi \simeq 0.01$ ev.

[19] W. Schottky, *Physik Z.*, **15**, 872 (1914).

[20] See, for example, J. Bardeen, *Phys. Rev.*, **49**, 653 (1936); **58**, 727 (1940).

[21] W. B. Nottingham, *Phys. Rev.*, **47**, 806 (1935); **58**, 927 (1940).

Field emission. When the external electric field becomes of the order of 10^6 volts per cm, cold emission or field emission sets in. This phenomenon is quite different from the Schottky effect: in the latter case the electrons cross over the potential barrier, in field emission they tunnel through the barrier. For simplicity, consider a metal at absolute zero and let us assume the surface potential barrier to be abrupt. The potential energy of an electron outside the metal is then equal to $-eEx$, represented by the line AB in Fig. 9-8. If the distance d in Fig. 9-8 is of the order of 10 Angstroms or less, electrons in the vicinity of the Fermi level will be

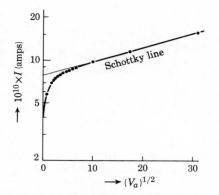

Fig. 9-7. Schottky line for tungsten. [After Nottingham, ref. 21]

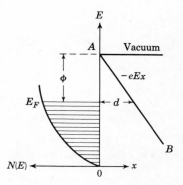

Fig. 9-8. To illustrate high-field emission; the distance d should be 10 Angstroms or less for appreciable tunneling to take place.

able to tunnel through the barrier.[22] For $\phi \simeq 3$ ev, this requires a field of the order of 10^7 volts cm^{-1}. As the field strength becomes larger, more and more electrons below the Fermi level begin to contribute to the emission current. According to Fowler and Nordheim, the emission current as function of the field strength E for a triangular barrier may be written in the form

$$I = BE^2 e^{-\beta/E} \tag{9-48}$$

where B and β are constants containing the work function.[23] Note that E plays the same role in this formula as T in the Dushman-Richardson expression for the thermionic current. Thus if $\log (I/E^2)$ is plotted versus $1/E$, a straight line should result. This has been confirmed by experiment.[24] Usually, field emission sets in at fields of the order of 10^6 volts cm^{-1}, probably as a consequence of high fields occurring at surface irregularities.

[22] See, for example, N. F. Mott and I. N. Sneddon, *op. cit.*

[23] R. H. Fowler and L. Nordheim, *Proc. Roy. Soc.* (*London*), **119A,** 173 (1928).

[24] See, for example, R. Haefer, *Z. Physik,* **116,** 604 (1940).

It will be evident from the above discussion that field emission is not strongly influenced by temperature. Of course, the temperature should be kept low enough to assure the absence of thermionic emission.

9-9. Changes of work function due to adsorbed atoms[25]

It is well known that the work function of metals such as tungsten can be lowered by surface adsorption of alkali or alkaline earth atoms. The lowest value of the work function is obtained roughly for a monatomic

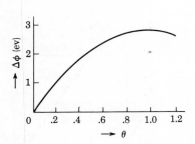

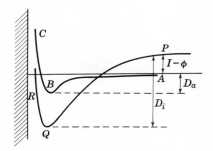

Fig. 9-9. The decrease $\Delta\phi$ of the work function of tungsten as function of the fraction θ covered with adsorbed Cs atoms; $\theta = 1$ corresponds to a monolayer. [After J. A. Becker, *Trans. Faraday Soc.*, **28**, 151 (1932)]

Fig. 9-10. *ABC* represents the potential energy of an atom as function of distance from the metal; *PQR* corresponds to an ion.

layer of adsorbed atoms, as may be seen from Fig. 9-9.[26] It is observed that the work function of tungsten (4.52 ev) may be lowered to 1.5 ev by Cs-adsorption. Adsorption of oxygen usually increases the work function of metals. We shall now investigate the reasons for such changes.

First consider the potential energy of an atom as function of its distance from a metallic surface. It is convenient to think of the metal as a huge molecule which is "perfectly" polarizable. Since any atom has a certain polarizability, the atomic potential energy curve will be of the type *ABC* in Fig. 9-10, the attraction resulting from van der Waals forces. The energy D_a corresponds to the energy required to dissociate the adsorbed atom from the metal surface. Suppose now that in point A we ionize the atom by supplying the ionization energy I. The electron is then taken to the metal, yielding a gain in energy equal to the work function ϕ of the metal (see 9-42). Thus the potential energy curve for the ion starts $(I - \phi)$ above the atomic curve, in point P. When we now approach the metal with the ion, it will be under influence of an image force, i.e.,

[25] For an extensive discussion see J. H. de Boer, *Electron Emission and Adsorption Phenomena*, Cambridge, London, 1935.

[26] See also J. B. Taylor and I. Langmuir, *Phys. Rev.*, **44**, 423 (1933).

the attraction potential will be a Coulomb attraction, proportional to the reciprocal of the distance from the metal. On the other hand, the potential curve for the atom AB is of the van der Waals type and varies with a higher power of the distance. For the ion we thus obtain a curve such as PQR, which intersects the atomic curve. In this curve, D_i represents the binding energy of the ion. Thus, if Q lies lower than B, the foreign atom will be adsorbed as a positive ion rather than as an atom. The condition for ionic adsorption is therefore

$$D_i - I + \phi > D_a$$

Thus atoms with a low ionization energy may be adsorbed as positive ions and experiments indicate that this is indeed the case for alkali and alkaline earth atoms adsorbed on a metal with a relatively high work function like tungsten. We may note that $(I - \phi)$ may be negative, so that point P may be lower than point A in Fig. 9-10. This is the case for example with Cs on tungsten: $I_{Cs} = 3.9$ ev and $\phi_W = 4.5$ ev. This has been confirmed experimentally by heating a tungsten wire in cesium vapor; if the tungsten wire is made positive with respect to a surrounding metal cylinder, one observes that the cesium is ionized at the tungsten and evaporates as ions rather than as atoms.[27] The same is true for rubidium, which has an ionization energy of 4.2 ev. For sodium, on the other hand, the ionization energy is 5.1 ev, so that for Na adsorbed on tungsten point P in Fig. 9-10 is indeed above point A. Sodium therefore evaporates in the form of atoms from a tungsten surface, even though it is adsorbed in the form of ions.

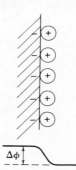

Let us now consider the influence of atoms adsorbed as positive ions on the work function of the base metal. Opposite the positive ions exists a negative surface charge on the metal, i.e., there exists a double layer (Fig. 9-11). According to electrostatics, the field outside the double layer vanishes, but inside the layer, the force on an electron is $4\pi\sigma e$, where σe is the surface charge density.

Fig. 9-11. Electric double layer on a metal resulting from the adsorption of atoms in the form of positive ions. The curve underneath represents the potential energy of an electron as it crosses the layer; $\Delta\phi$ is the lowering of the work function.

Thus as an electron is taken from the interior of the metal into vacuum there is an extra potential energy drop, resulting from the double layer, equal to

$$\Delta\phi = 4\pi\sigma e d = 4\pi N e^2 d \tag{9-49}$$

where d is the distance between the positive and negative charges and N

[27] J. B. Taylor and I. Langmuir, *Phys. Rev.*, **44**, 423 (1933); J. A. Becker, *Phys. Rev.*, **28**, 341 (1926).

is the number of adsorbed ions per cm². For example, if $d = 10^{-8}$ cm, one requires $N \simeq 0.5 \times 10^{14}$ cm^{-2} to produce a drop of 1 ev, which is approximately a complete monoatomic layer. It is therefore easier for the electrons to escape than without the double layer, and the effective work function of the metal is lowered by $\Delta\phi$. Similarly, if the double layer consists of negative ions adsorbed on the surface, as in the case of oxygen on tungsten, the work function is increased.

9-10. The contact potential between two metals

Consider two different metals of work functions ϕ_1 and ϕ_2 at absolute zero temperature. The energy levels of the electrons in the two metals

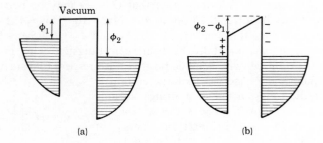

Fig. 9-12. Contact between two metals. In (a) no equilibrium has been established yet; (b) represents the equilibrium situation, showing the contact potential difference $\phi_2 - \phi_1$.

may then be compared with reference to the common "vacuum level." Suppose now the two metals are brought in contact with each other so that their separation is comparable to interatomic distances. Initially then, the situation is as indicated in Fig. 9-12a. Assuming $\phi_1 < \phi_2$, the energy can be lowered by taking an electron from metal 1 to metal 2, and evidently the situation depicted by Fig. 9-12a is unstable. A certain number of electrons will therefore move from 1 to 2 by tunnel effect or, for temperatures different from zero, by thermionic emission. Consequently, the surface of metal 2 will become negatively charged, that of metal 1 positively. Thus, as the number of electrons shifted from 1 to 2 increases, it becomes increasingly more difficult for other electrons to move from 1 to 2. Finally, an equilibrium will be established corresponding to Fig. 9-12b, in which the two Fermi levels coincide as a consequence of the potential rise (for electrons) across the gap associated with the surface charges. Obviously, the potential rise V is given by

$$eV = \phi_2 - \phi_1 \qquad (9\text{-}50)$$

where V is called the contact potential. We note that V is determined only by the two work functions and is independent of the depths of the potential energy wells.

In connection with the great importance of the Fermi level in equilibria between two or more sets of electronic energy levels, let us consider the problem from the thermodynamic viewpoint. Suppose two sets of energy levels, distinguished by the subscripts 1 and 2, are in thermal equilibrium at constant pressure and temperature. This means, according to Appendix A that the Gibbs thermodynamic potential of the combined systems should be a minimum; i.e., when one electron is transferred from system 1 to system 2, the resulting change $dG = dG_1 + dG_2$ should vanish. Now, according to thermodynamics,

$$T \, dS = dE + p \, dV - \mu \, dN \qquad (9\text{-}51)$$

where $-\mu/T$ is the change in entropy per particle added at constant E and V,

$$\mu = -T(\partial S/\partial N)_{E,V} \qquad (9\text{-}52)$$

At constant pressure and temperature, therefore,

$$dG = d(E - TS + pV) = \mu \, dN \qquad (9\text{-}53)$$

Applying this to the combined systems under consideration and keeping in mind that $dN_1 = -dN_2$, we may write as the condition for equilibrium at constant p and T,

$$\mu_1 \, dN_1 + \mu_2 \, dN_2 = 0 \quad \text{or} \quad \mu_1 = \mu_2 \qquad (9\text{-}54)$$

Equilibrium thus requires that the μ's of the two systems be the same. However, from (9-39), (9-40), and (9-52) it follows that $\mu = E_F$, showing that for two (or more) sets of electronic levels, *the Fermi levels must be the same in equilibrium.* This conclusion is of importance in the discussion of contacts between metals, semiconductors, and insulators.

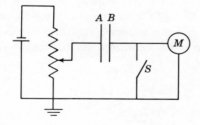

Fig. 9-13. Simple circuit to measure contact potentials.

Measurements of contact potentials may be used to determine the difference in work function of two surfaces and is thus important in cases where one is interested in changes in work functions. In Fig. 9-13, let A

and B be two such surfaces with different work functions. Thus, without external voltage, the plates will be charged as explained above. A sudden change in the distance between the plates (switch S open) will lead to a voltage pulse resulting from the change in capacitance and can be measured. If an external voltage is applied by means of a potentiometer (S closed), the levels of one metal are raised or lowered relative to those in the other. For a particular value of the external voltage the charges on the plates vanish and a change in distance (S open) will not yield a voltage pulse. Clearly, the external voltage then just compensates the contact potential and thus $(\phi_A - \phi_B)$ may be obtained. A method devised by Zisman employs a vibrating plate so that a-c techniques can be used and work functions can be measured in a matter of seconds.[28] In this way one has measured, for example, the change of work functions with temperature, with the result that for metals ϕ increases with about 10^{-4} ev per degree.

9-11. The photoelectric effect of metals

In the photoelectric effect, an electron absorbs a light quantum and is thereby excited into a state of higher energy; if the energy in the excited state is large enough, the electron may appear as a photoelectron outside the metal. The photoelectrons may originate from: (a) the interior of the metal (volume effect), (b) near the surface of the metal (surface effect), (c) foreign atoms adsorbed on the metal surface.

To begin with, it must be pointed out that completely free electrons cannot absorb photons; this may be shown from the expression for the quantum mechanical transition probability.[29] By means of the following simple argument, one arrives at the same conclusion. Consider the interaction between an electron and a photon as a collision in which momentum and energy are conserved. Let E_0 be the initial energy of the electron and $h\nu$ the energy of the photon. The energy of the electron after absorption is then $E = E_0 + h\nu$. When p and p_0 represent the absolute values of the momentum of the electron, respectively after and before the absorption process, and remembering that $h\nu/c$ is the momentum of the photon, conservation of momentum requires that

$$p \leqslant p_0 + h\nu/c \tag{9-55}$$

or
$$(2mE)^{1/2} \leqslant (2mE_0)^{1/2} + h\nu/c \tag{9-56}$$

This may be rewritten in the form

$$h\nu/2mc^2 + (2E_0/mc^2)^{1/2} \geqslant 1 \tag{9-57}$$

However, for the energies of interest we have $h\nu \ll mc^2$ and $E_0 \ll mc^2$.

[28] W. A. Zisman, *Rev. Sci. Instr.*, **3**, 367 (1932).
[29] See, for example, H. Fröhlich, *Elektronen Theorie der Metalle*, Springer, Berlin, 1936, p. 122; A. Sommerfeld and H. Bethe in *Handbuch der Physik*, Vol. 24/2.

One thus concludes that in the free electron approximation, the conservation laws cannot be satisfied and thus free electrons cannot absorb photons. This argument would hold for the electrons in the interior of the metal. The reason that there actually exists a volume effect is a consequence of the fact that the free electron approximation is not valid; even in the case of the alkali metals, for which this approximation is better than for any

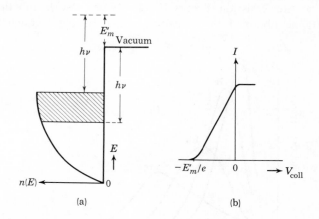

(a)   (b)

Fig. 9-14. Illustrating the photoelectric effect: for a frequency ν the electrons in the shaded part of the Fermi distribution may contribute to the emission (a); (b) represents the photo current as function of the collector voltage.

other metals, the volume effect may contribute to the surface effect (b).[30] The discussion given below is confined to process (b); because of lack of space, only some qualitative remarks will be made.

Notwithstanding the arguments given above, the free electron approximation applied to electrons near the surface leads to the possibility of photon absorption for these electrons; this follows from the wave-mechanical treatment of the problem.[31] One might say that the presence of the potential barrier at the surface makes it possible to satisfy the conservation laws in the sense that the surface itself acts as a possible source or sink for momentum. In other words, the system under consideration is no longer the electron plus a photon, but electron plus photon plus surface. With reference to Fig. 9-14a the following conclusions may then be drawn for the emission characteristics of a metal at absolute zero.

[30] H. J. Fan, *Phys. Rev.*, **68**, 43 (1945). In the volume effect, the excitation of electrons is governed by the selection rule that the transition should be "vertical" in the reduced zone scheme (see Chapter 10).

[31] K. Mitchell, *Proc. Roy. Soc.* (*London*), **A146**, 442 (1934); **153**, 513 (1936); I. Tamm and S. Schubin, *Z. Physik*, **68**, 97 (1931); A. G. Hill, *Phys. Rev.*, **53**, 184 (1938); R. E. B. Makinson, *Phys. Rev.*, **75**, 1908 (1949).

The minimum energy perpendicular to the surface required for an electron to escape from the metal is $E_F + \phi$. Thus, if $h\nu$ is the energy of the incident photons, electrons in the shaded portion of the Fermi distribution may contribute to the emission current. It is evident that the threshold frequency ν_t of the incident photons is given by

$$h\nu_t = \phi \qquad (9\text{-}58)$$

For $\nu < \nu_t$, no emission occurs. Evidently the work function of a metal may be obtained by measuring the threshold frequency ν_t. At

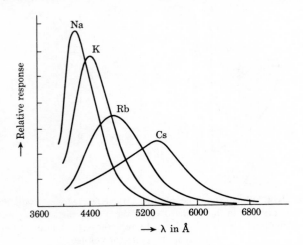

Fig. 9-15. Relative photoemissive current as function of the wavelength of the incident light for alkali metals. [After E. F. Seiter, *Astrophys. J.*, **52**, 129 (1920)]

temperatures different from zero, a method devised by Fowler may be used to determine ϕ.[32]

As the frequency is increased beyond ν_t, more and more electrons can contribute to the emission and thus the emission current rises with increasing frequency; for $h\nu \geqslant E_F + \phi$, saturation occurs. However, the transition probabilities decrease with increasing frequency, leading to a maximum in the current versus frequency curves (see Fig. 9-15).[31]

Besides measuring the total number of emitted electrons, one frequently measures the emission current for a given incident photon frequency as function of a retarding potential applied to a spherical collecting anode surrounding the target. The maximum energy with which an electron can leave the target at $T = 0$ is, according to Fig. 9-14a, equal to

$$E_m' = h\nu - \phi \qquad (9\text{-}59)$$

[32] R. H. Fowler, *Phys. Rev.*, **38**, 45 (1931).

Thus for a potential $-E'_m/e$ applied to the collector, all emitted electrons are stopped and the collected current $I = 0$. As the collector potential is made less negative, the collector current increases until for zero collector potential the current reaches its saturation value I_s for the particular incident frequency. The I versus $V_{collector}$ curve thus has the form as indicated in Fig. 9-14b; this is in agreement with the observations.[33] By differentiation of such curves, the energy distribution of the emitted electrons may be obtained.

Quantitatively, the theory may be set up in the following way: let $n(E) \, dE$ be the number of electrons in the metal occupying states in the energy range between E and $E + dE$. Also, let $P(\nu,E)$ be the probability that an incident photon of frequency ν excites an electron from a state E into the state $E + h\nu$. The number of electrons emitted by the metal originating from the range E, $E + dE$ is then per incident photon,

$$n(E)P(\nu,E)Q(E + h\nu) \, dE \qquad (9\text{-}60)$$

where $Q(E + h\nu)$ is the probability for an electron of energy $E + h\nu$ to escape. In most theories the assumptions made with regard to $P(\nu,E)$ and $Q(E + h\nu)$ are such that expression (9-60) is proportional to

$$F(\nu)(E - E_F - \phi) \, dE = F(\nu)E' \, dE' \qquad (9\text{-}61)$$

Here $F(\nu)$ is a function of the frequency only, and E' is the energy of the electron in the excited state relative to the vacuum level. From (9-61) an expression for the collector current as function of the retarding potential can be obtained.[33]

REFERENCES

L. Brillouin, *Die Quantenstatistik*, Springer, Berlin, 1933.

J. H. deBoer, *Electron Emission and Adsorption Phenomena*, Cambridge, London, 1935.

H. Fröhlich, *Elektronen Theorie der Metalle*, Springer, Berlin, 1936.

R. H. Good jr. and E. W. Müller, "Field Emission," *Encyclopedia of Physics*, Springer, Berlin, 1956, vol. 21, pp. 176-231.

C. Herring and M. H. Nichols, "Evaluation of Thermionic Data," *Revs. Mod. Phys.*, **21**, 185 (1949).

G. Herrmann and S. Wagener, *The Oxide Coated Cathode*, Chapman and Hall, London, 1951, Vol. 2, Chaps. 1, 2.

[33] For a discussion of the important difference in the slope of such curves for metals and semiconductors, see L. Apker, E. Taft, and J. Dickey, *Phys. Rev.*, **74**, 1462 (1948); we also refer the reader to this paper for many references to the existing literature.

N. F. Mott and H. Jones, *Theory of the Properties of Metals and Alloys*, Oxford, New York, 1936.

W. B. Nottingham, "Thermionic Emission," *Encyclopedia of Physics*, Springer, Berlin, 1956, vol. 21, pp. 1-176.

F. Seitz, *The Modern Theory of Solids*, McGraw-Hill, New York, 1940, Chap. 4.

Article by A. Sommerfeld and H. Bethe in *Handbuch der Physik*, Vol. 24/2, 1933, p. 333.

PROBLEMS

9-1. Discuss how one can determine E_s in Fig. 9-1 from electron diffraction experiments.

9-2. Calculate the average velocity of a conduction electron in sodium at $T = 0$. Compare the corresponding "classical temperature" with the melting point of Na. What is the electronic specific heat at $T = 300°K$?

9-3. Show that the derivative of the Fermi function is symmetrical about E_F and that

$$\int_{-\infty}^{+\infty} (\partial F/\partial E) dE = -1.$$

9-4. Give a derivation of the classical expression (9-20) for the paramagnetic susceptibility of free electrons.

9-5. Assuming $d\phi/dT = 10^{-4}$ ev per deg, what is the ordinate intercept of a Richardson plot? Compare this with $A = 120$ amp/cm²/deg².

9-6. Show that the average energy of the thermionically emitted electrons perpendicular to the surface is kT; show that the average energy parallel to the surface is kT.

9-7. On the basis of expression (9-61) derive an expression for the photoemission current as function of the retarding potential on the collecting anode.

9-8. A nondegenerate gas obeys the gas law $pV = RT$; derive a relation between p, V, and T for a degenerate electron gas. (*Hint*: first show that in general p equals two-thirds of the kinetic energy per unit volume).

9-9. Consider a gas of similar molecules in thermal equilibrium. Let the energy levels for the individual particles be denoted by E_n, where $n = 0, 1, 2, \ldots$. Let the energy level E_n correspond to Z_n possible states (wave functions including the spin) and let on the average N_n of these states be occupied in equilibrium. Consider a collision between two particles such that before the collision their energies are E_k and E_l, and after the collision E_m and E_n.

(a) Assume that the number of transitions k, $l \rightarrow m$, n per second is given by $AN_kN_lZ_mZ_n$, and that the number of transitions m, $n \rightarrow k$, l is given by $AN_mN_nZ_kZ_l$ where A is a constant. Show that the equilibrium condition and the law of conservation of energy lead to the distribution function $N_k = CZ_ke^{-\beta E_k}$ for all k. This is identical with the Boltzmann distribution if β is identified with $1/kT$.

(b) Suppose the number of transitions k, $l \rightarrow m$, n per second is given by $AN_kN_l(Z_m - N_m)(Z_n - N_n)$. Show that this leads to the Fermi-Dirac distribution function.

(c) Assuming that the number of transitions k, $l \rightarrow m$, n is proportional to $N_kN_l(Z_m + N_m)(Z_n + N_n)$, show that the same reasoning leads to the Bose-Einstein distribution.

(d) Comment on the physical meaning of the assumed expressions for the number of transitions k, $l \rightarrow m$, n for the three types of statistics.

9-10. For an ideally flat metal surface calculate the lowering of the work function resulting from a field outside the metal of 10^4 volts per cm. Also calculate the distance from the surface for which the potential barrier has its maximum value.

9-11. Discuss the theory of high-field emission of electrons for a metal at $0°K$ on the assumption that the potential barrier through which tunneling takes place is of a simple triangular form.

9-12. The equation of motion of a free electron in a metal under influence of light polarized along the x-direction may be written $d^2x/dt^2 + 2\pi\gamma(dx/dt) = -(e/m)E_0\exp(-2\pi i\nu t)$, where the second term is a damping term. Solve the equation for x and from it calculate the electric moment per unit volume. From this, show that the real part of the dielectric constant $\epsilon' = n^2 - k^2$ and the conductivity σ are given by

$$\epsilon' = 1 - \frac{n_e e^2}{\pi m(\nu^2 + \gamma^2)} \quad \text{and} \quad \sigma = nk\nu = \frac{n_e e^2 \gamma}{2\pi m(\nu^2 + \gamma^2)}$$

where n_e is the number of free electrons per cm³. Show that $\gamma = 1/2\pi\tau$ where τ is the relaxation time occurring in the static conductivity $\sigma_0 = n_e e^2 \tau/m$. Also show that metals are transparent for frequencies $\gtrsim 10^{15}$ per second and that they are reflecting in the region $10^{12} \leq \nu \leq 10^{15}$ per second. For background see Secs. 6-9 and 11-2; see also F. Seitz, op. cit., p. 638.

Chapter 10

THE BAND THEORY OF SOLIDS

10-1. Introductory remarks

In a solid one deals with a large number of interacting particles, and consequently the problem of calculating the electronic wave functions and energy levels is extremely complicated. It is thus necessary to introduce a number of simplifying assumptions. In the first place we shall assume that the nuclei in the crystalline solid are at rest. In an actual crystal this is of course never the case, but the influence of nuclear motion on the behavior of electrons may be treated as a perturbation for the case in which they are assumed to be at rest. As we shall see in the next chapter, the lattice vibrations play an important role in the interpretation of electrical resistivity and other transport phenomena. Even with the above assumption, however, we are still left with a many-electron problem which can be solved only by approximative methods. In the case of solids, the most important approximative method which has been applied extensively is the so-called one-electron approximation. In this approximation the total wave function for the system is given by a combination of wave functions, each of which involves the coordinates of only one electron. In other words, the field seen by a given electron is assumed to be that of the fixed nuclei plus some average field produced by the charge distribution of all other electrons. An extreme case of the one-electron approximation is the Sommerfield theory of metals discussed in the preceding chapter. There it was assumed that the potential seen by a given conduction electron is simply constant within the metal.

Within the framework of the one-electron theory there are two different approaches to the problem of the electronic structure of molecules and solids. One of these, the Heitler-London or valence bond scheme, is accurate when the atoms are far apart, i.e., when the atomic properties are pronounced. This scheme is thus based on atomic or localized orbitals. Another approach is that of Bloch; it is closely related to the Hund-Mulliken scheme which has been applied to molecules. In the Bloch scheme an electron is considered to belong to the crystal as a whole rather than to a particular atom. One speaks in this connection of the crystal orbital method and the discussion given below is essentially limited to this scheme. For a recent review of the one-electron method and many references we refer the reader to the article by Reitz cited at the end of this chapter. The problem as outlined above involves essentially that of the behavior of an electron in a potential which has the periodicity of crystal lattice. We shall see that this leads, among other things, to a natural distinction between metals, insulators, and semiconductors.

Before discussing the actual problem it may be useful to point out the analogy which exists between (i) electronic motion in a constant and a periodic potential, and (ii) the propagation of elastic waves in a continuum and in a periodic structure.

For elastic waves in a continuous medium the frequency is inversely proportional to the wavelength, i.e., there exists a linear relationship between frequency and wave number (or wave vector). This implies a velocity of propagation which is independent of the wavelength. Furthermore, there exists no upper limit for the frequency of the vibrational modes in a continuous medium. However, when one considers the modes of vibration in a lattice of discrete mass points which form a periodic structure, two characteristic features appear (see Chapter 2):

1. There exist allowed frequency bands, separated by forbidden regions.

2. The frequency is no longer proportional to the wave number but a periodic function of the latter.

Returning now to the motion of electrons, the reader is reminded of the fact that in a constant potential (free electron theory) the energy of the electron as function of the wave vector k is given by

$$E = \hbar^2 k^2 / 2m \qquad \text{where} \qquad k = 2\pi/\lambda = p/\hbar$$

Here λ is the wavelength associated with the electron and p is the momentum of the electron; the potential energy has been assumed zero. In this case, there is no upper limit to the energy, i.e., the energy spectrum is quasi-continuous (quasi, because the limited dimensions of the potential box produce closely spaced but discrete energy levels). However, if we consider the motion of an electron in a periodic potential we arrive at the following results:

1. There exist allowed energy bands separated by forbidden regions.

2. The functions $E(k)$ are periodic in k.

These results will be derived below. The analogy pointed out above is not too surprising if one recognizes that in both problems one deals with waves in periodic structures; in one case they are elastic waves, in the other they are waves associated with the electrons. For further details with regard to the general problem of wave motion in periodic structures we refer the reader to Brillouin.[1]

[1] L. Brillouin, *Wave Propagation in Periodic Structures*, Dover, New York, 1953. The existence of energy bands for electrons in crystals was first pointed out by M. S. O. Strutt, *Ann. Physik*, **84**, 485 (1927); **85**, 129 (1928).

10-2. The Bloch theorem

In the free electron theory one assumes that an electron moves in a constant potential V_0 leading to the Schrödinger equation for a one-dimensional case:

$$d^2\psi/dx^2 + (2m/\hbar^2)(E - V_0)\psi = 0$$

This equation can be solved by plane waves of the type

$$\psi(x) = e^{\pm ikx} \tag{10-1}$$

Upon substitution one obtains for the kinetic energy of the electron

$$E_{\text{kin}} = E - V_0 = \hbar^2 k^2/2m = p^2/2m$$

The physical meaning of k is that it represents the momentum of electron divided by $\hbar$. The complete solution for the wave function containing the time is obtained by multiplying $\psi(x)$ by $\exp(-i\omega t)$ where $\omega = E/\hbar$, so that actually solutions of the type (10-1) represent waves propagating along the x-axis.

Let us now consider the Schrödinger equation for an electron moving in a one-dimensional periodic potential. Thus, let the potential energy of an electron satisfy the equation

$$V(x) = V(x + a) \tag{10-2}$$

where a is the period. The Schrödinger equation is then

$$d^2\psi/dx^2 + (2m/\hbar^2)[E - V(x)]\psi = 0 \tag{10-3}$$

With reference to the solutions of this equation there is an important theorem which states that there exist solutions of the form

$$\psi(x) = e^{\pm ikx}u_k(x) \quad \text{where} \quad u_k(x) = u_k(x + a) \tag{10-4}$$

In other words, the solutions are plane waves modulated by the function $u_k(x)$, which has the same periodicity as the lattice. This theorem is known as the Bloch theorem;[2] in the theory of differential equations it is known as Floquet's theorem. Functions of the type (10-4) are called Bloch functions. Before giving a proof of this theorem we note that the Bloch function $\psi(x) = \exp(ikx)u_k(x)$ has the property

$$\psi(x + a) = \exp[ik(x + a)]\,u_k(x + a) = \psi(x)\exp(ika)$$

since $u_k(x + a) = u_k(x)$. In other words, Bloch functions have the property that

$$\psi(x + a) = Q\psi(x) \quad \text{where} \quad Q = \exp(\pm ika) \tag{10-5}$$

[2] F. Bloch, Z. Physik, **52**, 555 (1928).

It will be evident that if we can show that the Schrödinger equation (10-3) has solutions with the property (10-5), the solutions can be written as Bloch functions and the theorem is proved. This will now be done.[3]

Suppose $g(x)$ and $f(x)$ are two real independent solutions of the Schrödinger equation. Now a differential equation of the second order has only two independent solutions, and all other solutions are expressible as a linear combination of the independent ones. Then, since $f(x + a)$ and $g(x + a)$ are also solutions of the Schrödinger equation, we must have the relations

$$f(x + a) = \alpha_1 f(x) + \alpha_2 g(x)$$
$$g(x + a) = \beta_1 f(x) + \beta_2 g(x) \tag{10-6}$$

where the α's and β's are real functions of E. The solution of the Schrödinger equation may be written in the form

$$\psi(x) = Af(x) + Bg(x)$$

where A and B are arbitrary constants. According to (10-6) we must have

$$\psi(x + a) = (A\alpha_1 + B\beta_1)f(x) + (A\alpha_2 + B\beta_2)g(x)$$

In view of what has been said above about the property (10-5) of the Bloch functions, let us choose A and B such that

$$A\alpha_1 + B\beta_1 = QA$$
$$A\alpha_2 + B\beta_2 = QB \tag{10-7}$$

where Q is a constant. In this way we have obtained a function $\psi(x)$ with the property

$$\psi(x + a) = Q\psi(x) \tag{10-8}$$

Since equations (10-7) have nonvanishing solutions for A and B only if the determinant of their coefficients vanishes, we have the following equation for Q:

$$\begin{vmatrix} \alpha_1 - Q & \beta_1 \\ \alpha_2 & \beta_2 - Q \end{vmatrix} = 0$$

or　　　　$$Q^2 - (\alpha_1 + \beta_2)Q + \alpha_1\beta_2 - \alpha_2\beta_1 = 0 \tag{10-9}$$

Now, one can show that $\alpha_1\beta_2 - \alpha_2\beta_1 = 1$ in the following manner: from equations (10-6) one can derive that

$$\begin{vmatrix} f(x + a) & g(x + a) \\ f'(x + a) & g'(x + a) \end{vmatrix} = \begin{vmatrix} f(x) & g(x) \\ f'(x) & g'(x) \end{vmatrix} \begin{vmatrix} \alpha_1 & \alpha_2 \\ \beta_1 & \beta_2 \end{vmatrix} \tag{10-10}$$

[3] See H. A. Kramers, *Physica*, **2**, 483 (1935); F. Seitz, *The Modern Theory of Solids*, McGraw-Hill, New York, 1940, p. 279; N. F. Mott and H. Jones, *Theory of the Properties of Metals and Alloys*, Oxford, New York, 1936, p. 57; A. H. Wilson, *Theory of Metals*, 2d ed., Cambridge, London, 1953, p. 21.

where $f' = df/dx$, etc. If we multiply the Schrödinger equation for $g(x)$ by $f(x)$ and the equation for $f(x)$ by $g(x)$, we find upon subtracting,

$$0 = fg'' - gf'' = (d/dx)(fg' - gf')$$

Hence the so-called Wronskian is in this case a constant:

$$\begin{vmatrix} f(x) & g(x) \\ f'(x) & g'(x) \end{vmatrix} = \text{constant}$$

This result, together with equation (10-10), leads to the conclusion that $\alpha_1\beta_2 - \alpha_2\beta_1 = 1$. Instead of (10-9) we may therefore write

$$Q^2 - (\alpha_1 + \beta_2)Q + 1 = 0 \qquad (10\text{-}11)$$

where we should remember that $(\alpha_1 + \beta_2)$ is a real function of E. In general then, there are two roots Q_1 and Q_2, i.e., there are two functions $\psi_1(x)$ and $\psi_2(x)$ which exhibit the property (10-8). Note that the product $Q_1 Q_2 = 1$. For certain ranges of energy E, viz., for those corresponding to $(\alpha_1 + \beta_2)^2 < 4$, the two roots will be complex, and since $Q_1 Q_2 = 1$ they will be conjugates. In those regions of energy we may then write

$$Q_1 = e^{ika} \quad \text{and} \quad Q_2 = e^{-ika} \qquad (10\text{-}12)$$

The corresponding functions $\psi_1(x)$ and $\psi_2(x)$ then have the property

$$\psi_1(x + a) = e^{ika}\psi_1(x) \quad \text{and} \quad \psi_2(x + a) = e^{-ika}\psi_2(x) \qquad (10\text{-}13)$$

and thus are Bloch functions (see 10-5). In other regions of the energy E, viz., those corresponding to $(\alpha_1 + \beta_2)^2 > 4$, the two roots Q_1 and Q_2 are real and the reciprocals of each other. These roots correspond to solutions of the Schrödinger equation of the type

$$\psi_1(x) = e^{\mu x}u(x) \quad \text{and} \quad \psi_2(x) = e^{-\mu x}u(x)$$

where μ is a real quantity. Although such solutions are mathematically sound, they cannot in general be accepted as wave functions describing electrons, since they are not bounded. Thus there are no electronic states in the energy region corresponding to real roots Q_1 and Q_2. The above discussion thus leads also to the notion that the energy spectrum of an electron in a periodic potential consists of allowed and forbidden energy regions or bands. This will be illustrated further in the next section where we consider the motion of electrons in a particularly simple one-dimensional periodic potential.

10-3. The Kronig-Penney model

The essential features of the behavior of electrons in a periodic potential may be illustrated with reference to a relatively simple one-dimensional model first discussed by Kronig and Penney.[4] It is assumed that the potential energy of an electron has the form of a periodic array of square wells, as indicated in Fig. 10-1. The period of the potential is $(a + b)$; in regions such as $0 < x < a$ the potential energy is assumed equal to zero, in regions such as $-b < x < 0$ the potential energy is V_0. Each of the potential energy wells may be considered a rough approximation for the potential in the vicinity of an atom. The Schrödinger equations for the two regions are

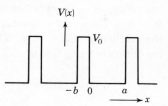

Fig. 10-1. One-dimensional Kronig-Penney potential.

$$d^2\psi/dx^2 + (2m/\hbar^2)E\psi = 0 \quad \text{for} \quad 0 < x < a \qquad (10\text{-}14)$$

$$d^2\psi/dx^2 + (2m/\hbar^2)(E - V_0)\psi = 0 \quad \text{for} \quad -b < x < 0 \qquad (10\text{-}15)$$

We shall assume that the energy E of the electrons under consideration is smaller than V_0. Defining two real quantities α and β by

$$\alpha^2 = 2mE/\hbar^2 \quad \text{and} \quad \beta^2 = 2m(V_0 - E)/\hbar^2 \qquad (10\text{-}16)$$

and making use of the fact that the solutions must be Bloch functions of the form $e^{ikx}u_k(x)$, one obtains upon substitution into (10-14) and (10-15) the following equations for $u_k(x)$:

$$d^2u/dx^2 + 2ik(du/dx) + (\alpha^2 - k^2)\,u = 0 \qquad 0 < x < a \qquad (10\text{-}17)$$

$$d^2u/dx^2 + 2ik(du/dx) - (\beta^2 + k^2)\,u = 0 \qquad -b < x < 0 \qquad (10\text{-}18)$$

The solutions of these equations are

$$\begin{aligned}
u_1 &= Ae^{i(\alpha - k)x} + Be^{-i(\alpha + k)x} & 0 < x < a \\
u_2 &= Ce^{(\beta - ik)x} + De^{-(\beta + ik)x} & -b < x < 0
\end{aligned} \qquad (10\text{-}19)$$

where A, B, C, and D are constants. These constants must be chosen in such a manner that the following four conditions are satisfied:

$$u_1(0) = u_2(0), \qquad u_1(a) = u_2(-b) \qquad (10\text{-}20)$$

$$(du_1/dx)_{x=0} = (du_2/dx)_{x=0}, \qquad (du_1/dx)_a = (du_2/dx)_{-b}$$

[4] R. de L. Kronig and W. G. Penney, *Proc. Roy. Soc.* (*London*), **A130**, 499 (1930); see for an extension of this work D. S. Saxon and R. A. Hutner, *Philips Research Repts.*, **4**, 81 (1949); J. M. Luttinger, *Philips Research Repts.*, **6**, 303 (1951); G. Allen, *Phys. Rev.*, **91**, 531 (1953). The case $V(x) = A \sin x$ has been discussed by Morse, *Phys. Rev.*, **35**, 1310 (1930). For another calculable one-dimensional case see J. C. Slater, *Phys. Rev.*, **87**, 807 (1952).

The two conditions on the left are imposed because of the requirement of continuity of the wave functions and of their derivatives; the two on the right are required because of the periodicity of $u_k(x)$. It is evident that application of (10-20) on (10-19) leads to four linear homogeneous equations in the constants A, B, C, D; thus the wave functions may be calculated. However, for our purpose we are more interested in determining the values of the energy for which satisfactory solutions are obtained. The four equations just mentioned have a solution only if the determinant of the coefficients of A, B, C, D vanishes. It can be shown that this leads to the following condition:

$$\frac{\beta^2 - \alpha^2}{2\alpha\beta} \sinh \beta b \sin \alpha a + \cosh \beta b \cos \alpha a = \cos k(a + b) \quad (10\text{-}21)$$

To obtain a more convenient equation, Kronig and Penney consider the case for which the potential barriers become delta functions, i.e., V_0 tends

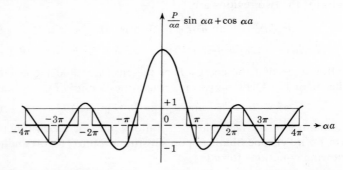

Fig. 10-2. The left hand side of (10-24) for $P = 3\pi/2$, plotted as function of αa. The allowed regions are heavily drawn.

to infinity and b approaches zero, but the product $V_0 b$ remains finite. Under these circumstances (10-21) reduces to

$$(mV_0 b/\hbar^2 \alpha) \sin \alpha a + \cos \alpha a = \cos ka \quad (10\text{-}22)$$

Let us now define the quantity

$$P = mV_0 ba/\hbar^2 \quad (10\text{-}23)$$

which is evidently a measure for the "area" $V_0 b$ of the potential barrier. In other words, increasing P has the physical meaning of binding a given electron more strongly to a particular potential well. From the last two equations we find that solutions for the wave functions exist only if

$$P \frac{\sin \alpha a}{\alpha a} + \cos \alpha a = \cos ka \quad (10\text{-}24)$$

As an example, we have represented in Fig. 10-2 the left-hand side of this equation as function of αa for the value $P = 3\pi/2$. The reader is reminded that α^2 is proportional to the energy E, i.e., the abcissa is a measure for the energy. Furthermore, it is important to realize that the right-hand side can accept only values between -1 and $+1$, as indicated by the horizontal lines in Fig. 10-2. Therefore the condition (10-24) can be satisfied only for values of αa for which the left-hand side lies between ± 1.

From the figure, the following interesting conclusions may be drawn:

(a) The energy spectrum of the electrons consists of a number of allowed energy bands separated by forbidden regions.

(b) The width of the allowed energy bands increases with increasing values of αa, i.e., with increasing energy; this is a consequence of the fact that the first term of (10-24) decreases on the average with increasing αa.

(c) The width of a particular allowed band decreases with increasing P, i.e., with increasing "binding energy" of the electrons. In the extreme case for which $P \to \infty$, the allowed regions become infinitely narrow and the energy spectrum becomes a line spectrum. In that case, (10-24) has only solutions if $\sin \alpha a = 0$, i.e., if $\alpha a = \pm n\pi$ with $n = 1, 2, 3,...$ According to this and (10-16), the energy spectrum is then given by

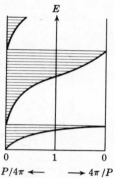

$$E_n = (\pi^2\hbar^2/2ma^2)n^2 \quad \text{for} \quad P \to \infty \quad (10\text{-}25)$$

which one recognizes as the energy levels of a particle in a constant potential box of atomic dimensions (see Appendix B). Physically, this could be expected because for large P, tunneling through the barriers becomes improbable.

Fig. 10-3. Allowed and forbidden energy ranges (shaded and open respectively) as function of P. The extreme left corresponds to $P = 0$ (free electrons), the extreme right to $P = \infty$.

These conclusions are summarized in Fig. 10-3, where the energy spectrum is given as function of P. For $P = 0$, we simply have the free electron model and the energy spectrum is (quasi) continuous; for $P = \infty$, a line spectrum results as discussed under (c) above. For a given value of P the position and width of the allowed and forbidden bands are obtained by erecting a vertical line; the shaded areas correspond to allowed bands.

From (10-24) it is possible also to obtain the energy E as function of the wave number k; the result is represented in Fig. 10-4a. This leads us to the conclusion that

(d) The discontinuities in the E versus k curve occur for

$$k = n\pi/a \qquad n = 1, 2, 3, ... \qquad (10\text{-}26)$$

These k-values define the boundaries of the first, second, etc. Brillouin zones. It must be noted that Fig. 10-4a gives only half of the complete $E(k)$ curve; thus the first zone extends from $-\pi/a$ to $+\pi/a$. Similarly, the second zone consists of two parts; one extending from π/a to $2\pi/a$, as shown, and another part extending between $-\pi/a$ and $-2\pi/a$.

A further important conclusion may be drawn from (10-24):

(e) Within a given energy band, the energy is a periodic function of k. For example, if one replaces k by $k + 2\pi n/a$, where n is an integer, the right-hand side of (10-24) remains the same. In other words, k is not

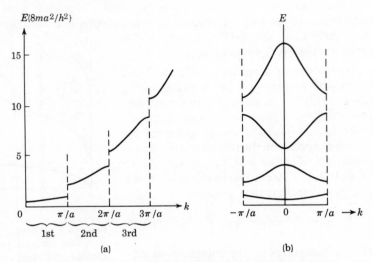

Fig. 10-4. In (a) the energy is represented as function of k for $P = 3\pi/2$; the Brillouin zones are indicated (note that this is only half the picture). In (b), E is plotted versus the reduced wave vector.

uniquely determined. It is therefore frequently convenient to introduce the "reduced wave vector" which is limited to the region

$$-\pi/a \leqslant k \leqslant \pi/a \qquad (10\text{-}27)$$

The energy versus reduced wave vector is represented in Fig. 10-4b. It may be noted here that the fact that k is not uniquely determined also follows quite generally from the form of the Bloch function (10-8). Consider the function $e^{ikx}u_k(x)$ and introduce a new wave vector $k' = k + 2\pi n/a$, where n is an integer. One may then write

$$\psi = e^{ik'x} u_k (x) e^{-2\pi inx/a} = e^{ik'x}u_{k'}(x) \qquad (10\text{-}28)$$

It will be noted that $u_{k'}(x)$ is also periodic with the lattice so that (10-28) is just as good a Bloch function as the initial function $e^{ikx}u_k(x)$.

The number of possible wave functions per band. So far, we have assumed the crystal to be infinite, but it will now be necessary to investigate the consequences of imposing boundary conditions. Since we have employed the running wave picture, it will be convenient to use cyclic or periodic boundary conditions (see Sec. 2-9 for the same problem in the theory of elastic waves in a chain of atoms). For a linear crystal of length L the boundary condition may be taken as

$$\psi(x + L) = \psi(x) \tag{10-29}$$

Strictly speaking, this applies to a circular lattice, but it may also be imposed on a linear lattice of macroscopic dimensions, as explained in Sec. 2-9. Making use of the fact that we are dealing with Bloch functions, this requires

$$e^{ik(x + L)}u_k(x + L) = e^{ikx}u_k(x)$$

Because of the periodicity of u_k, we have $u_k(x + L) = u_k(x)$, and the boundary conditions thus require

$$k = 2\pi n/L \quad \text{with} \quad n = \pm 1, \pm 2, ... \tag{10-30}$$

The number of possible wave functions (or k-values) in the range dk is therefore

$$dn = L \, dk/2\pi \tag{10-31}$$

Since k is limited in accordance with (10-26), it follows that the maximum value of n in (10-30) is $L/2a = N/2$, where N is the number of unit cells. This leads to a very important conclusion:

(f) The total number of possible wave functions in any energy band is equal to the number of unit cells N.

Now, as a result of the spin of the electrons and the Pauli exclusion principle each wave function can be "occupied" by at most two electrons.[5] Thus each energy band provides place for a maximum number of electrons equal to twice the number of unit cells. In other words, if there are $2N$ electrons in a band, the band is completely filled. This conclusion, as we shall see below, has far-reaching consequences for the distinction between metals, insulators, and semiconductors.

10-4. The motion of electrons in one dimension according to the band theory

The Kronig-Penney model is evidently an oversimplification of the actual potential encountered in real crystals. However, before we discuss the results obtained for more realistic models, it will be useful to consider the consequences of the conclusions reached so far for the motion of electrons in the band theory. First of all, let us consider the velocity of an electron described by a wave vector k. From the wavemechanical theory

[5] See Appendix C.

of particles it follows that the particle velocity is equal to the group velocity cf the waves representing the particle,[6] i.e.,

$$v = d\omega/dk \qquad (10\text{-}32)$$

Here ω is the angular frequency of the de Broglie waves; it is related to the energy of the particle by the relation $E = \hbar\omega$. Thus instead of (10-32), one may write in general for the velocity of the particle,

$$v = \hbar^{-1}(dE/dk) \qquad (10\text{-}33)$$

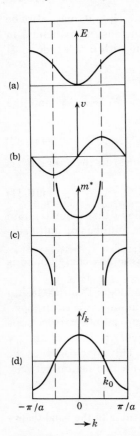

(a)

(b)

(c)

(d)

k_0

$-\pi/a \qquad 0 \qquad \pi/a$

$\rightarrow k$

Fig. 10-5. Energy, velocity, effective mass and f_k as function of k. The dashed lines correspond to the inflection points in the $E(k)$ curve.

This in itself shows the importance of the E versus k curves. In the case of free electrons $E = \hbar^2 k^2/2m$, and (10-33) simply leads to the identity $v = \hbar k/m = p/m$. In the band theory, however, E is in general not proportional to k^2, as may be seen from Fig. 10-4. Employing an $E(k)$ curve such as represented in Fig. 10-5a, one obtains, according to (10-33) for the velocity as function of k, a curve of the type illustrated in Fig. 10-5b. (Note that for free electrons v is proportional to k.) At the top and bottom of the energy band $v = 0$, because from the periodicity of the $E(k)$ curves it follows that there $dE/dk = 0$. The absolute value of the velocity reaches a maximum for $k = k_0$, where k_0 corresponds to the inflection point of the $E(k)$ curve. It is of importance to note that beyond this point the velocity decreases with increasing energy, a feature which is altogether different from the behavior of free electrons.

The effective mass of an electron. Let us now consider what happens to an electron when an external electric field F is applied.[7] It will be assumed that the Brillouin zone under consideration contains only one electron, so that the Pauli exclusion principle does not enter. Suppose the electron is initially in a state k. When the field has acted on the electron for a small time dt, it has gained an energy

$$dE = eFv\, dt = (eF/\hbar)(dE/dk)\, dt \quad (10\text{-}34)$$

[6] See, for example, M. Born, *Atomic Physics*, 5th ed., Hafner, New York, 1951.

[7] To avoid confusion with the energy, the electric field will be represented by F.

where we used (10-33).[8] Now $dE = (dE/dk)\,dk$ so that as a result of the applied field, the rate of change of the wave vector is given by

$$dk/dt = eF/\hbar \tag{10-35}$$

To obtain the acceleration of the electron, differentiate (10-33) with respect to t; this gives

$$a = dv/dt = (1/\hbar)(d^2E/dk^2)(dk/dt) \tag{10-36}$$

From the last two equations it follows that

$$a = (eF/\hbar^2)(d^2E/dk^2) \tag{10-37}$$

It is illustrative to compare this result with the acceleration of a free electron of mass m,

$$a = eF/m$$

From the last two expressions it follows that the electron behaves as if it had an effective mass m^* equal to

$$m^* = \hbar^2/(d^2E/dk^2) \tag{10-38}$$

Thus the effective mass is determined by d^2E/dk^2; this result indicates once more the importance of the $E(k)$ curves for the motion of the electrons. In Fig. 10-5c the effective mass is represented as a function of k; this curve shows the interesting feature that m^* is positive in the lower half of the energy band and negative in the upper half. At the inflection points in the $E(k)$ curves, m^* becomes infinite. Physically speaking, this means that in the upper half of the band the electron behaves as a positively charged particle, as will be explained further in Sec. 10-6. One arrives at the same conclusion by considering the $v(k)$ curve and making use of (10-35). Suppose an electron starts at $k = 0$; when an electric field is applied, the wave vector increases linearly with time. Until the velocity reaches its maximum value, the electron is accelerated by the field; beyond the maximum, however, the same field produces a decrease in v, i.e., the mass must become negative in the upper part of the band.

It is frequently convenient to introduce a factor

$$f_k = m/m^* = (m/\hbar^2)(d^2E/dk^2) \tag{10-39}$$

where f_k is a measure for the extent to which an electron in state k is "free." If m^* is large, f_k is small, i.e., the particle behaves as a "heavy" particle. When $f_k = 1$, the electron behaves as a free electron. Note that f_k is positive in the lower half of the band and negative in the upper half, as shown in Fig. 10-5d.

[8] Throughout this section, only the influence of the external field on the motion of the electron will be discussed. Actually, the electron also interacts with lattice vibrations, leading to resistivity. The problem of resistivity is discussed in Chapter 11.

It may be mentioned here that when the above treatment is extended to three dimensions, the effective mass may be represented by

$$1/m^* = (1/\hbar^2)\, \text{grad}_k\, \text{grad}_k\, E(k)$$

where $\text{grad}_k\, \text{grad}_k\, E(k)$ is a tensor with nine components of the general form $\partial^2 E/\partial k_i\, \partial k_j$ with $i, j = x, y, z$.[9]

10-5. The distinction between metals, insulators, and intrinsic semiconductors

Although a proper distinction between these three groups of materials is possible only by considering the results of a three-dimensional periodic potential, it is instructive at this point to indicate how the band theory leads naturally to the possibility of such a distinction. To see this, let us consider a particular energy band which we shall assume to be filled with electrons up to a certain value k_1, as indicated in Fig. 10-6. As far as the influence of an external electric field is concerned one would like to know with how many "free" electrons the N electrons in the band are equivalent.

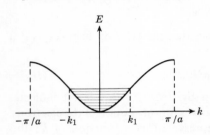

Fig. 10-6. Energy band filled up to states k_1 at $T = 0$.

Presumably, once we knew the answer to this question, it would be possible to draw conclusions about the conductivity associated with this band. The effective number of "free" electrons in the band is in accordance with the preceding section equal to

$$N_{\text{eff}} = \Sigma f_k \qquad (10\text{-}40)$$

where the summation extends over all occupied states in the band. Now, according to (10-31) the number of states in an interval dk (excluding the spin) for a one-dimensional lattice of length L is equal to $L\, dk/2\pi$. Because two electrons occupy each of these states in the shaded region of Fig. 10-6, one may write instead of (10-40),

$$N_{\text{eff}} = (L/\pi) \int_{-k_1}^{+k_1} f_k\, dk = (2Lm/\pi\hbar^2) \int_0^{k_1} (d^2E/dk^2)\, dk$$

where we used (10-39). Thus the effective number of electrons in the band is

$$N_{\text{eff}} = (2Lm/\pi\hbar^2)(dE/dk)_{k=k_1} \qquad (10\text{-}41)$$

[9] See, for example, F. Seitz, op. cit., p. 316.

From this result we draw the following conclusions:

(i) The effective number of electrons in a completely filled band vanishes, because dE/dk vanishes at the top of the band.

(ii) The effective number of electrons reaches a maximum for a band filled to the inflection point of the $E(k)$ curve, because then dE/dk is a maximum.

From the above discussion it follows that a solid for which a certain number of energy bands are completely filled, the other bands being

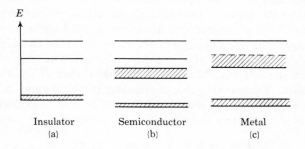

Insulator   Semiconductor   Metal
(a)   (b)   (c)

Fig. 10-7.   Electron distribution at $T = 0$ in an insulator, intrinsic semiconductor, and metal. The shaded regions are occupied by electrons.

completely empty, is an insulator (see Fig. 10-7a). On the other hand, a solid containing an energy band which is incompletely filled has metallic character (Fig. 10-7c). It will be evident that the situation depicted by Fig. 10-7a can occur actually only at absolute zero, when the crystal is in its lowest energy state. At temperatures different from zero, some electrons from the upper filled band will be excited into the next empty band ("conduction band") and conduction becomes possible. If the forbidden energy gap is of the order of several electron volts, however, the solid will remain an "insulator" for all practical purposes. An example is diamond, for which the forbidden gap is about 7 ev. For a small gap width, say about 1 ev, the number of thermally excited electrons may become appreciable and in this case one speaks of an intrinsic semiconductor. Examples are germanium and silicon. It is evident that the distinction between insulators and intrinsic semiconductors is only a quantitative one. In fact, all intrinsic semiconductors are insulators at $T = 0$, whereas all insulators may be considered semiconductors at $T > 0$. It may be noted here that the conductivity of semiconductors in general increases with increasing temperature, whereas the conductivity of metals decreases with increasing temperature. The properties of these materials will be further discussed in later chapters.

It must be noted that three-dimensional models allow the possibility of overlapping of bands (see Sec. 10-9); i.e., a solid which in the one-dimensional model should be an insulator may turn out to be a metal; the divalent metals are an example in point, as we shall see later.

10-6. The concept of a "hole"

It has just been mentioned that in an intrinsic semiconductor at temperatures different from zero, a certain number of electrons may be excited thermally from the upper filled band into the conduction band. Thus some of the states in the normally filled band are unoccupied. We shall see in the next chapter that these unoccupied states lie essentially near the top of the filled band. For the moment, let us consider a single "hole" in the filled band of a one-dimensional lattice and consider its influence on the collective behavior of this band when an external electric field is applied. Denoting the charge of an electron by $-e$ and the velocities of the electrons by v_i, we may write for the current associated with all electrons in a completely filled band in the absence of an external field,

$$I = -e \sum_i v_i = -e \left[v_j + \sum_{i \neq j} v_i \right] = 0 \qquad (10\text{-}42)$$

Thus if the electron j were missing, we should have

$$I' = -e \sum_{i \neq j} v_i = e v_j \qquad (10\text{-}43)$$

Applying an external field F, the rate of change of the current I' due to the field is

$$dI'/dt = e(dv_j/dt) = -e^2 F/m_j^* \qquad (10\text{-}44)$$

Now, since holes tend to reside in the upper part of a nearly filled band, m_j^* is negative and the right-hand side of (10-44) becomes positive. In other words, a band in which an electron is missing behaves as a "positive hole" with an effective mass $|m^*|$. This concept is of great importance in the theory of conductivity and Hall effect as we shall see later. It explains, for example, why certain materials show a positive rather than a negative Hall coefficient (free electrons give a negative Hall coefficient).

10-7. Motion of electrons in a three-dimensional lattice

So far, the discussion has been limited to a simple one-dimensional periodic potential. We shall now consider the motion of electrons in a three-dimensional lattice from a general point of view. The results are very similar, though more complicated, to those for the Kronig-Penney model.

The most fundamental property of an infinite crystal with primitive translation vectors a_1, a_2, a_3, is that if we make a translation corresponding to any vector,

$$d = d_1\, a_1 + d_2\, a_2 + d_3\, a_3 \qquad (10\text{-}45)$$

where d_1, d_2, d_3, are integers, we arrive at a point that is geometrically equivalent to the point we started from. Thus the physical properties remain unchanged when we make a translation defined by any vector of the type d. For example, if the potential energy of an electron is given by $V(r)$, we must have

$$V(r) = V(r + d) \qquad (10\text{-}46)$$

Vectors such as d are called direct lattice vectors; the adjective "direct" is included to distinguish such vectors from the "reciprocal" lattice vectors to be introduced below. In order to discuss the behavior of an electron in a periodic potential it will be convenient to consider first how one represents periodic functions such as (10-46) in terms of three-dimensional Fourier series. For a one-dimensional periodic potential which satisfies the condition

$$V(x) = V(x + d_1 a) \quad \text{where} \quad d_1 = \text{integer}$$

one may of course always write

$$V(x) = \sum_g V_g \exp\left(2\pi i g x/a\right) \quad g = \text{integer} \qquad (10\text{-}47)$$

where the summation extends over all integers from $-\infty$ to $+\infty$; the coefficients V_g are the Fourier coefficients. That this series indeed satisfies the periodicity requirement may readily be shown as follows. Replacing x in (10-47) by $x + d_1 a$, where d_1 is an integer, we obtain

$$V(x + d_1 a) = \sum_g V_g \exp\left(2\pi i g x/a + 2\pi i g d_1\right)$$

However, since $g d_1$ is an integer, $\exp\left(2\pi i d_1 g\right) = 1$ and the right-hand side of this expression equals $V(x)$.

Similarly, the potential in a cubic lattice satisfies the requirement

$$V(x,y,z) = V(x + d_1 a,\, y + d_2 a,\, z + d_3 a) \qquad (10\text{-}48)$$

where d_1, d_2, d_3 are integers. The reader may readily verify that $V(x,y,z)$ may be written in the form of the following three-dimensional Fourier series.

$$V(x,y,z) = \sum_{g_1}\sum_{g_2}\sum_{g_3} V_{g_1 g_2 g_3} \exp\left[(2\pi i/a)(g_1 x + g_2 y + g_3 z)\right] \qquad (10\text{-}49)$$

Returning now to the general three-dimensional lattice for which the primitive translations a_1, a_2, a_3 are not necessarily equal in magnitude, nor perpendicular to each other, it is not immediately obvious how one represents a potential with the periodicity (10-46) in terms of a three-dimensional Fourier series. It can be done rather easily, however, if we introduce the so-called reciprocal lattice. The reciprocal lattice is defined by three primitive translations b_1, b_2, b_3 which satisfy the conditions

$$a_i \cdot b_j = \delta_{ij} = \begin{cases} 1 & if \quad i = j \\ 0 & if \quad i \neq j \end{cases} \qquad (10\text{-}50)$$

Thus the vector b_1 is perpendicular to the plane through the direct lattice vectors a_2 and a_3. The explicit expressions for the b's are evidently of the form

$$b_1 = \frac{a_2 \times a_3}{a_1 \cdot (a_2 \times a_3)}, \quad \text{etc.} \qquad (10\text{-}51)$$

from which the absolute magnitudes of the b's may be obtained in terms of the primitive translations of the direct lattice. Any vector

$$n = n_1 b_1 + n_2 b_2 + n_3 b_3 \qquad n_1, n_2, n_3 \text{ integers} \qquad (10\text{-}52)$$

is called a reciprocal lattice vector. The end points of these vectors define the reciprocal lattice points. The reader may show himself that the reciprocal lattice of an f.c.c. lattice is b.c.c. and vice versa.[10]

We shall now show that the three-dimensional Fourier series,

$$V(r) = \sum_n V_n \exp(2\pi i n \cdot r) \qquad (10\text{-}53)$$

exhibits the periodicity requirement (10-46).[11] The symbol V_n stands for $V_{n_1 n_2 n_3}$ and the summation extends over all integers n_1, n_2, n_3 from $-\infty$ to $+\infty$. The proof is as follows. Applying to (10-53) a translation over a direct lattice vector d, we obtain

$$V(r + d) = \sum_n V_n \exp[2\pi i(n \cdot r + n \cdot d)]$$

However, $n \cdot d$ according to (10-45), (10-50), and (10-52) is equal to $n_1 d_1 + n_2 d_2 + n_3 d_3$, which is an integer. Hence the right-hand side of the last expression is equal to $V(r)$, which proves the statement.

Since we now have a method for representing periodic functions in three dimensions in terms of Fourier series, let us consider some of the general features of the motion of electrons in a potential of three-dimensional periodicity. First of all, the Bloch theorem concerning the form of the wave functions, discussed for the one-dimensional case in Sec.

---

[10] For other properties of the reciprocal lattice, see, for example, Brillouin's book quoted at the end of this chapter.

[11] Some authors define the reciprocal lattice by means of the relations $a_i \cdot b_j = 2\pi\delta_{ij}$; with this definition the factor 2π in the exponential of (10-53) is absent.

10-2, may be extended to three dimensions. The result is that the wave functions are, in analogy with (10-4), of the type

$$\psi(r) = e^{\pm i k \cdot r} u_k(r) \tag{10-54}$$

where $u_k(r)$ has the periodicity of the lattice. Hence, in general, we may write

$$u_k(r) = \sum_n c_n \exp(2\pi i n \cdot r) \tag{10-55}$$

where n is a vector in the reciprocal lattice. In analogy with what has been said in connection with equation (10-28), one can show that any two Bloch functions for which the wave vectors differ by 2π times a reciprocal lattice vector are physically equivalent. For example, let n be a reciprocal lattice vector and let us introduce instead of k another wave vector $k' = k + 2\pi n$ in (10.54). We may then write

$$\psi(r) = e^{\pm i k' \cdot r} e^{\mp 2\pi i n \cdot r} u_k(r) = e^{\pm i k' \cdot r} u_{k'}(r)$$

where $u_{k'}(r)$ as defined by the above expression is still periodic because $\exp(\pm 2\pi i n \cdot r)$ is periodic, i.e., we are still left with a Bloch function. We can say also that k is not uniquely determined and that k and $k + 2\pi n$ correspond to physically equivalent states. In order to avoid the occurrence of physically equivalent solutions with different k-values, it is convenient to restrict the range of k-values. This can be done most conveniently by limiting the components k_1, k_2, k_3 of k along the directions of b_1, b_2, b_3 to the ranges

$$-\pi b_1 \leqslant k_1 \leqslant \pi b_1$$
$$-\pi b_2 \leqslant k_2 \leqslant \pi b_2 \tag{10-56}$$
$$-\pi b_3 \leqslant k_3 \leqslant \pi b_3$$

In this case we refer to k as the reduced wave vector; the region of k-space defined by (10-56) is referred to as the first Brillouin zone or reduced zone.

As in the Kronig-Penney model, a given reduced wave vector k corresponds to a set of energy values $E_1(k)$, $E_2(k)$, ..., where the subscripts refer to a particular energy band. Within each energy band the k-values are restricted in accordance with (10-56). We shall now show that for a finite crystal the number of possible reduced k-values within a single energy band is equal to the number of unit cells contained in the crystal. This statement is the analogue of conclusion (f) in Sec. 10-3 for the Kronig-Penney model. Consider a crystal in the form of a parallelepiped with edges $N_1 a_1$, $N_2 a_2$, $N_3 a_3$, where N_1, N_2, N_3 are large integers. Employing cyclic boundary conditions (compare 10-29), the wave functions should satisfy the condition

$$w(r) = \psi(r + N_1 a_1 + N_2 a_2 + N_3 a_3) \tag{10-57}$$

Since $\psi(r)$ is a Bloch function of the type (10-54), for which $u_k(r)$ is periodic with the lattice, this condition is equivalent with the requirement

$$k \cdot (N_1 a_1 + N_2 a_2 + N_3 a_3) = 2\pi \text{ times an integer} \qquad (10\text{-}58)$$

This implies that the possible k-values are given by

$$k = 2\pi[(n_1/N_1)b_1 + (n_2/N_2)b_2 + (n_3/N_3)b_3] \qquad (10\text{-}59)$$

where n_1, n_2, n_3 are integers, since upon substituting this expression for k into (10-58) the left-hand side of (10-58) reduces to $2\pi(n_1 + n_2 + n_3)$; any k-value chosen not in accordance with (10-59) does not satisfy (10-58). Now the components of k along the reciprocal lattice vector directions are restricted in accordance with (10-56). From this and from (10-59) it thus follows that n_1, n_2, and n_3 can accept a total of, respectively, N_1, N_2, N_3 different values. In other words, the total number of k-values within an energy band is given by the product $N_1 N_2 N_3$, which is equal to the number of unit cells in the crystal. Each k-value corresponds to one wave function if we exclude the two possible spin directions; including the spin, the number of possible electronic states within an energy band is therefore equal to twice the number of unit cells in the crystal. The result obtained here may be expressed also in the following way. Consider a crystal of unit volume, the volume of the unit cell being $a_1 \cdot (a_2 \times a_3) = \Omega$. The crystal then contains $N = 1/\Omega$ unit cells. We leave it to the reader as a problem to show that the volume of a unit cell in the reciprocal lattice is given by $b_1 \cdot (b_2 \times b_3) = N$. Since the whole reduced zone contains N possible k-values, and since these values are uniformly distributed in the k-space, the number of electronic states dn_s corresponding to a volume element $d\Omega_k$ in k-space is, per unit volume of the crystal,

$$dn_s = (2/8\pi^3)\, d\Omega_k \qquad (10\text{-}60)$$

The factor 2 arises from the spin. The quantity dn_s is referred to as the density of states corresponding to the element $d\Omega_k$ in k-space. In subsequent discussions it will frequently be desirable to introduce the number of states per unit volume of the crystal per unit energy interval. Thus, consider in the k-space two surfaces of constant energy, one of E, the other of $E + dE$. The volume element $d\Omega_k$ in k-space corresponding to a differential area dS and bounded by the constant energy surfaces, is then given by

$$d\Omega_k = dS[|\text{grad}_k\, E(k)|]^{-1}\, dE$$

so that the density of states per unit energy interval is given by

$$dn_s/dE = (2/8\pi^3) \int \frac{dS}{|\text{grad}_k\, E(k)|} \qquad (10\text{-}61)$$

where the integral extends over the whole area of the constant energy planes.

10-8. The tightly bound electron approximation

As an example of evaluating the energy levels for an electron in a solid, we shall discuss one particular approximation in some detail, viz., the tightly bound electron approximation. In this approximation one starts from the wave function for an electron in a free atom and then constructs a crystal orbital, i.e., a Bloch function, which describes the electron in the periodic field of crystal as a whole. This method is abbreviated LCAO, since it is based on a linear combination of atomic orbitals. We shall see that the discrete electron levels corresponding to a free atom will broaden into energy bands as the atoms are brought together in the form of a crystal. The approximation used here is valid only for electrons corresponding to the inner electronic shells in the atoms, as will become clear below from the assumptions that will be introduced.

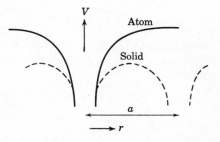

Fig. 10-8. Schematic representation of the potential energy of an electron in an atom (fully drawn) and in a solid (dashed curve).

Consider first an electron in a free atom. Suppose the potential energy of the electron in the field of the nucleus plus that of the other electrons in the atom is given by $V_a(r)$, where r represents the distance from the nucleus. The potential has a form as indicated by the fully drawn curve in Fig. 10-8. Let the wave function of the electron in the free atom be $\phi(r)$ and let its energy be E_0. The wave function then satisfies the Schrödinger equation,

$$-(\hbar^2/2m)\nabla^2\phi + V_a(r)\phi = E_0 \qquad (10\text{-}62)$$

We shall assume that the level is nondegenerate, i.e., there is only one wave function corresponding to E_0. Furthermore, we shall assume that the wave functions are normalized. Suppose then that similar atoms are brought together in the form of a crystal. The potential energy of the electron in the crystal then looks like the dashed curve in Fig. 10-8; the potential energy in this case will be represented by $V(r)$, where $V(r)$ has the periodicity of the lattice. Taking a particular atom as the origin of our coordinate system, the position of any atom may then be represented by a vector R_j where R_j is a lattice vector. In the tightly bound electron approximation it is assumed that the electron in the vicinity of a particular nucleus j is only slightly influenced by the presence of other atoms, i.e., when the end point of the vector r lies in the vicinity of R_j, the wave function for the electron is approximately given by $\phi(r - R_j)$ and the energy of the electron is still very close to the value E_0 in the free atom. Consequently, one calculates the energy of an electron with a wave vector k in the crystal on the basis of a linear combination of the form

$$\psi_k(r) = \sum_j c_j(k)\phi(r - R_j) \qquad (10\text{-}63)$$

since this expression satisfies the approximation just mentioned: if r lies close to R_j all contributions in the sum will be small except that from $\phi(r - R_j)$. However, since we are dealing with an electron in a periodic field, the wave function must be a Bloch function, and this restricts the choice of the coefficients c_j. If in expression (10-63) we take the coefficient $c_j(k)$ equal to exp $(ik \cdot R_j)$ we obtain

$$\psi_k(r) = \sum_j \phi(r - R_j) \exp(ik \cdot R_j) \qquad (10\text{-}64)$$

which indeed has the properties of a Bloch function. This can be seen by applying a transformation corresponding to a lattice vector, say R_m. This gives

$$\psi_k(r + R_m) = \sum_j e^{ik \cdot R_j}\phi[r - (R_j - R_m)]$$
$$= e^{ik \cdot R_m}\sum_j e^{ik \cdot (R_j - R_m)}\phi[r - (R_j - R_m)]$$

The sum in the last expression, however, is equal to $\psi_k(r)$, so that (10-64) satisfies the characteristic property of a Bloch wave. We shall now calculate the energy of an electron with wave vector k in the crystal, based on the wave function (10-64). This can be done by starting from the expression

$$E(k) = \int \psi_k^* \mathscr{H} \psi_k \, d\tau / \int \psi_k^* \psi_k \, d\tau \qquad (10\text{-}65)$$

where $\mathscr{H}$ is the Hamilton operator for an electron in the crystal; the denominator takes care of the proper normalization of the Bloch functions. The denominator becomes

$$\int \psi_k^* \psi_k \, d\tau = \sum_j \sum_m e^{ik \cdot (R_j - R_m)} \int \phi^*(r - R_m)\phi(r - R_j) \, d\tau$$

Now $\phi(r - R_m)$ has appreciable value only when the end point of the vector r lies in the vicinity of atom m; similarly, $\phi(r - R_j)$ has appreciable value only in the vicinity of atom j. In other words, there is very little overlap between the wave functions, even for nearest neighbors. To a first approximation, therefore, we shall neglect all overlapping, so that of the summation over j only the term $j = m$ will be retained. Since we have assumed that the atomic wave functions were normalized, we may then write

$$\int \psi_k^* \psi_k \, d\tau = \sum_m \int \phi^*(r - R_m)\phi(r - R_m) \, d\tau = N \qquad (10\text{-}66)$$

where N is the total number of atoms in the crystal. Let us now consider the numerator of (10-65). The Hamiltonian of an electron in the crystal may be written

$$\mathcal{H} = -(\hbar^2/2m)\nabla^2 + V(r) = -(\hbar^2/2m)\nabla^2 + V(r) - V_a(r - R_j)$$
$$+ V_a(r - R_j) = -(\hbar^2/2m)\nabla^2 + V'(r - R_j) + V_a(r - R_j) \quad (10\text{-}67)$$

where we have introduced the quantity

$$V'(r - R_j) \equiv V(r) - V_a(r - R_j) \quad (10\text{-}68)$$

The reason for this will become obvious below. The physical meaning of $V'(r - R_j)$ is that it represents the potential energy of the electron in the crystal at the point r, minus the potential energy of the electron in the same point if there were only a single atom, viz., the one located at R_j. In other words, $V'(r - R_j)$ represents the potential energy of the electron in point r resulting from the presence of all atoms except the one located at R_j. It is, in a sense, a perturbation potential. According to Fig. 10-8, $V'(r - R_j)$ is a negative quantity. Substituting the Hamilton operator (10-67) into (10-65), making use of (10-66), and realizing that

$$-(\hbar^2/2m)\nabla^2\phi(r - R_j) + V_a(r - R_j)\phi(r - R_j) = E_0 \; \phi(r - R_j)$$

where E_0 is the energy of the electron in the free atom, we obtain

$$E(k) = (1/N) \sum_j \sum_m e^{ik \cdot (R_j - R_m)} \int \phi^*(r - R_m)[E_0 + V'(r - R_j)]\phi(r - R_j) \, d\tau$$

First consider the term containing E_0. Since the overlapping is small anyway, we may neglect in the summation over m all terms except $m = j$. Thus the term containing E_0 becomes

$$(1/N) \sum_j \int \phi^*(r - R_j)E_0\phi(r - R_j) \, d\tau = E_0$$

In the term containing the "perturbing" potential $V'(r - R_j)$ we shall neglect all overlap except for wave functions ϕ corresponding to nearest neighbors. Furthermore, we shall assume that the atomic wave functions ϕ are spherically symmetric, which would be the case if they corresponded to s functions. Defining two positive quantities α and γ such that

$$\alpha = -\int\phi^*(r - R_j)V'(r - R_j) \; \phi(r - R_j) \, d\tau \quad (10\text{-}69)$$

$$\gamma = -\int \phi^* (r - R_m)V'(r - R_j)\phi(r - R_j) \, d\tau \quad (10\text{-}70)$$

where the vector R_m is understood to correspond to the location of one of the nearest neighbors of atom j, we may finally write

$$E(k) = E_0 - \alpha - \gamma \sum_m e^{ik \cdot (R_j - R_m)} \quad (10\text{-}71)$$

where the summation extends over nearest neighbors of atom j only. Note that α and γ are positive because $V'(r - R_j)$ is negative. It is observed that the energy of the electron in the crystal differs from the energy of the electron in the free atom by a constant factor α plus a term which depends on the wave vector $\boldsymbol{k}$. It is this last part which transforms the discrete atomic level into an energy band in the solid. In order to see this more clearly, we shall apply this result to the case of cubic crystals in the next section.

Another important approximation is the so-called nearly free electron approximation. In this case it is assumed that the Fourier coefficients of the periodic potential are small relative to the constant potential. This approximation may therefore be expected to be applicable to the conduction electrons in monovalent metals. The energy versus wave vector curves obtained for a one-dimensional lattice on the basis of this approximation resemble closely those given in Fig. 10-4 for the Kronig-Penney model.

For a discussion of the nearly free electron approximation as well as other approximations we refer the reader to the literature.

10-9. Application to a simple cubic lattice

In order to appreciate the consequences of the results obtained in the preceding section we shall first apply expression (10-71) to a simple cubic lattice. In this lattice a given atom has six nearest neighbors, located such that

$$\boldsymbol{R}_j - \boldsymbol{R}_m = (\pm a, 0, 0); \quad (0, \pm a, 0); \quad (0, 0, \pm a)$$

Evaluation of the sum in (10-71) then yields for the energy of an s electron in the crystal

$$E(\boldsymbol{k}) = E_0 - \alpha - 2\gamma(\cos k_x a + \cos k_y a + \cos k_z a) \qquad (10\text{-}72)$$

From this we may draw a number of important conclusions. In the first place it is observed that the part of $E(\boldsymbol{k})$ which depends on the wave vector $\boldsymbol{k}$ is periodic with $\boldsymbol{k}$. In order for $\boldsymbol{k}$ to be uniquely determined we should restrict the components to the regions $-\pi/a \leq k_x \leq \pi/a$, etc. Since the reciprocal of a simple cubic lattice of edge a is again a simple cubic lattice with edge $b = 1/a$, this conclusion is in agreement with the general expressions (10-56); see also (10-27). The first Brillouin zone in this case is evidently a cube of edge $2\pi/a$ in $\boldsymbol{k}$-space, the origin of $\boldsymbol{k}$-space being located at the centre of the cube. Furthermore, since the cosine terms vary between ± 1, the energy levels are contained within an energy band of a total width 12γ. The bottom of the energy band is given by

$$E_{\text{bottom}} = E_0 - \alpha - 6\gamma$$

and the top is given by

$$E_{\text{top}} = E_0 - \alpha + 6\gamma$$

From the definition (10-70) of γ it follows that the width of the band increases as the overlap of the wave functions on neighboring atoms increases. Thus the inner electronic levels of the free atoms give rise to narrow bands in the solid; as one proceeds to the outer shells the corresponding band widths in the solid increase. This conclusion is in agreement with conclusion (c) in Sec. 10-3 derived from the Kronig-Penney model. By way of illustration we have represented in Fig. 10-9 the formation of energy bands for sodium according to Slater.[12]

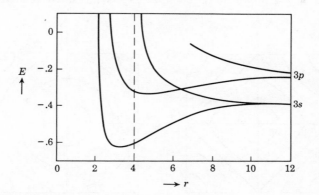

Fig. 10-9. Formation of the $3s$ and $3p$ bands in sodium. The energy E is plotted in Rydberg units as function of half the distance between nearest neighbors (in atomic units). The dashed line corresponds to the actual metal. [After Slater, ref. 12]

The bottom of the band corresponds to

$$\cos k_x a = \cos k_y a = \cos k_z a = 1$$

i.e., to $k = 0$ in this case. As long as k is small, the cosine terms may be expanded. Retaining only the first approximation of this expansion, one obtains from (10-72)

$$E \simeq E_0 - \alpha - 6\gamma + \gamma a^2 k^2 \quad \text{for small } k \qquad (10\text{-}73)$$

where $k^2 = k_x + k_y^2 + k_z^2$. It is observed that with reference to the bottom of the band, the energy of the electron is proportional to k^2, as in the case of free electrons; the constant energy surfaces are then spheres. Thus in this region the electrons may be considered free electrons with an effective mass m^* determined by

$$\hbar^2 k^2 / 2m^* = \gamma a^2 k^2 \quad \text{or} \quad m^* = \hbar^2 / 2\gamma a^2 \qquad (10\text{-}74)$$

As the band width decreases (decreasing γ), the effective mass of the electrons near the bottom of the band increases. This is consistent with the qualitative notion that strongly bound electrons do not move readily from

[12] J. C. Slater, *Phys. Rev.*, **45**, 794 (1934); **49**, 537 (1936).

one atom to another; they have a high effective mass, and the acceleration produced by an electric field will be relatively small.

The top of the band corresponds to $\cos k_x a = \cos k_y a = \cos k_z a = -1$, i.e., to $k_x, k_y, k_z = \pm \pi/a$. Thus the corner points of the reduced zone correspond to states at the top of the band. In the vicinity of such a corner point we may expand the cosines again; for example, if we expand about the point $k_x = k_y = k_z = \pi/a$ we may write $\cos k_x a = \cos(\pi - k'_x a)$ where the new component $k'_x = \pi/a - k_x$ is measured relative to the

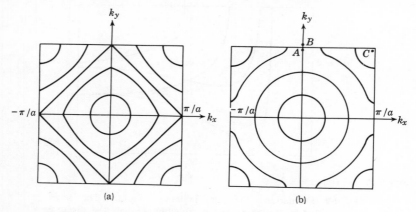

(a)   (b)

Fig. 10-10. Schematic representation of constant-energy curves for a two-dimensional square lattice: (a) for the tightly bound electron approximation; (b) for the nearly free electron approximation.

corner point. For small values of k'_x we then obtain $\cos(\pi - k'_x a) = -\cos k'_x a = -1 + (k'_x a)^2/2$. Hence near the top of the band, (10-72) leads to

$$E \simeq E_0 - \alpha + 6\gamma - \gamma a^2 k'^2 \quad \text{(near top)} \qquad (10\text{-}75)$$

Thus, relative to the top of the band, the electron energy is proportional to k'^2, where the new wave vector k' is measured from the corner point of the Brillouin zone. Constant-energy surfaces in this region are therefore again spherical, but with the corner point as center. By way of illustration we give in Fig. 10-10a a schematic representation of constant-energy surfaces in k-space for a two-dimensional square lattice, based on the tightly bound electron approximation. In the nearly free electron approximation, the proportionality with k^2 of the energy relative to the bottom of the band extends to much larger values of the wave vector than in the tightly bound approximation. Here again, however, constant energy surfaces near the top of the band are spherical relative to corner points of the reduced zone. This is illustrated for comparison in Fig. 10-10b.

It is left as a problem for the reader to discuss in a similar manner the application of the tightly bound electron approximation to body-centered and face-centered cubic lattices.

10-10. Brillouin zones; density of states; overlapping of energy bands

In order to understand the electronic properties of solids the following topics need some discussion: 1. the structure of the Brillouin zones, 2. the shape of constant-energy surfaces in k-space, 3. the density of states as function of energy, 4. the possibility of overlapping of energy bands. Some of these topics have already been discussed to some extent above; in the present section we shall consider these topics somewhat further. The discussion will mainly be concerned with simple cubic lattices.

The structure of Brillouin zones. In the preceding section we had arrived at the conclusion that the first Brillouin zone of a simple cubic lattice is given by a cube of edge $2\pi/a$, where a is the lattice constant. Although for many purposes only the first or reduced Brillouin zone is sufficient, it is sometimes desirable to introduce higher zones. The structure of the Brillouin zones may be obtained on the basis of the general discussion of Sec. 10-7 involving the reciprocal lattice. Consider the set of vectors $2\pi(n_1 b_1 + n_2 b_2 + n_3 b_3)$, where n_1, n_2, n_3 are

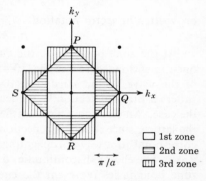

Fig. 10-11. The first three Brillouin zones for a square lattice of edge a.

1st zone
2nd zone
3rd zone

integers and b_1, b_2, b_3 are the primitive translations of the reciprocal lattice. The end points of the vectors so defined form a lattice which may be considered an enlarged reciprocal lattice, the enlargement factor being 2π. In this lattice we shall represent the k-vectors, choosing a particular lattice point as origin for the k-space. Suppose now we draw vectors from the origin to all other lattice points and that we draw planes which bisect these vectors perpendicularly. The smallest volume enclosed by these planes is then the first Brillouin zone. That this is consistent with our previous discussion may be seen from the definition of the first Brillouin zone according to (10-56). In order to illustrate the procedure with regard to higher zones, consider the case of a square lattice in Fig. 10-11. The lattice points of the "blown-up" reciprocal lattice are separated by a distance $2\pi/a$, forming again a square lattice. The first Brillouin zone in this case is a square of edge $2\pi/a$. The second Brillouin zone is defined by the area between the smallest and next smallest area enclosed by the lines bisecting the lattice vectors. Higher zones are obtained in a similar way. The zone boundaries are determined by the equations

$$n_x k_x + n_y k_y = \pi(n_x^2 + n_y^2)/a \qquad (10\text{-}76)$$

where n_x and n_y are integers. The first Brillouin zone is enclosed by the four lines corresponding to $n_x = \pm 1$, $n_y = 0$ and $n_x = 0$, $n_y = \pm 1$. The square $PQRS$ in Fig. 10-11 is determined by four lines corresponding to the four sets of integers n_x, $n_y = \pm 1$, ± 1. The area between $PQRS$ and the first zone forms the second Brillouin zone. Note that the areas of the zones are equal.

The extension of this procedure to the simple cubic lattice is relatively easy. The zone boundaries are in this case in analogy with (10-76) given by the solutions of the equation

$$n_x k_x + n_y k_y + n_z k_z = \pi(n_x^2 + n_y^2 + n_z^2)/a \qquad (10\text{-}77)$$

or, written in vector notation.

$$\boldsymbol{n} \cdot \boldsymbol{k} = \pi n^2/a \qquad (10\text{-}78)$$

At the zone boundaries, the energy exhibits a discontinuity as in the one-dimensional case (see Fig. 10-4). It is of interest to note that the values of the wave vector satisfying (10-78) are those for which the electron suffers a Bragg reflection.[13] We leave it as a problem to show that this is the case. An electron which satisfies the Bragg condition cannot penetrate the lattice, since it suffers reflections. Such an electron therefore does not correspond to a wave propagating through the crystal, but to a standing wave. The energy discontinuities or energy gaps occurring at the Brillouin zone boundaries represent the energy ranges for which it is impossible for an electron to move through the crystal. This is clearly borne out by the fact that if such electrons are incident on the crystal from the outside, they are totally reflected and unable to penetrate into the crystal. For the structure of Brillouin zones for various crystal structures we refer the reader to the literature.[14]

The density of states as function of energy. The number of electronic states per unit volume associated with a volume element $d\Omega_k$ in the k-space is, according to (10-60), equal to $(2/8\pi^3)\, d\Omega_k$. The density of states per unit energy interval is given by the general expression (10-61). Let us now consider the consequences of this for a simple cubic lattice. In order to simplify the problem, let us assume that the constant-energy surfaces are spheres or parts of spheres around the center of the first Brillouin zone. This situation is approached in the nearly free electron approximation (see Fig. 10-10b), although even there it does not hold in the vicinity of the corner points of the zone. With this assumption we have, as for free electrons, $E(k) = \hbar^2 k^2/2m^*$. Since the density of states corresponding to wave vectors for which the absolute magnitude lies between k and $k + dk$ is given by $(2/8\pi^3)4\pi k^2\, dk$, we obtain for the density of states $Z(E)\, dE$, corresponding to an energy interval dE

$$Z(E)\, dE = CE^{1/2}\, dE \quad \text{with} \quad C = 4\pi(2m^*/h^2)^{3/2} \qquad (10\text{-}79)$$

[13] See, for example, N. F. Mott and H. Jones, *op. cit.*, p. 64.
[14] See, for example, N. F. Mott and H. Jones, *op. cit.*, Chap. 5.

Hence $Z(E)$ increases as $E^{1/2}$; also note that as the effective mass increases, $Z(E)$ increases. For narrow energy bands, therefore, $Z(E)$ rises more rapidly than for broad bands. For the example under consideration, expression (10-79) will hold up to values of the wave vector equal to $k = \pi/a$ because for this k-value the spherical constant energy surface just touches the Brillouin zone boundary. For larger values of k and E, only the corners of the cube are available for electronic states, and (10-79) can no longer be used. In fact, for $k = (\pi/a)\sqrt{3}$ the density of states becomes zero. One thus obtains a $Z(E)$ curve as represented schematically in Fig. 10-12; the energy E_1 corresponds to $k = \pi/a$.

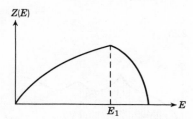

Fig. **10-12.** Schematic representation of the density of states versus energy for a simple cubic lattice, assuming spherical energy surfaces; the energy $E_1 = \pi^2 h^2/2m^* a^2$.

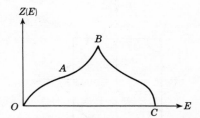

Fig. **10-13.** Schematic representation of the density of states as function of energy in an energy band.

Actually, the $E(k)$ surfaces are spherical around the point $k = 0$ only in the vicinity of the bottom of the band, as may be seen from Fig. 10-10. In general, therefore, the density of states as function of energy exhibits a shape of the type indicated in Fig. 10-13. Close to the bottom of the band, (10-79) holds (OA); as one approaches the zone boundary E does not change much with k (compare Fig. 10-4) and thus the density of states increases relative to (10-79), leading to a peak (AB); the subsequent drop (BC) is a result of the fact that only the corners of the zone are available. Near the top of the band, $Z(E)$ approaches zero as $(E_{\text{top}} - E)^{1/2}$ in agreement with the behavior expressed by equation (10-75).

Overlapping of energy bands. In the one-dimensional model there exists a clear-cut difference between metals and insulators: for a linear lattice to be a metal, there must exist an incompletely filled band. If the same simple picture were true for a three-dimensional lattice however, all divalent metals should be insulators, as will be explained further in Sec. 10-11. That elements such as Be, Ca, Ba, etc. are metallic is a result of overlapping of energy bands, a phenomenon which in the one-dimensional model is absent. This may be explained with reference to Fig. 10-10b, in particular by considering the energy corresponding to the points A, B, and C. (A and C lie within the first zone, B in the second zone.) Let these energies be denoted, respectively, by E_A, E_B, and E_C. In crossing the Brillouin zone from A to B, the energy changes discontinuously by the amount $\Delta E = E_B - E_A$. There exist now two possibilities with regard to E_B and E_C, viz.,

$$E_B > E_C \quad \text{or} \quad E_B < E_C$$

In the former case all energies inside the first Brillouin zone are lower than any of those in the second zone. This is likely to be the case when the energy discontinuity ΔE is large. In the second case, however, the lowest energy state in the second zone (E_B) lies below the top of the first

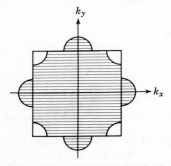

Fig. 10-14. Electron distribution (shaded) for the case of partial overlapping of the first and second energy bands; the number of holes in the first zone equals the number of electrons in the second zone if there are two electrons per atom.

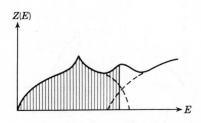

Fig. 10-15. Schematic representation of the density of states versus energy in the case of two overlapping bands. The shaded region may correspond to states occupied by electrons in case each atom contributes two electrons.

band (E_C). Thus the two bands overlap to some extent, and this may possibly happen when ΔE is relatively small. It is instructive to consider the consequences of this type of overlapping by filling up the available states with electrons. Suppose we use twice as many electrons as there are unit cells in the crystal; this number would just completely fill a band in the absence of overlapping. With overlapping, the electron distribution in the two-dimensional case would look as indicated in Fig. 10-14. The first zone is partly empty, the second zone is partly filled, because there are energy states available in the latter which lie below those at the top of the first zone. It will be evident that under these circumstances conduction becomes possible and the solid may behave as a metal, be it a "poor" one. In Fig. 10-15 we have represented schematically the density of states when overlap occurs.

10-11. The zone structure of metals

It is impossible within the scope of this volume to give a detailed account of the zone structure of metals; we shall therefore confine ourselves to a few general remarks.[15] First of all, for not too complicated structures such as the f.c.c., b.c.c., and hexagonal lattice, it is always possible to choose the unit cell in such a fashion that there is one atom per unit cell. For example, in the f.c.c. lattice one may use as translational vectors those joining a given corner atom with atoms at the center of three

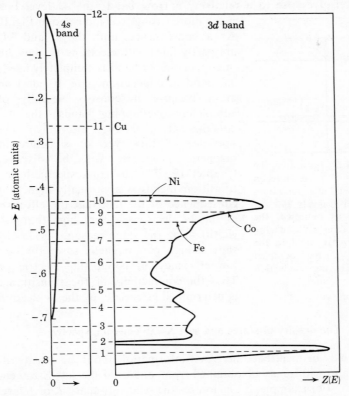

Fig. 10-16. The density of quantum states of copper in the 4s and 3d bands; the dashed lines indicate the highest filled levels for the transition metals, assuming the $Z(E)$ curves are the same as that for Cu. [After H. M. Krutter, *Phys. Rev.*, **48**, 664 (1935); see also J. C. Slater, *J. Appl. Phys.*, **8**, 385 (1937)]

faces (see Fig. 1-4a). Under these circumstances, each band can accommodate twice as many electrons as there are atoms in the lattice. It then follows that electronic shells which are filled in the atom will lead to completely filled bands in the solid state (at least if $T = 0$). It is therefore not difficult to understand that monovalent elements such as the alkalis, Cu, Ag, Au are metallic because they contain a half-filled band. In the

---

[15] For a review, see F. V. Raynor, *Repts. Progr. Phys.*, **15**, 173 (1952).

divalent metals such as Ca, Ba, Sr, etc. there is evidently overlapping between the energy bands associated with the valence electrons.

The zone structure of the transition elements is of considerable interest. For example, the elements of the iron group have an incompletely filled 3d shell in the atomic state. As the atoms are brought together, the 3d level gives rise to a relatively narrow band; the 4s level broadens much more strongly, as indicated in Fig. 10-16.[16]

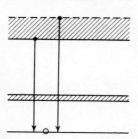

Fig. 10-17. Illustrating the process of X-ray emission by a metal after ionization of K or L levels. For the transitions indicated, the width of the emitted energy spectrum is equal to the width of the occupied region in the conduction band.

As a consequence, both the 4s and 3d bands are partly filled with electrons in these metals; in copper the 3d band is completely filled. (The 3d band can accommodate 10 electrons per atom because it consists actually of five completely overlapping bands; the 4s band contains at most two electrons.) The importance of this type of structure for the magnetic properties will be discussed in Chapter 19. The electronic specific heat of the transition metals is abnormally high. This is a consequence of the fact that the effective mass of the 3d electrons is very high (narrow band width). For the same reason, the 3d electrons show a high paramagnetic susceptibility and a low efficiency for conducting electric current. Thus the conductivity of the transition metals is determined essentially by the 4s electrons.

10-12. The density of states and soft X-ray emission spectra

It may be mentioned here that information about the density of states and band width may be obtained from studies of the soft X-ray emission spectra. For example, if one ionizes the relatively sharp K or L levels in a solid by bombardment with fast electrons, electrons from higher bands will make transitions to the vacated levels, with emission of X-rays. It is evident from Fig. 10-17 that the spectrum of the emitted radiation provides information about the energy distribution of the electrons in the higher energy bands.[17] Thus it is possible to determine the bandwidth of the upper bands, at least so far as they are occupied by electrons. One has found, for example, that the conduction electrons in Al cover a range of $\sim$12 ev, in Li $\sim$4.2 ev, and in Na $\sim$3.0 ev. This method may of course also be used to determine

[16] N. F. Mott, *Proc. Phys. Soc.* (*London*), **47**, 571 (1935); **49**, 258 (1937); **62**, 416 (1949).

[17] For a review see, for example, H. W. B. Skinner, *Repts. Prog. Phys.*, **5**, 257 (1939); *Trans. Roy. Soc.* (*London*), **A239**, 95 (1940). For recent work in this field see E. M. Gyorgy and G. G. Harvey, *Phys. Rev.*, **87**, 861 (1952); **93**, 365 (1954).

the bandwidth of the upper filled band in insulators. The exact shape of the emission spectrum also depends on the transition probabilities.

10-13. The Wigner-Seitz approximation and the cohesive energy of metals

In view of its importance, a few words may be said here about the Wigner-Seitz approximation, which is based on the following physical model.[18] Imagine a number of straight lines joining the nucleus of a particular atom in a metal with those of its nearest and next nearest neighbors. A set of planes bisecting these lines perpendicularly then defines what is known as an atomic polyhedron. An example is given in Fig. 10-18 for a body-centered cubic lattice. These polyhedra evidently fill the whole space occupied by the crystal. Confining ourselves to monovalent metals, each of the polyhedra contains a singly charged positive ion; one of the aims of this approximation is to obtain information about the behavior of the valence electrons in the field of these ions. Near the center of a polyhedron, the potential will be spherically symmetric;

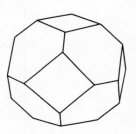

Fig. 10-18. Atomic polyhedron for a body-centered cubic lattice.

in the vicinity of the boundaries of the polyhedron the field will be small. In the Wigner-Seitz approximation it is assumed that the field is spherically symmetric inside the whole polyhedron; also, the field is assumed to be that of the singly charged positive ion at the center.

Consider now the wave function for an electron in the state $k = 0$. Then, because the wave function must be of the Bloch type, it follows that $\psi = u_k(r)$, i.e., the wave function itself must be periodic with the lattice. One may thus require that on the boundary of the polyhedron $\partial\psi/\partial n = 0$, where $\partial/\partial n$ stands for differentiation normal to the surface of the polyhedron. For simplicity, Wigner and Seitz approximate the polyhedron by a sphere of radius r_0 such that $(4\pi/3)r_0^3$ equals the volume of a polyhedron and then use as a boundary condition,

$$(\partial\psi/\partial r)_{r=r_0} = 0 \qquad (10\text{-}80)$$

The problem of calculating $\psi(r)$ then reduces to solving the spherically symmetric Schrödinger equation,

$$\frac{1}{r} \cdot \frac{d^2}{dr^2}(r\psi) + \frac{2m}{\hbar^2}[E - V(r)]\,\psi = 0 \qquad (10\text{-}81)$$

for the boundary condition (10-80). Note that because $V(r)$ represents the

[18] E. Wigner and F. Seitz, *Phys. Rev.*, **43**, 804 (1933); **46**, 509 (1934). See also J. C. Slater, *Phys. Rev.*, **45**, 794 (1934).

potential energy of an electron in the field of a free ion, the solution of (10-81) with the boundary condition $\psi \to 0$ for $r \to \infty$ would be identical with that for the valence electron in the free atom. As an example of the results of such calculations, we reproduce in Fig. 10-19 part of the wave function of a conduction electron (3s) in sodium in its lowest state. It is important to observe that the wave function is very flat over the region between 2 to 4 hydrogen radii. This means that the wave function for $k = 0$ is flat over about 90 per cent of the atomic volume; the total charge

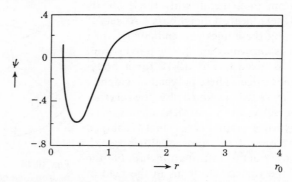

Fig. 10-19. Part of the wave function of a conduction electron in sodium for $k = 0$ as function of the distance from the center of an atomic polyhedron (r is expressed in atomic units).

distribution corresponding to the flat region is nearly equal to e. Now when a Bloch function for $k = 0$ is constant over a certain region of space, we may conclude that the periodic part u_k of the Bloch function is constant, i.e., the electron behaves as a free electron in that region. Thus the valence electrons in sodium and in the other alkali metals behave very much like free electrons. For copper and silver and presumably also for gold, the flat part of the wave functions extends over a relatively small region, and here the free electron model can hardly be applied.[19] It is interesting in this connection to point out that the ratio of the ionic to the metallic radii is much smaller for the alkali metals than for the monovalent noble metals.

	Li	Na	K	Cu	Ag	Au
r_{ionic}/r_{metal}:	0.39	0.51	0.58	0.75	0.88	0.95

Thus Cu, Ag, and Au may be pictured as consisting of a system of hard spheres (the ions) held together by the valence electrons. In the alkali metals on the other hand, the ions are separated by relatively large distances.

[19] N. F. Mott and H. Jones, *op. cit.*, p. 79; R. Fuchs, *Proc. Roy. Soc. (London)*, **A151**, 585 (1935); **153**, 622 (1936).

In Fig. 10-20 we have plotted the energy E_0 of the electron in sodium in the state $\boldsymbol{k} = 0$ as a function of the variable r_0. The physical meaning of E_0 is clearly this: it represents the energy corresponding to the bottom of the conduction band relative to the vacuum level. Thus the Wigner-Seitz approximation allows one to determine what we denoted by E_s in Fig. 9-1.

A "complete" theory of metals should allow one to calculate, among other things, the cohesive energy, the lattice constant, and the elastic constants. Although these problems are necessarily very complicated, a great

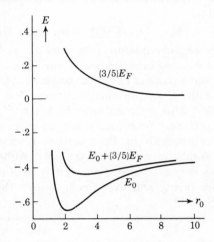

Fig. 10-20.   Curves for E_0, E_F and $E_0 + \frac{3}{5}E_F$ (all in Rydberg units)
versus r_0 (in atomic units) for sodium.

deal of progress has been made towards solving them for simple metals. We shall discuss here a simplified theory of the cohesive energy of metals based on the Wigner-Seitz approximation. In general, the total potential energy of the metal is determined by the interaction of the charges within a given polyhedron plus the interaction of the polyhedra with each other. Suppose now that the valence electrons are distributed such that each polyhedron contains one electron. In that case the polyhedra are neutral, and to a first approximation the interaction between them may be neglected. Doing this, the total energy of the crystal is then given simply by the sum of of the kinetic energy of the electrons plus the potential energy of each electron in the field of a positive ion. Now the latter quantity is given by E_0, represented as function of r_0 in Fig. 10-10. The kinetic energy of the electrons may be obtained to a first approximation by assuming a free electron model for the valence electrons, which for the alkali metals is quite good as we have seen above. In the preceding chapter we have seen that the average energy of such a system is equal to $\frac{3}{5}E_F$. Now, according to (9-9), E_F may be expressed in terms of the density of electrons; making use of the fact that $1/n = (4\pi/3)r_0^3$ one may write

$$E_{\text{kin}} = \tfrac{3}{5}E_F = \tfrac{3}{10}(\hbar^2/mr_0^2)(9\pi/4)^{2/3} \qquad (10\text{-}82)$$

This is represented for Na as function of r_0 in Fig. 10-20; the sum of the curves $E_{\text{kin}}(r_0)$ and $E_0(r_0)$ is also given. The position of the minimum of the curve $E_0 + \tfrac{3}{5}E_F$ determines the calculated lattice constant. From these results the cohesive energy may be obtained with reference to the system of free atoms at infinite separation. When E_I represents the ionization energy of a free atom, the cohesive energy (positive quantity) in the metal is, per atom, equal to

$$E_{\text{cohesive}} = -(E_0 + \tfrac{3}{5}E_F + E_I) \quad \text{with} \quad r_0 = (r_0)_{\text{min}} \qquad (10\text{-}83)$$

Here E_0 is the only negative quantity; E_F and E_I are both positive, and as they increase the binding becomes less strong. The above model is, of course, too simple and a number of corrections are required. For example it is estimated that the Coulomb energy between the valence electrons gives a term $0.6e^2/r_0$; also, account must be taken of the fact that the electrons tend to keep away from each other, an effect which depends on the relative spin orientations of the electrons involved. Furthermore, there are van der Waals forces between the ions. Although it is evident that the problem is a very complicated one, it may be of interest to indicate the extent to which theory and experiment agree; the following comparisons are from Seitz.[20]

	Lattice spacing (Å)		Sublimation energy (kcal/mole)	
Metal	Calc.	Obs.	Calc.	Obs.
Li	3.50	3.46	36.2	39
Na	4.51	4.25	24.5	26
K	5.82	5.20	16.5	23

In these figures, the minimum in the total energy versus r_0 curve was used to define the theoretical lattice spacing, and the cohesive energy was calculated for this particular value of r_0. Calculations of the compressibility are also in reasonable agreement with experiment. For Na the observed and calculated values are, respectively, 12.3 and 12.0 × 10^{-12} cm^2/dyne.[21]

Attempts have also been made to explain the crystal structure of metals in terms of the electronic structure; the differences in energy obtained for different crystal structures are in general too small to draw unique conclusions. For certain alloy structures, however, Jones has been able to account for structural transitions associated with particular compositions on the basis of the band theory.[22]

[20] F. Seitz, *op. cit.*, p.365.

[21] J. Bardeen, *J. Chem. Phys.*, **6**, 367, 372 (1938).

[22] H. Jones, *Proc. Roy. Soc. (London)*, **A144**, 225 (1934); *Proc. Phys. Soc. (London)*, **49**, 243 (1937); *Physica*, **15**, 13 (1949); *Phil. Mag.*, **41**, 663 (1950).

REFERENCES

An elementary treatment of the band theory may be found in:

L. Brillouin, *Wave Propagation in Periodic Structures; Electric Filters and Crystal Lattices*, 2d ed., Dover, New York, 1953.

A. H. Cottrell, *Theoretical Structural Metallurgy*, Arnold, London, 1948.

W. Hume-Rothery, *Atomic Theory for Students in Metallurgy*, Institute of Metals, London, 1947.

W. Hume-Rothery, *Electrons, Atoms, Metals and Alloys*, Cornwall Press, London, 1948.

Advanced discussions are given in:

H. Fröhlich, *Elektronen Theorie der Metalle*, Springer, Berlin, 1936.

N. F. Mott and H. Jones, *Theory of the Properties of Metals and Alloys*, Oxford, New York, 1936.

N. F. Mott, "Recent Advances in the Electron Theory of Metals," *Progr. Met. Phys.*, **3**, 76 (1952).

G. V. Raynor, "The Band Structure of Metals," *Repts. Progr. Phys.*, **15**, 173 (1952).

J. R. Reitz, "Methods of the One-Electron Theory of Solids," in F. Seitz and D. Turnbull (eds.), *Solid State Physics*, Academic Press, New York, 1955, Vol. 1.

F. Seitz, *The Modern Theory of Solids*, McGraw-Hill, New York, 1940.

J. C. Slater, "Electronic Structure of Metals," *Revs. Mod. Phys.*, **6**, 209 (1934).

A. Sommerfield and H. Bethe, in *Handbuch der Physik*, 1933, Vol. 24/2, pp. 333-622.

A. H. Wilson, *Theory of Metals*, 2d ed., Cambridge, London, 1953.

"International Conference on the Physics of Metals, 1948," special issue of *Physica*, 1949.

PROBLEMS

10-1. Let a_1, a_2, a_3 and b_1, b_2, b_3 represent the primitive translation vectors of the direct and reciprocal lattice. In the direct lattice consider a set of planes with Miller indices n_1, n_2, n_3. Show that the reciprocal lattice vector $n = n_1 b_1 + n_2 b_2 + n_3 b_3$ is perpendicular to these planes. Also show that the distance between consecutive planes is equal to $1/|n|$.

10-2. Consider an f.c.c. lattice with a cube edge a. Show that the reciprocal lattice is b.c.c. with an edge $2/a$. Also show that the reciprocal lattice of a b.c.c. lattice is f.c.c.

10-3. Show that the volumes of a unit cell in the direct and reciprocal lattices are the reciprocal of each other.

10-4. Suppose a beam of monochromatic X-rays is reflected by a crystal, i.e., the beam satisfies the Bragg condition. Let s_0 and s be unit vectors in the direction of the incident and reflected beams. Show that the Bragg condition is equivalent with the requirement that $(s - s_0)/\lambda$ must correspond to a vector in the reciprocal lattice; λ is the wavelength of the X-rays.

10-5. In Sec. 10-10 we concluded that the band theory for cubic crystals leads to discontinuities in the $E(k)$ surfaces whenever k satisfies the condition $n \cdot k = \pi n^2/a$ (see expression 10-78). Show that this condition is equivalent with that for Bragg reflection of the electrons by the set of planes with Miller indices n_1, n_2, n_3.

10-6. Show that in the tightly bound electron approximation the energy $E(k)$ for b.c.c. and f.c.c. lattices are given by

$$E(k) = E_0 - \alpha - 8\gamma \cos k_x a \cos k_y a \cos k_z a \qquad \text{(b.c.c.)}$$

$$E(k) = E_0 - \alpha - 4\gamma[\cos k_x a \cos k_y a + \cos k_x a \cos k_z a$$
$$+ \cos k_y a \cos k_z a] \qquad \text{(f.c.c.)}$$

where $2a$ is the cube edge. Show also that for small values of $|k|$ the energy varies proportionally with $|k|^2$. Discuss the shape of constant energy surfaces in k-space.

10-7. Calculate the width of the energy region occupied by electrons in the conduction bands of Li, Na, and Al on the basis of the free electron theory of metals, assuming that each atom contributes as many electrons as its chemical valence. With reference to the bandwidths quoted in Sec. 10-12, what average effective mass would one have to assume in order to obtain agreement?

10-8. Discuss the nearly free electron approximation for a one-dimensional lattice.

Chapter 11

THE CONDUCTIVITY OF METALS

In this chapter an elementary discussion is given of the electrical and thermal conductivities of metals; a brief account of the thermal conductivity of insulators is given in Sec. 11-9. Within the allowed space it did not seem possible to discuss superconductivity, thermoelectric, galvanomagnetic, and thermomagnetic effects, although a simplified derivation of the Hall effect is included as the last section.

11-1. Some features of the electrical conductivity of metals

Any theory of the electrical conductivity of metals must explain a number of pertinent experimental facts. Apart from deviations in special cases or under extreme conditions, the general features of the electrical conductivity of metals are the following.

1. In accordance with Ohm's law, the current density in the steady state is proportional to the field strength.
2. The specific resistivity of metals at room temperature is of the order of 10^{-5} ohm cm (1 ohm cm $\simeq 1.1 \times 10^{-12}$ cgs unit)
3. Above the Debye temperature the resistivity of metals increases linearly with temperature.
4. At low temperatures, but above approximately $20°K$, the resistivity of many metals is proportional to T^5; at liquid helium temperatures some metals exhibit a minimum in the resistivity versus temperature curve.
5. For most metals the resistivity decreases with increasing pressure.
6. According to Matthiessen's rule, the resistivity ρ of a metal containing small amounts of impurities may be written

$$\rho = \rho_0 + \rho(T) \tag{11-1}$$

where ρ_0 is a constant which increases with increasing impurity content and $\rho(T)$ is the temperature-dependent part of the resistivity.
7. The resistivity of alloys which exhibit order-disorder transitions shows pronounced minima corresponding to ordered phases (Fig. 11-7).

8. Above the Debye temperature the ratio of thermal to electrical conductivity is proportional to T, the constant of proportionality being approximately the same for all metals (Wiedemann-Franz law).

9. A number of metals exhibit the phenomenon of superconductivity, i.e., their resistivity disappears at temperatures above absolute zero.[1]

11-2. A simple model leading to a steady state; drift velocity and relaxation time

In order to appreciate the essential problem in the theory of conductivity it is useful to consider a simple model which shows the features of the more sophisticated theory. From the macroscopic point of view, the electrical conductivity of a metal is defined by

$$I_x = \sigma E_x \tag{11-2}$$

where I_x is the current density resulting from an applied electric field E_x in the x-direction. In the case of an anisotropic solid, the conductivity depends on direction, and σ becomes a tensor (see Sec. 1-12); we shall assume an isotropic solid. From an atomic viewpoint, we may ascribe the current to a flow of electrons, i.e.,

$$I_x = -ne\langle v_x \rangle \tag{11-3}$$

where n is the number of electrons per unit volume, $-e$ is the electronic charge, and $\langle v_x \rangle$ is the average velocity of the electrons in the x-direction (the average being taken over the electrons per unit volume). In the absence of an external field, the velocity distribution is isotropic and $\langle v_x \rangle$ vanishes. Now, a free electron under influence of an external field E_x obtains an acceleration $a_x = -eE_x/m$, and thus its velocity would continue to increase with time. It is evident that the influence of the electric field alone would not lead to a steady state as required by Ohm's law; it is therefore necessary to assume the occurrence of some kind of "frictional" process. This process together with the influence of the external field should then lead to an average velocity $\langle v_x \rangle$ which, according to (11-2) and (11-3), should be proportional to E_x. The origin of the "frictional" process must obviously be sought in a possible interaction of the conduction electrons with the atomic lattice, since collisions between the electrons themselves cannot provide the required result (the latter would not destroy momentum in the field direction).

---

[1] This topic will not be discussed here; for an introductory survey and references to the literature, see C. Kittel, *Introduction to Solid State Physics*, Wiley, New York, 1953 Chap. 20.

In its simplest phenomenological form the interaction of the electrons with the lattice may be described in the following manner: suppose the probability for an electron to collide with the lattice during a small time interval dt is dt/τ. For the moment we shall assume for simplicity that τ is constant, independent of the energy of the electron and of the direction of motion. Furthermore, let it be assumed that in a collision with the lattice, the electron loses all the energy it has gained from the external field and that its velocity after the collision is random (independent of the direction of motion before the collision). In other words, the collisions are assumed to be so designed that immediately after the collision the electron has no memory of what happened before the collision. Under the terms of the model specified above, we may argue in the following way: The rate of change of the average velocity in the x-direction due to the field alone is

$$(\partial \langle v_x \rangle / \partial t)_{\text{field}} = -eE_x/m \tag{11-4}$$

Also, the rate of change of $\langle v_x \rangle$ due to collisions with the lattice alone is

$$(\partial \langle v_x \rangle / \partial t)_{\text{coll}} = -\langle v_x \rangle / \tau \tag{11-5}$$

since $1/\tau$ is the probability for a collision per second and after the collisions the velocities are random. In the steady state we must have

$$d\langle v_x \rangle / dt = 0 = (\partial \langle v_x \rangle / \partial t)_{\text{field}} + (\partial \langle v_x \rangle / \partial t)_{\text{coll}} \tag{11-6}$$

From the last three equations it then follows that the average drift velocity in the field direction is given by

$$\langle v_x \rangle = (-e\tau/m)E_x \tag{11-7}$$

From (11-3) and (11-7) it then follows that the conductivity is given by

$$\sigma = ne^2\tau/m \tag{11-8}$$

Suppose that under influence of an electric field E_x the electrons have a certain average drift velocity and that at the instant $t = 0$ the field is suddenly switched off. As a result of the collisions with the lattice the average drift velocity will gradually approach zero; since the rate of change of $\langle v_x \rangle$ by collisions alone is given by (11-5), the decay will follow the expression

$$\langle v_x(t) \rangle = \langle v_x(0) \rangle e^{-t/\tau} \tag{11-9}$$

where $\langle v_x(0) \rangle$ is the average drift velocity at $t = 0$. Because of the exponential form of (11-9), the quantity τ is called the relaxation time.

We may note here already that with $n \simeq 10^{22}$ cm^{-3}, expression (11-8) requires $\tau \simeq 10^{-14}$ second in order to obtain agreement with experimental room temperature data (see point 2, Sec. 11-1).

For the particular type of collisions postulated above, τ also represents

the mean free time between collisions. This may be shown as follows:
Let $P(t)$ be the probability that t seconds after a certain collision has
occurred, an electron has not yet collided again; $P(t + dt)$ represents the
same quantity after $(t + dt)$ seconds. Then

$$P(t + dt) = P(t) + (dP/dt) \, dt$$

On the other hand, we may also write

$$P(t + dt) = P(t)P \, (dt) = P(t)(1 - dt/\tau)$$

where $(1 - dt/\tau)$ represents the probability for an electron not to collide
during the interval dt. From the last two equations one finds

$$P(t) = e^{-t/\tau}$$

since $P = 1$ for $t = 0$. Hence the mean free time between collisions is

$$\langle t \rangle = \int_0^\infty t \, (dP/dt) \, dt = \tau \qquad (11\text{-}10)$$

It must be emphasized, however, that the relaxation time and the mean
free time between collisions are identical only if the velocity after collision
is random. For example, if the scattering is not isotropic and τ_c is the
mean free time between collisions, the relaxation time can readily be
shown to be

$$\tau = \tau_c/(1 - \langle \cos \beta \rangle) \qquad (11\text{-}11)$$

where $\langle \cos \beta \rangle$ is the average of the cosine of the scattering angle.[2] Thus
when nearly all collisions involve small angles, the electron has a rather
strong "memory" and it takes a relatively large number of collisions to
erase this memory, i.e., $\tau \gg \tau_c$ in that case.

11-3. The Boltzmann transport equation

It will be evident that in a state of steady flow of heat or electricity,
the distribution function for the velocity components and spatial coordinates of the electrons will be different from that in thermal equilibrium
in the absence of flow. Thus the theory of transport phenomena is
concerned with determining this distribution function for given external
fields. We shall see in this section that the determination of the distribution
function requires solving an integrodifferential equation, viz., the
Boltzmann transport equation.[3]

    [2] See, for example, W. Shockley, *Electrons and Holes in Semiconductors*, Van
Nostrand, New York, 1950, p. 255.
    [3] L. Boltzmann, *Vorlesungen über Gastheorie*, Barth, Leipzig, 1923.

Let p_x, p_y, p_z represent the components of the momentum of an electron and let

$$f(p_x p_y p_z ; xyz ; t)\, dp_x\, dp_y\, dp_z\, dx\, dy\, dz \tag{11-12}$$

represent the number of electrons in the volume element $dx\, dy\, dz$ which at the instant t have momenta in the range $dp_x\, dp_y\, dp_z$. The steady state is then defined by

$$df/dt = 0 \tag{11-13}$$

In order to obtain information about the function f, it is necessary to consider the causes which, when operative by themselves, would tend to produce a change of f with time. First of all, we must consider the rate of change of f resulting from the velocities of the electrons and from the components X, Y, Z of the external forces which are assumed to act on the electrons. Consider the group of particles defined by (11-12) at an instant $t + \delta t$, where δt is a very small time interval. The momenta and spatial coordinates of this group of electrons at $t + \delta t$ are then to be found about the point

$$p_x + X\,\delta t; \qquad p_y + Y\,\delta t; \qquad p_z + Z\,\delta t$$

$$x + p_x\,\delta t/m; \quad y + p_y\,\delta t/m; \quad z + p_z\,\delta t/m \tag{11-14}$$

However, according to the definition of the distribution function (11-12) the number of electrons which at the instant $t + \delta t$ have their representative points in an element $dp_x\, dp_y\, dp_z\, dx\, dy\, dz$ around the point defined by (11-14) must be equal to

$$f(p_x + X\, dt, \ldots ; x + p_x\,\delta t/m \ldots ; t + \delta t)\, dp_x\, dp_y\, dp_z\, dx\, dy\, dz \tag{11-15}$$

Since (11-12) and (11-15) must be equal, one is led to the following result, obtained by expanding (11-15),

$$(\partial f/\partial t)_{\text{fields}} = -\frac{\partial f}{\partial p_x} X - \frac{\partial f}{\partial p_y} Y - \frac{\partial f}{\partial p_z} Z - \frac{\partial f}{\partial x} v_x - \frac{\partial f}{\partial y} v_y - \frac{\partial f}{\partial z} v_z \tag{11-16}$$

where v_x, v_y, v_z represent the velocity components. In the steady state there must be other processes which just balance the rate of change (11-16) produced by fields and gradients. As we noted already in the preceding section, such processes are provided by electron-lattice interactions. Thus condition (11-13) may be written in the form

$$(\partial f/\partial t)_{\text{fields}} + (\partial f/\partial t)_{\text{coll}} = 0 \tag{11-17}$$

where the first term is given by (11-16) and where the second term refers to electron-lattice scattering (compare 11-6). Since the force exerted on an electron by a combined electric and magnetic field is given by the Lorentz expression

$$F = -e\left(E + \frac{1}{c} v \times H\right)$$

where v is the velocity vector, we may write (11-17) combined with (11-16) in the general form

$$(\partial f/\partial t)_{\text{coll}} = -e\left(E + \frac{1}{c} v \times H\right) \cdot \text{grad}_p f + v \cdot \text{grad}_r f \qquad (11\text{-}18)$$

which is the Boltzmann transport equation for electrons.

The left hand side of this equation involves an integral operator, making the equation an integrodifferential equation; this may be seen as follows: The number of electrons per unit volume which, due to collisions with the lattice, change their momenta per unit time from the range $dp_x\, dp_y\, dp_z$ to another range $dp'_x\, dp'_y\, dp'_z$ can be represented by

$$f(p,r,t)\, dp_x\, dp_y\, dp_z\, P(p,p',r)\, dp'_x\, dp'_y\, dp'_z$$

where the transition probability $P(p,p',r)$ is determined by the type of electron-lattice interaction. Similarly, the corresponding number of electrons thrown from the range $dp'_x\, dp'_y\, dp'_z$ into $dp_x\, dp_y\, dp_z$ per unit time is

$$f(p',r,t)\, dp'_x\, dp'_y\, dp'_z\, P(p',p,r)\, dp_x\, dp_y\, dp_z$$

The net difference between the above quantities integrated over $dp'_x\, dp'_y\, dp'_z$ determines $(\partial f/\partial t)_{\text{coll}}$, i.e.,

$$(\partial f/\partial t)_{\text{coll}} = \iiint [f(p',r,t)P(p',p,r) - f(p,r,t)P(p,p',r)]\, dp'_x\, dp'_y\, dp'_z \qquad (11\text{-}19)$$

It is evident that since the left-hand side of (11-18) is given by expression (11-19), containing the transition probabilities P, the distribution function in the state of steady flow depends explicitly on the mechanism of interaction between the electrons and the lattice. From the atomic theory of electron scattering it can be shown that under certain circumstances it is possible to define a relaxation time such that $(\partial f/\partial t)_{\text{coll}}$ takes the form

$$(\partial f/\partial t)_{\text{coll}} = -\frac{f(p,r) - f_0}{\tau(p,r)} \qquad (11\text{-}20)$$

(compare 11-5). Here f_0 represents the distribution function in thermal equilibrium in the absence of external fields. The physical meaning of the relaxation time $\tau(p,r)$ is analogous to that of τ introduced in the preceding section: when the external fields are suddenly removed, $(f - f_0)$ decays to zero in the fashion

$$(f - f_0)_t = (f - f_0)_{t=0} e^{-t/\tau} \qquad (11\text{-}21)$$

When for a certain problem a relaxation time exists, the treatment is strongly simplified, since the integrodifferential equation then becomes an ordinary equation. An example of this type will be discussed in the next section.

Special cases for which a relaxation time can be defined consistently may be mentioned here.[4]

(i) In processes whereby the electrons may be considered to be scattered by elastic spheres; this is of importance for that part of the resistivity which is due to impurity scattering.

(ii) From the (approximate) theory of the interaction between electrons and lattice vibrations it follows that a relaxation time can be defined when $(\theta/T)^2 \ll 1$, where θ is the Debye temperature. This simplifies the theory of electrical and thermal conductivities at high temperatures.

11-4. The Sommerfeld theory of electrical conductivity

A theory of metallic conductivity based on average velocities, as employed in Sec. 11-2, was developed by Drude in 1900. Lorentz in 1905 reinvestigated the problem, using the Boltzmann transport equation and a simplified model for the collisions between the electrons and atoms in the lattice. However, the use of classical statistics led to serious difficulties; for a review of these theories we refer to the literature.[4] In 1928 Sommerfeld recalculated the conductivities along the lines of Lorentz' theory, but replacing classical statistics by Fermi-Dirac statistics.[5] Sommerfeld did not investigate the actual mechanism of interaction between the electrons and the lattice any further, but assumed that a relaxation time can be defined which is a function of the energy of the electrons only. As an application to the Boltzmann transport equation we shall discuss below Sommerfeld's theory of the electrical conductivity based on the free electron approximation; the thermal conductivity will be discussed later.

The number of electronic states per unit volume associated with an element $dp_x\, dp_y\, dp_z$ in momentum space is (including the spin) $(2/h^3)\, dp_x\, dp_y\, dp_z$. In thermal equilibrium and in the absence of fields, let the average number of occupied states be

$$(2/h^3)F_0(p)\, dp_x\, dp_y\, dp_z$$

where F_0 is the Fermi distribution function in terms of the total momentum p. Suppose we apply an electric field E_x along the x-direction, other

[4] See, for example, A. H. Wilson, *The Theory of Metals*, 2d ed., Cambridge, London, 1953, pp. 8, 264.

[5] A. Sommerfeld, *Z. Physik*, **47**, 1 (1928); see also the article by A. Sommerfeld and H. Bethe, in *Handbuch der Physik*, Vol. 24/2, 1934, or A. Sommerfeld and N. H. Frank, *Revs. Mod. Phys.*, **3**, 1 (1931).

fields or gradients being absent. When in the state of steady current the average number of electrons per unit volume in the range $dp_x \, dp_y \, dp_z$ is represented by

$$(2/h^3)F(p) \, dp_x \, dp_y \, dp_z \tag{11-22}$$

we may write immediately for the current density,

$$I_x = -\frac{2e}{h^3} \iiint v_x(F - F_0) \, dp_x \, dp_y \, dp_z \tag{11-23}$$

which is a generalization of (11-3). The term F_0 does not contribute anything to the current, since it is spherically symmetric with respect to p; it has been added, however, to emphasize the fact that the current is essentially determined by the deviation $(F - F_0)$ from the Fermi distribution. Thus, if one can calculate $(F - F_0)$, I_x may be obtained.

The Boltzmann transport equation (11-18) reduces for the case under consideration to

$$(\partial F/\partial t)_{\text{coll}} = -eE_x(\partial F/\partial p_x) \tag{11-24}$$

We shall now assume that there exists a relaxation time τ such that

$$(\partial F/\partial t)_{\text{coll}} = -(F - F_0)/\tau \tag{11-25}$$

(compare 11-20). Thus, according to the last two equations,

$$(F - F_0)/\tau = eE_x \, (\partial F/\partial p_x) \simeq eE_x \, (\partial F_0/\partial p_x) \tag{11-26}$$

where the last approximation is valid for small fields so that $(F - F_0)$ is relatively small (physically speaking this assumption is equivalent with a linear dependence of I on E). Making use of the fact that the energy of the electrons is given by $\epsilon = (p_x^2 + p_y^2 + p_z^2)/2m$, one may write instead of (11-26),

$$(F - F_0)/\tau = ev_x E_x \, (\partial F_0/\partial \epsilon) \tag{11-27}$$

Substituting (11-27) into (11-23), one obtains for the current density,

$$I_x = -(2e^2/h^3)E_x \iiint v_x^2 \tau (\partial F_0/\partial \epsilon) \, dp_x \, dp_y \, dp_z \tag{11-28}$$

We shall assume that τ is a function only of the energy and not of the direction of motion (compare 11-20). Since $\partial F_0/\partial \epsilon$ is also a function of ϵ alone, one may transform (11-28) into a single integral by replacing v_x^2 by $v^2/3$ and $dp_x \, dp_y \, dp_z$ by $4\pi p^2 \, dp$. Expressing the integrand in terms of ϵ, one obtains

$$I_x = -\frac{16\pi e^2 (2m)^{1/2}}{3h^3} \, E_x \int_0^\infty \epsilon^{3/2} \tau(\epsilon) \left(\frac{\partial F_0}{\partial \epsilon} \right) d\varepsilon \tag{11-29}$$

Now we have seen in Sec. 9-3 that $\partial F_0/\partial \epsilon$ has an appreciable value only in an energy range of a few kT about the Fermi level ϵ_F. To a good approximation $\epsilon^{3/2}\tau(\epsilon)$ under the integral sign may thus be replaced by the quantity $\epsilon_F^{3/2}\tau_F$ in front of the integral. Furthermore,

$$\int_0^\infty (\partial F/\partial \epsilon)\, d\epsilon = -1$$

and if one substitutes ϵ_F from formula (9-9), one finally obtains the simple result,

$$I_x/E_x = \sigma = ne^2\tau_F/m \qquad (11\text{-}30)$$

where n is the number of electrons per unit volume. It is interesting to note that although all electrons take part in the conduction mechanism only the relaxation time of the electrons at the Fermi level occurs in the conductivity. The reason for this may be explained with reference to Fig. 11-1. The full circle represents the Fermi distribution for a two-dimensional case in the absence of an external field. In the presence of a field along the x-direction, the velocity of all electrons is shifted by an amount Δv (the average drift velocity), leading to the dashed circle. It is evident that the distribution is changed only in the vicinity of the Fermi level, so that only the relaxation time of electrons near ϵ_F is of importance.

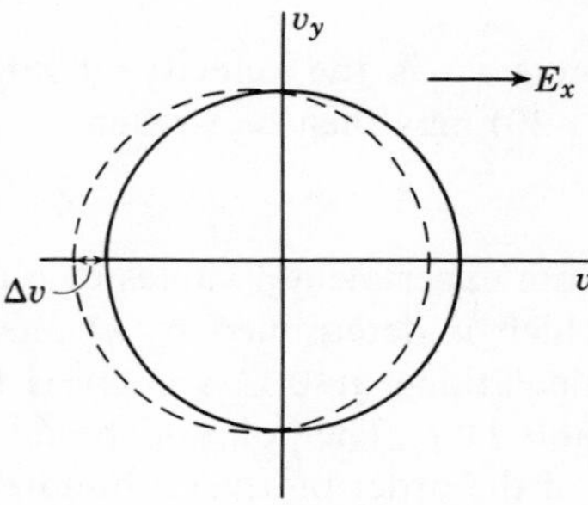

Fig. 11-1. Exaggerated representation of the influence of an electric field on the velocity distribution for a two-dimensional crystal. The fully drawn circle corresponds to the Fermi distribution in the absence of a field; the field E_x produces a shift Δv opposite to the field direction (dashed curve).

Note that (11-30) is essentially the same as (11-8), except that τ has been replaced by τ_F. Although the treatment given here was based on the free electron approximation, a similar treatment may be given for the band approximation.[6] The result of such a calculation is

$$\sigma = n_{\text{eff}} e^2 \tau_F/m \qquad (11\text{-}31)$$

i.e., n is replaced by the effective number of free electrons n_{eff} as defined in Sec. 10-5. It must be noted that (11-31) is based on the assumption that the energy of the electron as well as τ are functions of the absolute value of the wave vector only.

11-5. The mean free path in metals

If we confine ourselves to the conductivity of metals in the temperature region $T \gg 0$, the existence of a relaxation time is assured according to

[6] See, for example, N. F. Mott and H. Jones, *Theory of the Properties of Metals and Alloys*, Oxford, New York, 1936, p. 258.

what has been said in Sec. 11-3. So far, however, we have not paid any attention to the actual cause of resistivity, i.e., to the physical mechanism which determines τ_F. On the other hand, it follows from the basic formula (11-30) that features such as the temperature dependence, pressure dependence, etc. must be hidden in the quantity τ_F.

Let us assume that the scattering of the electrons is isotropic; from the discussion given at the end of Sec. 11-2 it then follows that we may introduce a mean free path Λ_F between collisions for electrons at the Fermi level by means of the relation

$$\Lambda_F = v_F \tau_F \tag{11-32}$$

where v_F is the velocity of an electron with the Fermi energy. Hence (11-30) may then be written

$$\sigma = ne^2 \Lambda_F / m v_F \tag{11-33}$$

From experimental values of σ and from a knowledge of the Fermi level (which is determined by n) one can thus calculate Λ_F. Results of such calculations at 0°C are given for a number of monovalent metals in Table 11-1. The point of special interest is the fact that the mean free path is of the order of several hundred Angstroms.

Table 11-1. Conductivity, Mean Free Path and Relaxation Time at 0°C for Some Monovalent Metals

Metal	$\sigma_{obs} \times 10^{17}$ (esu)	E_F (ev)	Λ_F (Å)	τ_F in 10^{-14} sec
Li	1.1	4.7	110	0.9
Na	2.1	3.1	350	3.1
K	1.5	2.1	370	4.4
Cu	5.8	7.0	420	2.7
Ag	6.1	5.5	570	4.1

Before the development of the band theory by Bloch and others, this fact presented a great difficulty. The electrons were supposed to move in the spaces between the ionic cores, as illustrated in Fig. 11-2, and such a model inevitably leads to a mean free path of a few Angstroms. This model also led to unsurmountable difficulties in explaining the temperature dependence, pressure dependence, influence of impurities on the conductivity, etc.

In Chapter 10 we have seen, however, that the wave vector of an electron moving in a perfectly periodic potential remains unchanged in the absence of external fields. Thus, as a result of the wave nature of the electrons, they can pass through a perfect crystal without suffering any resistance. This is a result of interference of the electron waves scattered by the periodic potential representing the lattice. It may be compared with the unattenuated passing of a light wave through a perfect crystal. The important consequence of this is that if all nuclei were at rest, the mean free path for electron scattering would be infinite.[7] The actual cause of resistivity must therefore be sought in deviations from the periodicity of the potential in which the electrons move. It is on this concept that the modern theory of conductivity is based.

Deviations from the periodicity of the potential causing resistivity may be due to:

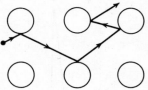

Fig. 11-2 The classical model for electron scattering by the atoms in a solid. This leads to $\Lambda \simeq 10^{-8}$ cm.

(i) Lattice vibrations

(ii) Lattice defects, such as vacancies, interstitials, and dislocations

(iii) Foreign impurity atoms

(iv) Boundaries

It is interesting to note that Wien in 1913, before the development of wave mechanics, put forward the hypothesis that the resistivity in pure metals was due to thermal vibrations of the atoms in the lattice. The justification of this idea had to await the development of the band theory.

11-6. Qualitative discussion of the features of the resistivity[8]

Temperature dependence of ρ. For the moment we shall assume scattering processes of the types (ii), (iii), and (iv) mentioned above to be negligible and confine ourselves to the temperature dependence of the resistivity. In the complete theory of the temperature-dependence of ρ it is necessary to investigate the influence of the lattice waves on the motion of the electrons. This is a complicated problem, and only on the basis of a number of simplifying assumptions is it possible to calculate the resistivity. One of the approximations involves the representation of the lattice waves by a Debye model (see Sec. 2-6); furthermore, certain assumptions must be made about the influence of such lattice waves on the potential seen by the electrons. We shall simplify matters even more strongly by assuming an Einstein model for the lattice vibrations (see Sec. 2-4) and by considering the interaction between the electrons and the atomic vibrations in a qualitative way. The results obtained in this way are, for the high temperature region, in agreement with the advanced theory and with experiment. In view of (11-33) we are particularly interested in the scattering of electrons with the Fermi energy.

[7] This was first pointed out by W. V. Houston, *Z. Physik*, **48**, 449 (1928); *Phys. Rev.*, **34**, 279 (1929).

When v represents the vibrational frequency of the atoms in the Einstein model, M the mass of an atom, and x its displacement from the equilibrium position along a given axis, the equation of motion of the atom is

$$M(d^2x/dt^2) + 4\pi^2 v^2 M x = 0 \qquad (11\text{-}34)$$

The average potential energy associated with the vibration is equal to half

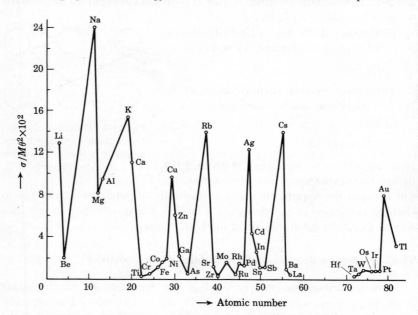

Fig. 11-3. Values of $\sigma/M\theta^2$ versus atomic number obtained from conductivity measurements at 0°C (the values employed are those given by Mott and Jones, l.c., page 246); σ is expressed in ohm^{-1} cm^{-1}, M in terms of the mass of a H atom.

the total thermal energy, i.e., equal to $kT/2$ for temperatures well above the critical temperature $\theta = hv/k$. Hence

$$2\pi^2 v^2 M \langle x^2 \rangle = kT/2 \qquad T \gg \theta \qquad (11\text{-}35)$$

The quantity $\langle x^2 \rangle$ is of particular interest for the scattering of electrons. In order to see this, we shall first introduce the "scattering cross section" Q_F associated with an atom with reference to its capability of scattering an electron with the Fermi energy. From the definition of Λ_F it follows that an electron traveling over Λ_F has unit probability of being scattered. Suppose we represent the atoms by obstacles with a cross section Q_F perpendicular to the direction of motion of the electron. Then Q_F may be defined by the relation

$$\Lambda_F N Q_F = 1 \qquad (11\text{-}36)$$

where N is the number of atoms per unit volume. Since there is no scatter-ing of electrons ($Q_F = 0$) when the atoms are all in their equilibrium position, one may expect that Q_F is proportional to $\langle x^2 \rangle$ (both have the dimensions of an area). Accepting this, it follows from the last two equations that

$$\Lambda_F = \text{const. } M\theta^2/T \qquad T \gg \theta \qquad (11\text{-}37)$$

Combining (11-37) with (11-33), we may write the conductivity in the form

$$\sigma = \text{const. } M\theta^2/T \qquad T \gg \theta \qquad (11\text{-}38)$$

Thus σ varies as T^{-1}, in agreement with the experimental fact (3) mentioned in Sec. 11-1. Expression (11-38) may be brought in harmony with Bloch's theory if θ is interpreted as the Debye rather than the Einstein temperature; this will be done from now on.

In comparing different metals, it is more meaningful to compare $\sigma/M\theta^2$ values than the σ values themselves. The reason is that the former quantity is a measure for the conductivity per unit amplitude of vibration of the atoms. In Fig. 11-3 we have plotted $\sigma/M\theta^2$ as function of atomic number for $T = 300°K$. It is observed that the alkali metals and the noble metals with one outer electron exhibit large values of this quantity, indicating a relatively small cross section for scattering. For the divalent metals next to them in the periodic table, $\sigma/M\theta^2$ is smaller by a factor between 2 and 4; this is a consequence of the small effective number of free electrons in these metals. Note also the low values of $\sigma/M\theta^2$ for the transition metals.

As a result of the expansion of the lattice and the associated reduction in the binding forces, θ decreases slightly at high temperatures; conse-quently σT is not exactly constant but decreases somewhat at high tem-peratures. The transition metals form an exception to this rule; they exhibit an increase of σT with increasing T which may be explained on the basis of the band structure of these metals.[8]

Matthiessen's rule. When a metal contains impurities, the field in the vicinity of the impurities is in general different from that near the host atoms. The impurities thus produce deviations from the periodicity of the potential and act as scattering centers for electrons. Thus electrons in an impure metal are scattered by impurity atoms as well as by the thermal vibrations of the atoms. Denoting the relaxation times associated with each of these processes by τ_i and τ_{th}, respectively, the resulting relaxation time τ is given by

$$1/\tau = 1/\tau_i + 1/\tau_{\text{th}} \qquad (11\text{-}39)$$

because the probabilities for scattering in this simple model are additive

---

[8] See also J. Bardeen, *J. Appl. Phys.*, **11**, 88 (1940).

and they are proportional to the reciprocals of the relaxation times. Since the resistivity is proportional to τ_F^{-1}, associated with electrons at the Fermi level, the impurity scattering leads to a constant term in Matthiessen's rule (11-1). Actually, τ_i will itself be slightly temperature-dependent, but in general the temperature-independent part predominates strongly. For not too high impurity concentrations, $1/\tau_i$ is proportional to the impurity concentration and so is ρ_0 in (11-1). As an example, we give in Fig. 11-4 the resistivity of pure copper together with that of copper containing small amounts of nickel, as function of temperature.[9]

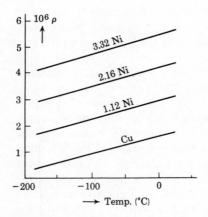

Fig. 11-4. Specific resistivity (ohm cm) as function of temperature for copper and copper-nickel alloys; the numbers refer to atomic percentages. [After J. O. Linde, ref. 9]

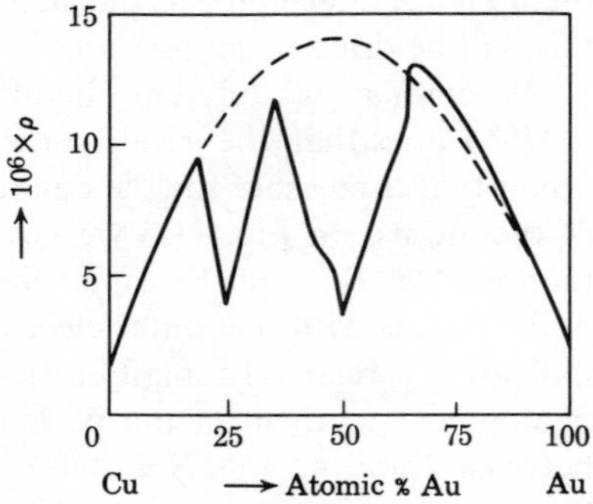

Fig. 11-5. Fully drawn curve represents the resistivity of copper-gold alloys annealed at 200°C (ordered); the dashed curve refers to alloys quenched from 650°C (disordered). [After Barrett, ref. 10]

Resistivity of alloys. As an example of the behavior of the resistivity of alloys, consider Fig. 11-5 for the copper-gold system.[10] The dashed curve refers to alloys quenched from 650°C, leading to disordered systems. The fully drawn curve refers to alloys which have been annealed at 200°C, leading to at least partly ordered alloys. For low concentrations of gold in copper (or copper in gold) the resistivity increases linearly with impurity concentration for reasons explained above. Particularly noteworthy are the resistivity minima corresponding to the ordered structures of the composition Cu_3Au and $CuAu$, and of course those corresponding to the pure elements; in all these cases the potential seen by the electrons is nearly periodic, in contrast with that of the disordered alloys. The amount

[9] J. O. Linde, *Ann. Physik*, **15**, 219 (1932).
[10] C. S. Barrett, *Structure of Metals*, 2d ed., McGraw-Hill, New York, 1952, p. 288.

of order in the lattice is thus clearly reflected by the resistivity of the material.[11]

Resistivity due to vacancies and interstitials. It may be remarked here that resistivity measurements play an important role in the study of radiation effects. For example, when a metal is exposed to a beam of neutrons or other types of radiation, a certain number of interstitial atoms and vacancies are formed. Each of these contribute to the scattering of electrons, i.e., to the resistivity. From resistivity measurements it is possible to obtain information about the numbers of defects produced, about the time required for these defects to anneal out at a given temperature, etc.

Variation of resistance with pressure. As mentioned under (5) in Sec. 11-1, the resistivity of most metals decreases with increasing pressure (exceptions are Li, Ca, Sr, Bi). Qualitatively, this may be understood by starting from expression (11-38). Under high pressures, the forces between the atoms are stronger, and as a result θ increases. Hence

$$d\sigma/dp = d(\theta^2)/dp > 0 \qquad (11\text{-}40)$$

The variation of θ with pressure or, rather, the so-called Grüneisen coefficient $d(\log \theta)/d(\log V)$, where V is the volume, may be deduced from the coefficient of expansion of the solid. Calculations carried out along these lines give fair agreement with the observed changes in σ. For a discussion of the exceptional cases the reader is referred to the literature.[12]

11-7. Thermal scattering described as electron-phonon collisions

Although the treatment followed in the preceding section gives a qualitative insight into the causes of resistivity, it does not touch upon the actual problem of calculating the perturbing influence of the lattice vibrations on the motion of the electrons. The problem of the coupling between the electrons and the lattice is a very complicated one, and in order to calculate the conductivity, strongly simplifying assumptions must be introduced. In a theory developed by Bloch the lattice vibrations are described in terms of a Debye model, and the interaction of the electrons with the lattice vibrations is assumed to be weak.[13] Furthermore, it is assumed that the lattice and the electronic system remain essentially in

[11] For a simplified treatment of the resistivity of completely disordered alloys see N. F. Mott and H. Jones, *op. cit.*, p. 297. Their treatment leads to $\rho_0 = \text{const.}\ x(1 - x)$, where x is the atomic concentration of one of the elements and $(1 - x)$ is that of the other. This type of curve is in rather good agreement with experimental results; it gives rise to the arch in Fig. 11-5.

[12] For references see N. F. Mott and H. Jones, *op. cit.*, p. 272.

[13] F. Bloch, *Z. Physik*, **52**, 555 (1928); **53**, 216 (1929); **59**, 208 (1930).

thermal equilibrium. For critical reviews of this subject and for the details of the theory we must refer the reader to the literature.[4] A few remarks will be made here in connection with the description of electron-lattice interaction in terms of electron-phonon collisions.

Suppose an elastic wave of wave vector q and angular frequency ω_q is propagated through a crystal lattice. The displacement of an atom at the lattice point r due to the vibrational mode may then be written in the form (see Chapter 2),

$$A_q e^{i(q \cdot r - \omega_q t)}$$

where A_q is the amplitude. For a transverse mode the displacement is perpendicular to q; for a longitudinal mode it is parallel to q. At the temperature T the average energy associated with this mode is given by Planck's formula,

$$\hbar\omega_q / [\exp(\hbar\omega_q / kT - 1)]$$

It is convenient to call $\hbar\omega_q$ the energy of a "phonon," in analogy with the photon concept in electromagnetic radiation. We may then say that the vibrational mode at the temperature T corresponds to $\exp(\hbar\omega_q / kT - 1)$ phonons. Note that the energy of a phonon may be written

$$\hbar\omega_q = \hbar c_s q$$

where c_s is the velocity of sound (if we use a Debye model, c_s is independent of q).

As a result of the atomic displacements, an electron of reduced wave vector k sees a potential which is somewhat different from that corresponding to the situation in which all nuclei are in their equilibrium positions. Thus there exists a nonvanishing transition probability for the electron to be scattered into another state k'. In order to deal with this type of problem, one usually applies time-dependent perturbation theory to the system consisting of the electron plus the lattice vibrations. It turns out that the transition probabilities vanish unless the following selection rules are satisfied

$$E_{k'} = E_k \pm \hbar c_s q \tag{11-41}$$

$$k' = k \pm q + 2\pi b \tag{11-42}$$

where either the upper or the lower signs should be used. The vector b is a vector in the reciprocal lattice and for a simple cubic lattice $2\pi b = (2\pi/a)n$, where n is a vector with integer components. For the moment we shall assume $b = 0$; in this case the selection rules have a simple physical interpretation: (11-41) expresses the conservation of energy in an electron-phonon collision, the $+$ sign corresponding to absorption, the $-$ sign corresponding to emission of a phonon by the electron. Similarly, (11-42) (with $b = 0$) may be considered as expressing the law of conservation of momentum in an electron-phonon collision; the momentum of the electron is given by $p = \hbar k$, the momentum associated with the phonon is $\hbar q = \hbar \omega_q / c_s$ in complete analogy with the momentum associated with a photon. The selection rules have interesting consequences, a few of which may be mentioned here. First of all, we may bear in mind that the values of q are limited to the range $0 < q < q_{max} \simeq \pi/a$. Hence the energy of the most energetic phonons is only $\hbar c_s q_{max} \simeq 0.01$ ev, assuming $c_s \simeq 10^5$ cm sec^{-1}. On the other hand, electrons near the Fermi level, the scattering of which determines essentially the conductivity of metals according to (11-30), have energies of several ev; hence when such electrons are scattered their energy remains essentially unaltered, although they may be scattered over large angles (when $k \simeq q$). The angle β over which an electron is scattered by phonon absorption or emission may also be found from the selection rules if the functions $E(k)$ and $E(k')$ are known. We leave it to the reader to show that when $E(k) = \hbar^2 k^2 / 2m^*$ and the electron energy is large compared to the phonon energy,

$$\sin (\beta/2) \simeq q/2k \qquad (11\text{-}43)$$

Since the absolute value of the left-hand side of this equation is $\leqslant 1$, the electrons can interact only with such phonons for which $q \leqslant 2k$. Thus low-energy electrons with small k-values can interact only with a fraction of the total spectrum of vibrational modes; electrons near the Fermi level can interact with essentially the whole spectrum of vibrations.

At temperatures far below the Debye temperature, there are essentially only phonons for which the wave vector q satisfies the inequality

$$\hbar \omega_q = \hbar c_s q \lessgtr k_0 T \quad \text{or} \quad q \lessgtr k_0 T / \hbar c_s \qquad (11\text{-}44)$$

(k_0 is Boltzmann's constant); the higher-frequency modes require too much excitation energy. Consequently, electrons near the Fermi level can be scattered only over small angles when the temperature is low. In fact, according to the last two equations,

$$\beta \lessgtr k_0 T / \hbar c_s k_F \quad \text{or} \quad \beta \lessgtr T/\theta \quad \text{for} \quad T \ll \theta \qquad (11\text{-}45)$$

A few remarks may be made here about the case for which $b \neq 0$ in equation (11-42); such processes are called "Umklapp-Prozesse" ("reversal processes").[14] For cubic crystals they are described by

$$k' = k \pm q + (2\pi/a)n \qquad (11\text{-}46)$$

where n has integer components. Such processes, viz., with $q = 0$, we have encountered in the preceding chapter; in fact, $k' = k + (2\pi/a)n$ represents the condition for Bragg reflection of an electron by a set of atomic planes with Miller indices $(n_1 n_2 n_3)$. The only difference which arises presently is that $k + q$ satisfies the Bragg condition rather than k

[14] R. Peierls, *Ann. Physik*, **4**, 121 (1930); **5**, 244 (1930).

alone. Since q may accept a great variety of values, an electron in state k has many more possibilities for such reflections. It is evident that in an Umklapp process there is no conservation of momentum of the system electron plus phonon. In fact, in such a process an electron absorbs a phonon and thereby arrives in a state at the boundary of a Brillouin zone, whereupon it suffers a reflection.

Peierls has suggested that Umklapp processes are essential in maintaining thermal equilibrium in the phonon system when an electric current flows at low temperatures.[15] The problem involved here is the following. When there is an electric field in the positive x-direction, the electrons gain momentum in the negative x-direction. This momentum is given off to the lattice by the electron-lattice interaction, and thus the phonon equilibrium is disturbed. In the theory of conductivity it is usually assumed that the phonons are in thermal equilibrium; at normal temperatures the interaction between the phonons (due to anharmonic forces) is probably strong enough to maintain essentially thermal equilibrium. However, at low temperatures, the "self-relaxation" of the lattice may require long periods; in that case the lattice waves would accumulate momentum in the direction of the electronic current, and consequently further transfer of momentum from the electronic system to the phonon system would be inhibited. In an Umklapp process, however, electronic momentum may be destroyed without the necessity of having this momentum absorbed by phonons; thus Peierls suggests that these processes must be responsible for maintaining phonon equilibrium at low temperatures.[15] His suggestion has been criticized by Klemens, who claims that the anharmonicity of the lattice forces is strong enough to maintain phonon equilibrium.[16] The problem of "phonon-drag" has received much attention in recent years.

11-8. The electrical conductivity at low temperatures

From the Bloch theory,[13] in which the interaction between the conduction electrons and the lattice vibrations is investigated by approximative methods, it follows that for $(T/\theta)^2 \gg 1$, a relaxation time can be defined. Thus once τ_F has been calculated, the conductivity can be obtained immediately from (11-30) (or from its more general form). In that temperature region his theory leads for free electrons to

$$\sigma = 2.83 \times 10^{-32} n M \theta^2 / C^2 T \quad \text{(cgs)} \quad (11-47)$$

where n is the number of electrons per cm^3, M is the atomic weight, θ is the Debye temperature, and C is a constant characteristic of the metal, with the dimensions of an energy; C may be calculated from experimental

[15] R. Peierls, *Ann. Physik*, **12**, 154 (1932).
[16] P. G. Klemens, *Proc. Phys. Soc.* (*London*), **A64**, 1030 (1951).

σ-values by means of (11-47) and turns out to be roughly equal to the Fermi energy. The value of C is determined by the coupling between the electrons and the lattice vibrations. We note that this formula confirms expression (11-38) which we used in our qualitative discussion of the conductivity in the high-temperature range.

At low temperatures ($T \ll \theta$), a relaxation time cannot be defined consistently. It is, of course, always possible to define τ_F in accordance with (11-30) by $\tau_F = m\sigma/ne^2$; however, if one defines τ_F in a similar way from the thermal conductivity, the two values of τ_F are no longer equal (for $T \ll \theta$) and the concept has lost its usefulness. On the other hand, for the electrical conductivity it is still possible to find a relatively simple solution to the Boltzmann transport equation in the region $T \ll \theta$; for the thermal conductivity this is not the case (because it is a second-order phenomenon). For low temperatures, Bloch's analysis leads to a resistivity proportional to T^5. In an oversimplified way, one may make the T^5 law plausible by the following arguments. First of all, at low temperatures the specific heat of the metallic lattice is proportional to T^3 (in the Debye model); therefore the density of phonons and the probability for scattering are proportional to T^3. Furthermore, the angle of scattering at low temperatures is proportional to T according to (11-45). Now, if one substitutes (11-45) into (11-11) one finds that the influence of the small scattering angles alone would lead to a factor T^{-2} in the conductivity, i.e., T^2 in the resistivity. Consequently, ρ is proportional to $T^3 \cdot T^2 = T^5$. Since this argument implies the existence of a relaxation time, it is not very satisfactory; on the other hand, it points to the two essential causes for the T^5 law: the decrease in density of phonons and the decrease of the scattering angle with decreasing temperature.

On the bases of certain approximations it is possible to obtain from Bloch's theory a formula which covers the whole temperature range:[17] this formula had been used previously by Grüneisen[18] on a semiempirical basis and is of the form

$$\rho(T) = A(T/\theta)^5 \int_0^{\theta/T} \frac{x^5 \, dx}{(e^x - 1)(1 - e^{-x})} \qquad (11\text{-}48)$$

where A is a constant characteristic of the metal. Note that for $T \gg \theta$ the integral $\simeq \frac{1}{4}(\theta/T)^4$, so that in that region ρ is proportional to T, in agreement with experiment. For $T \ll \theta$ we may replace the upper limit of the integral by ∞, leading to the T^5 law. When one plots $\rho(T)/\rho(\theta)$ versus (T/θ), one obtains from (11-48) the universal curve given in Fig. 11-6, which represents the experimental data above $\sim 20°K$ very well for many metals. On the basis of (11-48) one may determine the Debye temperature

[17] See, for example, M. Köhler, *Z. Physik*, **125**, 679 (1949).
[18] E. Grüneisen, *Ann. Physik*, **16**, 530 (1933).

θ from resistivity measurements; in fact, when two temperatures T_1 and T_2 satisfy the condition $T_1 \ll \theta \ll T_2$, one finds from (11-48),

$$\rho(T_1)/\rho(T_2) = 497.6(T_1/\theta)^4(T_1/T_2) \tag{11-49}$$

A comparison of Debye temperatures so obtained with those determined from specific heat data is given in Table 11-2; the agreement is good.

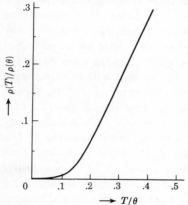

Fig. 11-6. The reduced resistivity $\rho(T)/\rho(\theta)$ as function of the reduced temperature (T/θ), according to the Bloch-Grüneisen formula (11-48).

However, systematic studies by the Leiden[19] and Oxford[20] low-temperature groups have shown that deviations from (11-48) occur in the region between 4° and 20°K. One type of deviation is illustrated in Fig. 11-7, which represents the "apparent" Debye temperature as function of T for Rb; the apparent θ at a given temperature is calculated from (11-49) on the basis of resistivity measurements. It is observed that instead of being constant, θ varies with T. Such discrepancies may be compared with those observed at low temperatures for the apparent θ calculated from the T^3 law of the specific heat (see Sec. 2-13). The occurrence of such deviations is not too surprising in view of the approximations involved in the theory, in particular the use of the Debye approximation for the lattice vibrations, which is known to be inaccurate at low temperatures.

Deviations of a more fundamental character in the region $\lesssim 10$°K were first reported by de Haas, de Boer, and van den Berg;[19] they found a minimum in the resistivity versus T curve of gold specimens, the minimum shifting to lower temperatures as the sample becomes more pure. The effect has since been observed in other metals as well; the explanation of the effect is still in doubt.

Table 11-2. Comparison of Characteristic Temperatures in Degrees Absolute Obtained from Specific Heat and from Resistivity Data. [After D. K. C. MacDonald, *Progress in Metal Physics*, **3**, 42 (1952).]

Metal	Na	Cu	Ag	Au	Al	Pb	W	Ta
θ (sp. heat)	159	315–330	210–215	163–186	390	82–88	305–337	245
θ (resist.)	202	333	223	175	395	86	333	228

[19] Work by W. J. de Haas, J. de Boer, and G. J. van den Berg has been reported in *Physica* **1**, 609 (1934); **1**, 1115 (1934); **2**, 453 (1935); **3**, 440 (1936); **4**, 683 (1937).
[20] D. K. C. MacDonald and K. Mendelssohn, *Proc. Roy. Soc.* (*London*), **A202**, 523 (1950).

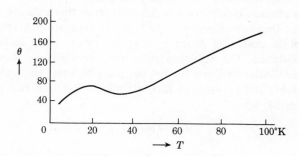

Fig. 11-7. The "apparent" characteristic temperature θ for Rb, as deduced from resistivity measurements by employing (11-49). [After MacDonald and Mendelssohn, ref. 20]

11-9. The thermal conductivity of insulators

A thermal gradient in a cubic crystal gives rise to a flow of heat in a direction opposite to that of the gradient. Thus if there exists a thermal gradient dT/dx along the x-direction and Q_x is the resulting heat current density, the thermal conductivity K is defined as

$$K = -Q_x/(dT/dx) \tag{11-50}$$

In normal insulators the heat flow is carried by lattice waves. In metals, the thermal conductivity is, at least in principle, determined by the conduction electrons as well as by the lattice waves. Usually the electronic contribution dominates strongly in metals; however, in poor metals such as bismuth, or in metals containing large amounts of impurities (alloys), the lattice conductivity may be important. For the moment we shall confine ourselves to the thermal conductivity in insulators to obtain some insight into the lattice conductivity.

A theory of the thermal conductivity of insulators was developed in 1914 by Debye;[21] as in his theory of the specific heat (1912), he assumed that the lattice vibrations may be described by a model in which elastic waves are propagated through a continuum. Since solids expand upon heating, these waves cannot be purely harmonic but must be anharmonic. This anharmonicity was, according to Debye, the source of coupling between the lattice waves, so that mutual scattering of the waves becomes possible. (He pointed out that mutual scattering is not possible for purely harmonic waves.) As a measure for the coupling, Debye introduced a mean free path Λ, which measures the distance of travel of a wave required to attenuate its intensity by a factor e.

[21] P. Debye, *Vorträge über die kinetische Theorie der Materie und der Elektrizität*, Teubner, Berlin, 1914, pp. 19–60.

These ideas were extended by Peierls and translated in terms of phonon-phonon interaction.[22] When a temperature gradient is present in a solid, the phonon distribution is different from that existing in thermal equilibrium; the phonon-phonon collisions tend to restore this equilibrium, the rate of the restoring process being the determining factor for the thermal resistance. The selection rules for the collisions between two phonons are similar to those for the collision between an electron and a phonon (11-41) and (11-42); in fact, a collision between two phonons 1 and 2 is possible when

$$\omega_1 + \omega_2 = \omega_3 \tag{11-51}$$

$$q_1 + q_2 = q_3 + (2\pi/a)n \tag{11-52}$$

where a is the cube edge in a cubic crystal and n is a vector with integer components. According to (11-51), two phonons may give rise to a single phonon with an energy $\hbar\omega_3$ equal to the sum of the energies of the original phonons (conservation of energy). If in (11-52) we assume for the moment $n = 0$, this equation expresses the law of conservation of momentum. However, collisions of the type $n = 0$ do not contribute to the thermal resistance because after such a collision the energy is still flowing in the same direction as before. On the other hand, when the vector $n \neq 0$, the direction of flow of energy has changed after the collision; these so-called "Umklapp" processes (compare Sec. 11-7) are therefore responsible for the thermal resistance in Peierls' theory. Since the vector n may accept a number of directions in space, e.g., along the six directions corresponding to the cube edges in a cubic lattice, the scattering may be considered as approximately random.

In order to set up an expression for the thermal conductivity, we remind the reader of a well-known formula for the thermal conductivity of a gas:[23]

$$K = \tfrac{1}{3}Cv\Lambda \tag{11-53}$$

where C is the specific heat (at constant volume) of the gas per unit volume, v is the average velocity of the molecules, and Λ is the mean free path. In analogy, we may write for the conductivity associated with the Umklapp processes,[24]

$$K_u = \tfrac{1}{3}\sum_i\sum_j C_{ij}v_{ij}\Lambda_{ij} \tag{11-54}$$

The subscript j refers to the direction of polarization of the phonons; the summation over i extends over the complete frequency range of the

[22] R. Peierls, *Ann. Physik*, **3**, 1055 (1929).
[23] For a derivation, see any textbook on the kinetic theory of gases.
[24] See, for example, R. Berman, *Advances in Physics*, **2**, 103 (1953).

vibrational spectrum. In a Debye model for the lattice vibrations the velocities v_{ij} are all equal (to the velocity of sound c_s).

For a given solid the thermal resistance may arise as a result of a variety of causes:

(i) Umklapp processes (K_u)

(ii) Scattering of phonons by boundaries (K_b)

(iii) Scattering by impurities and lattice imperfections (K_i)

If we consider these processes independent, their scattering probabilities may be added, and the resultant conductivity is then given by

$$1/K = 1/K_u + 1/K_b + 1/K_i \qquad (11\text{-}55)$$

For the moment we shall consider an ideal crystal of infinite dimensions, and inquire about the temperature-dependence of K_u. As long as the temperature is well above the Debye temperature, the specific heats C_{ij} in (11-54) are all the same and independent of T (viz., equal to k_0 per mode, where k_0 is Boltzmann's constant). Furthermore, the mean free path for a given phonon ij is inversely proportional to the density of all other phonons with which it can interact. Since the number of phonons of a given type is equal to $kT/\hbar\omega_{ij}$, the density of all phonons is proportional to T. We thus conclude that

$$\Lambda_{ij} \propto T^{-1} \quad \text{and} \quad K_u \propto T^{-1} \quad \text{for} \quad T \gg \theta \qquad (11\text{-}56)$$

For macroscopic crystals which are well annealed, (ii) and (iii) may usually be neglected in this range of temperatures. For example, for NaCl at $0°C$, $K = 0.017$ cal cm^{-1} degree^{-1} sec^{-1}; assuming $K = K_u$, we find by using the simple expression (11-53) that $\Lambda_u \simeq 20$ Å on the basis of a specific heat of 0.45 cal cm^{-3} and a velocity of sound of $\sim 5 \times 10^5$ cm sec^{-1}. When processes (ii) and (iii) lead to a mean free path of the same order as Λ_u or smaller, they can, of course, no longer be neglected. It is obvious that (ii) and (iii) may be expected to become important at low temperatures and in imperfect crystals.

In considering the Umklapp processes at low temperatures $(T \ll \theta)$, we must point out that equation (11-52) indicates that Umklapp processes can occur only when the phonons have an energy larger than a certain minimum value. In fact, we want at least one of the q's to be of the order $1/a$, corresponding to a phonon energy $\sim k_0\theta$ (k_0 is Boltzmann's constant). Peierls takes as a threshold energy $k_0\theta/2$.[22] Now the number of phonons with this energy is proportional to $1/[\exp(\theta/2T) - 1]$. From this we deduce that the temperature-dependences of Λ_u and K_u at low temperatures are essentially given by

$$\Lambda_u \propto e^{\theta/2T} \quad \text{and} \quad K_u \propto e^{\theta/2T} \quad \text{for} \quad T \ll \theta \qquad (11\text{-}57)$$

Thus the Umklapp processes lead to a thermal conductivity which decreases exponentially with T in the low-temperature region; in the high-temperature region it decreases as T^{-1}. Although $K_u \to \infty$ for $T \to 0$, the total thermal conductivity remains finite even in a perfect crystal, as a result of boundary scattering. Qualitatively, the influence of the latter at low temperatures may be seen from (11-53): since the specific heat is proportional to T^3 and the mean free path Λ_b is determined by the dimensions of the crystal, K_b is proportional to T^3 and to the crystal dimensions. A quantitative calculation of this effect has been made by

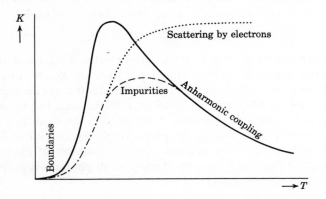

Fig. 11-8. The fully drawn curve represents the general theoretical form of the thermal conductivity of an insulator; in metals, phonons are scattered by electrons as well (dotted curve), leading to the dashed resultant curve. [After R. E. B. Makinson, *Proc. Cambr. Phil. Soc.*, **34**, 474 (1938)]

Casimir.[25] The general form of the thermal conductivity of an ideal insulating crystal is given by the fully drawn curve in Fig. 11-8, indicating the occurrence of a maximum. In order to observe the exponential behavior predicted by Peierls, one must measure K in the range between $\theta/10$ to $\theta/20$. The lower limit of this temperature region is determined not only by the boundary scattering, which must be negligible, but also by the fact that scattering by imperfections must be avoided. Results for the mean free path obtained in this region are represented in Fig. 11-9 for sapphire, diamond, and solid helium. The conductivity in this range fits a relation of the type $K \propto T^n e^{\theta/bT}$, where b is approximately 2 (compare 11-57). For further details on this topic we refer to the literature.[24] In general, Peierls' theory combined with Casimir's calculation of the influence of crystal size at low temperatures describes the experiments satisfactorily.

[25] H. B. G. Casimir, *Physica*, **5**, 595 (1938); see also H. B. G. Casimir, *Magnetism at Very Low Temperatures*, Cambridge, London, 1940.

11-10. The thermal conductivity of metals

Although lattice conductivity may become important in metals under certain circumstances (low T, high magnetic fields, large impurity content), we shall assume for the moment that their thermal conductivity is determined solely by the conduction electrons. Thus, let there be a thermal gradient dT/dx in a metal and a thermal current density Q_x. Since the gradient produces a drift velocity of the electrons and since the heat flow is determined under conditions of zero electric current, a small electric field must be set up internally to counteract the drift velocity due to the gradient; this is achieved by a slight redistribution of the electrons. Thus, in the Boltzmann equation (11-18) we must include, besides the thermal gradient dT/dx (which leads to a term $\partial f/\partial x$), a term containing an electric field E_x. We shall first consider the region $T \gg \theta$, since in this region one can define a relaxation time, which simplifies the calculation of the conductivity tremendously. Using the notation of Sec. 11-3 we obtain for this case from (11-18),

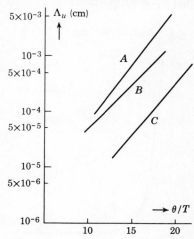

Fig. 11-9. The mean free path for Umklapp processes as function of θ/T: A, synthetic sapphire ($\theta \simeq 980$); B, diamond ($\theta \simeq 1840$, C, solid helium (θ, 22–35). [After R. Berman, F. E. Simon, and J. Wilks, *Nature*, London, **168**, 277 (1951)]

$$-(f - f_0)/\tau = -eE_x(\partial f/\partial p_x) + v_x(\partial f/\partial x)(\partial T/\partial x) \qquad (11\text{-}58)$$

As long as the electric field and $(\partial T/\partial x)$ are small, we may replace f on the right-hand side by f_0, as we did in calculating the electrical conductivity. The thermal current density in terms of the distribution function $F(p_x p_y p_z)$ introduced in Sec. 11-4 is given by

$$Q_x = (2/h^3) \iiint v_x F \epsilon \, dp_x \, dp_y \, dp_z \qquad (11\text{-}59)$$

where ϵ is the energy of an electron. When Q_x is calculated by solving (11-58) under the condition that the electric current

$$I_x = -(2e/h^3) \iiint v_x F \, dp_x \, dp_y \, dp_z$$

vanishes, one finds for the electronic thermal conductivity K_e in the free electron approximation,[26]

$$K_e = \pi^2 k^2 T n \tau_F / 3m, \qquad T \gg \theta \qquad (11\text{-}60)$$

Here τ_F is again the relaxation time for electrons at the Fermi level. From the theory of interaction of electrons with lattice vibrations one can show that τ_F is proportional to T^{-1}, so that

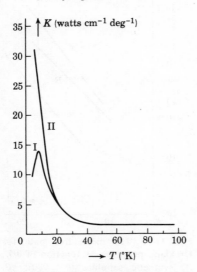

Fig. 11-10. The thermal conductivity of two samples of sodium; sample II is purer than sample I. [After Berman and MacDonald, ref. 27]

$$K_e = \text{constant} \qquad T \gg \theta \quad (11\text{-}61)$$

in good agreement with experimental data. Note that combination of (11-60) and (11-31) leads to the Wiedemann-Franz law [see point (8) in Sec. 11-1].

$$L \equiv K_e / \sigma T = (\pi^2/3)(k/e)^2$$
$$= 2.7 \times 10^{-13} \text{ cgs unit} \quad (T \gg \theta)$$
$$(11\text{-}62)$$

Here L is called the Lorenz number; the theoretical value is in rather good agreement with experimental data in the high-temperature region.

It can be shown that the existence of a relaxation time is a sufficient condition for the constancy of the Lorenz number. Experimentally one finds, however, that as the temperature decreases, L decreases, indicating that the concept of a relaxation time cannot be extended to low temperatures. At this point we may mention that, like the electrical resistivity, the thermal resistivity associated with electrons may be considered to consist of two parts: one due to scattering by lattice vibrations, another due to scattering by impurities or other lattice imperfections. Denoting these parts, respectively, by subscripts l and i, we may write, if they are independent,

$$1/K_e = 1/K_{el} + 1/K_{ei} = 1/K_{el} + 1/L\sigma_i T \qquad (11\text{-}63)$$

The last equality follows from the fact that for impurity scattering one may always define a relaxation time (see the end of Sec. 11-3). Thus, by plotting T/K_e versus T, one can obtain $1/L\sigma_i$ from the intercept at $T = 0$ and K_{el} may be determined by subtraction.

In the case of the electrical conductivity one can, even in the low-temperature region where no relaxation time can be defined properly,

[26] See, for example, A. H. Wilson, *op. cit.*, pp. 18, 201.

arrive at a relatively simple solution for the Boltzmann transport equation. For the thermal conductivity, which is a second-order phenomenon, this is much more complicated; for a discussion of this subject we refer the reader to the literature. As an example of the thermal conductivity of metals we represent in Fig. 11-10 measured curves for two sodium samples of different purity.[27] The theory leads to curves of a similar type.

In alloys, the lattice conductivity must also be taken into account, since the electronic thermal resistance is increased as a result of impurity scattering. Furthermore, the lattice conductivity is modified as a result of phonon scattering by electrons, as indicated in Fig. 11-8.

For pure metals, one may estimate the ratio of the electronic and lattice conductivities at high temperatures as follows: according to (11-60) and (11-53) we may write

$$K_{\text{electrons}}/K_{\text{lattice}} = \pi^2 k_0^2 T n \tau_F / m \Lambda C c_s$$

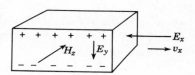

Considering a monovalent metal for which the density of electrons n is equal to the density of atoms, one finds with a specific heat (at constant volume) of $3nk_0$, a velocity of sound $c_s \simeq 5 \times 10^5$ cm sec^{-1}, $\tau_F \simeq 3 \times 10^{-14}$ sec, and a phonon mean free path $\Lambda \simeq 100$ Å for this ratio $\sim 10^2$.

Fig. 11-11. Illustrating the Hall effect, in a metal, produced by an electric field E_x and a magnetic field H_z perpendicular to the front face. The electrons move with a drift velocity v_x as indicated; the Lorentz force acts downward along the y-axis. For positive charge carriers, E_y will be reversed.

11-11. The Hall effect in metals

Consider a slab of material subjected to an external field E_x along the x-axis and a magnetic field H_z along the z-axis as illustrated in Fig. 11-11. As a result of the applied electric field, a current density I_x will flow in the direction of E_x. For the moment let us assume that the current is carried by electrons of a charge $-e$. Under influence of the magnetic field the electrons will be subjected to a Lorentz force such that the lower surface collects a negative charge, the upper surface a positive charge. Ultimately, a stationary state is obtained in which the current along the y-axis vanishes and a field E_y is set up. If the charge carriers were positive, the upper surface would become negative relative to the lower surface, i.e., E_y would be reversed. From this it is evident that a measurement of the "Hall voltage" in the y-direction gives information about the sign of the charge carriers. Measurements of this kind are thus useful in semiconductor research. Furthermore, the density of the charge carriers may

[27] R. Berman and D. K. C. MacDonald, *Proc. Roy. Soc. (London)*, **A209**, 368 (1952).

be obtained, at least if the current is carried either by electrons or holes. To illustrate this, let us assume a free electron model for a metal; the derivation given here is strongly simplified, but leads to the same result as obtained from the Boltzmann transport equation.[28] The force exerted on an electron of charge $-e$ by a combined electric and magnetic field is given by the Lorentz formula,

$$F = -e\left[E + \frac{1}{c}\ v \times H\right] \qquad (11\text{-}64)$$

For the configuration of Fig. 11-11 we have from $F_y = 0$ in the steady state

$$E_y = (1/c)v_x H_z$$

where v_x is the average drift velocity of the electrons. Also, the current density may be expressed in terms of the number of electrons n per unit volume as

$$I_x = -nev_x$$

From the last two equations one obtains for the Hall coefficient,

$$R_H \equiv E_y/I_x H_z = -1/nec \qquad (11\text{-}65)$$

Thus the Hall coefficient is determined essentially by the sign and density of the charge carriers. Observed Hall coefficients for a number of metals are given in Table 11-3. It is observed that a number of metals have positive Hall coefficients. Qualitatively, this can be explained on the basis of the band theory of metals, since a metal with a nearly filled band is equivalent to a conductor in which the current is carried by positive holes; this would change the sign of R. For further details on the Hall effect see Chapter 13. We should mention that the same information as obtained from Hall coefficient measurements can be obtained from the thermoelectric force.

Table 11-3. Hall Coefficient of a Number of Metals at Room Temperature, in volts/cm-abamp-gauss. (After Seitz, *Modern Theory of Solids*, McGraw-Hill, New York, 1940, p. 183)

$10^{12}R_H$		$10^{12}R_H$		$10^{12}R_H$	
Cu	−5.5	Be	24.4	Fe	100
Ag	−8.4	Zn	3.3	Co	24
Au	−7.2	Cd	6.0	Ni	−60
Li	−17.0	Al	−3.0		
Na	−25.0				

Negative signs indicate electron conduction, positive signs indicate hole conduction.

[28] See, for example, F. Seitz, *The Modern Theory of Solids*, McGraw-Hill, New York, 1940, p. 181.

REFERENCES

Besides the books referred to at the end of the preceding chapter, the following review papers may be consulted:

J. Bardeen, "Electrical Conductivity of Metals," *J. Appl. Phys.*, **11**, 88 (1940).

R. Berman, "The Thermal Conductivity of Dielectric Solids at Low Temperatures," *Advances in Physics* (quarterly supplement of the *Philosophical Magazine*), **2**, 103 (1953).

P. G. Klemens, "Thermal Conductivity of Solids at Low Temperatures," *Encyclopedia of Physics*, Springer. Berlin, 1956, vol. 14, pp. 198–276.

D. K. C. MacDonald, "Properties of Metals at Low Temperatures," *Progress in Metal Physics*, **3**, 42 (1952).

D. K. C. MacDonald, "Electrical Conductivity of Metals and Alloys at Low Temperatures," *Encyclopedia of Physics*, Springer, Berlin, 1956, vol. 14, pp. 137–197.

J. L. Olsen and H. M. Rosenberg, "On the Thermal Conductivity of Metals at Low Temperatures," *Advances in Physics*, **2**, 28 (1953).

"Proceedings of the International Conference on Electron Transport in Metals and Solids," *Can. J. Phys.* **34**, Dec. 1956, No. 12A.

PROBLEMS

11-1. From the observed electrical conductivity of copper at room temperature, calculate the relaxation time and the mean free path for electrons at the Fermi level on the basis of (11-30); assume one free electron per atom. Also calculate the average drift velocity of these electrons in a field of 1 volt per cm and compare the result with the average velocity in the absence of a field.

11-2. Show that on the basis of the classical picture of electron scattering by rigid spheres (the atoms) and on the assumption that the electrons obey Boltzmann statistics, the electrical conductivity should be proportional to $T^{-1/2}$. How does this compare with experiment?

11-3. Set up a simple classical theory for the thermal conductivity K of a metal and show that in this theory $K/\sigma T = 3(k/e)^2 = 2.48 \times 10^{-13}$ cgs unit, where σ is the electrical conductivity. This is the Wiedemann-Franz law. See for example the first chapters of the books by A. H. Wilson, *op. cit.*, and by N. F. Mott and H. Jones, *op. cit.*

11-4. Show that if the ions in a metal behave as rigid spheres with respect to electron scattering, a relaxation time can be properly defined (see, for example, A. H. Wilson, *op. cit.*, p. 8).

11-5. Consider a group of similar particles which at the instant $t = 0$ all move in the x-direction with the same velocity v_{0x}. Suppose the particles are scattered by obstacles such that the average time between collisions is τ_c. The scattering is not isotropic. Show that the average velocity of the group measured along the x-direction decreases exponentially to zero with a relaxation time $\tau = \tau_c/(1 - \langle \cos \beta \rangle)$, where β is the scattering angle and $\langle \cos \beta \rangle$ is the average of $\cos \beta$.

11-6. Give a rough estimate of the density of vacancies or interstitial atoms required in a metal such as copper to make the impurity resistivity comparable to the resistivity associated with lattice vibrations at room temperature; do this on the basis of mean free path considerations. Do the same problem for liquid air and liquid helium temperatures.

11-7. In the simplified discussion of Sec. 11-6 it was assumed that the cross section for scattering of an electron by an atom was proportional to the mean square displacement of the vibrating atom. Calculate the mean square displacement of a silver atom in the metal at room temperature, assuming that the frequency is equal to the Debye frequency. Also, calculate the cross section Q_F for scattering per silver atom from the observed conductivity at room temperature. Find the proportionality factor relating Q_F and $\langle x^2 \rangle$ for this case.

11-8. Consider a collision between an electron and a phonon in which the phonon is absorbed by the electron. Assume that the energy of the electron may be written $E(k) = \hbar^2 k^2/2m$, and that the electron energy is much larger than the energy of the phonon. From the conservation laws, show that $\sin (\beta/2) \simeq q/2k$ where β is the angle over which the electron is scattered and q is the magnitude of the wave vector of the phonon. Also, calculate the scattering angle if the electron has an energy of 4 ev and the phonon has a wavelength of 10 Å; assume that the velocity of sound is 10^5 cm sec^{-1}. For this case, what is the required angle between k and q before the collision?

11-9. Consider a metal subject to an electric field and a constant temperature gradient, both in the x-direction. Set up the Boltzmann transport equation for this case and show that in the free electron approximation, if a relaxation time exists, the thermal conductivity is given by (11-60). See, for example, F. Seitz, *op. cit.*, pp. 174 ff.

11-10. Define the thermoelectric effects: the Thomson effect, the Peltier effect, and the Seebeck effect. Discuss these effects for metals on the basis of the free electron approximation. See F. Seitz, *op. cit.*, 178, or A. H. Wilson, *op. cit.*, p. 202.

11-11. Discuss the influence of a magnetic field on the resistivity of metals (magnetoresistance effect). For this and other galvanomagnetic effects see A. H. Wilson. *op. cit.*, or N. F. Mott and H. Jones. *op. cit.*

Chapter 12

THE ELECTRON DISTRIBUTION IN INSULATORS AND SEMICONDUCTORS

The electrical properties of semiconductors are determined essentially by the following quantities:

(i) The number of electrons and holes per unit volume.

(ii) The mobility of the electrons and holes.

It is therefore convenient to discuss the temperature-dependence of the density of charge carriers for some frequently occurring cases before going into the details of specific types of semiconductors.

12-1. The Fermi distribution

As shown in Appendix D, the number of electrons per unit volume occupying states in the energy range between E and $E + dE$ in any electronic system in thermal equilibrum is given by

$$n(E)\, dE = Z(E)F(E)\, dE \qquad (12\text{-}1)$$

where $F(E)$ is the Fermi distribution function,

$$F(E) = \frac{1}{e^{(E-E_F)/kT} + 1} \qquad (12\text{-}2)$$

and $Z(E)$ represents the number of possible states per unit volume, (including the spin). So far we have had an opportunity to employ this distribution law only in the free electron theory of metals, in which case $Z(E)$ is proportional to $E^{1/2}$ when E is measured from the bottom of the potential well representing the metal. In that case, the physical meaning of E_F at $T = 0$ was simply that it represented the highest occupied state. In the case of insulators and intrinsic semiconductors where $Z(E)$ may be a complicated function of E which vanishes in the forbidden energy ranges, the physical meaning of E_F may not be immediately obvious. In general, of course, we may say that E_F corresponds to that level which has a probability of $\frac{1}{2}$ for being occupied; this follows immediately from (12-2). However, E_F in the case of insulators and semiconductors is usually located somewhere between the valence and conduction bands, i.e., in general E_F is not a level which can actually be occupied by an electron. The physical meaning in these cases is therefore somewhat more abstract than that in the case of metals. The position of the Fermi level in any case may be determined from the condition

$$\int n(E)\, dE = \int Z(E)F(E)\, dE = n \qquad (12\text{-}3)$$

where n is the total number of electrons per unit volume. The general procedure of calculating $n(E)$ for given $Z(E)$ and T therefore is this: from (12-3) one calculates E_F and from it $n(E)$ may be determined by substitution into (12-1).

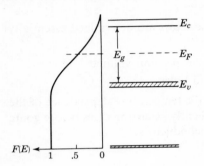

Fig. 12-1. Insulator with Fermi level half-way between valence and conduction bands. The band widths are assumed small compared with E_g. The Fermi distribution function is indicated on the left.

12-2. A simplified model of an insulator

In order to indicate the general features of the electron and hole distribution in insulators and intrinsic semiconductors as functions of temperature, we shall first consider a simplified model. It will be assumed that the widths of the valence and conduction bands are small compared with the forbidden gap between the two bands. In this case we may associate a single energy E_c with all states in the conduction band and a single energy E_v with all states in the valence band (see Fig. 12-1). This situation resembles closely the system of discrete energy levels in an atom. Let each band contain Z possible states per unit volume; $Z \simeq 10^{22}$ per cm³. At $T = 0$ the electrons are in their lowest state, and because the solid is assumed to be an insulator at this temperature, the valence band and all lower bands are completely filled; the conduction band at $T = 0$ is completely empty. At temperatures different from zero, the density of electrons in the conduction band is given by

$$n_c = \frac{Z}{\exp\left[(E_c - E_F)/kT\right] + 1} \qquad (12\text{-}4)$$

Similarly, the density of electrons in the valence band is

$$n_v = \frac{Z}{\exp\left[(E_v - E_F)/kT\right] + 1} \qquad (12\text{-}5)$$

It will be evident that for gap widths of the order of several electron volts, practically all electrons in the conduction band originate from the valence band, so that the presence of bands below the latter may be neglected.[1] In other words, we may write

$$n_c + n_v = Z \qquad (12\text{-}6)$$

Substituting (12-4) and (12-5) into this expression, one obtains an equation for E_F, leading to:

$$E_F = \tfrac{1}{2}(E_v + E_c) \qquad (12\text{-}7)$$

Thus, in this model, the Fermi level is located exactly halfway between the valence and conduction bands. Also, its position is independent of temperature in this approximation.

The density of electrons in the conduction band may now be found by substituting E_F from (12-7) into (12-4). If we assume that the Fermi level is more than about $4kT$ away from the conduction band, the term unity in the denominators of (12-4) and (12-5) may be neglected to a good approximation. In that case,

$$n_c \simeq Z e^{-E_g/2kT} \simeq 10^{22} e^{-E_g/2kT} \qquad (12\text{-}8)$$

where $E_g = E_c - E_v$ represents the width of the forbidden gap. This result may be compared with the improved formula (12-19). The number of holes in the valence band is, of course, equal to n_c. Note the occurrence of half the gap width in the Boltzmann factor (see Problem 12-1). Clearly, when $\log n_c$ is plotted versus $1/T$, a straight line with a slope of $-E_g/2k$ results (see Fig. 12-6). In this connection it is of interest to note that the conductivity of a material is given by

$$\sigma = n_e e \mu_e + n_h e \mu_h \qquad (12\text{-}9)$$

where μ represents the mobility of the charge carriers, (i.e., the velocity per unit electric field); the subscripts e and h refer to electrons and holes, respectively. In the case under discussion $n_e = n_h = n_c$. One speaks in this case of intrinsic conductivity. Now we shall see in the next chapter that μ_e and μ_h are much less strongly temperature-dependent than the density of electrons and holes. The temperature-dependence of σ in the intrinsic region is therefore essentially given by (12-8); i.e., $\log \sigma$ versus $1/T$ yields a straight line with a slope of $-E_g/2k$. We shall see below that the same result is obtained with a more sophisticated model. Note that the conductivities of insulators and intrinsic semiconductors increase with increasing temperature. In contrast to this, the conductivity of metals decreases with increasing T; the reason is that in metals the density of charge carriers remains constant and the mobility decreases with increasing T.

---

[1] The reader is reminded of the fact that at room temperature $kT \simeq 0.025$ ev; the gap width in a good insulator is several ev.

12-3. Improved model for an insulator and intrinsic semiconductor

It is evident that when the width of the allowed energy bands becomes comparable with the width of the forbidden region, one is no longer justified in using a single energy for a complete band. Thus, in general, (12-4) should be replaced by

$$n_c = \int_{E_c}^{\text{top}} Z(E)F(E)\, dE \qquad (12\text{-}10)$$

where E_c represents the bottom of the conduction band and $Z(E)$ is the

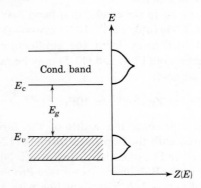

Fig. 12-2. Schematic representation of the density of states in an insulator. Near the bottom of the conduction band $Z(E)$ is proportional to $(E - E_c)^{1/2}$; near the top of the valence band $Z(E)$ is proportional to $(E_v - E)^{1/2}$.

density of the states (see Fig. 12-2). Because we expect from the results obtained above that E_F lies roughly halfway between E_v and E_c, the Fermi function $F(E)$ decreases strongly as one moves up in the conduction band. In other words, to evaluate the integral (12-10) it is sufficient to know $Z(E)$ near the bottom of the conduction band and one may then integrate from $E = E_c$ to $E = \infty$. Near the bottom of the conduction band we have, in accordance with (10-79),

$$Z(E) = (4\pi/h^3)(2m_e^*)^{3/2}(E - E_c)^{1/2}\, dE \qquad (12\text{-}11)$$

where m_e^* is the effective mass of an electron near E_c. Hence the density of electrons in the conduction band is

$$n_c = (4\pi/h^3)(2m_e^*)^{3/2} \int_{E_c}^{\infty} \frac{(E - E_c)^{1/2}\, dE}{e^{(E - E_F)/kT} + 1} \qquad (12\text{-}12)$$

For simplicity we shall assume that $(E_c - E_F) \geqslant 4kT$, in which case the

term unity in the denominator may be neglected to a good approximation.[2]
The integral (12-12) may then be reduced to the type

$$\int_0^\infty x^{1/2} e^{-x}\, dx = \pi^{1/2}/2$$

and one obtains

$$n_c = 2(2\pi m_e^* kT/h^2)^{3/2} e^{(E_F - E_c)/kT} \qquad (12\text{-}13)$$

In order to find E_F, which so far is an unknown quantity, we make use of
the fact that n_c must be equal to the number of holes in the valence band.
To calculate the latter, we note that $[1 - F(E)]$ represents the probability
for a state of energy E to be unoccupied. The density of holes in the
valence band may thus be written

$$n_h = \int_{\text{bottom}}^{E_v} Z(E)[1 - F(E)]\, dE \qquad (12\text{-}14)$$

where the integration extends over the valence band.

It is readily verified that the factor $[1 - F(E)]$ decreases rapidly as one
goes down below the top of the valence band (i.e., the holes reside near
the top of the valence band). Hence, to evaluate the integral (12-14) one
is essentially interested in $Z(E)$ near the top of the valence band. According
to the results obtained in Chapter 10, $Z(E)$ varies in this region in the
following fashion:

$$Z(E)\, dE = (4\pi/h^3)(2m_h^*)^{3/2}(E_v - E)^{1/2}\, dE \qquad (12\text{-}15)$$

where m_h^* represents the effective mass of a hole near the top of the valence
band. If we make the assumption that the Fermi level lies more than about
$4kT$ above E_v, we may use the approximation

$$1 - F(E) \simeq e^{(E - E_F)/kT} \qquad (12\text{-}16)$$

Substituting the last two expressions into (12-14) and integrating from
$-\infty$ to E_v, one obtains in the same way as above

$$n_h = 2(2\pi m_h^* kT/h^2)^{3/2} e^{(E_v - E_F)/kT} \qquad (12\text{-}17)$$

Employing the fact that $n_c = n_h$, it follows from (12-13) and (12-17) that

$$E_F = (E_c + E_v)/2 + \tfrac{3}{4}kT \log(m_h^*/m_e^*) \qquad (12\text{-}18)$$

In case $m_h^* = m_e^*$, the Fermi level lies again exactly halfway between the

---

[2] For numerical tables of integrals of the type (12-12), see J. McDougall and E. C.
Stoner, *Phil. Trans.*, **A237**, 67 (1929).

top of the valence band and the bottom of the conduction band; (12-18) is then identical with (12-7). In general $m_h^* > m_e^*$ and the Fermi level is raised slightly as T increases. This is indicated schematically in Fig. 12-5 by the "intrinsic Fermi level."

The density of electrons in the conduction band n_c and the density of holes in the valence band n_h may be obtained by substituting (12-18) into (12-13). This gives

$$n_c = n_h = 2(2\pi kT/h^2)^{3/2}(m_e^* m_h^*)^{3/4} e^{-E_g/2kT} \qquad (12\text{-}19)$$

where E_g represents the gap width. It is observed that the temperature-dependence is the same as in the simplified model. The temperature-dependence of n_c is represented schematically by the curve labeled "intrinsic" in Fig. 12-6. It is convenient to remember that at room temperature

$$2(2\pi mkT/h^2)^{3/2} \simeq 10^{19} \text{ per cm}^3 \qquad (12\text{-}20)$$

where m is the mass of a free electron. Note that the constant in front of the exponential in (12-8) is much larger than that in (12-19). We emphasize again that (12-18) and (12-19) are good approximations only if the Fermi level is more than a few kT away from the bottom of the conduction band and from the top of the valence band.

12-4. Models for an impurity semiconductor

Most semiconductors owe their conductivity to impurities, i.e., either to foreign atoms built into the lattice or to a stoichiometric excess of one of its constituents. At absolute zero such a solid may contain a certain concentration of occupied electronic levels which lie in the normally forbidden region between the valence and conduction bands. These electrons are localized in the vicinity of the impurities and therefore do not contribute to the conductivity unless they are excited into the conduction band. Centers of this kind are called donor levels. In the energy level scheme they are represented by a short bar, to indicate that they are localized (see Fig. 12-3a). Similarly, an impurity semiconductor may contain a certain density of holes which at $T = 0$ are trapped in levels lying in the forbidden gap. Such levels are called acceptor levels because they may become occupied by electrons excited from the filled band; these excited electrons leave a hole in the valence band and conduction becomes possible in this band (see Fig. 12-3b). The physical reasons for the existence and location of donor and acceptor levels will be discussed in the next chapter.

We shall now consider the density of free electrons and holes for two simple models.

(i) The simplest model for an *n*-type semiconductor consists of a conduction band below which there are n_d donor levels per cm³ of energy E_i (see Fig. 12-3a).[3] The influence of the valence band will be neglected for the moment, i.e., the model may be applied only at relatively low temperatures. Let us assume that at $T = 0$ all donor levels are filled with electrons. At low temperatures, when only a small fraction of donors is ionized, we expect the Fermi level to lie about halfway between the donor levels and the bottom of the conduction band. We shall assume for

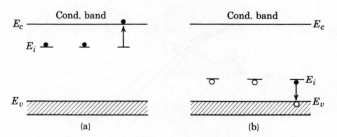

Fig. 12-3. Donor levels are indicated in (a); one of the donors is ionized, leading to a free electron in the conduction band. Acceptor levels are indicated in (b); one of them is ionized (i.e., occupied by an electron from the valence band), leading to a free hole.

simplicity that E_F lies more than a few kT below the bottom of the conduction band. In that case, the density of conduction electrons n_c is given by (12-13). This number must be equal to the density of ionized donors. If we assume that E_F lies more than a few kT above the donor levels, the density of empty donors is equal to

$$n_d[1 - F(E_i)] \simeq n_d e^{(E_i - E_F)/kT} \qquad (12\text{-}21)$$

Equating (12-13) and (12-21), one obtains for the location of the Fermi level the expression,

$$E_F = \tfrac{1}{2}(E_i + E_c) + (kT/2) \log \left[\frac{n_d}{2(2\pi m_e^* kT/h^2)^{3/2}} \right] \qquad (12\text{-}22)$$

Thus at $T = 0$, E_F lies exactly halfway between the donor levels and the bottom of the conduction band. As T increases, the Fermi level drops. This is illustrated in Fig. 12-4 for the case $E_c - E_i = 0.2$ ev for three

[3] Semiconductors in which the current is carried predominantly by electrons are called *n*-type semiconductors, (n = negative); a hole conductor is referred to as a *p*-type (p = positive) semiconductor.

different values of n_d.[4] Within the triangular region ABC the Fermi level is more than $2kT$ away from the conduction band and from the donor levels; only in this region is (12-22) applicable (with an accuracy of about 8 per cent). Outside this region, the term unity in the Fermi distribution entering in (12-21) must be retained. Note that for this model, E_F falls indefinitely; in an actual case, however, the presence of the valence

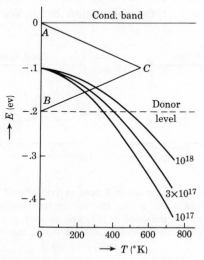

Fig. 12-4. The Fermi level as function of T for a set of donor levels 0.2 ev below the conduction band; the presence of the valence band is neglected. The numbers next to the curves represent the number of donors per cm³. Within ABC, the Fermi level is more than $2kT$ away from the donors and from the conduction band. [After Hutner, Rittner, and DuPré, ref. 4]

band would ultimately keep the Fermi level about halfway between the valence and conduction bands (see Fig. 12-5).

For the region in which (12-22) is applicable, the density of free electrons in the conduction band is obtained by substituting E_F into (12-13), leading to

$$n_c = (2n_d)^{1/2}(2\pi m_e^* kT/h^2)^{3/4}e^{-\Delta E/2kT} \qquad (12\text{-}23)$$

where $\Delta E = E_c - E_i$ represents the ionization energy of the donors. Note again the occurrence of $\Delta E/2$ rather than ΔE; also note that n_c is proportional to the square root of the donor concentration (see Problem 12-2).

The case of acceptor levels above the valence band may be treated in

    [4] R. A. Hutner, E. S. Rittner, and F. K. DuPré, *Philips Research Repts.* **5**, 188, (1950).

the same way. The density of holes in the valence band, making similar assumptions as above, is given by an expression similar to (12-23). In this case the Fermi level lies halfway between the acceptor levels and the top of the valence band at $T = 0$; as T increases, the Fermi level rises (see Problem 12-3 and Fig. 12-5).

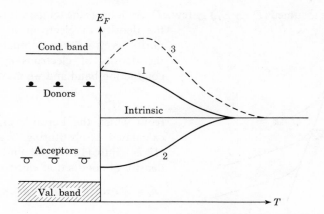

Fig. 12-5. Schematic representation of the Fermi level as function of temperature; curve 1 for insulator with donors, curve 2 for insulator with acceptors. The intrinsic Fermi level slopes slightly upward, in accordance with (12-18). The dashed curve, 3, corresponds to the case in which the electron gas in the conduction band is degenerate over a certain range of temperatures, as discussed in Sec. 12-6.

From these results it follows that the logarithm of the density of carriers plotted versus the reciprocal temperature should yield a straight line of slope $-\Delta E/2k$. However, as the temperature is increased to such values that the intrinsic excitation becomes important, the slope changes gradually to $-E_{\mathrm{gap}}/2k$. The reason is that the density of electrons in the filled band is of the order of 10^{22} per cm³, whereas the density of impurity centers is usually $\leqslant 10^{19}$ per cm³. This is illustrated schematically in Fig. 12-6. Similar curves are encountered when the logarithm of the conductivity is plotted against $1/T$, as we shall see in later chapters.

(ii) The above model applies to a large extent to semiconductors such as germanium and silicon, containing trivalent or pentavalent impurities; the former produce acceptor levels, the latter donor levels. In other cases, such as the alkali halides containing excess metal, the density of available levels may be larger than the number of excess electrons. In other words, it is possible that at $T = 0$ only a fraction of the available levels is occupied. As an extreme case, we shall assume that the density of donor electrons n_d is very small compared with the density of available levels Z_i. In this case, the Fermi level evidently lies below the donor levels. At any temperature T, the number of filled "impurity" levels is equal to

$$\frac{Z_i}{e^{(E_i - E_F)/kT} + 1} \simeq Z_i e^{(E_F - E_i)/kT}$$

where we assumed $(E_i - E_F) \gtrsim$ few kT. As long as the temperature is low, the density of electrons in the impurity levels is large compared with the density of electrons n_c in the conduction band and we may write

$$Z_i e^{(E_F - E_i)/kT} \simeq n_d \quad (12\text{-}24)$$

from which the Fermi level may be calculated. Substituting E_F from (12-24) into (12-13) we find for the density of conduction electrons,

$$n_c = 2(2\pi m_e^* kT/h^2)^{3/2}(n_d/Z_i)e^{-\Delta E/kT} \quad (12\text{-}25)$$

It is interesting to compare this expression with (12-23); in the present case n_c is proportional to n_d (instead of $n_d^{1/2}$), and the exponential contains ΔE (instead of $\Delta E/2$). This shows that in some cases one must be careful in interpreting the slope of the log n_c versus $1/T$ curve as giving half the ionization energy of the donors.

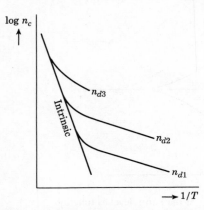

Fig. 12-6. Schematic representation of the logarithm of the density of conduction electrons versus $1/T$ for an impurity semiconductor containing different donor densities, $(n_{d1} < n_{d2} < n_{d3})$. At high temperatures the slope is determined by $E_{\text{gap}}/2k$; at lower temperatures by $\Delta E/2k$.

12-5. Thermionic emission from semiconductors

The importance of the Fermi level in the discussion of contacts between conductors has been stressed in Sec. 9-10. It was shown there that in such contacts the Fermi levels of the materials must coincide. We shall show here another important aspect of the Fermi level, viz., the fact that it determines the thermionic work function of a semiconductor.

In Sec. 9-6 we derived the Richardson expression from the free electron model for the thermionic emission of metals;

$$I = (4\pi m e k^2 T^2/h^3)e^{-\phi/kT} \quad (12\text{-}26)$$

We neglect reflection for simplicity. We shall now consider the thermionic emission from a semiconductor, assuming that the electrons in the conduction band may be treated as free electrons with an effective mass m^*.

Let the vacuum level (i.e., the energy of an electron at rest outside the semiconductor) be higher than the bottom of the conduction band by an amount χ as indicated in Fig. 12-7; χ is called the electron affinity of the crystal. If x is the direction perpendicular to the surface, an electron needs at least a momentum in the x-direction given by

$$p_{x_0}^2 = 2m^*\chi \qquad (12\text{-}27)$$

in order to escape. As a result of thermal excitation let there be n_c electrons per unit volume in the conduction band. If the Fermi level is assumed to lie more than a few kT below the bottom of the conduction band, the conduction electrons have a Max-wellian velocity distribution accord-ing to the discussion of the preceding sections. We leave it as a problem to the reader to show that the density of electrons with momenta in the range dp_x, dp_y, dp_z is then equal to

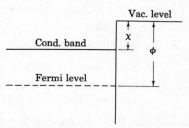

Fig. 12-7. Illustrating the electron affinity χ and the work function ϕ of a semiconductor.

$$n(p_x,p_y,p_z)\,dp_x\,dp_y\,dp_z = [n_c/(2\pi m^*kT)^{3/2}]e^{-p^2/2m^*kT}\,dp_x\,dp_y\,dp_z \quad (12\text{-}28)$$

Following the same treatment as in the thermionic emission of metals, one may then write for the emission current density,

$$I = \frac{en_c}{(2\pi m^*kT)^{3/2}} \int\int\int (p_x/m^*)e^{-p^2/2m^*kT}\,dp_x\,dp_y\,dp_z \qquad (12\text{-}29)$$

The integrations over p_y and p_z go between $\pm\infty$; the integration over p_x extends from p_{x_0} to ∞. This yields

$$I = \frac{en_c}{(2\pi m^*kT)^{3/2}} 2\pi m^*k^2T^2 e^{-\chi/kT} \qquad (12\text{-}30)$$

The value of n_c is for intrinsic as well as for impurity semiconductors given by (12-13). Substitution gives finally

$$I = (4\pi m^*ek^2T^2/h^3)e^{-\phi/kT} \qquad (12\text{-}31)$$

where the work function ϕ represents the energy difference between the Fermi level and the vacuum level, as indicated in Fig. 12-7. It is observed that (12-31) becomes identical with (12-26) if one replaces the effective mass of the conduction electrons by that of a free electron. It is of interest to note that according to (12-30) the thermionic emission is proportional to n_c, i.e., the emission current density is correlated with the conductivity of the material.

12-6. Electronic degeneracy in semiconductors

In the preceding sections it was assumed that the Fermi level was located at least a few kT below the bottom of the conduction band. In that case the electrons in the conduction band follow closely Boltzmann statistics, i.e., the electron gas is nondegenerate. Under certain circumstances, however, the Fermi level may enter the conduction band and the electron gas in the conduction band may become degenerate. From the preceding discussions it should be clear that the conditions favorable for such a situation are the following:

(i) Relatively high donor densities ($\sim 10^{19}$ per cm^3)

(ii) Small donor ionization energy

(iii) Low density of states near the bottom of the conduction band, i.e., small effective electronic mass (see Sec. 10-9).

When these conditions are fulfilled, the Fermi level as function of temperature varies as indicated by the dashed curve 3 in Fig. 12-5. As T increases from absolute zero, the donors begin to ionize and as a result of the low density of states, the lower energy states in the conduction band become completely filled. The position of the Fermi level relative to the bottom of the conduction band is then given by (9-9),

$$E_F = (h^2/2m_e^*)(3n_c/8\pi)^{2/3}$$

where n_c is the density of electrons in the conduction band. As long as $E_F \gg kT$, the electron gas is degenerate. Clearly, as the effective electronic mass is reduced, degeneracy may occur at lower electron densities. As T is increased further, the degeneracy is removed and the Fermi level leaves the conduction band again.

The circumstances described here are believed to occur in InSb, containing donor levels in concentrations of about 10^{18} per cm^3; the effective mass of the conduction electrons is probably only about $m/30$ in this case.

REFERENCES

J. S. Blakemore, "Carrier Concentrations and Fermi Levels in Semiconductors," *Elec. Commun.*, June 1952, pp. 131–153.

R. A. Hutner, E. S. Rittner, and F. K. DuPré, "Fermi Levels in Semiconductors," *Philips Research Repts.*, **5**, 188 (1950).

F. Seitz, *The Modern Theory of Solids*, McGraw-Hill, New York, 1940, pp. 186 ff.

W. Shockley, *Electrons and Holes in Semiconductors*, Van Nostrand, New York, 1950.

PROBLEMS

12-1. With reference to the problem discussed in Secs. 12-2 and 12-3, consider the reaction

electron in valence band $\leftrightarrows$ electron in conduction band
+ hole in valence band

Applying the law of mass action as used in chemical reactions, show that the equilibrium concentration of the conduction electrons is proportional to $\exp(-E_{gap}/2kT)$.

12-2. With reference to the problem discussed in Sec. 12-4, consider the reaction

bound electron $\leftrightarrows$ free electron + empty donor

Making use of the law of mass action, answer the following questions:

(a) Assuming that at $T = 0$ all donor levels are filled, show that the density of free electrons is proportional to $n_d^{1/2} \exp(-\Delta E/2kT)$.

(b) Assuming that at $T = 0$ only a small fraction of the donor levels is filled, show that the density of free electrons is proportional to $Z_i \exp(-\Delta E/kT)$, where Z_i is the density of impurity levels and ΔE is the ionization energy of the donor levels.

12-3. For an intrinsic semiconductor with a gap width of 1 ev, calculate the position of the Fermi level at $T = 0$ and at $T = 300°$, if $m_h^* = 5m_e^*$. Also, calculate the density of free electrons and holes at $T = 300°$ and at $T = 600°$.

12-4. Assuming a Maxwellian velocity distribution for the electrons in the conduction band, derive expression (12-28).

12-5. Assuming a valence band above which there are n_a acceptor levels per unit volume, derive an expression for the Fermi level and for the density of free holes in the valence band as function of T.

12-6. What is roughly the temperature range over which an electron gas in the conduction band is degenerate if $n_c = 10^{18}$ per cm³ and $m_e^* = m/30$? Compare this with perfectly free electrons.

12-7. If the Fermi level in a semiconductor lies more than a few kT below the bottom of the conduction band and more than a few kT above the top of the valence band, show that the product of the number of free electrons and the number of free holes per cm³ is given by

$$n_e n_h = 2.33 \times 10^{31} T^3 e^{-E_g/kT}$$

where E_g is the gap width. Note that this holds irrespective of the presence of donors or acceptors in the gap, as long as the condition imposed on the Fermi level is satisfied.

12-8. Consider a crystal which at $T = 0$ is an insulator; the crystal contains N_d donor levels per cm³, which at $T = 0$ are all occupied, and N_t electron traps per cm³, which at $T = 0$ are all empty (the traps lie above the donor levels). Discuss in detail the distribution of electrons at a temperature T and the various approximations which may hold under particular circumstances.

Chapter 13

NONPOLAR SEMICONDUCTORS

13-1. Introductory remarks

Semiconductors are characterized by an electrical conductivity (associated with the motion of electrons or holes or both) which on the one hand is considerably smaller than that of metals, and on the other hand, is much larger than that of "insulators." Furthermore, the conductivity increases with temperature, in contrast with the behavior of metals at normal temperatures. The number of current carriers per unit volume in a semiconductor is in general much smaller than the number of atoms per unit volume. This situation is encountered, for example, in a solid for which the forbidden energy gap between the highest normally filled band and the conduction band is small, i.e., of the order of one electron volt. At absolute zero such a solid is an insulator, and as the temperature is raised, the density of free electrons and holes increases as explained in the preceding chapter. In this case the density of free electrons equals that of the free holes and one speaks of intrinsic semiconductors; the properties are then characteristic of the solid itself. Semiconductor properties may also be exhibited by solids which in the pure state are good insulators, viz., when impurities are present which either donate free electrons to the conduction band (donors) or free holes to the upper filled band (acceptors); in this case one speaks of extrinsic or impurity semiconductors. Impurity conductivity may of course be superimposed on the intrinsic semiconductor properties of a solid.

The semiconducting elements are those appearing within the area enclosed by the lines drawn in Table 13-1; this table represents the A subgroup elements in a number of columns of the periodic table. Of these, silicon and germanium have received a great deal of attention because of their great technical importance, particularly in the field of crystal diodes and transistors. The discussion in this chapter will be concerned mainly with the properties of Si and Ge; the amount of literature on this subject is so vast that the discussion is necessarily very incomplete. A review which is up to date until the beginning of 1955 may be found in H. Y. Fan in F. Seitz and D. Turnbull (eds.), *Solid State Physics*, Academic Press, New York, 1955, Volume 1.

319

Extensive studies have recently been initiated on intermetallic compounds formed between the elements of the third and fifth columns in Table 13-1; these will be discussed briefly in the last section of this chapter.

Table 13-1. The A Subgroups of the 3rd, 4th, 5th, 6th, and 7th Columns
of the Periodic System of Elements

IIIA	IVA	VA	VIA	VIIA
B	C	N	O	F
Al	Si	P	S	Cl
Ga	Ge	As	Se	Br
In	Sn	Sb	Te	I
Tl	Pb	Bi	Po	At

Of the semiconducting salts in which the binding is essentially ionic, the alkali halides containing color centers have been investigated most thoroughly; we shall return to these compounds in Chapter 15.

13-2. Some lattice properties of the elements of the fourth group

Structure. Diamond, silicon, germanium, and grey tin all have the diamond structure represented in Fig. 13-1. Each atom is surrounded by four others, occupying the corner points of a tetrahedron, to which it is bound by electron pair bonds. The structure may be described by an f.c.c. point lattice in which each lattice point corresponds to two atoms, one located at $(0,0,0)$ and another at $(\frac{1}{4},\frac{1}{4},\frac{1}{4})$. The free atoms of the elements have an outer electron configuration in which two electrons occupy an s state and two others occupy a p state. In the solid state the total of four outer electrons per atom is just sufficient to produce electron pair bonds with four other atoms; in this configuration the s and p wave functions form hybrid wave functions giving rise to four equivalent chemical bonds, the angle between any two of them being approximately $109°$.[1] This type of covalent binding may be contrasted with the ionic bonds in crystals such as the alkali halides; in the latter, the particles are charged and the field around a given ion is spherically symmetric, i.e., the restriction on the coordination number is essentially of geometrical origin. In terms of a two-dimensional picture one arrives at an electron distribution as indicated schematically in Fig. 13-2.

One expects the electrons taking part in the electron pair bonds to be rather strongly bound, i.e., one expects that a certain amount of energy is required in order to set them free to the extent that they can move about in the crystal. This is in agreement with the fact that at very low temperatures these elements are insulators. In terms of the energy band scheme,

[1] See L. Pauling, *The Nature of the Chemical Bond*, 2d ed., Cornell University Press, Ithaca, 1945, p. 81.

this means that at absolute zero the electron distribution is such that a certain number of energy bands is completely filled, the higher ones being completely empty.

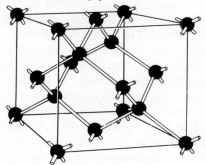

Fig. 13-1. The crystal structure of diamond, showing the tetrahedral bond configuration. [After W. Shockley, *Electrons and Holes in Semiconductors*, Van Nostrand, New York, 1950]

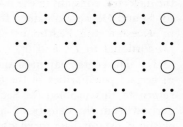

Fig. 13-2. Schematic two-dimensional representation of the electronic distribution in the diamond structure, showing the electron pair bonds.

Physical constants. It is of interest to consider how some of the physical properties of these elements vary in a regular fashion with their position in the periodic table. As the atomic number increases, the interatomic distances increase, i.e., the binding forces become weaker, and the solids become "softer." In Table 13-2 some physical constants are given for diamond, silicon, and germanium to illustrate this. In this order, the lattice parameter a (the edge of the f.c.c. lattice) increases, the elastic constants, the melting point, the Debye temperature, and the forbidden energy gap decrease. Qualitatively, this regularity can be explained on the basis of the relative strengths of the chemical bonds between the atoms. It is also observed that the dielectric constant increases in the order C, Si, Ge; this is to a large extent a result of the increase in the number of electrons per atom, leading to a larger polarizability. With reference to the quantities given in Table 13-2, some remarks should be made. The lattice constants for Si and Ge are those obtained at 20°C by

Table 13-2. Some Physical Constants of Diamond, Silicon, and Germanium
(see text for details)

	a (Å)	m.p. (°C)	ϵ	θ_D (°K)	E_{gap} (ev)	c_{11}	c_{12}	c_{44} (10^{12} dynes/cm)
C	3.561	3550	5.7	1800	~7	9.2	3.9	4.3
Si	5.43086	1420	12	658	1.21	1.674	0.652	0.796
Ge	5.65748	936	16	362	0.785	1.298	0.488	0.673

Straumanis and Aka from X-ray diffraction data; the coefficients of expansion, measured between 10°C and 50°C, obtained by these authors are 4.15×10^{-6} and 5.92×10^{-6} per °C for Si and Ge, respectively.[2] The dielectric constant ϵ given above is based on measurements of the index of refraction in the optical region as well as on measurements of the dielectric constant in the microwave region.[3] The Debye temperatures for Si and Ge were obtained from specific heat measurements below 4°K by Keesom and Pearlman;[4] in this region the lattice specific heat is proportional to T^3, and θ_D may be calculated on the basis of formula (2-37). The energy gap in Si and Ge is not a well-defined quantity because of certain peculiarities in the band structure of these elements; we shall return to this problem in Sec. 13-6. The values given in the table are derived from the density of charge carriers in the intrinsic region. The elastic constants have been obtained from measurements of the velocity of propagation of elastic waves.[5]

Influence of impurities. Of great interest is the fact that Si and Ge can be "doped" with foreign elements. For example, Pearson and Bardeen have shown that boron and phosphorus form substitutional solid solutions in Si.[6] Evidence for this was obtained from the decrease in the lattice constant with increasing concentration of these elements (the atomic radii of Si, B, P are, respectively, 1.17, 0.89, and 1.1 Å). If the solute atoms were incorporated interstitially, the lattice constant should have increased. Thus, consider a phosphorus atom at a position which is normally occupied by Si. The phosphorus atom has five outer electrons, one in excess of the number required to form electron pair bonds with four nearest neighbors. As a result, the extra electron is relatively weakly bound and only a small amount of energy is required to set the electron free. In terms of the energy band picture, this means that phosphorus and other pentavalent atoms give rise to donor levels close to the conduction band.

The order of magnitude of the energy required to ionize the phosphorus atom, i.e., the energy difference between the donor level and the bottom of the conduction band may be estimated according to a suggestion by Bethe as follows: the extra electron of the phosphorus atom may be pictured as moving in the field of a single positive charge, i.e., the problem is somewhat

[2] M. E. Straumanis and E. Z. Aka, *J. Appl. Phys.*, **23**, 330 (1952).

[3] See, for example, K. Lark-Horovitz and K. W. Meissner, *Phys. Rev.*, **76**, 1530 (1949); W. C. Dunlap and R. L. Watters, *Phys. Rev.*, **92**, 1396 (1953).

[4] P. H. Keesom and N. Pearlman, *Phys. Rev.*, **91**, 1347 (1953); N. Pearlman and P. H. Keesom, *Phys. Rev.*, **88**, 398 (1952).

[5] W. L. Bond, W. P. Mason, H. J. McSkimin, K. M. Olsen, and G. K. Teal, *Phys. Rev.*, **78**, 176 (1950); H. J. McSkimin, W. L. Bond, E. Buehler, and G. K. Teal, *Phys. Rev.*, **83**, 1080 (1951).

[6] G. L. Pearson and J. Bardeen, *Phys. Rev.*, **75**, 865 (1949); also F. H. Horn, *Phys. Rev.*, **97**, 1521 (1955).

analogous to that of the hydrogen atom.[7] The difference is, however, that the extra electron and the positive charge are embedded in a medium of rather high dielectric constant (see Table 13-2). As a result, the radius of the orbit covers several atomic distances and the binding energy is small. In fact, if one employs for an estimate the simple Bohr picture modified by taking into account the dielectric constant ϵ and the effective mass m^*, one obtains for the radius and the energy of the ground state

$$r = \epsilon\hbar^2/m^*e^2 \quad \text{and} \quad E_d = -m^*e^4/2\hbar^2\epsilon^2 \tag{13-1}$$

The energy E_d is measured relative to the bottom of the ionization continuum, i.e., relative to the bottom of the conduction band. Assuming for the moment the effective mass m^* to be equal to the free electron mass, one finds

	ϵ	r	E_d (Bohr)	E_d exp
Si	12	6.4 Å	−0.09 ev	−0.05
Ge	16	8.5 Å	−0.05 ev	−0.01

The last column gives the experimental ionization energy of the donor levels for doping with P, As, or Sb.[8] A detailed calculation of the ionization energy of donors by Kittel and Mitchell gives 0.009 ev as a lower limit for germanium and 0.03 ev as a lower limit for silicon, in good agreement with the experimental values.[9] These calculations made use of recent information about the $E(k)$ surfaces as revealed by cyclotron resonance experiments (see Sec. 13-6).

Silicon and germanium may also be doped with trivalent elements such as B, Al, Ga, and In. In these cases the added atoms are one electron short for four electron pair bonds. Each added trivalent atom thus gives rise to a vacant electron level slightly above the valence band. These levels are acceptor levels because they may accept an electron from the filled band if the electron is excited thermally. One may picture the acceptor level as a hole describing a Bohr orbit about the impurity atom; the binding energies are approximately equal to those for the donors. Ionization of the acceptor level in this type of picture is equivalent to the excitation of a valence electron into the hole. In the energy band scheme, electrons are excited upward, holes downward (see Fig. 13-3).

From what has been said above, it is evident that ionization of donor levels (P, As, Sb) gives rise to electronic carriers in the conduction band; ionization of acceptor levels (B, Al, Ga, Sn) produces hole conductivity in the valence band. In germanium at room temperature nearly all donor or

[7] G. Wannier, *Phys. Rev.*, **52**, 191 (1937); see also G. F. Koster and J. C. Slater, *Phys. Rev.*, **95**, 1167 (1954); **96**, 1208 (1954).

[8] J. A. Burton, *Physica*, **20**, 845 (1954).

[9] C. Kittel and A. H. Mitchell, *Phys. Rev.*, **96**, 1488 (1954).

acceptor levels will be ionized, because $kT \simeq 0.025$ ev, which is larger than the binding energy of donor electrons and acceptor holes. Also, the ionization energy decreases with increasing concentration, as may be seen from Fig. 13-4.[10] Thus, even at low temperatures the fraction of ionized donors or acceptors may be rather large.

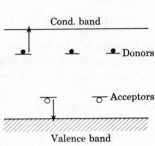

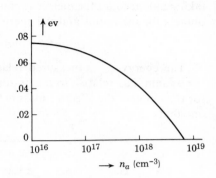

Fig. 13-3.   Energy level scheme for donor and acceptor levels.

Fig. 13-4.   Ionization energy of acceptor levels in Si as function of the acceptor density n_a. [After Pearson and Bardeen, ref. 10]

Crystal growth. Single crystals of silicon and germanium, either doped or not, can be obtained by placing a seed crystal in contact with the melt and then withdrawing the seed slowly.[11] The concentration of a particular impurity in crystals so obtained is determined by the segregation coefficient of the impurity under consideration; this quantity is defined as the ratio of the impurity concentration in the solid phase to that in the melt in thermal equilibrium. For most impurities the segregation coefficient is $\ll 1$, except for boron, which has a coefficient larger than unity in germanium. It will be evident that in general, therefore, the concentration of impurities in the melt increases as the crystal is withdrawn, so that the impurities are concentrated at the end of the crystal. Based on this principle is the so-called zone-refining technique by which crystals of high purity may be obtained: when one moves a heating coil slowly along a crystal, the impurities are swept towards one end of the crystal; this process may of course be repeated many times.[12] In this way it is now possible to produce single crystals of Ge and Si with impurity concentrations as small as one part in 10^{10} or 10^9, at least if one considers the

[10] For *p*-type Si, see G. L. Pearson and J. Bardeen, *Phys. Rev.*, **75**, 865 (1949); for *n*-type Ge, see P. P. Debye and E. M. Conwell, *Phys. Rev.*, **93**, 693 (1954).

[11] G. K. Teal and J. B. Little, *Phys. Rev.*, **78**, 647 (1950); see also G. K. Teal and E. Buehler, *Phys. Rev.*, **87**, 190 (1952).

[12] W. G. Pfann, *J. Metals*, **4**, 747 (1952); W. G. Pfann and K. M. Olsen, *Phys. Rev.*, **89**, 322 (1953).

electrical resistivity a measure for the purity. It should be mentioned in this connection that the use of crucibles and the contamination resulting from the crucible material may be avoided by employing the so-called floating zone technique.[13] In this technique one produces a molten section in a polycrystalline rod of the material (which is held vertically) by induction heating. One end of the material is in contact with a single crystal seed and the molten zone is moved slowly from that end to the other, leading to recrystallization of the polycrystalline material.

Diffusion of impurities. We mentioned above that elements of the third and fifth columns in the periodic system, used as doping material in Si and Ge, are believed to be incorporated substitutionally in the lattice. This belief is supported by the fact that the diffusion coefficients of these elements lie in the same range as those for self-diffusion, i.e., the elements probably diffuse by a vacancy mechanism.[14] There are, however, some notable exceptions, viz., copper, nickel, and lithium. The diffusion coefficients of these elements in silicon and germanium are very high ($\sim 10^{-5}$ cm²/sec at temperatures of 700° or 800°C) and it seems likely that the diffusion process in these cases involves the migration of interstitials. It is believed that copper migrates through germanium in the form of positive ions.[15] At normal temperatures there is strong evidence that copper acts as an acceptor for electrons, i.e., it should then be negatively charged.

Influence of lattice defects. When a germanium crystal, doped with donor impurities, is irradiated with high-energy particles, the conductivity initially decreases. Upon further irradiation with a sufficiently large flux it may convert from *n* type (electron carriers) to *p* type (hole carriers) and the conductivity may then increase. Irradiation effects of this type are evidently associated with the formation of vacancies and interstitial atoms in the lattice; in fact, when the crystals are annealed, the changes essentially disappear. It is not unlikely that the interstitials correspond to donor levels and the vacancies to acceptor levels, although several details of the interpretation of irradiation effects are not yet settled.

Dislocations produced by plastic deformation of silicon and germanium also produce pronounced effects on the electrical conductivity. In *n*-type Ge, for example, plastic deformation leads to a reduction in the conductivity, i.e., the deformation introduces acceptor levels.[16] The physical

[13] P. H. Keck and M. J. E. Golay, *Phys. Rev.*, **89**, 1297 (1953).

[14] See, for example, H. Letaw, L. M. Slifkin, and W. M. Portnoy, *Phys. Rev.*, **93**, 892 (1954); W. C. Dunlap, *Phys. Rev.*, **94**, 1531 (1954).

[15] C. S. Fuller, J. D. Struthers, J. A. Ditzenberger, and K. B. Wolfstirn, *Phys. Rev.*, **93**, 1182 (1954); F. van der Maesen and J. A. Brenkman, *J. Electrochem. Soc.*, **102**, 229 (1955).

[16] C. J. Gallagher, *Phys. Rev.*, **88**, 721 (1952).

picture of the acceptor levels according to Shockley and Read is the following. Slip in these crystals takes place along the $\{111\}$ planes and along a $\langle 110 \rangle$ direction. The extra half plane associated with an edge dislocation leads to a row of "dangling" bonds since the atoms of this row have no neighbors on one side. An electron paired with one of those dangling bonds would not be as "free" as an electron in the conduction band, so that the corresponding level should lie below the bottom of the conduction band. On the other hand, the paired electron is not as strongly bound as one corresponding to a normal electron pair bond between two neighboring atoms, i.e., the level associated with the dangling bond should lie above the filled band. Consequently, an edge dislocation corresponds to a row of acceptor levels lying in the forbidden energy region. For a detailed discussion of the implications of this model for the electrical properties of these materials we refer the reader to a series of three papers by Read.[17]

13-3. Conductivity and Hall effect in semiconductors with a single type of charge carrier

Before discussing the electrical properties of Si and Ge, some remarks on the conductivity and Hall effect of semiconductors should be made. In this section we shall limit ourselves to the case of a single type of charge carrier. The conductivity of such a material is given by

$$\sigma = ne\mu \qquad (13\text{-}2)$$

where n is the density of carriers and μ is their mobility (drift velocity per unit field). It is observed that measurements of $\sigma(T)$ provide information only about the product $n(T)\mu(T)$, and in general do not allow one to determine these quantities separately. However, if we assume for the moment that the Hall coefficient for a semiconductor is given by the formula applicable to metals we would have (see 11-65),

$$R_{\mathrm{H}} = 1/nec \quad \text{and} \quad c\sigma R_{\mathrm{H}} = \mu \qquad (13\text{-}3)$$

Thus $R_{\mathrm{H}}(T)$ would provide information about $n(T)$, and combined measurements of R_{H} and σ thus permit determination of n and μ separately. Although this type of analysis is indeed applied to semiconductors, there are some modifications in the formula for R_{H} which will be discussed below. Also, the temperature-dependence of μ is different from that for metals.

We shall give here a simple theory for n-type material based on the assumption that the electrons in the conduction band behave as nearly free electrons with an effective mass m^*; this implies that constant-energy surfaces in momentum space are assumed to be spheres. There exists at

[17] W. T. Read, *Phil. Mag.*, **45**, 775 (1954); **45**, 1119 (1954); **46**, 111 (1955).

present a great deal of evidence (see Sec. 13-6) that this is not correct, but in many instances the simple theory still gives rather good agreement with the experiments. It is also assumed that the electron gas in the conduction band is nondegenerate, and thus that it has a Maxwellian distribution.

As an example, consider a semiconductor in which the current is carried only by electrons in the conduction band. Suppose an electric field E_x and a magnetic field H_z are applied to the material as indicated in Fig. 13-5. The current density I_x along the x-direction may then be obtained from the Boltzmann transport equation in the same way as for metals. Thus from (11-28) it follows that

$$I_x = -\frac{e^2 E_x}{3} \int_0^\infty \frac{\partial F_0}{\partial E} v^2 \tau(E)(8\pi/h^3)p^2 \, dp \tag{13-4}$$

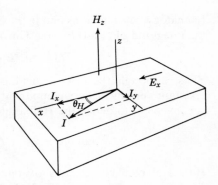

The relaxation time τ is assumed to be a function only of the energy of the electrons, not of their direction of motion. Now it can readily be shown that the Fermi function $F_0(E)$ satisfies the relation

$$-(\partial F_0/\partial E) = F_0(1 - F_0)/kT \simeq F_0/kT \tag{13-5}$$

The last approximation is valid only if the density of the electrons in the conduction band is small enough so that $F_0 \ll 1$, i.e., if the system is nondegenerate. Recognizing that $8\pi p^2 \, dp \, F_0/h^3$ equals the number of electrons with momentum in the range dp, it follows that

Fig. 13-5. Showing the Hall effect; the current I_y flows only if front and back faces are connected; normally, this is not the case and an electric field in the y-direction is set up. The electrons actually flow in the direction opposite to the current vectors.

$$I_x = \frac{ne^2 E_x}{3kT} \langle v^2 \tau \rangle = \sigma E_x = ne\mu E_x \tag{13-6}$$

Here $\langle v^2 \tau \rangle$ is the average value of $v^2 \tau(E)$, the average being taken over the Maxwellian distribution of the conduction electrons. Since $3kT = m^* \langle v^2 \rangle$, one may also express the mobility as

$$\mu = \frac{e}{m^*} \cdot \frac{\langle v^2 \tau \rangle}{\langle v^2 \rangle} \tag{13-7}$$

Note that if τ were independent of the velocity of the electrons, this would reduce simply to $\mu = e\tau/m^*$, as in the simplified model discussed in Sec. 11-2. We shall return to this expression in the next section.

The Hall effect may be discussed by considering the case for which the front and back faces in Fig. 13-5 are short-circuited, allowing the flow of a current along the y-direction. An electron of velocity v_x under influence of the magnetic field H_z will develop a velocity along the y-direction such that

$$(\partial v_y/\partial t)_{H_z} = ev_xH_z/m^*c = \omega v_x \tag{13-8}$$

On the other hand, due to collisions with the lattice,

$$(\partial v_y/dt)_{\text{coll}} = -v_y/\tau$$

Hence, in the steady state,

$$v_y = ev_xH_z\tau/m^*c = \omega\tau v_x \tag{13-9}$$

In analogy, one may thus obtain the current along the y-axis by multiplying the integrand of (13-4) by $\omega\tau$. This finally leads to

$$I_y = (ne^2E_x\omega/3kT)\langle v^2\tau^2\rangle \tag{13-10}$$

Thus, although the electric field is applied along the x-direction, the resultant current has a y-component due to the magnetic field. In fact, it is convenient to define the Hall angle θ_{H} (see Fig. 13-5), where

$$\tan\theta_{\text{H}} \simeq \theta_{\text{H}} = I_y/I_x = \omega\frac{\langle v^2\tau^2\rangle}{\langle v^2\tau\rangle} \tag{13-11}$$

If the Hall contacts are not short-circuited, a field E_y is set up to counteract the influence of the magnetic field. The Hall coefficient then becomes

$$R_{\text{H}} = E_y/I_x\,H_z = I_y/\sigma I_xH_z = \frac{1}{nec}\cdot\frac{\langle v^2\tau^2\rangle\langle v^2\rangle}{\langle v^2\tau\rangle^2} \tag{13-12}$$

where σ has been substituted from (13-6). Note that the sign of the carrier in the above derivation is contained in e; for electrons R_{H} is negative, for holes it is positive. It should be mentioned that one frequently employs the Hall mobility μ_{H} defined in analogy with (13-3) by

$$\mu_{\text{H}} = c\sigma R_{\text{H}} = \frac{e}{m^*c}\cdot\frac{\langle v^2\tau^2\rangle}{\langle v^2\tau\rangle} \tag{13-13}$$

Comparing this with the "normal" mobility given by (13-7), it is observed that in general μ_{H} is not equal to μ.

From the foregoing discussion it is evident that the relaxation time τ plays an essential role in the interpretation of conductivity and Hall effect data. The relaxation time in general is determined by collisions of the carriers with

(i) Lattice vibrations

(ii) Ionized impurities

(iii) Neutral impurities, dislocations, vacancies, and interstitials.

13-4. Mobility and Hall effect as determined by different scattering processes

(i) *Scattering by lattice vibrations.* From the theory of interaction of thermal electrons with lattice vibrations in nonpolar solids,[18] it follows that

(a) The scattering is isotropic.

(b) The mean free path Λ is independent of the velocity of the carriers.

(c) The mean free path is inversely proportional to T, down to temperatures of the order of $1°K$.

The selection rules for electron-phonon interaction mentioned in Sec. 11-7 play an essential role in arriving at these conclusions. For a given temperature it thus follows from (a) and (b) that one may write[19]

$$\tau = \Lambda/v \qquad (13\text{-}14)$$

Substituting τ into the results obtained in the preceding section, one is thus left with the simple problem of finding averages over a Maxwellian distribution of quantities on the type v^n. Thus, if only lattice scattering is present, (13-7) and (13-13) give

$$\mu = \tfrac{4}{3}e\Lambda \,/(2\pi mkT)^{1/2} \quad \text{and} \quad \mu_H = (3\pi/8)\mu \qquad (13\text{-}15)$$

Combining this result with (c) above, one concludes that the mobility μ should be proportional to $T^{-3/2}$ in this case. Bardeen and Shockley[18] find from their calculation of Λ,

$$\frac{e\tau}{m^*} = \mu = \frac{(8\pi)^{1/2}\hbar^4 c_{ll}}{3E_1^2 m^{*5/2}(kT)^{3/2}} = \text{const. } T^{-3/2} \qquad (13\text{-}16)$$

Here, c_{ll} is the average longitudinal elastic constant, and E_1 is the shift of the edge of the conduction band per unit dilation; the temperature-dependence of both these quantities may be neglected. For holes, E_1 represents the shift of the edge of the valence band per unit dilation. Experiments indicate that $E_1 \simeq 10$ ev for germanium. The formula obtained by Seitz[18] is written in terms of the Debye temperature θ, the mass M of the atoms, and their number per unit volume N,

$$\mu = \frac{2^{1/2} \times 6^{1/3}}{4\pi^{5/6}} \cdot \frac{N^{1/3}e\hbar^2 k^2\theta^2 M}{m^{*5/2}C^2(kT)^{3/2}} \qquad (13\text{-}16a)$$

The constant C has the dimensions of an energy and is of the same order of magnitude as E_1 in the Bardeen-Shockley formula; it is a measure for the electron-phonon interaction. The mobility determined by lattice scattering alone is usually referred to as the "lattice mobility."

---

[18] F. Seitz, *Phys. Rev.*, **73**, 549 (1948); J. Bardeen and W. Shockley, *Phys. Rev.*, **80**, 72 (1950).

[19] Compare expression (11-11) for the relation between collision time, relaxation time, and scattering angle.

The Hall coefficient as determined by lattice scattering for semiconductors containing one or two types of carriers is given, respectively, by

$$R_H = \pm \frac{3\pi}{8nec} \quad \text{and} \quad R_H = \frac{3\pi}{8ec} \cdot \frac{n_h \mu_h^2 - n_e \mu_e^2}{(n_h \mu_h + n_e \mu_e)^2} \tag{13-17}$$

where the subscripts e and h in the last formula refer to electrons and holes, respectively. The conductivity for two types of carriers is of course equal to $(n_e e \mu_e + n_h e \mu_h)$.

(ii) *Ionic scattering predominates.* When the concentration of ionized donors is high, the charge carriers suffer Rutherford scattering due to the presence of ions, as illustrated in Fig. 13-6. If one assumes that the ions are distributed throughout the lattice in a regular fashion, the average distance between the ions a_i is given by $a_i^3 = 1/N_i$, where N_i is the number of ions per unit volume. Thus if v is the velocity of an electron, the mean free time between collisions is $\tau_c \simeq a_i/v$. The relaxation time according to (11-11) is in general given by

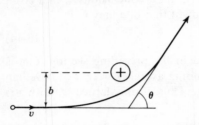

Fig. 13-6. Rutherford scattering of an electron by an ionized donor. It can be shown that tan $(\theta/2) = e^2/\varepsilon m v^2 b$, where ε is the dielectric constant of the material.

$$\tau = \tau_c/(1 - \langle \cos \beta \rangle)$$

where $\langle \cos \beta \rangle$ is the average of the cosine of the scattering angle. Making use of the Rutherford scattering formula, Conwell and Weisskopf have calculated an approximate expression for τ with the result that

$$\mu = \frac{e\tau}{m^*} = \frac{\epsilon^2 m^* v^3}{2\pi N_i e^3} \left[\log \left(1 + \frac{\epsilon^2 m^{*2} v^4}{4 e^4 N_i^{2/3}} \right) \right]^{-1} \tag{13-18}$$

where ϵ is the dielectric constant.[20] It is observed that this type of scattering leads to a mobility which varies approximately as $T^{3/2}$, in contrast with the $T^{-3/2}$ law for lattice scattering.

The Hall coefficient and Hall mobility associated with ionic scattering are found to be [21]

$$R_H = \pm 1.93/nec, \qquad \mu_H = 1.93\mu \tag{13-19}$$

(iii) *Neutral impurity scattering.* The scattering of charge carriers by neutral impurities is quite similar to the scattering of electrons by hydrogen

---

[20] E. M. Conwell and V. F. Weisskopf, *Phys. Rev.*, **77**, 388 (1950); see also W. Shockley, *Electrons and Holes*, Van Nostrand, New York, 1950, pp. 258 ff.; for a quantum mechanical treatment, see H. Brooks, *Phys. Rev.*, **83**, 879 (1951).

[21] W. Shockley, *op. cit.*, p. 279.

atoms. Thus, by suitably modifying the theory of the latter, Erginsoy has calculated the mobility associated with this type of scattering alone.[22] He finds

$$e\tau/m^* = \mu = \frac{m^*e^3}{20N\epsilon\hbar^3} \tag{13-20}$$

where N is the density of neutral impurities and ϵ is the dielectric constant. The relaxation time is independent of the velocity in this case, so that the Hall coefficient is the same as that for metals, viz., $R_H = \pm 1/nec$, as can readily be seen from (13-12).

Dislocations are also scattering centers for charge carriers as a result of the dilation they produce in the lattice. According to calculations by Dexter and Seitz the probability for scattering is proportional to the number of dislocation lines per cm² and proportional to the temperature T.[23]

Scattering of charge carriers by vacancies and interstitials is used in studying radiation effects in solids by resistivity measurements.

In general, lattice scattering, ionic scattering, and scattering by neutral impurities are all present. The relaxation time for a given velocity of the charge carriers may then be obtained from

$$1/\tau = 1/\tau_{\text{lattice}} + 1/\tau_{\text{ionic}} + 1/\tau_{\text{neutral}} \tag{13-21}$$

because the probabilities for scattering are additive, each of them being proportional to the reciprocal of the corresponding relaxation time.

13-5. Comparison with experiment

The first extensive investigation of the electrical properties of the elements of the fourth group was carried out by Pearson and Bardeen on silicon and silicon alloys containing boron and phosphorus.[24] In these experiments polycrystalline materials were used. More recently, the electrical conductivity and Hall effect of single crystals of silicon containing arsenic (n type) and boron (p type) have been studied by Morin and Maita over a temperature range between 10°K and 1100°K.[25] The mobilities in single crystals are appreciably larger than those in polycrystalline materials (see Table 13-3). Similar measurements on germanium crystals containing arsenic have been reported by Debye and Conwell; these extend over the temperature range between 11°K and 300°K.[26]

[22] C. Erginsoy, *Phys. Rev.*, **79**, 1013 (1950).

[23] D. L. Dexter and F. Seitz, *Phys. Rev.*, **86**, 964 (1952).

[24] G. L. Pearson and J. Bardeen, *Phys. Rev.*, **75**, 865 (1949).

[25] F. J. Morin and J. P. Maita, *Phys. Rev.*, **96**, 28 (1954).

[26] P. P. Debye and E. M. Conwell, *Phys. Rev.*, **93**, 693 (1954).

As an example we reproduce in Fig. 13-7 and 13-8 the resistivity and Hall coefficient for some of the samples measured by Debye and Conwell, (they actually measured eleven samples). The intrinsic resistivity is indicated by the dashed line in Fig. 13-7. Sample 55 is nearly pure, whereas

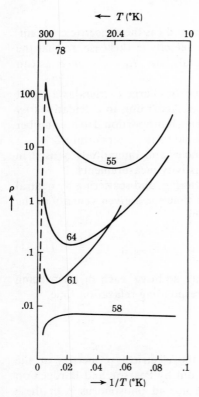

Fig. 13-7. The specific resistivity in ohms cm for n-type germanium samples (doped with arsenic), as function of T^{-1}. [After Debye and Conwell, ref. 26]

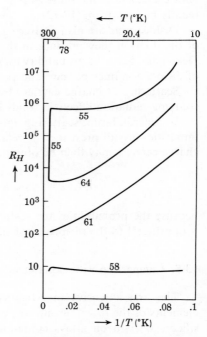

Fig. 13-8. Hall coefficient (cm³/ coulomb) versus T^{-1} for arsenic doped germanium samples; the numbers refer to the same samples as in Fig. 13-7. [After Debye and Conwell, ref. 26]

sample 58 contains enough arsenic to make the electron gas in the conduction band degenerate over most of the temperature range. The other samples have intermediate impurity densities.

In accordance with (13-13), the Hall mobility may be obtained from the relation $\mu_{\mathrm{H}} = c R_{\mathrm{H}}/\rho$; the results are given in Fig. 13-9. It is observed that the nearly pure sample 55 follows closely the $T^{-3/2}$ law down to the lowest temperatures. The reason for this is that neutral impurity scattering and ionic scattering are negligible for low impurity concentrations. As the impurity concentration increases, ionized donors become important as scattering centers at lower temperatures where the amplitude of the lattice vibrations becomes small. Sample 61 contains a sufficient number of ionized donors at low temperatures to give a positive slope for the $\mu(T)$ curves. In most of the samples, however, the slope gets steeper again after the initial flattening resulting from ionic scattering; the reason for this is that electrons fall back into donor levels at low temperatures, thus reducing the influence of ionic scattering.

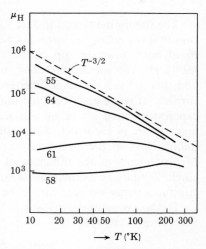

A quantitative analysis of these results shows that in the range where scattering of electrons by the lattice is predominant, the mobility varies as $T^{-1.64}$ rather than as $T^{-1.5}$. This deviation from the simple theory is probably in part due to the fact that the constant energy surfaces in the momentum space are not spheres. We shall return to this in Sec. 13-6. Similar deviations have been observed by Morin and Maita for silicon. A summary of mobility data is given in Table 13-3.

Fig. 13-9. Hall mobility for some arsenic-doped germanium samples as function of T; the sample numbers are the same as those in Figs. 13-7 and 13-8. [After Debye and Conwell, ref. 26]

Table 13-3. Mobilities in cm^2 $volt^{-1}$ sec^{-1}

	Room temp.	$\mu_{lattice}$ (arbitrary temp.)
C (diamond), electrons[a]	900	
Si (polycryst.) electrons	300	
Si (polycryst.) holes	100	
Si (single cryst.) electrons	1450	$4.0 \times 10^9 T^{-2.6}$
Si (single cryst.) holes	500	$2.5 \times 10^8 T^{-2.3}$
Ge (single cryst.) electrons	3600	$4.9 \times 10^7 T^{-1.66}$
Ge (single cryst.) holes	1700	$1.05 \times 10^9 T^{-2.33}$
Sn (grey) electrons[b]	3000	

[a] C. C. Klick and J. Maurer, *Phys. Rev.* **81**, 124 (1951).
[b] G. Busch, I. Wieland, and H. Zoller, *Helvetia Phys. Acta*, **24**, 49 (1951).

Debye and Conwell conclude from their measurements that the mobility associated with ionic scattering increases with a power of T .

between 1.0 and 1.5, i.e., less rapidly than predicted by the Conwell-Weisskopf formula. The Erginsoy formula for neutral impurity scattering fits their data well for an effective electron mass equal to about $m/3$. They find scattering by dislocations negligible in their samples.

13-6. Constant-energy surfaces and effective mass in silicon and germanium

The theory developed in Sec. 13-3 and 13-4 was based on the assumption that the energy of electrons near the bottom of the conduction band or of holes near the top in the valence band could be represented by $\hbar^2 k^2/2m^*$. This implies that constant-energy surfaces in k-space are spheres and that m^* is a constant independent of the direction of motion of the carriers. It is presently believed that the discrepancies between theory and experiment cited above are, at least in part, due to the fact that this assumption is incorrect. Thus values of the effective mass calculated indirectly from the electrical properties must be considered unreliable. Measurements of the influence of a magnetic field on the resistivity of single crystals of germanium also drew attention to the fact that the constant-energy surfaces cannot be spheres.[27]

If the constant-energy surfaces are spheres, the effective mass is, according to (10-38),

$$m^* = \hbar^2/(d^2E/dk^2)$$

However, if the energy is a function also of the direction of the wave vector k, the effective mass is a tensor rather than a scalar, as was mentioned in Sec. 10-4. By a suitable choice of axes, this tensor may be diagonalized in such a way that along the three principal axes the effective mass is given by

$$m_i^* = \hbar^2/(d^2E(k)/dk_i^2) \quad \text{where} \quad i = x, y, z \quad \text{(13-22)}$$

For example, for motion along the x-axis, the electron behaves as a particle of effective mass $\hbar^2/(d^2E/dk_x^2)$, etc. Until recently, experimental information about the effective mass, and hence about the curvature of constant-energy surfaces in the k-space, could be obtained only indirectly, viz., from experimental results for transport phenomena in which m^* occurs. However, cyclotron resonance experiments of electrons and holes have made it possible for the first time to measure m^* directly.[28] In this type of experiment, electrons in the conduction band and holes in the valence band describe spiral orbits about the axis of a constant magnetic field H.

---

[27] G. L. Pearson and H. Suhl, *Phys. Rev.*, **83**, 768 (1951).

[28] Dresselhaus, Kip, and Kittel, *Phys. Rev.*, **92**, 827 (1953); Lax, Zeiger, Dexter, and Rosenblum, *Phys. Rev.*, **93**, 1418 (1954); Dexter, Zeiger, and Lax, *Phys. Rev.*, **95**, 557 (1954).

The angular frequency of rotation ω_c can be obtained immediately from the equality of the centrifugal force and the force due to the magnetic field:

$$m^* v^2 / r = \pm Hev/c \quad \text{or} \quad \omega_c = \pm eH/m^* c \qquad (13\text{-}23)$$

where r is the radius of the orbit; the plus or minus sign indicates the opposite senses of rotation for electrons and holes. Resonant absorption of energy from a radio-frequency electric field perpendicular to the static

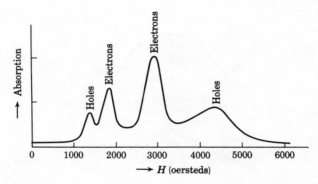

Fig. 13-10. Typical cyclotron resonance absorption (arbitrary units) for silicon near 24,000 mc/sec at 4°K; static magnetic field in a (110) plane, 30° from an [001] axis. [After Dresselhaus, Kip, and Kittel, *Phys. Rev.*, **98**, 368 (1955)]

magnetic field occurs when the frequency of the radio-frequency field is equal to that determined by (13-23). Evidently, by measuring ω_c for different directions of H relative to the crystal axes, one measures essentially the effective mass as function of direction. Usually, one employs a constant frequency of the radio-frequency field and then varies H until resonance is observed. A typical result is reproduced in Fig. 13-10 for an angular frequency $\omega_c \simeq 1.5 \times 10^{11}$ radians per sec for silicon at 4°K. The assignment of a given peak to electrons or holes may be made on the basis of a circularly polarized radio-frequency field or by using n- or p-type material and exciting a particular type of carrier. The width of the lines is determined by the relaxation time τ of the electrons or holes. In order to obtain distinct resonance peaks, it is necessary that $\omega_c \tau \geqslant 1$. Thus the mean free path of the carriers should be large enough so that they can cover at least one radian of a circle between successive collisions. Since the relaxation times τ are of the order of 10^{-13} or 10^{-14} second at room temperature, it is necessary to work with high-purity samples at liquid nitrogen or helium temperatures if one employs frequencies $\omega \simeq 10^{11}$ radians per second.

Since it is not possible to enter into a detailed discussion of this subject, it may suffice here to mention some of the results obtained for silicon and germanium.[29] As an example of the band structures obtained, we give in Fig. 13-11 the energy as function of the wave vector along the $\langle 100 \rangle$ direction for silicon. It is observed that the minimum energy in the conduction band does not correspond to $k = 0$ but that there are in all six minima located somewhere along the six $\langle 100 \rangle$ axes. In the vicinity of these minima, the constant energy surfaces are prolate ellipsoids of

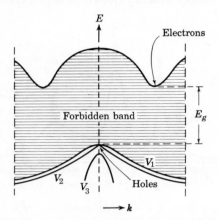

Fig. 13-11. Schematic representation of the energy band structure in Si along a $\langle 100 \rangle$ axis. [After F. Herman, *Proc. IRE*, **43**, 1703 (1955)]

revolution. Similar minima occur for the conduction band in germanium along the $\langle 111 \rangle$ axes. Choosing one of these minima as origin, the surfaces of constant energy may thus be represented by an expression of the form

$$E(k) = \hbar^2 \left(\frac{k_x^2 + k_y^2}{2m_t} + \frac{k_z^2}{2m_l} \right) \tag{13-24}$$

where m_t and m_l are called, respectively, the transverse and longitudinal electron mass. For Si and Ge the cyclotron resonance experiments lead to the following results at $4°K$:

$$\text{Silicon:} \qquad m_t = 0.19m; \qquad m_l = 0.98m$$

$$\text{Germanium:} \qquad m_t = 0.082m; \qquad m_l = 1.57m$$

where m is the free electron mass.

[29] The energy band structure of Si and Ge derived from cyclotron experiments was, at least in part, predicted by a theoretical study of F. Herman, *Physica*, **20**, 801 (1954); *Phys. Rev.*, **95**, 847 (1954). See also his excellent review in *Proc. IRE*, **43**, 1703–1732 (1955) (solid state issue).

The maximum energy for the valence band in both silicon and germanium occurs for $k = 0$, according to the results of cyclotron resonance experiments; furthermore, this maximum is common to two bands which meet at $k = 0$. The constant-energy surfaces near $k = 0$ for these two bands are warped and are given by the expression

$$E(k) = -\frac{\hbar^2}{2m}[Ak^2 \pm \sqrt{B^2k^4 + C^2(k_x^2k_y^2 + k_y^2k_z^2 + k_z^2k_x^2)}] \quad (13\text{-}25)$$

where A, B, and C are constants. The negative and positive roots correspond, respectively, to the highest (V_1) and second highest (V_2) valence band. If one approximates the warped surfaces by spheres, one may determine the average hole mass in the two bands from the experimental values of A, B, and C. In this approximation, one obtains

$$\text{Silicon:} \qquad m_{V_1}^* = 0.49m; \quad m_{V_2}^* = 0.16m$$

$$\text{Germanium:} \qquad m_{V_1}^* = 0.28m; \quad m_{V_2}^* = 0.044m$$

We should note here that the form of expression (13-25) was indicated by the theory of spin-orbit splitting for these crystals.[30]

It is observed from Fig. 13-11 that there is a third valence band V_3 which is separated from the V_1 and V_2 bands as a result of spin-orbit interaction. The maximum of the V_3 band lies slightly below that of the two other bands. Near the maximum of the V_3 band, the constant energy surfaces are spherical; the effective masses are:

$$\text{Silicon:} \qquad m_{V_3}^* = 0.24m$$

$$\text{Germanium:} \qquad m_{V_3}^* = 0.077m$$

The energy difference between the top of the V_3 band and the common maximum of the V_1 and V_2 bands has been estimated to be 0.035 ev for Si and 0.28 ev for Ge. It will be evident that the relative hole populations of the V_3 and V_1, V_2 bands is a function of temperature.

The energy gap. A few remarks may be made here about the consequences of the above results for the concept of the forbidden energy gap and its experimental determination. When an electron is thermally excited from the valence band into the conduction band, the electron absorbs a phonon. This process is governed by the selection rules corresponding to conservation of momentum and energy:

$$k' = k + q + 2\pi n$$
$$E(k') = E(k) + \hbar\omega_q \qquad (13\text{-}26)$$

[30] G. Dresselhaus, A. F. Kip, and C. Kittel, *Phys. Rev.*, **95**, 568 (1954); **98**, 368 (1955); R. J. Elliott, *Phys. Rev.*, **96**, 266 (1954); **96**, 280 (1954).

Here k' and k are, respectively, the final and the initial wave vector of the electron; q is the wave vector of the absorbed phonon, and $\hbar\omega_q$ is the energy of the phonon; n is a vector in the reciprocal lattice, and $2\pi n$ in (13-26) guarantees that k' is a vector in the reduced zone. The "cheapest" thermal excitation of an electron from the valence band to the conduction band evidently involves a phonon of energy $\hbar\omega_q = E_g$ where E_g is the energy difference between the highest electronic level in the valence band and the lowest level in the conduction band (see Fig. 13-11). Thus E_g may be obtained from the variation of the carrier concentration with temperature, We should note here that E_g itself is a function of temperature (resulting from the expansion of the lattice).

Let us now consider what one measures if one determines the long wavelength threshold for optical excitation of an electron from the valence band into the conduction band in substances such as Si and Ge. If one considers the optical excitation as a collision between an electron of wave vector k and a photon of wave vector σ the selection rules require

$$k' = k + \sigma \quad \text{and} \quad E(k') = E(k) + h\nu \tag{13-27}$$

where $h\nu$ is the energy of the photon. Now, the wavelength of a photon corresponding to infrared or visible radiation is large compared to a lattice constant. Hence σ may in general be neglected in comparison with the electron wave vector k. In other words, optical transitions of this kind occur "vertically" in the reduced zone scheme because we then have $k' = k$. It is evident from Fig. 13-11 that the "cheapest" vertical transition involves always more energy than E_g because the minimum of the conduction band occurs for a different k-value than the maximum of the valence band. In other words, the optical threshold energy should be larger than E_{gap}. However, the observed threshold photon energies correspond closely to the energy gap E_g determined from the variation of carrier concentration with temperature. Hall, Bardeen, and Blatt have therefore suggested that the observed optical threshold is determined by an indirect or nonvertical transition in which the absorption of a photon is accompanied by the absorption or emission of a phonon.[31] Under these circumstances the momentum and energy conservation laws for an optical transition are:

$$k' = k + \sigma \pm q + 2\pi n \simeq k \pm q + 2\pi n$$
$$E(k') = E(k) + h\nu \pm \hbar\omega_q \tag{13-28}$$

where the symbols have the same meaning as above. The presence of the phonon momentum q thus makes it possible for the transition to be non-vertical. The $+$ and $-$ signs refer, respectively, to absorption and emission of a phonon. It is of interest to recognize that at very low

[31] L. H. Hall, J. Bardeen, and F. J. Blatt, *Phys. Rev.*, **95**, 559 (1954).

temperatures few phonons are present and thus absorption of a phonon becomes improbable. Thus at $T = 0$ we shall have an optical threshold frequency ν_t such that

$$h\nu_t = E_{\text{gap}} + \hbar\omega_q$$

At high temperatures, on the other hand, there are sufficient phonons present to make optical transitions possible at a threshold frequency ν_t such that

$$h_{vt} = E\,\nu_{\text{gap}} - \hbar\omega_q$$

In other words, the optical threshold frequency will vary with temperature.

Transport phenomena. It will be evident that the above results for the energy-band structure have an important bearing on the theory of electrical conductivity, Hall effect, magneto resistance, infrared absorption, etc. In fact, the resulting energy-band scheme and the numerical values for the effective mass parameters are consistent with magneto resistance measurements on *n*-type germanium and silicon.[32] Deviations from the $T^{-1.5}$ law for the mobility may also be explained as a result of the nonisotropic mass.

Infrared absorption. A few remarks may be made here about the infrared absorption of charge carriers in Ge and Si. For the moment, consider a charge carrier with an isotropic mass m^* under influence of an electromagnetic field. Suppose the electric field is along the *x*-direction and let the magnetic field be neglected. The velocity component v_x of the charge carriers then varies with time according to

$$dv_x/dt = (\partial v_x/\partial t)_{\text{field}} + (\partial v_x/\partial t)_{\text{coll}} = (e/m^*)E_0 e^{i\omega t} - v_x/\tau$$

The stationary solution of this equation is

$$v_x = (e\tau/m^*)E_0 e^{i\omega t}\,\frac{1}{1 + i\omega t} \tag{13-29}$$

As long as the angular frequency of the field $\omega \ll 1/\tau$, v_x varies in phase with the external field, and the conductivity of the material containing N carriers per unit volume is equal to the static conductivity σ_0, where

$$\sigma_0 = Nev_x/E_x = Ne^2\tau/m^* \qquad (\omega\tau \ll 1)$$

In the general case, however, it follows from (13-29) that the conductivity is complex; the real part varies with frequency as

$$\sigma' = Ne^2\tau/m^*(1 + \omega^2\tau^2) = \sigma_0/(1 + \omega^2\tau^2)$$

[32] S. Meiboom and B. Abeles, *Phys. Rev.*, **95**, 31 (1954); I. Estermann and A. Foner, *Phys. Rev.*, **79**, 365 (1950); G. L. Pearson and C. Herring, *Physica*, **20**, 975 (1954).

The absorption coefficient of the radiation K is of course proportional to the real part of the conductivity, and in fact equal to

$$K = (4\pi/nc)\sigma' = 4\pi Ne^2\tau/ncm^*(1 + \omega^2\tau^2)$$

where n is the index of refraction and c is the velocity of light. When $\omega\tau \gg 1$, this may be written approximately as

$$K \simeq 4\pi Ne^3/nc(m^*)^2\omega^2\mu \qquad (13\text{-}30)$$

where μ is the mobility of the carriers. Now if the constant-energy surfaces are prolate spheroids, one can use (13-30) by replacing m^* by an average effective mass m_{av}^* given by

$$1/m_{av}^* = \tfrac{1}{3}(1/m_l + 2/m_t) \qquad (13\text{-}31)$$

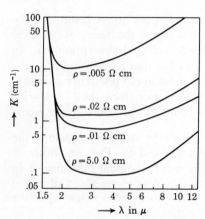

Fig. 13-12. The absorption coefficient of n-type Ge. [After Fan and Becker, ref. 33]

where m_l and m_t are the longitudinal and transversal mass parameters. Thus by measuring K as function of ω, m_{av}^* may be determined from known values of μ. In Fig. 13-12 we have represented the absorption coefficients of n-type germanium samples in the infrared, as determined by Fan and Becker.[33] The resistivity of the samples at room temperature is indicated. The sharp rise in the K versus wavelength curves is associated with transitions of electrons from the valence band to the conduction band. For wavelengths > 6 micron ($\omega < 3 \times 10^{14}$ radians per second), K varies approximately as $1/\omega^2$ in accordance with (13-30). From the four curves given in Fig. 13-12, Kahn finds by applying (13-30) for the average effective mass of the electrons, 0.11, 0.12, 0.20, and 0.14, taking the mass of a free electron as unit.[34] Using the values for m_t and m_l for electrons in Ge as determined from the cyclotron resonance experiments, one finds from (13-31) that $m_{av}^* = 0.14m$, in reasonable agreement with the experimental values. The infrared absorption bands observed in p-type Ge can be interpreted in terms of transitions of holes between the three energy bands lying near the top of the valence band, as suggested by the cyclotron resonance experiments.

[33] H. Y. Fan and M. Becker, *Proc. Reading Conference*, Butterworths Scientific Publications, London, 1951, pp. 132–147.

[34] A. H. Kahn, *Phys. Rev.*, **97**, 1647 (1955).

13-7. The lifetime and diffusion of minority carriers

Consider a semiconductor containing a relatively high concentration of donor levels so that the conductivity is essentially due to electrons in the conduction band (n-type). The electrons are then called the majority carriers. There are, of course, always some holes in the valence band as a result of thermal excitation of electrons from the filled band, but at not too high temperatures the number of holes is relatively small. The holes are called the minority carriers in this case. In thermal equilibrium the number of holes recombining with electrons per second is equal to the number of electron pairs produced per second by thermal excitation. The concentration of minority carriers may be increased artificially in a number of different ways.[35] For example, if a metal in contact with n-type material is made positive relative to the semiconductor, holes are injected into the latter, as will be explained further in Sec. 14-4. Also, the semiconductor may be exposed to light; absorption of photons by electrons in the filled band will then lead to the formation of electron-hole pairs. The minority carriers so produced will diffuse about in the crystal; however, because the density of the minority carriers is not equal to the equilibrium concentration, they will ultimately disappear by recombination with the majority carriers. Suppose now that a certain number of minority carriers is produced during a short time interval somewhere in a crystal. As long as the excess concentration is small compared with the equilibrium concentration, the rate of recombination is proportional to the excess concentration, i.e., the excess number will decay according to $\exp(-t/\tau)$, where τ is the lifetime of the carriers (the lifetime should not be confused with the relaxation time). Measurements of the lifetime of minority carriers are of interest, since by varying the conditions under which the experiments are carried out, one obtains information about the factors determining the recombination process. Experiments of this kind essentially involve the following idea: minority carriers are injected from an emitter into a crystal; the carriers diffuse away from the emitter, and their arrival at another point is detected by a collector. For a given number of injected carriers the collector pulse decreases with increasing distance from the emitter as a result of the disappearance of a fraction of the carriers on their way to the collector. Frequently an electric field is used to drive the carriers from the emitter toward the collector.

The interpretation of this type of experiment is based on some fundamental principles, which will now be considered. In an n-type semiconductor let the equilibrium concentration of holes (minority carriers) be n_0, and let the actual concentration be n_h. The basic equation governing

[35] See Shockley, *op. cit.*, p. 60; F. S. Goucher, *Phys. Rev.*, **81**, 475 (1951); R. Bray, *Phys. Rev.*, **76**, 152, 458 (1949).

the behavior of these carriers under conditions in which n_h is a function of space and time is the continuity equation,

$$\partial n_h/\partial t = -(1/e) \text{ div } \boldsymbol{I}_h - (n_h - n_0)/\tau_h + g_h \qquad (13\text{-}32)$$

The terms on the right-hand side have the following meaning: the first represents the number of holes leaving unit volume per unit time due to the hole current density $\boldsymbol{I}_h$; the second represents the number of holes disappearing per second per unit volume due to recombination (τ_h is the lifetime of the holes); the last represents the number of holes generated per unit volume per second by external means (injection).

The hole current is made up of two terms: one results from the external electric field $\boldsymbol{E}$, the other is due to the diffusion of the holes. The diffusion current is proportional to minus the gradient of the hole concentration so that

$$\boldsymbol{I}_h = n_h e \mu_h \boldsymbol{E} - e D_h \text{ grad } n_h \qquad (13\text{-}33)$$

where D_h is the diffusion coefficient of the holes and μ_h is the hole mobility. There exists a fundamental relationship between the diffusion coefficient and the mobility. According to elementary diffusion theory,

$$D = (\Lambda/3)\langle v \rangle \qquad (13\text{-}34)$$

where Λ is the mean free path for scattering and $\langle v \rangle$ is the average velocity of the carriers. On the other hand, it follows from (13-7) and (13-14) that

$$\mu = \frac{e}{m} \Lambda \frac{\langle v \rangle}{\langle v^2 \rangle} \qquad (13\text{-}35)$$

For thermal holes, $m\langle v^2 \rangle = 3kT$, so that we obtain the Einstein relation,

$$\mu/D = e/kT \qquad (13\text{-}36)$$

The same relationship is obtained from (13-33) by considering an equilibrium situation in which $\boldsymbol{I}_h = 0$. Under these circumstances, we should have, according to Boltzmann,

$$n_h = A e^{-eV/kT}$$

where V is the electrostatic potential and A is a constant. Combining this with (13-33) for $\boldsymbol{I}_h = 0$, we may write

$$0 = e\mu_h n_h \boldsymbol{E} - e D_h n_h \left(-\frac{e}{kT} \text{ grad } V \right)$$

$$= e n_h \boldsymbol{E}(\mu_h - e D_h/kT)$$

which leads immediately to (13-36).

Equations (13-32) and (13-33) govern the theory of the injection experiments; a simple one-dimensional example may be given here.[36]

---

[36] For further examples, see Shockley, *op. cit.*, pp. 318ff.

Consider an infinite medium consisting of n-type material in which at $t = 0$ a number of holes is produced by a plane source at $x = 0$. Let $n(x,t)$ be the excess hole concentration and τ the lifetime of the holes. Assuming that no electric field is present, we have, according to (13-33),

$$I_x = -eD \; \partial n/\partial x$$

(we leave out the subscripts h). In (13-32), the term g_h is zero for $t > 0$, so that

$$\partial n/\partial t = D \; \partial^2 n/\partial x^2 - n/\tau \qquad (13\text{-}37)$$

The solution of this equation is

$$n(x,t) = \frac{N}{(4\pi Dt)^{1/2}} \, e^{-x^2/4Dt - t/\tau} \qquad (13\text{-}38)$$

where N measures the strength of the source. It is recognized that the finite lifetime of the carriers produces a factor $\exp(-t/\tau)$ which does not occur in the "normal" solution for Brownian motion ($\tau = \infty$). We leave it to the reader as a problem to show that the average distance relative to the point of origin traveled by the carriers during life is equal to

$$L = (D\tau)^{1/2} \qquad (13\text{-}39)$$

where L is called the diffusion length of the carriers. It may be compared with the well-known expression $\langle x^2 \rangle = 2Dt$ for the mean square displacement of a particle carrying out a one-dimensional random walk. Clearly, the distance between collector and emitter in an injection experiment should be of the same order or less than L in order to detect the arrival of the carriers at the collector.

Results of injection experiments show that recombination takes place not only in the bulk of the sample, but also at the surface. In fact, the surface treatment influences the lifetime in many instances. A few examples of lifetimes of holes in an n-type single crystal of Ge are given below; the resistivity of the sample was 19 ohm cm at room temperature.[37] The dimensions indicated refer to the cross section perpendicular to the direction of current flow. The values τ_g refer to roughly ground surfaces, τ_e to carefully etched surfaces.

Table 13-4. Hole Lifetimes for Ground and Etched Surfaces

Dimensions of cross-section (cm²)	τ_g (microsec)	τ_e (microsec)
0.371×0.737	144	280
0.202×0.716	78	340
0.100×0.705	16.5	290
0.071×0.48	9.2	280
0.036×0.48	3.1	235

[37] D. Navon, R. Bray, and H. Y. Fan, *Proc. IRE*, **40**, 1342 (1952).

This shows clearly the important role played by the surface in the recombination process in the roughly ground samples. The exact nature of the centers at which the electron-hole recombination takes place is not understood. Estimates of direct recombination of electrons and holes under photon emission indicate lifetimes of the order of one second.[38] So far, the longest lifetimes observed are of the order of 10^{-3} second, indicating that the direct recombination process is relatively unimportant. It seems, therefore, that centers are required which act as a catalyst in the recombination process. It is of interest to note that when a Ge crystal is heated to higher temperatures and then quenched, the lifetime of the carriers decreases.[37] This implies that certain types of frozen-in lattice defects are at least in part responsible for recombination.

13-8. Intermetallic compounds

As a result of the search for new semiconductors with properties similar to those of silicon and germanium, Welker successfully initiated a study of intermetallic compounds consisting of the elements of the third and fifth column in the periodic system.[39] Presently, a great deal of effort is being expended in studies of the physical properties of this new group of semiconductors. From Table 13-1 it is observed that column IIIA contains elements with an outer electron configuration in which two electrons occupy an s state and one occupies a p state; similarly, the elements in column VA have an outer electron configuration consisting of two s electrons and three p electrons. One may then expect a close relationship in structure and physical properties of compounds of the type $A^{III}B^{V}$ with elements such as Si, Ge, Sn. Of particular interest are combinations of the six elements

Al	P
Ga	As
In	Sb

The nine compounds which can be made by combination of the elements of one group with those of the other all crystallize in the zincblende structure, which is closely related to the diamond structure; in fact if the elements in the zincblende structure are made identical, the diamond structure results. The nearest neighbor distances in Angstroms for these compounds are given below; for comparison, those of Ge, Si, and grey Sn are included.

AlP	2.36	GaP	2.36	InP	2.54	Si	2.34
AlAs	2.44	GaAs	2.44	InAs	2.62	Ge	2.44
AlSb	2.62	GaSb	2.62	InSb	2.80	Sn	2.80

[38] See Shockley, op. cit., p. 69.
[39] H. Welker, Z. Naturforsch., 7a, 744 (1952); 8a, 248 (1953).

The binding in these compounds is to a large extent homopolar, as in the fourth group elements; however, as a result of the somewhat larger electronegativity of the fifth group elements, there is a small ionic contribution to the binding energy. The essentially covalent character of the bonds is consistent with the fact that the interatomic distances are approximately equal to the covalent radii of the atoms; the sum of the ionic radii is considerably smaller. Thus the trivalent atoms and the pentavalent atoms contribute an average of four electrons to the formation of four electron pair bands per atom. From this model one may expect that it is rather difficult to replace a pentavalent atom by a trivalent one. In other words, it should not be too difficult to grow crystals of nearly stoichiometric composition. That this is indeed the case is confirmed by the fact that InSb can be made to conform to the chemical formula so well that at room temperature the conductivity is essentially intrinsic.

A method of growing large single crystals (several cm) has been described by Gremmelmaier and Madelung.[40]

In order to vary the electrical properties of these materials, one can add elements of the second group such as Cd, Zn, or elements of the sixth group, such as Se, Te; in the former case the compounds become hole conductors, in the latter electronic conductors.

For InSb, measurements of the electrical conductivity and Hall coefficient show that the electron mobility as a function of temperature can be represented by[41]

$$\mu_e = 65,000(T/300)^{-1.66} \text{cm}^2/\text{volt sec.}$$

Thus at room temperature the electron mobility in InSb is about 20 times that in germanium. This is presumably a consequence of a very small electronic mass in the conduction band. In fact, Burstein has explained the anomalous behavior of optical properties of this material on the basis of $m_e^* = 0.03 \, m$.[42] If m_e^* is small, the curvature of the $E(k)$ curves near the bottom of the conduction band is strong; consequently, the density of states is low and the electron gas degenerates at relatively low densities. This leads to a shift in the long-wave optical absorption edge to smaller values as the density of electrons increases beyond the degeneracy density.

According to Madelung and Weiss the forbidden gap in InSb is given by[41]

$$E_{\text{gap}} = 0.27 - 3 \times 10^{-4}T \quad \text{(ev)}$$

New information on the properties of intermetallic compounds is

[40] R. Gremmelmaier and O. Madelung, Z. Naturforsch., 8a, Heft 5 (1953).

[41] O. Madelung and H. Weiss, Z. Naturforsch., 9a, 527 (1954).

[42] E. Burstein, Phys. Rev., 93, 632 (1954); M. Tanenbaum and H. B. Briggs, Phys. Rev.; 91, 1561 (1953).

being obtained at a rapid rate and this may be expected to continue for a number of years to come. Some further references are given below.[43]

REFERENCES

H. Y. Fan, "Valence Semiconductors, Germanium and Silicon," in F. Seitz and D. Turnbull (eds.), *Solid State Physics*, Academic Press, New York, 1955, Vol. 1, pp. 284–367.

F. Herman, "The Electronic Energy Band Structure of Silicon and Germanium," *Proc. IRE*, **43** 1703–1732 (1955) (solid state issue).

W. Shockley, *Electrons and Holes*, Van Nostrand, New York, 1950.

Proc. IRE, **40**, (1952) (transistor issue); **43**, (1955) (solid state issue).

"Semiconducting Materials," *Proc. Reading Conference*, Butterworths Scientific Publications, London, 1951.

PROBLEMS

13-1. Calculate the distance between nearest neighbors in the germanium and silicon lattices.

13-2. Consider an n-type semiconductor containing N_d donors per cm^3; let there also be N_a acceptor levels per cm^3, close to the conduction band. Discuss the density of electrons in the conduction band as function of temperature.

13-3. Discuss how the elastic constants given in Table 13-2 can be obtained from measurements of the velocity of elastic longitudinal and shear waves.

13-4. On the basis of the Debye approximation, calculate the Debye temperature for Si and Ge from the elastic constants given in Table 13-2; compare the results with θ_D obtained from specific heat measurements.

13-5. From the dielectric constants given in Table 13-2 calculate the polarizability per Si and per Ge atom in the crystalline state, assuming for simplicity an internal field of the Lorentz type.

13-6. A germanium crystal contains 10^{-4} atomic per cent of arsenic; assuming all donors are ionized, calculate the resistivity at room temperature.

[43] For InSb, see R. G. Breckenridge *et al.*, *Phys. Rev.*, **96**, 571 (1954); for GaSb, R. F. Blunt, W. R. Hosler, and H. P. R. Frederikse, *Phys. Rev.*, **96**, 576 (1954); and, D. P. Detwiler, *Phys. Rev.*, **97**, 1575 (1955); for AlSb, R. F. Blunt, H. P. R. Frederikse, J. H. Becker, and W. R. Hosler, *Phys. Rev.*, **96**, 578 (1954).

13-7. On the basis of the Rutherford scattering formula, rederive the Conwell-Weisskopf formula by formulating your own simplifying assumptions; compare the result with expression (13-18).

13-8. Show that the Hall coefficient for a semiconductor in which the current is carried by electrons as well as holes is given by expression (13-17).

13-9. Consider an electron in the conduction band of a semiconductor with the average thermal energy at room temperature. Discuss the collision between this electron and a phonon on the basis of the laws of conservation of momentum and energy. Show that the energy gain or loss for the electron is always relatively small compared with its initial energy. See Sec. 11-7 for details.

Chapter 14

RECTIFIERS AND TRANSISTORS

14-1. Rectifying properties of a barrier layer between two metals

Although in solid-state rectifiers one usually employs one semiconducting contact, semiconduction itself is not essential for the rectification process. This may be illustrated by considering two metals of different work function separated by a thin vacuum gap. As we have seen in Sec. 9-10, the Fermi levels of the two metals must coincide in thermal equilibrium, leading to the situation depicted in Fig. 14-1a; the metal of low work function acquires a positive surface charge, the other acquires a negative surface charge. The total potential drop across the gap is

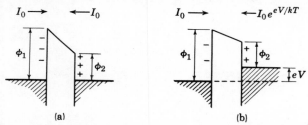

Fig. 14-1. (a) Shows the equilibrium between two metals of different work functions separated by a thin vacuum gap. In (b) a forward voltage is applied (metal 2 negative).

equal to $(\phi_1 - \phi_2)/e$. It is convenient to consider this situation a dynamic equilibrium in which the electronic current from 1 to 2 is equal to that from 2 to 1. Let us denote this current density by I_0. Suppose now metal 2 is made negative with respect to 1 by applying an external voltage smaller than the voltage drop $(\phi_1 - \phi_2)/e$. The energy levels of 2 are then raised relative to those in 1, and the situation corresponding to Fig. 14-1b results. The current $I_{1\to2}$ is still equal to I_0 because the barrier viewed from the position of metal 1 has not changed. On the other hand, the potential energy hill as viewed from metal 2 is lowered by an amount eV, which makes the probability for an electron to cross the hill larger by a factor $e^{eV/kT}$. Hence the net electron current is

$$I_f = I_0 \left(e^{eV/kT} - 1 \right) \tag{14-1}$$

Similarly, if the applied voltage has such polarity as to make metal 2

348

positive with respect to 1, we have again $I_{1\to 2} = I_0$. However, the current from $2 \to 1$ is now $I_0 e^{-eV/kT}$, yielding a net current of

$$I_r = I_0(1 - e^{-eV/kT}) \qquad (14-2)$$

where I_f and I_r are referred to, respectively, as the forward current and the reverse current. Now I_f increases exponentially with the voltage applied in the forward direction; I_r, on the other hand, saturates rapidly to the low value I_0. The current-voltage characteristic of the contact is similar to that given in Fig. 14-8 and can be used for rectifying purposes.

14-2. The Schottky theory of a metal-semiconductor contact

A simple theory for the contact between a metal and a semiconductor has been developed by Schottky.[1] It leads to the formation of a physical

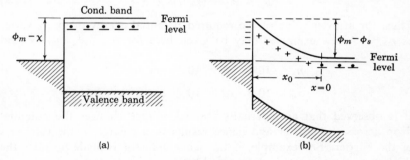

Fig. 14-2.   (a) Refers to a metal-semiconductor contact not yet in equilibrium; χ is the electron affinity of the semiconductor. In (b) equilibrium has been established by the formation of a Schottky layer; the total potential drop is $(\phi_m - \phi_s)/e$.

barrier layer at the metal-semiconductor interface as explained below. Such barriers must be distinguished from chemical barrier layers which may be present between the metal and semiconductor as a result of chemical preparation.

To explain the nature of the physical barrier layer, consider an ideal contact between a metal of work function ϕ_m and an n-type semiconductor with an electron affinity χ.[2] Before equilibrium has been established, the energy band scheme may be represented by Fig. 14-2a. According to Sec. 12-5, the effective work function of the semiconductor is given by the energy difference between its Fermi level and the vacuum level; let this difference be ϕ_s. Thus, if $\phi_s < \phi_m$, electrons will flow from the

[1] W. Schottky, *Z. Physik*, **113**, 367 (1939).

[2] The electron affinity is defined as the energy required to transfer an electron from the bottom of the conduction band to vacuum.

semiconductor into the metal. Consequently, the metal acquires a negative surface charge and the semiconductor charges up positively. Now, because the density of donors is relatively small, the donors will be come ionized over a region which extends into the semiconductor, i.e., a space charge rather than a surface charge is created (see Fig. 14-2b). The thickness of the barrier layer thus formed may be estimated as follows: Let us assume that all donors in the region between $x = 0$ and $x = x_0$ in Fig. 14-2b are ionized. The potential energy of an electron ϕ in this region is then determined by the Poisson equation

$$d^2\phi/dx^2 = (4\pi/\epsilon)n_d e^2 \qquad (14\text{-}3)$$

where n_d is the donor concentration and ϵ the dielectric constant. Taking $\phi = 0$ at $x = 0$ and $\phi = \phi_m - \phi_s$ at $x = x_0$, one readily finds that the thickness x_0 of the barrier must satisfy the relation

$$\phi_m - \phi_s = (2\pi/\epsilon)n_d e^2 x_0^2 \qquad (14\text{-}4)$$

Thus, for a given value of the required potential energy drop, x_0 varies as $n_d^{-1/2}$. A few examples may be given here for $\phi_m - \phi_s = 1$ eV and $\epsilon = 10$.

n_d	10^{15}	10^{17}	10^{19}	per cm^3
x_0	10^{-4}	10^{-5}	10^{-6}	cm

It is observed that an externally applied voltage changes the potential drop across the barrier and hence results in a change in the thickness of the barrier. For example, if the semiconductor is made positive, the thickness increases and is determined by

$$\phi_m - \phi_s + eV = (2\pi/\epsilon)n_d e^2 x_0^2 \qquad (14\text{-}5)$$

For an applied voltage in the opposite direction, x_0 decreases. Note that the barrier thickness increases with increasing dielectric constant. If the dielectric constant of the material is known, the thickness of the barrier can be determined from capacitance measurements with a small ac signal for a given bias. To a first approximation the equivalent circuit of the contact may be represented by a voltage-dependent capacitor in parallel with a nonlinear resistor, the combination being in series with the bulk resistance of the semiconductor. Changes as indicated by (14-5) can indeed be observed.

The above model is admittedly simplified and neglects, for example, the influence of the image force; for high dielectric constants ($\geqslant 10$) he image force has little influence. Also, the influence of surface states has been neglected; these may play an important role.

The Schottky barrier layer forms an essential factor in the theory of rectifying contacts as we shall see below. It is left to the reader to discuss the barrier formed at a metal-p-type-semiconductor contact.

14-3. Single-carrier theories of rectification

As an example of the rectifying properties of a metal-semiconductor contact we represent in Fig. 14-3 the current-voltage characteristic of a metallic point contact on p-type AlSb.[3] In general, the forward current is observed under the following circumstances: for n-type material the semiconductor should be negative, for p-type material the semiconductor should be positive.

In the conventional theories of rectification it is assumed that either electrons or holes take part in the current flow across the barrier; i.e., they are single-carrier theories. In order to explain certain properties of Ge rectifiers, a two-carrier theory has been developed. In the present section we shall consider only the single-carrier case.

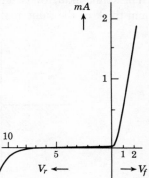

Fig. 14-3. The current in mA as function of forward and reverse voltage (in volts) for a point-contact AlSb rectifier. [After Welker, ref. 3]

The tunnel theory. The oldest theory of rectification was developed in 1932 by Wilson and Nordheim.[4] These authors assumed that for an n-type semiconductor the electrons crossed the barrier by tunnel effect, i.e., the carriers penetrate through rather than cross over the potential barrier. Such a mechanism of course requires thin barrier layers ($\sim 10^{-7}$ cm); as we have seen above, the barrier is usually considerably thicker. The strongest objection against the tunnel theory is, however, that it predicts the wrong sign for rectification. For example, the reader can readily convince himself that for a metal-n-type-semiconductor contact, the tunnel theory predicts the forward current when the metal is negative. This is simply because the number of electrons available for tunneling in the metal is much larger than that in the conduction band of the semiconductor. The tunnel theory will therefore not be discussed here, although it should be kept in mind that under special circumstances tunneling may well occur.

The Mott-Schottky theory for thick barriers. A new theory of rectification in which it is assumed that the carriers surmount the potential barrier by thermal excitation was proposed by Mott[5] and further developed by Schottky.[6] Mott was particularly concerned with selenium and with Cu-Cu_2O rectifiers. In these rectifiers, as a result of the chemical way in

[3] H. Welker, *Z. Naturforsch.*, **8a**, 248 (1953).

[4] H. Wilson, *Proc. Roy. Soc.* (*London*), **136**, 487 (1932); L. W. Nordheim, *Z. Physik*, **75**, 434 (1932).

which they are prepared, the density of donors (or acceptors) is very small near the metal and gradually increases to a constant value as one moves into the semiconductor. In some instances one produces deliberately an insulating layer between the metal and the semiconductor by chemical means.

As an idealized model for this type of system we shall consider the following case.[5] An n-type semiconductor contains n_d donors per cm³. The semiconductor is separated from the metal by a layer of 10^{-4}–10^{-5} cm thick of the same material but without donor levels. We shall further

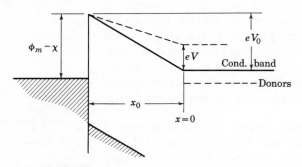

Fig. 14-4. Metal-insulator-semiconductor contact; the voltage drop across the insulating layer in equilibrium is $V_0 = (\phi_m - \phi_s)/e$. With an applied forward voltage V, the voltage drop is $(V_0 - V)$ as indicated by the dashed conduction band.

assume that any potential difference between the metal and semiconductor exists essentially across the insulating layer, the field strength in the layer being constant (see Fig. 14-4).[6] Since the thickness of the layer x_0 is large compared with the mean free path for scattering of the electrons by lattice vibrations, the electron current through the layer is due to (1) the electric field and (2) diffusion. Let E represent the field strength for a unit negative charge, and let I be the electronic current density.

We may then write

$$I = n(x)e\mu E - De\, dn/dx \qquad (14\text{-}6)$$

where $n(x)$ is the density of electrons. The diffusion coefficient D in terms of the mobility μ is given by the Einstein relation $D = \mu kT/e$. Integrating (14-6), one thus obtains

$$n(x) = I/\mu eE + Ce^{eEx/kT} \qquad (14\text{-}7)$$

where C is a constant. In order to calculate the current I, we make use

[5] N. F. Mott, *Proc. Roy. Soc. (London)*, **A171**, 27 (1939).

[6] W. Schottky, *Z. Physik*, **118**, 539 (1942); also, W. Schottky and E. Spenke, *Wiss. Veröffentl. Siemens Werken*, **18**, 225 (1939). These references also take account of the space charge region in the semiconductor.

of the following boundary conditions: for $x = 0$, the density of electrons is equal to that in the conduction band in the bulk semiconductor $n(0)$. Also, the density of electrons for $x = x_0$ in the absence of an external field must be equal to

$$n(x_0) = n(0)e^{-(\phi_m - \phi_s)/kT} = n(0)e^{-eV_0/kT} \qquad (14\text{-}8)$$

where ϕ_m and ϕ_s are the work functions of the metal and insulator, respectively; the total voltage drop is then $V_0 = (\phi_m - \phi_s)/e$. We shall assume that $n(x_0)$ is not influenced by the current flow resulting from an external field, although this is only approximately true. The first boundary condition leads to $C = n(0) - I/\mu eE$. Substituting this into (14-7) and applying the second boundary condition in the form (14-8), one obtains for the current density,

$$I = \mu eE \frac{n(0)e^{eEx_0/kT} - n(x_0)}{e^{eEx_0/kT} - 1} \qquad (14\text{-}9)$$

Now when V is the applied voltage in the forward direction as indicated in Fig. 14-4, $Ex_0 = -(V_0 - V)$; also, as long as we are interested in cases for which the potential barrier is large compared with kT, the denominator in (14-9) reduces to -1. Thus (14-9) may be written in the form

$$I(V) = [\mu e(V_0 - V)/x_0]n(x_0)(e^{eV/kT} - 1) \simeq A(e^{eV/kT} - 1) \quad (14\text{-}10)$$

where A is approximately constant. The form of the current-voltage characteristic is thus essentially the same as (14-1); for the reverse current one obtains a relation similar to (14-2). For the type of rectifiers for which this theory is developed (thick barriers), it is generally in accord with the experimental results; refinements involving the image force may be found in footnotes 5 and 6.

The diode theory.[7] In germanium and silicon rectifiers the barrier layer thickness is of the order of 10^{-6} cm, i.e., comparable with the mean free path of the carriers. In that case, the diffusion theory cannot be applied, and the so-called diode theory has been developed. In this theory it is assumed that collisions of carriers with the lattice are absent and the problem reduces to that of two thermionic emitters facing each other. We leave it to the reader to show that the electronic current density from the semiconductor to the metal in this case is given by

$$(\tfrac{1}{2})n(0)e\langle v \rangle e^{-e(V_0 - V)/kT} \qquad (14\text{-}11)$$

where $\langle v \rangle = (2kT/\pi m)^{1/2}$ is the average thermal velocity of the electrons in the conduction band of the semiconductor; the other symbols have

[7] See, for example, H. C. Torrey and C. A. Whitmer, *Crystal Rectifiers*, McGraw-Hill, New York, 1948, p. 81.

the same meaning as above. The electronic current density from the metal to the semiconductor is obtained by putting $V = 0$ in expression (14-11), since for $V = 0$ the two currents are equal and opposite. The resultant current is then

$$I(V) = (\tfrac{1}{2})n(x_0)e\langle v\rangle(e^{eV/kT} - 1) = A'(e^{eV/kT} - 1) \qquad (14\text{-}12)$$

Comparing this with (14-10), it is observed that the form of the two expressions is essentially the same. However, $\langle v\rangle$ may be considerably smaller than μE, leading to $A' \ll A$. For example, at room temperature $\langle v\rangle \simeq 10^7$ cm sec^{-1}; for a barrier of 10^{-6} cm and a voltage drop of 1 eV, $E \simeq 10^6$ volts per cm, and with $\mu \simeq 10^3$ cm per volt sec, we obtain $\mu E \simeq 10^9$ cm sec^{-1}. It should be remarked here that V represents the voltage across the barrier, i.e., it is equal to the applied voltage minus the voltage drop across the bulk semiconductor.

Although the diode theory has been applied in the past to interpret the rectifying properties of germanium and silicon diodes, a number of observations remained unexplained. For example, according to the above theory, the magnitude of the currents should depend strongly on the work function of the metal because $n(x_0)$ is proportional to exp $(-eV_0/kT)$ and V_0 is determined by $(\phi_m - \phi_s)$. Thus, for a variation of 0.5 ev in the work function of the metals used, the currents should vary by a factor of $\sim 10^8$. Experiments indicate variations by a factor of 10 or less for different metal points. The origin of this discrepancy will be discussed in the next section.

14-4. Surface states on semiconductors

In 1948 Shockley and Pearson reported the following relatively simple but crucial experiment.[8] Consider a thin layer of n-type germanium on an insulating support. Opposite the layer and separated from it is a metal plate, the system as a whole forming a parallel plate condenser. When the metal plate is made negative relative to the germanium layer, a negative charge is induced in the latter, which, if it were free to move, should enhance the conductivity of the layer. For example, if the applied field is 3×10^4 volts cm^{-1} the induced charge per cm^2 corresponds to about 3×10^{10} electrons. On the other hand, if the layer is 5000 Å thick and contains 10^{15} electrons per cm^3, the number of electrons per cm^2 of the layer without external field is 5×10^{10}. It should thus be possible to measure this effect. The experiments indicated, however, that only about one-tenth of the total induced charge contributed to the increase in conductivity. It was proposed by Bardeen that the immobile fraction of the induced charge resides in electronic states at the surface of the

[8] W. Shockley and G. L. Pearson, *Phys. Rev.*, **74**, 232 (1948).

material.[9] Such states, which may lie within the normally forbidden region, may arise partly as a consequence of the sudden departure from periodicity of the potential at the surface or in part from adsorbed atoms. In other words, the simple band picture which one normally employs for the bulk properties is in general not applicable close to the surface. Thus a certain number of these surface states may be occupied without giving rise to an excess surface charge. When the material is placed opposite a positively charged metal, more surface states may be filled by the induced charge.

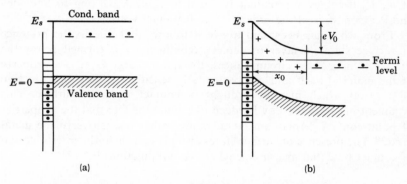

Fig. 14-5. In (a) there is no equilibrium; a number of surface states are filled but no surface charge exists. In (b) equilibrium is established, leading to a surface charge equal to the space charge extending over x_0.

The existence of surface states has an important consequence for the electron distribution near the surface of a neutral germanium crystal. The reason is that the Fermi level associated with the surface states should coincide with that of the bulk material. Thus, in the absence of a net surface charge, let the surface states of an n-type Ge crystal be filled up to the level $E = 0$ as indicated in Fig. 14-5a. Let the conduction band be located at E_s. Evidently, electrons in the conduction band will tend to fill up more surface states until a potential drop V_0 is built up such that the highest filled surface state coincides with the Fermi level of the bulk material (see Fig. 14-5b). Let the density of surface states in the vicinity of $E = 0$ be equal to n_s per cm² per electron volt. The neutrality of the crystal then requires that per cm² the number of ionized donors extending over a thickness x_0 must equal the excess number of electrons in surface states. Thus, if we assume that the bottom of the conduction band practically coincides with the Fermi level in n-type Ge, we may write

$$n_d x_0 = n_s(E_s - eV_0) \tag{14-13}$$

[9] J. Bardeen, *Phys. Rev.*, **71**, 717 (1947).

According to (14-4) we also have

$$eV_0 = 2\pi n_d e^2 x_0^2/\epsilon \qquad (14\text{-}14)$$

so that x_0 may be eliminated, leading to

$$n_s^2 = n_d \epsilon e V_0/2\pi e^2 (E_s - eV_0)^2 \qquad (14\text{-}15)$$

We note that for very small values of n_s, the voltage drop V_0 is very small because a small number of extra electrons will bring the Fermi level at the surface up to that of the bulk material. For very large values of n_s, V_0 becomes approximately equal to E_s/e. According to Snockley and Pearson, n_s is of the order of 5×10^{13} cm^{-2} volts^{-1}.

From what has been said above it follows that due to the presence of surface states, a layer of depleted conductivity is formed below the surface. Under these circumstances, the space charge layer is a property of the material itself and not particularly sensitive to the work function of a metal which may be brought in contact with the surface. This argument has been used by Bardeen to explain the fact that the properties of point-contact germanium rectifiers are rather insensitive to the metal used.[10] The presence of surface states also play a role in the interpretation of contact potential measurements across n-p junctions.[11]

14-5. The two-carrier theory of rectification

In Sec. 14-3 we have seen that if V is the applied voltage in the forward direction the forward current of a rectifying contact should be given by

$$I = A[e^{\alpha(V - Ir)} - 1] \qquad (14\text{-}16)$$

where r is the bulk resistance of the rectifier. Although this formula is in agreement with results obtained for germanium point-contact rectifiers up to about 0.2 or 0.3 volts, deviations occur at higher voltages; these deviations are such that they require a decrease in the resistance r. This difficulty has been explained by Bardeen and Brattain in terms of the model represented in Fig. 14-6.[12] They assume that as a result of surface states the Fermi level in n-type material crosses the surface near the top of the valence band. From Fig. 14-5b it may be seen that this is possible if the density of surface states per unit energy interval is sufficiently large. Under these circumstances, the concentration of holes in the valence band near the surface will be larger than the concentration of electrons in the conduction band. Hence a thin layer of the n-type material

[10] J. Bardeen, *Phys. Rev.*, **71**, 717 (1947); see also S. Benzer, *J. Appl. Phys.*, **20**, 804 (1949).

[11] W. H. Brattain, "Semiconducting Materials," *Proc. Reading Conference*, Butterworths Scientific Publications, 1951, p. 37.

[12] J. Bardeen and W. H. Brattain, *Phys. Rev.*, **74**, 230, 231 (1948).

will become p-type. Suppose now that the semiconductor is made negative relative to a metal in contact with it. This will lead to an increase in the electronic current from the semiconductor into the metal but at the same time a hole current will begin to flow from the surface into the semiconductor. In other words, two types of carriers contribute to the current. This has the effect of decreasing the apparent value of r in (14-16), because r is based on electronic conductivity only. Because of lack of space it is not possible to discuss the quantitative aspects of the two-carrier theory for point contacts here.[13] It will be evident that this model also explains the hole injection into n-type material by metals biased in the forward direction, as referred to in Sec. 14-6.

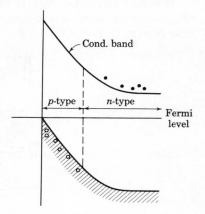

Fig. 14-6. As a result of surface states, the valence band at the surface lies close to the Fermi level; this gives rise to a thin p-type layer near the surface of n-type material.

14-6. The p-n junction rectifier

When a piece of p-type material is in contact with an n-type region, one speaks of a p-n junction. Such junctions may be made in several ways; in germanium they have been produced by converting part of an n-type region into p-type by heating or by nuclear bombardment. In other cases, these junctions are formed during the growth of single crystals as a result of segregation of impurities. In general, the acceptor concentration and the donor concentration will not change abruptly at the junction, but for simplicity we shall assume this to be the case (Fig. 14-7a). The Fermi level in the bulk p-type is located close to the top of the valence band; the Fermi level in the n-type region lies close to the bottom of the conduction band. As a consequence, the situation of Fig. 14-7b is unstable; electrons will flow from n to p and holes from p to n until two space charge regions are established, producing a voltage drop V_0 (see Fig. 14-7c). The space charge in the n-region results from ionized donors, that in the p-region from ionized acceptors. The voltage drop V_0 is approximately equal to the width of the forbidden gap. For an ideal case, assuming a simple variation of donor and acceptor

[13] J. Bardeen and W. H. Brattain, *Phys. Rev.*, **75**, 1208 (1949); J. A. Swanson, *J. Appl. Phys.*, **25**, 314 (1954); for a discussion of the reverse characteristics of high inverse voltage point contacts on Ge, see J. H. Simpson and H. L. Armstrong, *J. Appl. Phys.*, **24**, 25 (1953).

concentration at the junction, the potential may be calculated in a way similar to that used in a metal-semiconductor contact (Sec. 14-2).

It is convenient to consider the equilibrium situation in the absence of an external field as a dynamic one. Thus, there must be a certain hole current I_{h_0} flowing from P to n and an equal but opposite one from

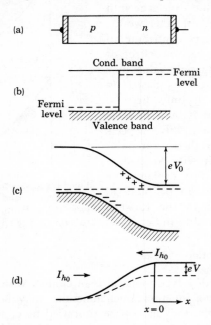

Fig. 14-7. (a) p-n junction; (b) non-equilibrium energy band scheme; (c) equilibrium energy band scheme with space charge regions; (d) full curve represents the potential energy for a hole in equilibrium and the two compensating hole currents I_{h_0} are indicated; the dashed curve represents the potential energy for a hole when the junction is biased in the forward direction; in that case the hole current to the left remains I_{h_0}, the hole current to the right equals $I_{h_0} \exp (eV/kT)$.

n to p (Fig. 14-7d). The same is true for the equilibrium electron current I_{e_0}. This implies that there must be a certain concentration of holes in the n-region as well as a certain concentration of electrons in the p-region. This is a result of the continuous thermal creation of electron-hole pairs, the creation being compensated by recombination. For example, if g is the rate of production of pairs and n_{e_0} and n_{h_0} are the equilibrium concentrations anywhere, we must have $r n_{e_0} n_{h_0} = g$, where r is the recombination coefficient. Thus in either region, $n_{e_0} n_{h_0} = g/r$, which is constant at a given temperature. If one assumes that the ratio g/r is independent of the donor or acceptor concentration, g/r must also be equal to n_i^2, where n_i is the density of carriers in intrinsic material. Under these circumstances

$$n_{e_0} n_{h_0} = g/r = n_i^2 \tag{14-17}$$

Suppose now that a negative voltage $-V$ is applied to the n-region. If we assume that the voltage drop is essentially across the space-charge region, the hole current from n to p is still I_{h_0}. However, holes going

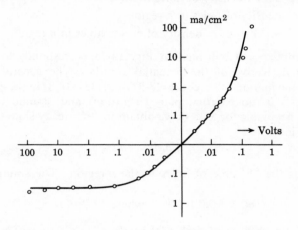

Fig. 14-8. Current-voltage characteristic of a p-n junction. The circles are experimental points, the curve is theoretical. [After W. Shockley, ref. 14]

from p to n have to climb a smaller potential hill (Fig. 14-7d) and will give rise to a current $I_{h_0} \exp (eV/kT)$. Hence

$$I_h(V) = I_{h_0}(e^{eV/kT} - 1) \tag{14-18}$$

For the electron current one finds a similar expression and the total forward current across the junction should be

$$I_f(V) = (I_{h_0} + I_{e_0})(e^{eV/kT} - 1) \tag{14-19}$$

For positive voltages applied to the n-type region the reverse current is obtained,

$$I_r = (I_{h_0} + I_{e_0})(1 - e^{-eV/kT}) \tag{14-19a}$$

In Fig. 14-8 we have represented the experimental points obtained for a p-n junction characteristic;[14] the fully drawn curve is the theoretical one. The agreement is very good indeed.

[14] W. Shockley, *Proc. IRE*, **40**, 1289 (1952).

Let us now consider the rectification process in some more detail; we shall discuss only the hole current because a similar reasoning may be given for the electron current. We shall use the following symbols:

$V_0 =$ equilibrium potential drop

$-V =$ voltage applied to n-region

$n_0 =$ equilibrium density of holes in bulk n-region

$n_h(x) =$ actual density of holes in n-region

$n_p =$ density of holes in p-region

$n(x) = n_h(x) - n_0 =$ density of excess holes in n-region

The point $x = 0$ indicated in Fig. 14-7d corresponds to the point where the derivative of the potential vanishes. The general equations governing the motion of holes are (13-32) and (13-33). If in these equations we put $g_h = 0$ (no external pair generation) and assume the electric field to be negligible for $x > 0$, we obtain for the steady state ($\partial n/\partial t = 0$) in that region,

$$D_h \, d^2n/dx^2 = n/\tau_h \qquad (14\text{-}20)$$

where τ_h is the life time of holes in the n-region. The solution of this equation is

$$n(x) = n(0)e^{-x/L_h} \quad \text{where} \quad L_h^2 = D_h\tau_h \qquad (14\text{-}21)$$

where L_h is the diffusion length of the holes. Thus the excess hole density in the n-region decreases by a factor $1/e$ over a distance L_h. According to equation (13-33) the hole current density diffusing across the junction is equal to

$$I_h = -eD_h(\partial n_h/\partial x)_{x=0} = (eD_h/L_h)n(0) \qquad (14\text{-}22)$$

In order to find an expression for $n(0)$ in terms of the applied voltage, we make use of the fact that according to Boltzmann,

$$n(0) = n_h(0) - n_0 = n_pe^{-e(V_0-V)/kT} - n_pe^{-eV_0/kT} \qquad (14\text{-}23)$$

From the last two equations it then follows that

$$I_h = \frac{eD_h}{L_h} n_0(e^{eV/kT} - 1) \qquad (14\text{-}24)$$

Comparing this with (14-18) it is observed that the equilibrium current $I_{h_0} = eD_hn_0/L_h = en_0L_h/\tau_h$. This result has a simple physical interpretation: n_0/τ_h represents the number of holes recombining per second in equilibrium, and hence also represents the rate of creation of holes. The created holes diffuse about and recombine at an average distance L_h from their point of origin. Therefore the holes diffusing across the barrier are essentially those created within a range L_h on the right of $x = 0$

(Fig. 14-7d). For electrons in Ge, the diffusion constant $D \simeq 100$ cm²/sec and a typical lifetime is 10^{-4} sec. This gives a diffusion length of the order of 0.1 cm.

The correctness of the diffusion theory for the rectifying p-n junction has been tested further by using junctions as a photoconductive device. For example, let photons of sufficient energy to create electron-hole

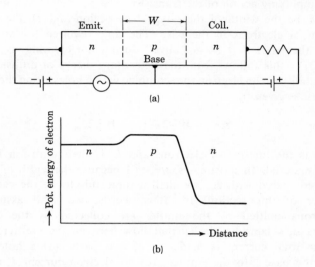

(a)

(b)

Fig. 14-9. (a) Represents schematically an n-p-n junction transistor with the emitter biased in the forward direction, the collector in the reverse direction. Actually, the p-region is much narrower than indicated. In (b) the potential energy of an electron is represented for the biased transistor.

pairs be incident on the n-type region at a distance x from $x = 0$. According to what has been said above, the current response should vary as $\exp(-x/L)$ and this has indeed been verified experimentally by Goucher and coworkers.[15] Also, the value of L so obtained is consistent with the one required by the rectifier equation (14-24). When the light is incident at the junction itself, the electron and hole are separated by the strong field at the junction and a current of one electron per absorbed photon may be obtained.

14-7. Transistors

An n-p-n junction transistor is built up of two n-type regions separated by a thin layer of weakly p-type material. It is mainly this type of transistor which will be discussed below. The same reasoning applies to p-n-p

[15] F. S. Goucher et al., *Phys. Rev.*, **78**, 816 (1950); **81**, 637 (1951).

junction transistors. When the junction transistor is used as an amplifier, one of the n-p junctions is biased in the forward direction, the other in the reverse direction, as indicated in Fig. 14-9a. The former is called the emitter because the corresponding n-type region emits electrons into the p-region (the base); these electrons are collected at the junction with the reverse bias (the collector). The discussion below deals with the reasons for the amplifying action of the transistor.

Let W be the width of the p-type base region and D_e the diffusion coefficient of electrons in the base. The time required for an electron to cross the base, if it stays "alive" during the crossing, is equal to $t = W^2/2D_e$; this follows from the elementary theory of diffusion. Thus the probability for an electron to recombine with a hole during the crossing of the base is given by

$$t/\tau_e = W^2/2D_e\tau_e = W^2/2L_e^2 \qquad (14\text{-}25)$$

where τ_e is the lifetime of electrons and L_e is their diffusion length in the base material. In most cases, $t/\tau_e \ll 1$ because the width of the base is small compared with L_e; we shall assume this to be the case in the remainder of this section. In other words, we shall assume that all electrons emitted by the emitter are collected by the collector.

Let us now consider the current flow between the emitter and the base. The total current is made up of two parts: (a) a hole current I_h from the base into the emitter; (b) an electron current I_e from the emitter into the base. The ratio of these currents is important for the amplifying action of the transistor, and we shall now show that $I_e/I_h = L_h\sigma_e/W\sigma_h$, where σ_e and σ_h are the conductivities of the emitter and base regions, and L_h is the diffusion length of holes in the emitter region.

According to (14-24), the hole current is given by

$$I_h = \frac{eD_h}{L_h}n_{h_0}(e^{eV/kT} - 1) \qquad (14\text{-}26)$$

where V is the applied voltage between base and emitter and n_{h_0} is the equilibrium concentration of holes in the emitter region. Because of what follows it is important to realize that I_h is determined by the diffusion length of holes in the emitter region. In the same way, the electronic current from emitter to base is determined by the diffusion length of electrons in the base region. However, because the width of the base region is $W \ll L_e$, one should use W rather than L_e for the electronic current. Hence

$$I_e = \frac{eD_e}{W}n_{e_0}(e^{eV/kT} - 1) \qquad (14\text{-}26a)$$

where n_{e_0} is the equilibrium density of electrons in the base. From (14-26a) and (14-26) it then follows that

$$I_e/I_h = D_e n_{e_0} L_h / D_h n_{h_0} W \qquad (14\text{-}27)$$

We may now apply expression (14-17) to the base and emitter regions, giving

$$n_{e_0} = n_i^2/n_h \quad \text{and} \quad n_{h_0} = n_i^2/n_e \qquad (14\text{-}28)$$

where n_i is the density of carriers in intrinsic material, n_h is the density

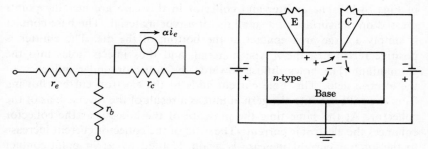

Fig. 14-10. Equivalent circuit of the transistor.   Fig. 14-11. A point-contact transistor.

of holes in the base, and n_e is the density of electrons in the emitter. Substituting into (14-27) we obtain

$$I_e/I_h = D_e L_h n_e / D_h W n_h = L_h \sigma_e / W \sigma_h \qquad (14\text{-}29)$$

Here we have made use of the fact that in general $\sigma = ne\mu$ and $\mu = De/kT$, where μ is the mobility.

Suppose now that the base potential is altered; this will give rise to a change in the hole current from the base to the emitter, and at the same time, to a change in the electron current from the emitter into the base. However, the latter is collected completely by the collector, and it thus follows that the current gain is simply given by (14-29); the current gain so obtained may be 100 or more. Other factors also favor a high gain. The collector impedance is very high because of the reverse bias; it is evident from the reverse junction characteristic in Fig. 14-8 that for voltages larger than a few times kT/e, the collector current is essentially independent of the bias, i.e., the impedance would approach infinity. Actual collector impedances are of the order of 10^6 ohms or higher. Furthermore, the resistance r_e of the emitter is very low; in fact, it follows from the forward characteristic that

$$r_e = (kT/eI)$$

where I is the emitter current. For $I = 1$ ma, this gives at room temperature, $r_e = 25$ ohms.

From the above discussion one arrives at the equivalent circuit represented in Fig. 14-10. Here r_e is the emitter junction resistance, r_b represents the resistance of the thin p-type base region, and r_c is the resistance of the collector junction. These resistances are, of course, functions of the bias voltages. The collecting action may be represented by a current generator αi_e, where i_e is the emitter alternating current and α is the fraction of the emitter current collected by the collector. For a good junction transistor, α is nearly unity, as was assumed above.

A point-contact transistor (called type A) is represented schematically in Fig. 14-11. The emitter and collector in this case are metallic points pressed on the surface of a small die of n-type material. The base contact is simply a large area contact at the bottom of the die. The emitter is positive relative to the n-type material, and thus injects holes into the germanium. The holes diffuse towards the collector under influence of the electric field. This hole current adds to the electron current flowing from the collector into the germanium as a result of the reverse bias of the collector. At the same time the presence of the holes near the collector enhances the electronic current. The ratio of the collector current increase to the emitter current increase is again denoted by α; in point-contact transistors α is therefore larger than unity (see table below). Since the collector current flows through the high collector impedance, whereas the emitter current is injected through the low emitter impedance, one also obtains a voltage gain. Some typical values for a point-contact type A transistor and a junction transistor are given below; the resistances are in ohms.

	Junction	Point-contact
r_e	25	125
r_b	200	75
r_c	5×10^6	2×10^4
α	0.95-0.99	2-3

REFERENCES

J. Bardeen and W. H. Brattain, *Phys. Rev.*, **75**, 1208 (1949); Bell System Tech. J., **28**, 239 (1949).

J. S. Blakemore, A. E. De Barr, and J. B. Gunn, "Semiconductor circuit Elements," *Repts. Progr. Phys.*, **16**, 160 (1953).

H. K. Henisch, *Metal Rectifiers*, Oxford, New York, (1949).

Proc. IRE., **40**, (1952) (transistor issue).

W. Shockley, *Electrons and Holes in Semiconductors*, Van Nostrand, New York, 1950.

H. C. Torrey and C. A. Whitmer, *Crystal Rectifiers*, McGraw-Hill, New York, 1948.

PROBLEMS

14-1. Two metallic surfaces with work functions of 3 and 4 ev are separated by a gap of 10 Å. Calculate the surface charge density in equilibrium at room temperature in terms of a number of electrons.

14-2. A metal with a work function of 3 ev is in contact with a semiconductor with an electron affinity of 1 ev; the semiconductor contains 10^{16} donors per cm^3 close to the conduction band. Calculate the capacitance of the barrier layer per cm^2 for zero applied voltage, when the dielectric constant is 12. Do the same problem for a reverse bias of 5 volts.

14-3. Consider a block of semiconducting material with a large area contact on one of its faces; the opposite face has a small circular point contact of radius a. Show that the bulk or spreading resistance of the system is $r = 1/4\sigma a$, where σ is the conductivity of the semiconductor.

14-4. Consider an idealized p-n junction in which the acceptor concentration is constant for $x < 0$, and the donor concentration is constant for $x > 0$. Find an expression for the barrier thickness in terms of the acceptor and donor concentrations and the forbidden energy gap; assume that the donor and acceptor levels lie very close, respectively, to the conduction and valence bands. Also discuss the variation of the barrier thickness with an applied voltage.

14-5. Repeat Problem 14-4 for a junction consisting of a p-type region containing N acceptors per cm^3 and an n-type region containing N donors per cm^3, the two regions being separated by a transition region in which the concentrations vary linearly with x. Assume that the transition region is large compared with the physical barrier layer.

14-6. Consider a p-n junction with an area of 0.25 cm^2 in which the current is carried mainly by holes. Given that for small forward voltages the junction resistance is 800 ohms, calculate the density of holes in the n-region if the life time of the holes in this region is 10^{-4} sec and their mobility is 1800 cm^2 volt^{-1} sec^{-1}.

Chapter 15

ELECTRONIC PROPERTIES OF
ALKALI HALIDES

In the class of solids which may be referred to as ionic semiconductors, the alkali halides have been investigated more thoroughly than any other group. In this respect they occupy a place similar to Si and Ge in the class of nonpolar semiconductors. The reason for this is twofold: in the first place large single crystals of the alkali halides may be grown with relative ease; second, they have a simple structure. In the present chapter some of the most outstanding electronic properties of these materials will be discussed. This discussion is necessarily very incomplete, and for further details we must refer the reader to the bibliography at the end of this chapter.

15-1. Optical and thermal electronic excitation in ionic crystals

In this chapter much of the discussion will be devoted to the excitation of the electronic system of ionic crystals. Electronic excitation may be accomplished in various ways:

  (i) The electrons may be excited thermally.

 (ii) They may absorb photons.

(iii) They may absorb energy from incident charged particles.

The excitation processes are discussed in terms of energy level diagrams, and a few words may be said about the use of such diagrams.

First, the reader is reminded that in ionic crystals one must distinguish between the high-frequency dielectric constant ϵ_0 and the static dielectric constant ϵ_s. The former is a result of electronic displacements only, the latter is due to electronic displacements plus ionic displacements (see Chapter 6). For ionic crystals ϵ_s is considerably larger than ϵ_0. These quantities enter in the discussion of energy level diagrams as a consequence of the so-called Franck-Condon principle, which states that when an electron is excited optically, the nuclei of the ions may be considered to remain at rest during the process.[1] In other words, an optical excitation process takes place in a time interval small compared with the period

---

[1] J. Franck, *Trans. Faraday Soc.*, **21**, 536 (1925); E. U. Condon, *Phys. Rev.*, **28**, 1182 (1926); **32**, 858 (1928).

associated with lattice vibrations. The consequences of this principle may first be illustrated with reference to the optical excitation of a diatomic molecule XY; later we shall generalize the picture to apply to a solid. In Fig. 15-1 let the curve ABC represent the potential energy of the molecule as function of the separation r between the X and Y atoms. Similarly, let curve PQR represent the potential energy of the electronically excited atom Y* as function of its distance relative to atom X; the point R lies above C by an amount equal to the excitation energy Q_e of the free

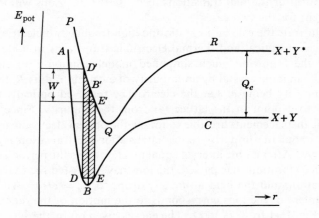

Fig. 15-1.   Illustrating the Franck-Condon principle (see text).

Y atom. In general, the minima B and Q will not correspond to the same separation. Suppose now the molecule XY is in the state B. It may then absorb a photon $h\nu$, after which its representative point will arrive at B', in accordance with the Franck-Condon principle (the separation between the nuclei does not change during the transition). However, point B' represents a highly excited vibrational state of the XY* molecule and ultimately the system will move toward a point on the PQR curve near Q, by energy exchange with the surroundings. In other words, some of the optically absorbed energy is wasted in the sense that after the optical transition a certain fraction of it is transformed into heat. The thermal activation energy is simply given by the energy difference between B and Q; evidently the optical activation energy is always larger than or equal to the thermal activation energy. This was first pointed out by de Boer and van Geel.[2]

We should note that actually the atoms in the XY molecule vibrate relative to each other, even at $T = 0$. Thus, let the molecule XY be in the vibrational level DE. Depending on where the representative point finds itself along the DE level, the optical excitation energy may lie anywhere in

[2] J. H. de Boer and W. Ch. van Geel, *Physica*, **2**, 286 (1935).

the shaded region of Fig. 15-1. Thus the absorption spectrum is a band spectrum in contrast with the line spectra observed for single atoms. The band width W will increase with increasing temperature.

The same reasoning may be applied to an electronic transition in a solid by interpreting the coordinate r as representing the configuration of the nuclei in the vicinity of the position in the crystal where the transition takes place. It follows from the above discussion that when one introduces an energy-level diagram, it is necessary to specify whether one is talking about optical or thermal transitions, because the diagrams will in general be different for the two cases.

To illustrate the role of the static and high-frequency dielectric constant in the case of optical and thermal electronic transitions in ionic crystals, consider the following much simplified model.[3] Suppose an electron is trapped in an ionic crystal by an impurity of a certain radius R, the charge of the impurity being e. Let the electron be removed optically from the impurity to a point in the lattice far from the impurity. Since only the electronic displacements are able to follow the optical electronic transition, the field about the impurity immediately after the transition is equal to $E_1 = e/\epsilon_0 r^2$. After a time interval equal to a few times the period associated with lattice vibrations has passed, the ions have adjusted themselves to the new situation, and the field ultimately drops to $E_2 = e/\epsilon_s r^2$. The process of adjustment of the ions corresponds to the motion of the representative point in Fig. 15-1 from B' to Q. The energy given off by the system during this process may be estimated as follows. The energy per unit volume in the dielectric is given by $(E \cdot D)/8\pi$. In our example E and D are both radial vectors; hence, per unit volume there is a change in energy equal to

$$(E_1 - E_2)D/8\pi = (e^2/8\pi r^4)(1/\epsilon_0 - 1/\epsilon_s)$$

Integrating this from $r = R$ to $r = \infty$, one obtains for the difference between the optical and thermal activation energy in this model,

$$\int_R^\infty \frac{e^2}{8\pi r^4}\left(\frac{1}{\epsilon_0} - \frac{1}{\epsilon_s}\right) 4\pi r^2\,dr = \frac{e^2}{2R}\left(\frac{1}{\epsilon_0} - \frac{1}{\epsilon_s}\right) \tag{15-1}$$

This may be of the order of a few ev when $R \simeq 1$ Å.

We may note that in nonpolar crystals such as silicon and germanium, the optical and thermal activation energies are equal within the experimental error; this is a result of the fact that the atoms are neutral and any atomic displacements occurring after an optical transition give off a very small amount of energy indeed.

---

[3] See N. F. Mott and R. W. Gurney, *Electronic Processes in Ionic Crystals*, Oxford, New York, 1940, p. 160.

15-2. The upper filled band and the conduction band in ionic crystals

In the present section it will be assumed that the crystals under consideration are perfect in the sense that they are of stoichiometric composition and that they do not contain lattice defects of any kind. Although such crystals do not actually exist, it is useful to consider the properties of an idealized model as a starting point; the influence of lattice defects on the electronic properties will be considered later.

Ionic crystals such as the alkali and silver halides, the oxides of the alkaline earth metals, etc. are usually good insulators. Thus, according to

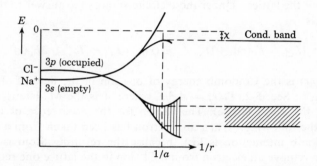

Fig. 15-2. Schematic representation of the variation of the occupied $3p$-levels and the empty $3s$-levels in NaCl as function of the separation between the ions. The actual lattice constant is a, leading to the filled band and the conduction band as indicated on the right. The energy χ required to take an electron from the bottom of the conduction band to vacuum is called the *electron affinity*.

the band theory, the electron distribution may be represented by a system of completely filled and completely empty energy bands, at least at $T = 0$. For many purposes in this chapter it will be convenient to discuss the electronic properties by considering the crystals as a system of interacting ions rather than from the collective electron viewpoint. Thus, in this section, the upper filled band and the empty band (conduction band) will be associated with certain electronic states of the composing ions.

As a particular example, consider NaCl. Suppose a NaCl lattice is uniformly expanded so that the separation of the ions is large enough to consider the ions as free. In order to locate the electronic levels we shall take the energy of a free electron at rest as zero.[4] The lowest unoccupied level of a free Na^+ ion is a $3s$ state, located below the zero level by an amount equal to the ionization I_{Na} energy of a sodium atom, i.e., located at -5.12 ev (see Fig. 15-2). The highest occupied state of the Cl^- ion is a

[4] NaCl has been discussed by W. Shockley, *Phys. Rev.*, **40,** 754 (1936).

$3p$ level, located below zero by an energy difference equal to the electron affinity E_{Cl} of the Cl atom, i.e., at -4 ev. Thus, in the infinitely expanded lattice, the empty $3s$ level lies below the occupied $3p$ level by an amount $I_{Na} - E_{Cl} = 1.12$ ev; this is true for the "optical" energy level diagram as well as for the "thermal" one. As the ions are brought together, however, the relative position of these levels varies as indicated schematically in Fig. 15-2, where r represents the shortest interionic distance. The reason for this change may be understood by asking the following question: What is the energy required to transfer an electron from a Cl^- ion to a remote Na^+ ion, when the ions are incorporated in an ionic lattice? For the moment let us neglect any polarization effects associated with the dielectric constant of the lattice. Under these circumstances the answer to the above question is

$$[E_{Cl} + E_C(r)] - [I_{Na} - E_C(r)] = E_{Cl} - I_{Na} + 2E_C(r) \qquad (15\text{-}2)$$

where $E_C(r)$ is the Coulomb energy of one ion in the field of all others; according to Sec. 5-2, $E_C(r) = Ae^2/r$, where A is the Madelung constant (1.75 for the NaCl lattice). The reason for the occurrence of the $E_C(r)$ terms is the following. When an electron has been taken from a Cl^- ion, the Coulomb interaction is lost, because the resulting atom is neutral. Hence, to remove an electron from a Cl^- ion in the lattice one requires an energy $E_{Cl} + E_C(r)$. In a similar way, the energy gained by putting an electron on a Na^+ ion is $I_{Na} - E_C(r)$ because again the Coulomb energy is lost. Thus, as r decreases, $E_C(r)$ increases, leading to the variation of the energy levels as indicated; for a certain value of r they cross over, and for still smaller values of r the occupied $3p$ levels fall below the empty $3s$ levels.

Actually, the $E_C(r)$ terms should be corrected for polarization effects. Thus, when an electron is excited optically from a certain Cl^- ion to a remote Na^+ ion, one should subtract from (15-2) the polarization energy around the neutral Cl and Na atoms, using the high-frequency dielectric constant ϵ_0. If the excitation is thermal, the polarization energy must be calculated on the basis of the static dielectric constant ϵ_s. Here again the thermal excitation energy will be smaller than the optical excitation energy. Hence one arrives at two possible electron level schemes: an optical one and a thermal one.

When the lattice parameter r reaches values such that the wave functions of neighboring ions of equal sign begin to overlap, the discrete atomic levels broaden into bands (see Chapter 10). The actually observed lattice parameter $r = a$ determines the distance between the bands as well as the widths of the bands, as indicated on the right in Fig. 15-2.

One thus arrives at the conclusion that the upper filled band in NaCl is associated with the occupied $3p$ levels of the Cl^- ions, the empty band corresponding to the unoccupied $3s$ levels of the Na^+ ions. Similar identifications may be made in other ionic crystals. Actually, the conduction band in ionic crystals probably corresponds to an ionization continuum, i.e., other empty bands will overlap with the one identified above.

Information about the width of the upper filled band may be obtained from soft X-ray emission spectra, as explained in Sec. 10-12. Results of such studies for a number of ionic and semi-ionic crystals are given in Table 15-1.[5] It is observed that the band width for the alkali halides and

**Table 15-1.   The Width of the Upper Filled Band in ev
for a Number of Solids**

LiF	2.1	LiBr	1.2	Li_2O	12.8
NaF	1.7	NaBr	0.75	CaO	10.8
KF	1.5	KBr	0.55	SrO	9.2
		RbBr	0.45	BaO	8.4
..		AgBr	1.1		

silver halides is of the order of 1 ev; for the oxides it is of the order of 10 ev. From this one might expect the effective mass of a hole to be larger in the halides than in the oxides.

The energy difference between an electron at rest in vacuum and an electron at the bottom of the conduction band is called the electron affinity χ of the crystal (see Fig. 15-2). For alkali halides χ is probably of the order of 0.5 ev or less.

15-3. The ultraviolet spectrum of the alkali halides; excitons

A great deal of experimental information about the electronic structure of ionic crystals has been obtained from optical absorption measurements.[6] As an example we give in Fig. 15-3 the absorption spectrum of KBr.[7] The alkali halides are transparent in the visible region of the spectrum, and the absorption spectrum associated with electronic transitions lies entirely in the ultraviolet. It consists of a number of absorption peaks which are best resolved at low temperatures. In the vicinity of the peaks, the absorption coefficient is of the order of 10^6 per cm, so that thin evaporated layers are used in these experiments. The high energy region is very difficult to investigate experimentally so that virtually nothing is known about the

[5] N. F. Mott and R. W. Gurney, op. cit., pp. 75, 79.

[6] For a review, see R. W. Pohl, Physik. Z., 39, 36 (1938); E. G. Schneider and H. M. O'Bryan, Phys. Rev., 51, 293 (1937); L. Apker and E. Taft, Phys. Rev., 81, 698 (1951). New studies, with emphasis on the range from 950 Å to 1700 Å are presently being carried out at Cornell University by Hartman, Siegfried, and Nelson.

[7] R. Hilsch and R. W. Pohl, Z. Physik, 59, 817 (1929).

short wavelength tail of the absorption region. The tail on the long-wavelength side is at least in part due to imperfections, as will be explained further in Sec. 15-5; it is therefore temperature-sensitive.

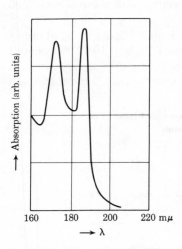

It is important to note that when photons are absorbed in the long wave-length tail or in the first absorption peak, no photoconductivity results. This indicates that the first absorption peak does not give rise to an electronic transition from the filled band into the conduction band. It is believed, therefore, that the first absorption peak gives rise to an excited state of the halogen ions, i.e., an electron from the filled band is raised to a level below the conduction band. This situation may be compared with the excited states of an atom. Complete ionization of an atom may then be compared with the transition of an electron from the filled band into the conduction band.

Fig. 15-3. Absorption spectrum of pure KBr. [After Hilsch and Pohl, ref. 7]

It is for this reason that the energy band scheme of a perfect ionic crystal contains a number of narrow "exciton bands" below the conduction band, as indicated in Fig. 15-4. One may also look at this by saying that when a photon corresponding to the first absorption peak is absorbed by an electron in the filled band, the excited electron is still bound to some extent by the Coulomb field produced by the hole it left behind. This will be further illustrated in the next section. The combination of an electron in an excited state and the associated hole is called an exciton; the unit as a whole is neutral. It has been suggested that an exciton may be thought of as resulting from an electronic transition from a negative ion to a nearest neighbor positive ion. A transition from the filled band to the conduction band in this type of picture then corresponds to an electron transfer from a negative ion to a faraway positive ion. This is probably an oversimplification, although it illustrates the electron-hole interaction.

At present it is not known where the ultraviolet absorption spectrum goes over from exciton bands into the ionization continuum. A rough estimate may be made on the basis of the following simplified model. Consider the exciton as an electron and a hole revolving about each other as a result of Coulomb interaction. The energy of this system may be estimated from the analogy with a hydrogen atom in the ground state. Two modifications are required: (1) the mass of the electron is approximately equal to that of the hole; (2) the field between the two particles is reduced by a factor equal to the high-frequency dielectric constant ϵ_0. Now the binding energy of an electron in the hydrogen atom is 13.54 ev. Introducing the two modifications suggested above, one obtains for the binding energy of the exciton in electron volts $13.54/2\epsilon_0^2$. This is of the order of 1 ev for most ionic crystals. One thus estimates that the band-to-band transitions should occur approximately 1 ev beyond the first absorption peak. From these arguments it follows that as ϵ_0 increases, the exciton bands should be crowded into a smaller energy region.

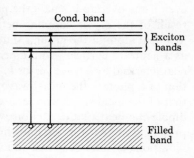

Fig. 15-4. Energy band scheme of an insulator, showing exciton bands below the conduction band. The combination of an electron in an excited state (black dot) and the hole left behind in the filled band (open circle) is called an *exciton.*

The first absorption peak shifts to higher values as the temperature is lowered. This is a result of the thermal contraction of the lattice, leading to larger binding energies. Also, the peaks broaden at higher temperatures as a result of the increased amplitudes of the lattice vibrations.

As an example we give in Table 15-2 the position of the first absorption peak for a number of alkali halides, together with the corresponding photon energy in ev. It is observed that as the ions become larger, the absorption peak shifts generally to lower energy values, as one might expect. It is of great importance to realize that once an exciton is produced at the location of a certain halide ion, it will in general not stay there. In fact, there is a great deal of experimental and theoretical evidence that excitons move about in the lattice. Thus an excited halide ion may transfer its energy to the next halide ion and by repeated transfers of this kind the exciton is propagated through the lattice. In the earlier work on this topic

Table 15-2. Position of the First Ultraviolet Absorption Peak at Room Temperature for a Number of Alkali Halides

Salt	Å	ev	Salt	Å	ev	Salt	Å	ev
LiCl	1430	8.6						
NaCl	1580	7.8	NaBr	1900	6.5			
KCl	1620	7.6	KBr	1890	6.5	KI	2200	5.6
RbCl	1660	7.4	RbBr	1930	6.4	RbI	2230	5.5
CsCl	1620	7.6	CsBr	1870	6.6			

by Frenkel[8] and by Slater and Shockley[9] the possibility of exciton propagation was related to the overlapping of the excited-state wave functions on neighboring atoms. More recently, Heller and Marcus have shown that even if the overlap is small, the propagation of excitons may be good as a result of the dipole coupling between the excited ion and a neighboring identical atom in the ground state.[10] Thus an exciton may be represented as a neutral "particle" with a certain effective mass m^*, its motion being characterized by a wave vector k. If the exciton is produced by the absorption of a photon, the initial wave vector of the exciton will be the same as that of the incident photon (conservation of momentum). In this case, the dipole moment of the exciton will be perpendicular to the direction of propagation. As the exciton propagates, it may interact with lattice vibrations or imperfections, and scattering results. Excitons for which the dipole moment is parallel to the direction of propagation are also possible and the two types can be converted into each other by scattering processes. The optical lifetime τ of an exciton, i.e., the average period elapsing between the production of the exciton and the instant that the electron and hole recombine under emission of a photon, is probably of the order of 10^{-8} second (corresponding to the emission of dipole radiation). However, long before the optical lifetime is up, the exciton may give off its energy to lattice imperfections. For example, an exciton may transfer its energy to an F center, thereby raising the trapped electron into the conduction band. Excitons may also transfer their energy to an electron in the filled band in the vicinity of a negative ion vacancy, leading to the production of an F center. These matters will be further discussed in Sec. 15-9. According to Marcus and Heller, the effective mass of an exciton is given by

$$m^* \simeq m(3\pi/4n)^{1/3}/f_{n_0}a_e \tag{15-3}$$

where n is the number of ions per unit volume, m is the free electron mass, a_e is the effective Bohr radius of the excited atom, and f_{n_0} is the oscillator strength connecting the ground state and the excited state. When $f_{n_0} \simeq 1$, as it is in the alkali halides, it follows from (15-3) that $m^* \simeq m$. Hence at room temperature the velocity of an exciton is approximately equal to that of a thermal electron, i.e., $v \simeq 10^7$ cm/sec. During the optical lifetime the total path covered by an exciton is thus of the order of $10^7 \times 10^{-8} \simeq 0.1$ cm. As a result of the scattering by phonons and imperfections, the path is actually curled up as in any type of Brownian motion. If one

[8] J. Frenkel, *Phys. Rev.*, **37**, 17, 1276 (1931); *Phys. Z. Sowjetunion*, **9**, 158 (1936); see also G. H. Wannier, *Phys. Rev.*, **52**, 191 (1937).

[9] J. C. Slater and W. Shockley, *Phys. Rev.*, **50**, 705 (1936).

[10] W. R. Heller and A. Marcus, *Phys. Rev.*, **84**, 809 (1951).

assumes a mean free path for scattering $\lambda_s \simeq 10$ Angstroms, one finds for the mean square displacement

$$\langle r^2 \rangle = 2D\tau = \tfrac{2}{3}\lambda_s v\tau \simeq 10^{-8} \text{ cm}^2 \tag{15-4}$$

Thus, during the optical life, the excitons may on the average undergo a displacement of approximately 10^{-4} cm relative to point of origin.

15-4. Illustration of electron-hole interaction in single ions

In view of the importance of the concept of an exciton, it may be useful to consider the following example of the Coulomb interaction between an electron and a hole. To remove the $3s$ electron in a free sodium atom, the ionization energy (5.12 ev) is required. To remove a second electron, another 47 ev is required, as illustrated in Fig. 15-5a. At first sight one

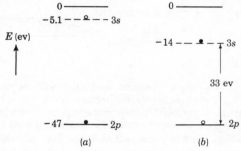

Fig. 15-5. Schematic representation of the energy levels of a singly charged sodium ion (a); the excitation of the $2p$-electron into the $3s$-level requires only 33 ev (b) rather than 42 ev, illustrating the electron-hole interaction.

might thus expect that an energy of about 42 ev would be necessary to excite the $2p$ electron in a sodium ion into the $3s$ level. However, experimentally one finds only about 33 ev. This leads to the electron level scheme for the excited ion given in Fig. 15-5b. Thus the electron in the $3s$ level is now more strongly bound than in the atom as a result of the Coulomb interaction between the electron and the hole in the $3p$ level. In this case, the interaction energy is approximately 9 ev.

15-5. Qualitative discussion of the influence of lattice defects on the electronic levels

So far, we have considered only perfect crystals. However, as we have seen in previous chapters, any crystal contains a certain number of lattice defects of various kinds (vacancies, aggregates of vacancies, interstitials, dislocations) quite apart from chemical impurities. The presence of such defects will alter the charge distribution and one expects a change in the electronic levels in the vicinity of the defects. As a simple example, consider a positive ion vacancy in a lattice such as NaCl. The $3p$ electrons of the Cl⁻ ions neighboring the vacancy will not be so strongly bound as they normally would be, because the positive ion vacancy acts as a negative charge. Thus it should be easier to ionize or excite an electron from such Cl⁻ ions (A in Fig. 15-6) than is normally the case. In other words, the outer electrons of these Cl⁻ ions do not reside in the filled band but occupy levels above the filled band. This is indicated in Fig. 15-6; the levels are

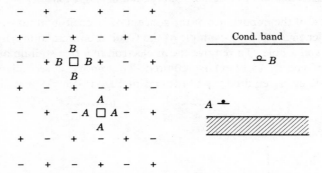

Fig. 15-6. The outer electrons associated with negative ions surrounding a positive ion vacancy occupy levels above the filled band (A); the empty levels corresponding to positive ions surrounding a negative ion vacancy lie below the conduction band (B). The excited states of levels such as A have been omitted.

represented by a short bar, and it is understood that this implies that the level is localized in the vicinity of a particular vacancy. Each positive ion vacancy gives rise to six of these levels because there are six Cl⁻ ions surrounding the vacancy. To a lesser extent, similar considerations hold for the next-nearest Cl⁻ ions; the levels for the $3p$ electrons on these ions will be much closer to the filled band.

It may be noted that if in some way or other a free hole should be created in the filled band, the hole may be trapped at one of the A levels mentioned above. This is not surprising, because a position where a positive ion is missing would be a favorable site for a positive hole to reside. The trapped hole may then be represented as a Cl atom neighboring a positive ion vacancy. Actually, the hole will probably be shared by the six surrounding halogen ions, because they are all equivalent. Trapped holes of this kind are called V centers; these will be discussed in Sec. 15-12.

The situation around a negative ion vacancy may be discussed in a similar way. Suppose by some means one had created a free electron in the conduction band. A likely place for this electron to get trapped would be a negative ion vacancy; the latter has an effective positive charge and thus attracts the electron. In this case the electron is shared by six surrounding Na⁺ ions and the resulting center is called an F center. In the energy level scheme this means that the empty $3s$ states of the Na^+ ions surrounding a negative ion vacancy (B in Fig. 15-6) do not lie in the conduction band but below it.

Summarizing, we may say, that positive ion vacancies give rise to occupied electronic levels above the filled band; negative ion vacancies give rise to unoccupied states below the conduction band. It will be evident that as a result of these changes in the energy level scheme, new absorption bands will arise, the extent of the absorption being proportional to the density of lattice defects. More complicated lattice defects, such as pairs, triplets, etc., will also change the absorption spectrum. Usually the new absorption bands lie in the tail of the first fundamental absorption band. Thus, although changes in the tail may be observed, for example, by variations in temperature, it is difficult to resolve the new bands. At low temperatures, however, one has observed the so-called α band, which is believed to be associated with the presence of single negative-ion vacancies.[11]

15-6. Nonstoichiometric crystals containing excess metal

A great deal of fundamental information about semiconducting ionic crystals has been obtained by studying the properties of nonstoichiometric crystals, i.e., crystals containing an excess of one of their constituents. For example, when an alkali halide crystal is heated in the vapor of its metallic constituent, an excess of metal is incorporated in the crystal. Some properties resulting from the excess metal will now be discussed.

F centers. In the first place, crystals heated in the metal vapor and quenched to room temperature show an absorption band in the visible or ultraviolet, whereas the original crystals were transparent in that region. This absorption band is called the F band (the German word for color is Farbe). As an example we show in Fig. 15-7 the F band in KBr at various temperatures according to Mollwo.[12] The width of the band increases and its position shifts to lower energies when the crystals are heated. At room temperature the position of the F band peak in the alkali halides is as given in Table 15-3. It is interesting to note that according to Mollwo[12] the F-absorption frequency ν_F is related to the shortest interionic distance a by the approximate expression

$$\nu_F a^2 \simeq 0.5 \text{ cm}^2 \text{ sec}^{-1} \tag{15-5}$$

[11] Delbecq, Pringsheim, and Yuster, *J. Chem. Phys.*, **19**, 574 (1951); **20**, 746 (1952); see also W. Martienssen, *Z. Physik*, **131**, 488 (1952); W. Martienssen and R. W. Pohl, *Z. Physik*, **133**, 153 (1952).

[12] E. Mollwo, *Z. Physik*, **85**, 56, 62 (1933); the fact that ν_F is essentially determined by a and only very slightly by the dielectric constant of the material may be explained on the basis of calculations by L. Pincherle, *Proc. Phys. Soc.* (*London*), **64**, 648 (1951).

As a result of the presence of the F band, the crystals have a colored appearance; for example, LiF containing excess Li looks pink; KCl with excess K looks violet, NaCl with excess Na looks brown-yellow, etc.

The peak height of the absorption band at a given temperature is proportional to the number of F centers per unit volume. From dispersion theory, Smakula has derived the following formula for the F-center density n_F:[13]

$$fn_F = 1.31 \times 10^{17} \frac{n}{(n^2 + 2)^2} K_{\max} H \text{ per cm}^3 \qquad (15\text{-}6)$$

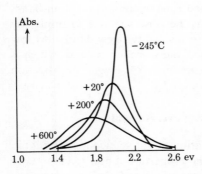

Fig. 15-7. The optical absorption as function of photon energy for KBr resulting from an excess of potassium, measured at various temperatures (°C). [After Mollwo, ref. 12]

where f is the oscillator strength, n is the index of refraction, $K_{\max}$ is the absorption coefficient in cm^{-1} at the peak, and H is the half width of the band in ev. By measuring the excess metal chemically and comparing the result with formula (15-6), Kleinschrod obtained an oscillator strength $f = 0.81$ for KCl.[14] When f is not known, formula (15-6) can be used only to determine the order of magnitude of the F center density. It should be added that the derivation of Smakula's formula is somewhat doubtful in the light of recent results obtained from spin resonance studies.[15]

F center density as function of metal vapor pressure and temperature. The absorption of alkali metal by the crystal can be described as a diffusion phenomenon, as will be explained further below. For a given temperature of the crystal and a given number of metal atoms (alkali vapors are monatomic) per unit volume in the container, a certain saturation density of F centers is obtained. Some results obtained for K in KBr by Rögener

Table 15-3. F-Center Absorption Energies in ev for the Alkali Halides

LiF	5.0	NaF	3.6	KF	2.6				
LiCl	3.1	NaCl	2.7	KCl	2.2	RbCl	2.0	CsCl	2.0
LiBr	2.7	NaBr	2.3	KBr	2.0	RbBr	1.8		
				KI	1.8	RbI	1.6		

[13] See R. Hilsch and R. W. Pohl, *Z. Physik*, **68**, 721 (1931); F. Seitz, *Revs. Mod. Phys.*, **18**, 384 (1946); **26**, 7 (1954).

[14] F. G. Kleinschrod, *Ann. Physik*, **27**, 97 (1936).

[15] See, for example, F. Seitz, *Revs. Mod. Phys.*, **26**, 7 (1954).

are represented in Fig. 15-8.[16] It may be noted that he assumed $f = 1$ in formula (15-6), so that actually the F center densities are somewhat larger than in the figure. Several conclusions may be drawn from these measurements. In the first place, the saturation value, for brevity simply denoted by n_F, is proportional to the number of K atoms per unit volume n_v in the

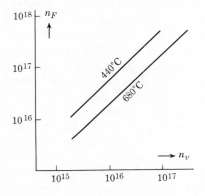

Fig. 15-8. The saturation density of F centers (n_F) in KBr as function of the density of atoms in the metal vapor (n_v), for a crystal temperature of 440°C and 680°C. [After Rögener, ref. 16]

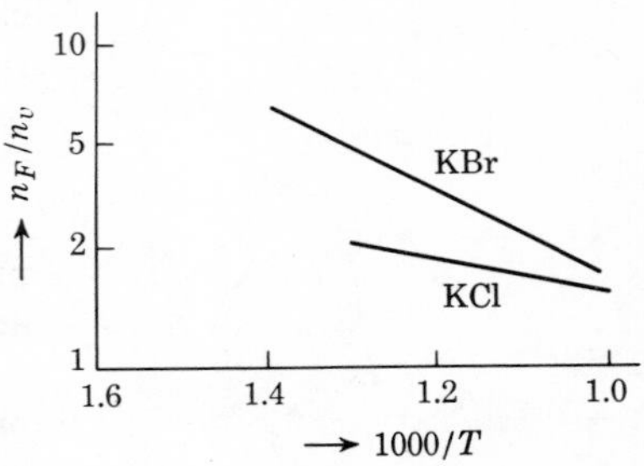

Fig. 15-9. The ratio n_F/n_v (plotted logarithmically) versus the reciprocal absolute temperature for KBr and KCl. [After Rögener, ref. 16]

vapor. Hence the chemical reaction corresponding to the incorporation of excess metal may be written

$$\text{metal atom in vapor} \leftrightarrows F \text{ center}$$

According to the law of mass action, we then have

$$n_F/n_v = \text{const. } e^{-\phi/kT} \tag{15-7}$$

where ϕ is the energy required to take an atom from the vapor and incorporate it as an F center in the crystal. In Fig. 15-9 we have plotted n_F/n_v as function of T^{-1} as given by Rögener for KBr and KCl.[16] From the slopes it follows that

$$\text{for K in KBr} \quad \phi = -0.25 \text{ ev}$$

$$\text{for K in KCl} \quad \phi = -0.10 \text{ ev}$$

Note that in both cases ϕ is negative, i.e., energy is released by taking an atom from the vapor into the crystal. It is observed that $n_F > n_v$ for these crystals.

[16] H. Rögener, *Ann. Physik*, **29**, 386 (1937).

The F-center model. Although some other interpretations had been given previously it is now generally accepted that an *F* center is an electron trapped at a negative ion vacancy. This model was first suggested by de Boer[17] and was further developed by Gurney and Mott.[18] In the light of this model the incorporation of excess metal by the crystal may then be pictured in the following manner. The first step is the adsorption of a metal atom from the vapor on the surface of the crystal, for example, at point *A* in Fig. 15-10. The atom may then split up into a positive ion and an

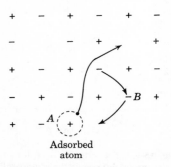

Fig. 15-10. Possible mechanism for the incorporation of excess metal in an alkali halide (see text).

electron. A negative ion from the lattice such as *B* may then jump into a position next to *A* to form the beginning of a new layer on the surface of the crystal. The electron and the negative ion vacancy produced at *B* diffuse into the crystal, and the electron will become trapped in a region where the potential is such that it provides a level below the conduction band. Evidently a lattice site where a negative ion is missing provides such a region. The trapped electron is shared by the six positive ions surrounding the vacancy. We emphasize that in the above picture the number of "empty" negative ion vacancies remains constant, because for each electron added, a negative ion vacancy is created. Seitz has pointed out that the actual mechanism of the formation of *F* centers may be somewhat different in the sense that positive and negative ion vacancies tend to associate to pairs or higher aggregates because of Coulomb attraction.[19] However, if an electron meets a pair of ion vacancies, the electron may first be trapped by the pair, whereupon the positive ion vacancy wanders off, because the binding energy of an electron and a negative ion vacancy (∼2 ev) is larger than the binding energy of a pair of vacancies (∼1 ev). In other words, a negative ion vacancy prefers an electron as a partner over a positive ion vacancy. The result of such a mechanism is, of course, the same as the one described above.

This *F*-center model is confirmed, for example, by the fact that heat treatment of KCl in sodium vapor produces exactly the same absorption band as excess K in KCl, i.e., the *F* band is independent of the added metal. Also, the same band is formed when the stoichiometric crystals are irradiated with ultraviolet, X-rays, or other types of radiation which

[17] J. H. de Boer, *Rec. trav. chim.*, **56,** 301 (1937).

[18] R. W. Gurney and N. F. Mott, *Trans. Faraday Soc.*, **34,** 506 (1938).

[19] F. Seitz, *Revs. Mod. Phys.*, **18,** 384 (1946).

produce free electrons. Such free electrons ultimately become trapped at negative ion vacancies, forming F centers.

Also in agreement with the above F-center model is the observation by Witt that the density of the crystals decreases when excess metal is introduced.[20] Within the experimental error, the observed decrease in density of KCl is compatible with the notion that one negative ion vacancy is created for each F center formed.

Although the experimental evidence will be given later, it may be noted here that the F-absorption band is believed to be due to the excitation of the F-center electron into an excited state close to the conduction band (see Fig. 15-11), but not into the conduction band. In this connection it is of interest to note that Kleinschrod observed that the F band has not a simple bell shape but possesses a shoulder and a tail on the short-wave length side.[21] Seitz has suggested the name "K band" for this shoulder. The K band itself may correspond to transitions of the electron to excited states lying between the first excited state and the conduction band; the tail may be associated with transitions from the ground state of the F center into the conduction band.

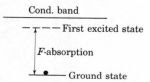

Fig. 15-11.   Energy level diagram for an F center. The F-absorption band arises from a transition from the ground state to the first excited state below the conduction band.

Theoretical calculations on F centers. Theoretical calculations of the motion of an electron in the field of a negative ion vacancy have been carried out by a number of investigators.[22] In these calculations self-consistent field methods must be used because the potential in which the electron finds itself is a function of the wave function of the electron. Because of lack of space it is not possible to discuss these models here, and we refer the reader to the literature on this topic. In all papers except the last one mentioned in footnote 22, the electron is assumed to move in a spherically symmetric field. In the spherical approximation, the ground state of the electron in an F center is a $1s$ state, and the F absorption band corresponds to transitions form $1s$ to $2p$. The calculated absorption frequencies are in fair agreement with the experimental values.

We mentioned above that the width of the F band increases with temperature, the peak shifting at the same time to lower energies. Although

[20] H. Witt, *Nachr. Akad. Wiss. Göttingen*, **1952**, 17.

[21] F. Kleinschrod, *Ann. Physik*, **27**, 97 (1936).

[22] S. R. Tibbs, *Trans. Faraday Soc.*, **35**, 1471 (1939); J. H. Simpson, *Proc. Roy. Soc. (London)*, **A197**, 269 (1949); L. Pincherle, *Proc. Phys. Soc. (London)*, **64**, 648 (1951); J. A. Krumhansl and N. Schwartz, *Phys. Rev.*, **89**, 1154 (1953); T. Inui and Y. Uemura, *Progr. Theoret. Phys. (Japan)*, **5**, 252, 395 (1950).

qualitatively this can be understood on the basis of lattice vibrations and lattice expansion, the first serious attempt to interpret these effects quantitatively was made not earlier than 1950.[23] It is not possible to discuss here the rather complicated calculations on this topic that have been published since that time.

Magnetic properties of F centers. Since an *F* center contains an unpaired electron, one expects the crystals additively colored with metal to be paramagnetic; the static paramagnetism has been observed by Jensen.[24]

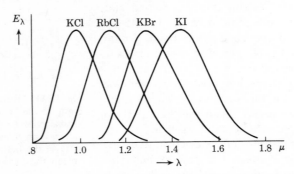

Fig. 15-12. *F*-center luminescence emission spectra for some alkali halides at 20°K. [After Botden, van Doorn and Haven, ref. 26]

More recently, spin resonance techniques have been employed to study the structure of *F* centers.[25] The gyromagnetic ratio *g*, which determines the splitting of the energy levels per unit magnetic field, is 1.995 ± 0.001 rather than 2.0023 corresponding to a free electron. This result, together with results obtained from measurements of the line width, show that the *F*-center electron overlaps to a considerable extent the surrounding positive and negative ions, as one might have expected. For details concerning the interpretation of such experiments we refer to the literature.

Luminescence of F centers. One might expect that an excited *F* center would return to the ground state with emission of a photon. From the foregoing discussions it is evident that experiments attempting to detect this type of luminescence should be conducted at low temperatures,

[23] K. Huang and A. Rhys, *Proc. Roy. Soc.* (*London*), **A204**, 406 (1950); see also H. J. G. Meyer, *Physica*, **20**, 181 (1954); **20**, 1016 (1954); **21**, 253 (1955).

[24] P. Jensen, *Ann. Physik*, **34**, 161 (1939).

[25] C. A. Hutchison, *Phys. Rev.*, **75**, 1769 (1949); C. A. Hutchison and G. A. Noble, *Phys. Rev.*, **87**, 1125 (1952); E. E. Schneider and T. S. England, *Physica*, **17**, 221 (1951); M. Tinkham and A. F. Kip, *Phys. Rev.*, **83**, 657 (1951); A. H. Kahn and C. Kittel, *Phys. Rev.*, **89**, 315 (1953); Kip, Kittel, Levy, and Portis, *Phys. Rev.*, **91**, 1066 (1953); A. M. Portis, *Phys. Rev.*, **91**, 1071 (1953).

because otherwise the electron will not remain in the excited state but will be further excited thermally into the conduction band. The luminescence of F centers in additively colored alkali halides has recently been observed by Botden, van Doorn, and Haven.[26] The crystals were irradiated with light in the F band and luminescence in the infrared was observed at 20°K and at 77°K. In Fig. 15-12 we reproduce the emission spectra at 20°K. The energy of the emitted photons at 20°K are given in ev below, together with the corresponding photon energy for F absorption at room temperature. It is observed that the absorption frequency is nearly twice the emission frequency, and this difference would actually be larger if the absorption energies were referred to 20°K. This illustrates again clearly the importance of the Franck-Condon principle in ionic crystals. After the optical excitation has taken place, the ions in the vicinity of the excited F center will adjust themselves to the new charge dis-

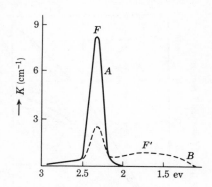

Fig. 15-13. Formation of the F' band at the expense of the F band, by irradiation of an additively colored crystal with F light at 173°K. [After Hilsch and Pohl, ref. 27]

tribution, thereby giving off energy (corresponding to the representative point moving from B' to Q in Fig. 15-1). When the electron returns to the ground state after this ionic displacement has taken place, an infrared quantum is emitted.

Table 15-4. F-Center Absorption and Emission Energies (ev)

	Absorption	Emission
KCl	2.2	1.25
RbCl	2.0	1.10
KBr	2.0	0.96
KI	1.8	0.85

15-7. The transformation of F centers into F' centers and vice versa

When an additively colored crystal containing F centers is irradiated with light in the F band, a new band appears at the long-wavelength side of the F band. The new band grows at the expense of the F band and is called the F' band. For example in Fig. 15-13, curve A represents the

[26] Th. P. J. Botden, C. Z. van Doorn, and Y. Haven, *Philips Research Repts.*, **9**, 469 (1954).

optical absorption spectrum of a KCl crystal containing 1.6×10^{16} F centers per cm³, measured at 38°K.[27] After irradiation with F light at 173°K, the F band has decreased and the F' band appears (curve B, Fig. 15-13, measured again at 38°K). The F' centers are stable only at rather low temperatures, because the electrons causing F' absorption are more loosely bound than those in the F centers. Thus at higher temperatures, the F' centers dissociate thermally and form F centers again. To investigate the transformation of F centers into F' centers and vice versa, Pick carried out a number of interesting experiments on the quantum efficiency of these processes at different temperatures.[28] For example, Fig. 15-14 gives the number of destroyed F centers as function of the number of absorbed F center quanta for KCl at different temperatures. The slope of the curves give the quantum yield, i.e., the number of destroyed F centers per absorbed quantum. We note that above 140°K the curves start off with a quantum yield of 2, i.e., in that region one destroys two F centers for each absorbed quantum. This suggests the following interpretation: at temperatures above about 140°K (but

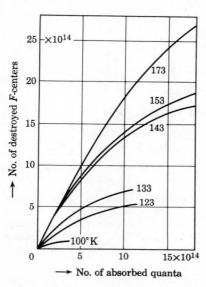

Fig. 15-14. The number of destroyed F centers as function of the total number of absorbed F quanta at various temperatures. [After Markham, ref. 28]

below the temperature above which F' centers become unstable) each absorbed F quantum produces an electron in the conduction band; the free electron wanders about in the crystal and is then trapped by another F center, forming an F' center. Hence an F' center then corresponds to two electrons trapped at a negative ion vacancy. Because the negative ion vacancy is equivalent to a single positive charge, the two electrons are only weakly bound (see Fig. 15-15). More evidence for the correctness of this picture has been obtained from photoconductivity measurements, which will be discussed in the next section. Markham has shown that from Pick's data one can conclude that the capture cross section for an electron in the conduction band to form an F' center is much larger than the cross section to form an F center from a negative ion vacancy.

[27] R. Hilsch and R. W. Pohl, *Z. Physik*, **68**, 721 (1931).

[28] H. Pick, *Ann. Physik*, **31**, 365 (1938); **37**, 421 (1940). The interpretation given here is due to J. J. Markham, *Phys. Rev.*, **88**, 500 (1952).

The rather sudden drop in the quantum yield in the beginning of the irradiation with F light at temperatures below 140°K is explained as follows: an F center corresponds to an electron trapped at a negative ion vacancy, so that for large distances the electron moves in an electric field $-e^2/\epsilon_0 r^2$, where ϵ_0 is the high-frequency dielectric constant.[29] As in a hydrogen atom, there must therefore be a number of excited states below the ionization continuum, i.e., below the conduction band. Mott assumes that the absorption of an F quantum raises the electron from the ground

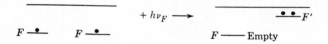

$$F \underline{\bullet} \qquad F \underline{\bullet} \qquad \xrightarrow{+ h\nu_F} \qquad \underline{\bullet\ \bullet}F'$$
$$F \text{----- Empty}$$

Fig. 15-15. Schematic diagram of the reaction $2F \rightarrow F'$. The reaction proceeds only if the temperature is high enough so that absorption of an F photon produces a free electron in the conduction band, which may then be captured by another F center. At the same time the temperature should be low enough for the F' center to be stable.

state to the first excited state, which is close to but not in the conduction band (Fig. 15-11). At temperatures above 140°K the thermal lattice vibrations are intense enough to provide the additional energy required to raise the electron from the excited state into the conduction band, but at low temperatures the probability for the electron to fall back to the ground state takes over. Hence, at low temperatures, absorption of an F quantum does not liberate the electron, leading to the drop in quantum yield of the reaction $2F \rightarrow F'$.

The decrease in quantum yield as the time of irradiation increases is a result of the increase in the number of negative ion vacancies; this increases the probability for an electron in the conduction band to be trapped by a negative ion vacancy.

Another set of interesting data has been obtained by Pick employing an additively colored KCl crystal in which 80 per cent of the F centers had been transformed into F' centers. In such crystals one can study the reverse process viz., the transformation of F' centers into F centers by irradiating with F' light. In Fig. 15-16 we reproduce Markham's representation of Pick's data for the number of F centers formed as function of the number of F' photons absorbed.[28] It is observed that at low temperatures up to about 90°K two F centers are formed per absorbed F' photon, at least in the beginning of the irradiation. This is in agreement with the model of an F' center discussed above: an F' center from which an electron is released is transformed into an F center; the free electron captured by a negative ion vacancy produces the second F center. The drop in the

[29] N. F. Mott, *Proc. Phys. Soc.* (*London*), **50**, 196 (1938).

quantum yield at higher temperatures may be explained by considering the trapping of an electron by a negative ion vacancy as a two-step process: the electron is first captured in the excited state; it may then drop to the ground state or may be released again by absorbing energy from the lattice vibrations. Thus, as the temperature increases, the capture cross section

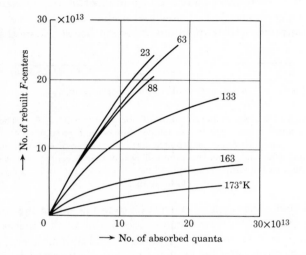

Fig. 15-16. The number of rebuilt F centers as function of the total number of F' quanta absorbed. [After Markham, ref. 28]

for a free electron to form an F center from a negative ion vacancy decreases. The decrease of the quantum yield as the irradiation proceeds is a consequence of the increase in the number of F centers and the decrease in the number of negative ion vacancies.

15-8. Photoconductivity in crystals containing excess metal

We have seen above that absorption of an F photon by an F center produces a free electron if the temperature is not too low. Thus when a crystal containing F centers is irradiated with F light and at the same time an electric field is applied to the crystal, a photocurrent is observed. However, if only the electrons are mobile, a space charge will soon be built up in the crystal, thereby lowering the field and the current. The space charge may be neutralized by electrons entering the crystal from the anode, or by electrolytic conduction in the crystal. If this is not the case, space charge difficulties may be avoided by employing low light intensities for a short period. Before discussing briefly some classical experiments by Pohl's group it may be useful to make some general remarks on the process of photoconductivity, assuming that space charge effects have been avoided.

An electron liberated from, say, an F center, will carry out a random motion in the conduction band. In the presence of an electric field E, it will drift in the direction towards the anode with a velocity

$$v_d = \mu E$$

where μ is the mobility. After a certain time it will be trapped at some lattice imperfection and for the moment it will be assumed that it remains trapped, so that we may associate with the electrons in the conduction band a certain life time τ. The distance over which the electrons drift in the field direction is then

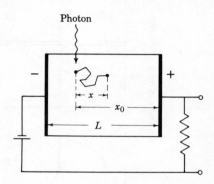

$$x = v_d \tau = \mu E \tau \qquad (15\text{-}8)$$

unless the electron has arrived at the anode before being trapped. Suppose the electron is liberated at a distance x_0 from the anode, and let L be the distance between the electrodes (Fig. 15-17). The charge passing through the external circuit is then ex/L or

Fig. 15-17. Illustrating the displacement x associated with the drift of a photo electron during a lifetime τ in an external electric field.

ex_0/L, depending on whether $x < x_0$ or $x > x_0$. Let N_p represent the number of photons absorbed by the crystal per second, and let η be the probability that an absorbed photon actually produces a free electron. On the assumption that $x < x_0$ for all electrons under consideration, we find by using (15-8) for the current,

$$I = \eta N_p ex/L = \eta N_p E \mu e \tau / L \quad \text{for } x < x_0 \qquad (15\text{-}9)$$

Hence I should be proportional to the field strength E. However, as E is increased, x increases, and x may become larger than x_0. One thus expects that the I versus E curve will saturate for high field strengths. In fact, for a crystal illuminated in a thin slab at a distance x_0 from the anode we shall have

$$I_{\text{max}} = \eta N_p ex_0/L \qquad (15\text{-}10)$$

Similarly, for a uniformly illuminated crystal

$$I_{\text{max}} = \eta N_p e/2 \qquad (15\text{-}10a)$$

It seems that for alkali halides saturation occurs only for crystals that are too thin to be used in photoconductivity experiments. Saturation has been observed, however, in the silver halides, in zinc sulfide, and in diamond.

The above considerations are based on equation (15-8), i.e., on a mean lifetime τ of the liberated electrons. In other words, free electrons that have been trapped are not supposed to contribute any longer to the current unless they are liberated again by absorption of energy. Such currents are called "primary currents." However, suppose that an electron liberated by absorption of a photon from, say, an F center, is ultimately

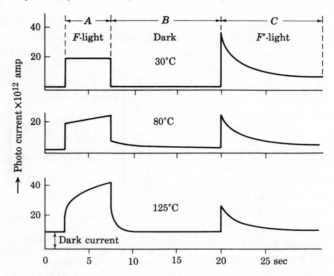

Fig. 15-18. Time dependence of the photocurrent in NaCl containing 8×10^{15} excess Na atoms per cm³, at various temperatures. [After Glaser and Lehfeldt, ref. 30]

trapped by another F center so as to form an F' center. If the temperature is high enough, it may become free again by thermal excitation. Evidently, such processes would increase the effective lifetime; the resulting "excess" current is called a "secondary current." It is obvious that the magnitude of the secondary current will depend strongly on temperature, contrary to the primary current.

As a specific example, we shall briefly discuss some of the classical experiments on the photoconductivity of alkali halides containing F centers resulting from an excess of the metallic constituent. In Fig. 15-18 we have represented the photocurrent observed in a colored NaCl crystal as function of time for different temperatures.[30] During the interval A the crystal is irradiated with light in the F band. Then follows a dark interval (B) and finally the crystal is irradiated with light in the F' band (C). At temperatures below 30°C one observes a constant current during the

[30] G. Glaser and W. Lehfeldt, *Nachr. Akad. Wiss. Göttingen*, **2**, 91 (1936); see also R. W. Pohl, *Physik. Z.*, **39**, 36 (1938).

interval A. This is a true primary current for which relation (15-9) holds. Thus the quantity $\eta x/E$ should be independent of the field strength, in agreement with the experiments. From what has been said in the preceding section one expects F' centers to be formed during the irradiation with F light. That this is indeed the case may be seen from the intervals C, which also indicate a larger production of F' centers at lower temperatures,

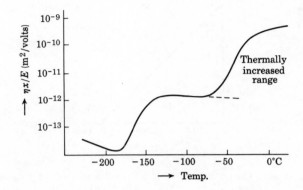

Fig. 15-19. The quantity $\eta x/E$ as function of temperature for a KCl crystal containing 2.7×10^{16} F centers per cm³. [After Pohl, ref. 30]

as expected. The increase in the current during interval A at higher temperatures is a result of the thermal liberation of electrons from F' centers; this effect produces the secondary current mentioned above. For the same reason there is still some current flow at higher temperatures during the dark interval B.

The existence of an excited state of an F center close to the conduction band (see preceding section) is confirmed by Fig. 15-19 where the quantity

$$\eta x/E = IL/N_p eE \qquad (15\text{-}11)$$

has been plotted as function of temperature for a KCl crystal containing F centers. The sharp drop below $-140°C$ is a result of a drop in the quantum efficiency η for liberation of an electron from an F center. The increase in the effective displacement above room temperature is a consequence of thermal excitation of electrons from F' centers. The region below $-180°C$ probably corresponds to photoelectrons liberated from colloidal sodium particles.

Another result of great interest which confirms the conclusions of the preceding section is represented in Fig. 15-20 where x/E for KCl has been plotted as function of the density of F centers n_F for a fixed temperature of $-100°C$. At this temperature, η may be taken equal to unity. We note that the slope of the line in this double logarithmic plot is 45°, showing that for the region of F center densities involved, x is inversely proportional to n_F. From (15-8) it thus follows that the mean free path for capture of an electron is proportional to n_F^{-1}, indicating again that F centers are efficient

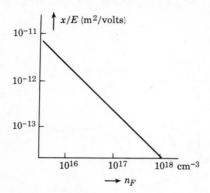

Fig. 15-20.   The quantity x/E for KCl as function of the F center density n_F at $-100°C$. [After Pohl, ref. 30]

traps for free electrons. We leave it to the reader to show that from Fig. 15-20 one may estimate a capture cross section of about 10^{-14}–10^{-15} cm^2.

15-9. The photoelectric effect in alkali halides

Although the photoelectric effect of insulators has not been studied very thoroughly, some recent experiments by Apker and Taft[31] on alkali halides show that such investigations can provide useful information about the behavior of imperfections in crystals. As in the study of this effect from metals, one can measure the number of photoelectrons emitted per incident quantum as function of the frequency of the light employed, and the energy distribution of the emitted electrons. In pure alkali halides, the energy required to produce a free electron in the conduction band is of the order of 8 ev, and in order to observe the photoelectric effect, photons of an energy of this order of magnitude are required. On the other hand, if F centers are present in the crystal, i.e., electrons trapped in levels about 2 ev below the conduction band, one expects an appreciably lower threshold frequency. That this is indeed the case may be seen from Fig. 15-21, representing the photoelectric yield in electrons per quantum for potassium iodide containing F centers. For $h\nu \simeq 2.3$ ev, about 10^{-8}

[31] For a review of this work see the article by Apker and Taft in W. Shockley (ed.), *Imperfections in Nearly Perfect Crystals*, Wiley, New York, 1952, p. 246.

electron is emitted per incident quantum, but the curve rises rapidly to a plateau with a yield of 10^{-4}. The sample contained about 10^{19} F centers per cm³ produced by electron bombardment. The rise beyond the plateau is interpreted as follows. The first fundamental absorption peak of KI occurs at $h\nu = 5.66$ ev at room temperature. Thus photons of 5 ev

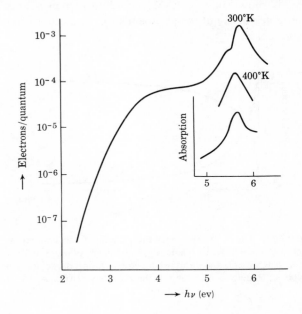

Fig. 15-21. Spectral distribution of the photoelectric yield in electrons per quantum for KI containing F centers. In the inset the fundamental optical absorption of KI at 293°K is given for comparison. [After Apker and Taft, ref. 33]

correspond to irradiation in the tail of this band and therefore produce excitons in the crystal. The excitons may diffuse through the crystal as mentioned in Sec. 15-3 and may give up their energy to an F center, thereby giving rise to an electron in the conduction band of several ev. From Fig. 15-21 we see that this process of ionization via excitons increases the yield by a factor of 20. This reasoning is confirmed by the fact that the shape of the peak in Fig. 15-21 is the same as that of the first fundamental absorption band. The Apker-Taft experiment constitutes the most direct experimental evidence for the motion of excitons. For a quantitative treatment of these results, we refer the reader to a paper by Hebb.[32]

It has also been observed that excitons may interact with negative ion vacancies in such a manner than an F center and presumably a free hole

[32] M. H. Hebb, *Phys. Rev.*, **81**, 702 (1951).

are formed. Thus, when a crystal which initially contains no color centers is irradiated with light in the first fundamental absorption band, the excitons produce F centers which may thereupon be ionized by other excitons. One thus expects a build up of the F-center concentration as function of time, and associated with this, an increase in the photoemission current. This is shown in Fig. 15-22 according to Apker and Taft.[33] In the same figure, the decay of the photoemission resulting from heating the crystal is represented.

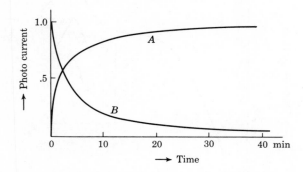

Fig. 15-22. Curve A represents the growth of the photocurrent (arbitrary units) in KI by irradiating with 5.66 ev photons at 300°K. Curve B represents the decay obtained by raising the temperature to 400°K, leading to bleaching of the F centers. [After Apker and Taft, ref. 33]

15-10. Coagulation of F centers and colloids

When a crystal containing F centers is irradiated with F light at room temperature, a number of bands on the long-wavelength side of the F band appear. It is believed that the negative ion vacancies produced by the ionization of the F centers join with positive ion vacancies, forming pairs. These pairs are highly mobile (see Sec. 7-5) and thus provide a vehicle for the transport of negative ion vacancies. The observed absorption bands are probably due to aggregates of F centers and vacancies. The first products of this type of coagulation are the so-called R_1 and R_2 bands and the M band (see Fig. 15-24).

Related to the coagulation mentioned above is the formation of colloidal particles of metal in the crystals. We have seen in Sec. 15-6 that when an alkali halide is heated in the metal vapor at, say, 600°C and then quenched, F centers are observed. However, if the crystals are cooled slowly, or when a quenched crystal is heated at higher temperatures (say above 250°C), the atomically dispersed F centers condense in the form of

[33] L. Apker and E. Taft, *Phys. Rev.*, **79**, 964 (1950).

colloidal particles. At high temperatures the colloids are again transformed into F centers. In other words, there exists an equilibrium between the colloidal particles and the F centers. For details on this topic, see F. Seitz, *Revs. Mod. Phys.*, **18**, 384 (1946); **26**, 7 (1954).

15-11. The Hall effect and electron mobility

The Hall effect of NaCl containing excess sodium has recently been measured by Redfield, using a technique which is particularly suitable for relatively high resistivity materials.[34] The electron mobility measured at 82°K is 260 ± 30 cm²/volt sec; at 200°K he finds 40 ± 20 in the same units. According to MacDonald, the electron mobility at room temperature in NaCl is equal to 12.5 cm²/volt sec.[35] It may be noted here that a theoretical calculation of the electron mobility in ionic crystals has been carried out recently by Low and Pines.[36] Earlier calculations of the mobility of electrons were made by Fröhlich and Mott.[37]

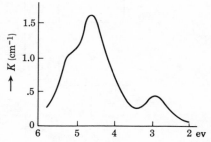

Fig. 15-23. The V bands observed by Mollwo in KBr containing excess bromine. The main peak is designated as the V_2 band, and the unresolved peak on the left as the V_3 band.

15-12. Color centers resulting from excess halogen

In the preceding sections we have been mainly concerned with the electronic properties associated with excess metal. In some cases, however, it is also possible to obtain an excess of halogen in alkali halides. For example, heat treatment of KI in iodine vapor results in new absorption bands in the ultraviolet, as shown by Mollwo.[38] Similar bands observed by Mollwo for KBr when heated in Br_2 vapor are represented in Fig. 15-23. Color centers of this type are referred to as V centers, and the reason for their presence may be understood on the basis of a picture analogous to that used for F centers.

The excess bromine is presumably incorporated in the lattice in the form of negative ions, occupying normal lattice sites. Thus the introduction of each extra bromine atom leads to the formation of a positive

[34] A. Redfield, *Phys. Rev.*, **91**, 244, 753 (1953).
[35] J. R. MacDonald, *Phys. Rev.*, **92**, 4 (1953).
[36] F. E. Low and D. Pines, *Phys. Rev.*, **91**, 193 (1953).
[37] H. Fröhlich, *Proc. Roy. Soc. (London)*, **A160**, 230 (1937); H. Fröhlich and N. F. Mott, *Proc. Roy. Soc. (London)*, **171**, 496 (1939); see also F. Seitz, *Phys. Rev.*, **76**, 1376 (1949).
[38] E. Mollwo, *Ann. Physik*, **5**, 394 (1937).

hole. These holes are most likely to be found near a positive ion vacancy where they can be trapped. The optical absorption associated with a trapped hole may be, for example, the transition of an electron from the filled band into the hole. A hole trapped at a positive ion vacancy is called a V_1 center. There is good evidence to believe, however, that the dominant peak observed by Mollwo is not of this simple type. The reason for this is the following. According to Mollwo's experiments the saturation density

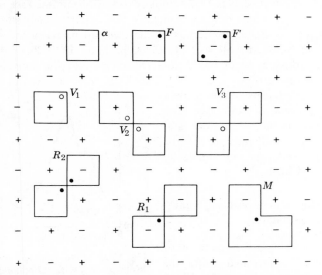

Fig. 15-24. Models for a number of color centers. The squares indicate ion vacancies, the dots electrons, and the open circles holes.

of color centers for a given temperature is proportional to the number of Br_2 molecules in the vapor. According to the law of mass action, each molecule absorbed from the vapor must therefore give rise to one color center in the crystal. Seitz has therefore suggested that the centers corresponding to the main peak are of a molecular type, i.e., two holes are trapped by a pair of positive ion vacancies, as shown in Fig. 15-24. These centers are called V_2 centers. The details of the properties of V centers are at present not so well understood as the corresponding ones for F centers. For a review of the present situation we refer the reader to F. Seitz, *Revs. Mod. Phys.*, **26**, 7 (1954).

15-13. Color centers produced by irradiation with X-rays

When an X-ray quantum passes through an ionic crystal it will usually give rise to a fast photoelectron with an energy of the same order as that of the incident quantum. Such electrons, because of their small mass, do not have sufficient momentum to displace ions and therefore lose their energy by producing free electrons and holes, excitons, and phonons. It is evident that this will give rise to trapped electrons as well as trapped holes. Hence, color centers of both the F type and V type are formed. In contrast with the additively colored crystals, the color centers in X-ray irradiated crystals are not permanent. They can be bleached by irradiation with light or by heating, because ultimately the excited electrons and holes will recombine. Without going into details, it will be evident that studies of the coloration, photoconductivity, and bleaching at various temperatures provide information about the pro- perties of the color centers and their interaction. As an example, we give in Fig. 15-25 the absorption spectrum induced in KCl by irradiation with X-rays at 20°C.[39]

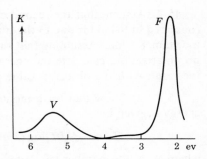

Fig. 15-25. The F and V bands pro- duced in KCl by irradiation with X-rays at room temperature. [After Dorendorf and Pick, ref. 39]

It is of interest to note that measure- ments of the change in density of alkali halides during X-ray irradiation show that the lattice starts to expand as soon as the irradiation begins. It thus seems that during the irradiation vacancies are formed.[40] Eventually the expansion saturates, a typical value being 5×10^{-5} cm for a crystal with dimensions of 1 cm. At present the interpretation of the production of vacancies upon X-ray irradiation is still rather speculative, although it seems very likely that dislocations play an important role in the process.[41]

REFERENCES

J. H. de Boer, *Electron Emission and Adsorption Phenomena*, Cambridge, London, 1935.

N. F. Mott and R. W. Gurney, *Electronic Processes in Ionic Crystals*, Oxford, New York, 1940.

R. W. Pohl, *Proc. Phys. Soc. (London)*, **49** (extra part), 3 (1937); *Physik. Z.*, **39**, 36 (1938).

F. Seitz, *Revs. Mod. Phys.*, **18**, 384 (1946); **26**, 7 (1954). (These papers constitute the most extensive review of the properties of alkali halides.)

[39] H. Dorendorf and H. Pick, *Z. Physik*, **128**, 106 (1950).
[40] K. Sakaguchi and T. Suita, *Technol. Repts. Osaka Univ.*, **2**, 177 (1952).
[41] See J. J. Markham, *Phys. Rev.*, **88**, 500 (1952); also, F. Seitz, *Revs. Mod. Phys.*, **26**, 7 (1954).

PROBLEMS

15-1. Assume that the first characteristic absorption peak for KCl (observed at 7.6 ev) is due to the transfer of an electron from a Cl^- ion to a neighboring K^+ ion. Calculate the energy required for this process on the assumption that the positions of the nuclei remain fixed and that there is no polarization. Compare the answer with the observed value, and from this calculate the polarization energy.

15-2. Assume that the second characteristic absorption peak for KCl (observed at 9.4 ev) is due to the transfer of an electron from a Cl^- ion to a distant K^+ ion. Assuming that the nuclei remain fixed and that there is no polarization, calculate the energy required for the transfer. Compare the result with the observed value and calculate the polarization energy.

15-3. (a) Show that for a monatomic gas at a temperature T the free energy is given by

$$F = -N_v kT[\log (2\pi mkT/h^2)^{3/2} + 1 - \log n_v]$$

where n_v is the number of atoms per unit volume and N_v is the total number of atoms in the system; m is the mass per atom.

(b) What is the configurational entropy of an alkali halide crystal containing N ion pairs and n_F F centers, relative to the crystal without F centers?

(c) Consider an alkali halide crystal containing N ion pairs in equilibrium with the vapor of the alkali metal at a temperature T. The vapor contains n_v atoms per cm³; the crystal contains n_F F centers per cm³. Set up an expression for the change in the free energy ΔF of the system crystal plus vapor if one atom is transferred from the vapor to the crystal; neglect thermal entropy changes. Show that because $\Delta F = 0$ in equilibrium,

$$n_F \simeq Nn_v \left(\frac{2\pi mkT}{h^2}\right)^{-3/2} e^{-\phi/kT} \quad \text{for} \quad n_F \ll N$$

where ϕ is the energy required to take an atom from the metal vapor into the crystal, thereby forming an F center. Compare the result with equation (15-7).

15-4. Calculate the paramagnetic susceptibility of KCl at room temperature containing 5×10^{17} F centers per cm³ and compare this with the diamagnetic susceptibility. Do the same for liquid air and for liquid helium temperatures.

15-5. From the data given in Fig. 15-20, estimate the cross section for capture of an electron by an F center and compare the result with that stated at the end of Sec. 15-8.

15-6. Assuming that the thermal ionization energy of an F center is 0.94 ev, estimate the electronic conductivity of a sodium chloride crystal containing 10^{17} F centers per cm³ at room temperature; for mobility data see Sec. 15-11.

15-7. Discuss the derivation of Smakula's formula (15-6). See for example F. Seitz, *The Modern Theory of Solids*, McGraw-Hill, New York, 1940, p. 661.

Chapter 16

LUMINESCENCE

16-1. General remarks

When a substance absorbs energy in some form or other, a fraction of the absorbed energy may be re-emitted in the form of electromagnetic radiation in the visible or near-visible region of the spectrum. This phenomenon is called luminescence, with the understanding that this term does not include the emission of black-body radiation, which obeys the laws of Kirchhoff and Wien. Luminescent solids are usually referred to as phosphors.

Luminescence is a process which involves at least two steps: the excitation of the electronic system of the solid and the subsequent emission of photons. These steps may or may not be separated by intermediate processes. This will be further discussed in the next sections. Excitation may be achieved by bombardment with photons (photoluminescence), with electrons (cathodoluminescence), or with other particles. Luminescence can also be induced as the result of a chemical reaction (chemiluminescence) or by the application of an electric field (electroluminescence).

When one speaks of fluorescence, one usually has in mind the emission of light during excitation; the emission of light after the excitation has ceased is then referred to as phosphorescence or afterglow. These definitions are not very exact since strictly speaking there is always a time lag between a particular excitation and the corresponding emission of a photon, even in a free atom. In fact, the lifetime of an atom in an excited state for which the return to the ground state is accompanied by dipole radiation is $\sim 10^{-8}$ second. For forbidden transitions, involving quadrupole or higher-order radiation, the lifetimes may be 10^{-4} second or longer. One frequently takes the decay time of $\sim 10^{-8}$ second as the demarcation line between fluorescence and phosphorescence.[1] Some authors define fluorescence as the emission of light for which the decay time is temperature-independent, and phosphorescence as the temperature-dependent part.[2] In many cases the latter definition is equivalent to the former, but there are exceptions.

[1] See, for example, G. F. J. Garlick, *Luminescent Materials*, Oxford, New York, 1949, p. 1.

[2] See, for example, F. A. Kröger, *Some Aspects of the Luminescence of Solids*, Elsevier, New York, 1948, p. 36.

One of the most important conclusions reached already in the early studies of luminescence, is that frequently the ability of a material to exhibit luminescence is associated with the presence of "activators." These activators may be impurity atoms occurring in relatively small concentrations in the host material, or a small stoichiometric excess of one of the constituents of the material. In the latter case one speaks of self-activation. The presence of a certain type of impurity may also inhibit the luminescence of other centers, in which case the former are referred to as "killers." Since small amounts of impurities may play such an important role in determining the luminescent properties of solids, studies aimed at a better understanding of the mechanism of luminescence must be carried out with materials prepared under carefully controlled conditions. A great deal of progress has been made in this respect during the last two decades.

A number of important groups of luminescent crystalline solids may be mentioned here.

(i) Compounds which luminesce in the "pure" state. According to Randall, such compounds should contain one ion or ion group per unit cell with an incompletely filled shell of electrons which is well screened from its surroundings.[3] Examples are probably the manganous halides, samarium and gadolinium sulfate, molybdates, and platinocyanides.

(ii) The alkali halides activated with thallium or other heavy metals.

(iii) ZnS and CdS activated with Cu, Ag, Au, Mn, or with an excess of one of their constituents (self-activation).

(iv) The silicate phosphors, such as zinc orthosilicate (willemite, Zn_2SiO_4) activated with divalent maganese, which is used as oscilloscope screens.

(v) Oxide phosphors, such as self-activated ZnO and Al_2O_3 activated with transition metals.

(vi) Organic crystals, such as anthracene activated with naphtacene; these materials are often used as scintillation counters.

16-2. Excitation and emission

Before discussing the properties of specific luminescent materials, it is perhaps useful to consider first some simple models which, at least in principle, could give rise to luminescence. This will be done in the present section and the next; the results may then be used as a guide in the interpretation of the mechanism of luminescence in specific cases. For

[3] J. T. Randall, *Trans. Faraday Soc.*, **35**, 2 (1939); *Proc. Roy. Soc.* (*London*), **A170**, 272 (1939).

the moment let us assume that the luminescence is associated with the presence of activator atoms. The incorporation of an activator atom in a crystalline solid will in general give rise to localized energy levels in the normally forbidden energy gaps. These localized levels may be classified into two categories: (i) levels which belong to the activator atoms themselves and (ii) levels belonging to host atoms which are under the perturbing influence of the activators. The levels of group (ii) may be associated with host atoms in the immediate vicinity of the impurity atoms, but they may also be associated with lattice defects (e.g., vacancies) whose existence is tied up with the incorporation of the activator. For example, if Mn^{4+} ions were incorporated on sites normally occupied by Zn^{2+} in a ZnS lattice, there may be localized levels associated with the Mn^{4+} ion, levels associated with the S^{2-} and Zn^{2+} ions in the vicinity of the Mn^{4+} ion, and levels associated with ions in the vicinity of a positive ion vacancy (produced as a result of the presence of the Mn^{4+} ion to compensate for the excess positive charge).

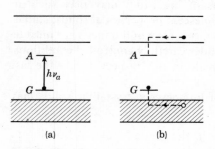

Fig. 16-1. The ground state G and an excited state A of a luminescence center. In (a) excitation takes place by direct absorption of a photon $h\nu_a$. In (b) excitation is achieved by capture of a hole at G and of an electron at A.

In terms of the energy band picture of Fig. 16-1 let G and A be two levels corresponding to one of the categories (i) and (ii) mentioned above. In the ground state, level G is occupied by an electron and A is empty; in the excited state the reverse is true. The excitation from G to A may be accomplished in at least three ways:

(a) It is possible that an incident photon of the proper frequency is absorbed directly by the electron in level G, whereupon it arrives in A (see Fig. 16-1a). As a result of lattice vibrations the absorption will correspond to a band centering about a certain frequency ν_a.

(b) The excitation process may also involve the diffusion of an exciton (see Sec. 15-3). Suppose, for example, that in some part of the crystal an exciton is produced; since the exciton may diffuse about in the crystal, it may reach a center such as AG, whereupon it may give off its energy to the center, resulting in excitation of the electron. This consideration is of importance, since it provides a mechanism whereby energy can be transferred from the exciting source to the impurities via the host crystal. In other words, the exciton mechanism makes it possible for the activators to receive more energy than they ought to on the basis of their relative concentration in the lattice.

(c) The excitation process may also involve the motion of free electrons and holes. For example, let electron-hole pairs be created somewhere in the crystal, as for example, by bombardment with photons or electrons. If the center AG is in its ground state, the level G may capture a hole from the valence band and A may trap an electron from the conduction band. In this way, excitation of the center has been achieved, as indicated in (Fig. 16-1b). Evidently this type of excitation process should be associated with conductivity, in contrast with processes (a) and (b).

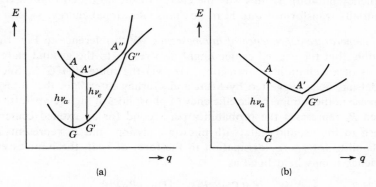

Fig. 16-2. Energy of the ground state G and of an excited state A as function of a configurational coordinate q. The situation (a) gives luminescence; (b) corresponds to dissipation in the form of heat.

The Franck-Condon principle. From the simple energy level diagram of Fig. 16-1 one might get the impression that the return of the electron from the excited state A to the ground state G should be accompanied by emission of a photon of a frequency equal to the absorption frequency. This is not the case, since the Franck-Condon principle must be taken into account, as discussed in Sec. 15-1. In Fig. 16-2 we have represented the levels A and G as function of a configurational coordinate q; each value of q corresponds to a particular configuration of the nuclei in the vicinity of the luminescence center. During the optical excitation from G to A the nuclei remain essentially at rest, leading to an absorption energy $h\nu_a$. After the absorption act the nuclei do not occupy the equilibrium position proper for the excited state, and the system will move gradually to the minimum of the A curve, with emission of phonons. This process is possible since the lifetime of the excited state is $\sim 10^{-8}$ second, as compared with periods of the order of 10^{-13} second associated with lattice vibrations. The emission act itself, like the absorption act, takes place vertically in Fig. 16-2a, so that $\nu_e < \nu_a$. Thus luminescence centers are in general transparent, or nearly so, with respect to their own emission bands.

Radiationless transitions. An excited center in a crystal can return to the ground state either with or without the emission of a photon. A model corresponding to the former case is the one represented in Fig. 16-2a. For nonluminescent materials Seitz has suggested a model in which the return to the ground state of an excited center can take place by means of a radiationless transition.[4] Thus in Fig. 16-2b the system may move after the absorption act from A to A' and then cross the narrow gap to point G' associated with the ground state (perhaps with emission of a low-frequency photon). In this way the energy of the absorbed photon GA is essentially transformed into heat, i.e., into vibrational energy.

Temperature-dependence of luminescence. With reference to Fig. 16-2a we note that the excited center might also return to the ground state by means of a radiationless transition, viz., via the route $A'A''G''G$. Such a model has been suggested by Mott and Gurney to explain the observed decrease in the luminescence efficiency of phosphors at high temperatures.[5] When P_e represents the probability per second for an excited center to return to the ground state with photon emission, and P_h represents the probability for energy dissipation in the form of heat, the luminescence efficiency η may be defined as

$$\eta = P_e/(P_e + P_h) = [1 + (P_h/P_e)]^{-1} \qquad (16\text{-}1)$$

Since it seems reasonable to assume that P_e is nearly temperature-independent, P_h must be mainly responsible for the temperature effect. For a model such as in Fig. 16-2a the probability P_h is determined by the probability to find the excited state in a vibrational level corresponding to A'' or higher; one may then write $P_h = \nu \exp(-\epsilon/kT)$ where ϵ is the energy difference between A'' and A', and ν is a frequency. Thus for this model P_h increases as T increases and the efficiency decreases. A detailed account of the temperature-dependence of luminescence may be found in F. A. Kröger, *op. cit.*

16-3. Decay mechanisms

One of the aims of studies of luminescent materials is the identification of the luminescence centers and their energy levels. A good deal of information for this purpose can be obtained from the decay characteristics, and it is therefore useful to consider some simple decay mechanisms for further reference.

Temperature-independent exponential decay. A model of luminescence centers exhibiting a temperature-independent exponential decay of the

[4] F. Seitz, *Trans. Faraday Soc.*, **35**, 74 (1939).
[5] N. F. Mott and R. W. Gurney, *Electronic Processes in Ionic Crystals*, 2d ed., Oxford, New York, 1948, p. 221.

intensity of luminescence after excitation has ceased can readily be set up. Let the instant at which the exciting source is removed be denoted by $t = 0$. Suppose at any instant t the number of electrons in excited states such as A in Fig. 16-1 is given by $n(t)$. Let us assume that the probability for an electron in A to return to the ground state G is $1/\tau$ per second, and that such a transition is associated with the emission of a photon. If the center is well screened from its environment, the average lifetime τ of the excited state is independent of temperature and of the number of other excited centers. Hence the intensity of luminescence $I(t)$, i.e., the number of photons emitted per unit time, is given by

$$I(t) = -(dn/dt) = n/\tau \qquad (16\text{-}2)$$

This leads to $n(t) = n_0 \exp(-t/\tau)$ and to

$$I(t) = (n_0/\tau)e^{-t/\tau} = I_0 e^{-t/\tau} \qquad (16\text{-}3)$$

where I_0 is the intensity at $t = 0$. If the transition from A to G is associated with dipole radiation, $\tau \simeq 10^{-8}$ second.

In some cases, e.g., in ammonium uranyl phosphate and in uranyl nitrate, τ may be of the order of milliseconds; one then presumably deals with quadrupole or higher-order radiation.[6]

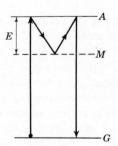

Fig. 16-3. Schematic representation of a center with a metastable level M.

(ii) *Temperature-dependent exponential decay.* In certain phosphors, e.g., in the thallium-activated alkali halides, one observes exponential decays of the form (16-3) but with τ of the order of several minutes; furthermore, τ decreases exponentially with increasing temperature. A model of a luminescence center which exhibits such properties involves the existence of a "metastable" state, as illustrated schematically in Fig. 16-3. The physical nature of such states will be further explained in the next section. Suppose that the excitation act involves a transition of an electron from G to A and that from A it may either return to G with emission of a photon or it may fall into the metastable state M. We shall assume that the direct transition from M to G is forbidden. When the exciting source is removed at the instant $t = 0$, a certain number of electrons n_0 will reside in the metastable M levels. These electrons can presumably return to the ground state only via level A. If the energy difference between M and A is equal to E, the probability per unit time for an electron in M to be excited into A will be given by an expression of the type

$$1/\tau = (1/\tau_0)e^{-E/kT} \qquad (16\text{-}4)$$

[6] J. T. Randall and M. H. F. Wilkins, *Proc. Roy. Soc.* (*London*), **A184**, 379 (1945).

where $1/\tau_0$ represents a frequency. Let us assume that once an electron has arrived in a level such as A, the probability of returning to the ground state G with emission of a photon is much larger than the probability of falling back into M. Under these circumstances the intensity of the luminescence at any instant is simply determined by the rate at which transitions from M to A take place. Hence (16-2) and (16-3) are still valid, but since τ depends on T in accordance with (16-4), one obtains

$$I(t) = (n_0/\tau_0)e^{-E/kT} \exp\left[-(t/\tau_0)e^{-E/kT}\right] \qquad (16\text{-}5)$$

If the temperature is low, the intensity will be low; at high temperatures the electrons in M levels may be "boiled off" at a high rate.

(iii) *Power-law decay.* The simplest model leading to a power-law decay is the following: suppose that upon excitation of a particular type of luminescence center the electron is released into the conduction band. Let us further assume that the emission of a photon requires the recombination of a free electron and an empty center. If there are n free electrons and n empty centers, the intensity would be given by an expression of the type

$$I(t) = -(dn/dt) = \alpha n^2 \qquad (16\text{-}6)$$

Such a process is called bimolecular, in contrast with a monomolecular process described by an equation of type (16-1). From (16-6) one finds

$$n(t) = n_0/(n_0\alpha t + 1) \quad \text{and} \quad I(t) = \alpha n_0^2/(n_0\alpha t + 1)^2 \qquad (16\text{-}7)$$

For large values of t, the intensity decays as t^{-2}. Several variations of this mechanism may be found in the literature involving trapping of the released electrons. It is evident that the same equations hold if holes are released in the valence band. Other power-law decays may be obtained by superposition of processes of type (ii). For example, let the metastable levels M in (ii) be distributed in energy such that after the excitation is removed the number of occupied M levels with activation energies in the range dE is given by $n_0(E)\,dE$. One then obtains for the intensity of the luminescence instead of (16-5),

$$I(t) = \int_0^\infty [n_0(E)/\tau_0]e^{-E/kT} \exp\left[-(t/\tau_0)e^{-E/kT}\right] dE \qquad (16\text{-}8)$$

If one now assumes that τ_0 is essentially independent of E and that $n_0(E)$ is given by an exponential distribution $C\exp(-\beta E)$, it is shown in Problem 16-11 that for large t,

$$I(t) = \text{const.}/t^{(\beta kT + 1)} \qquad (16\text{-}9)$$

Thus power-law decay does not exclude the occurrence of exponential decay of individual components.

Thermoluminescence and glow curves. Let us again consider luminescence centers involving a metastable state M as discussed under (ii) above. For simplicity we shall assume a single level M of an activation energy E below level A in Fig. 16-3. Suppose that the centers are excited at a low temperature T_0 such that the rate of decay at T_0 is very small. Let the crystal now be warmed up at a uniform rate $dT/dt = \theta$. Qualitatively one expects the following behavior of the intensity of the luminescence as function of time. As long as the temperature is low such that $kT \ll E$, the intensity will remain low; when $kT \simeq E$, the intensity should become high, and finally it should drop as a result of the depletion of the M levels. Thus $I(t)$ is expected to have a bell shape in the vicinity of $kT \simeq E$. If there are several discrete M levels of different E values, one will presumably obtain a superposition of such curves. The emission of light resulting from heating after excitation is referred to as thermoluminescence. A curve of I versus t resulting from a uniform rate of heating is called a glow curve; in studies of luminescence such glow curves are often used, since they provide information about the energy of the metastable levels involved as well as about the occupation of such levels at $t = 0$.

For centers with a single metastable level M located in the energy-level scheme of Fig. 16-3 below A by an amount E, the glow curve is governed by the following equations:

$$I = -(dn/dt) = (n/\tau_0)e^{-E/kT}$$

Since $dt = dT/\theta$, this leads to

$$\log\left(\frac{n}{n_0}\right) = -\frac{1}{\theta\tau_0}\int_{T_0}^{T} e^{-E/kT}\, dT \qquad (16\text{-}10)$$

Since the temperature T_0 has been chosen such that $kT_0 \ll E$, the lower limit of integration may be replaced by zero. One thus obtains

$$I = (n_0/\tau_0)e^{-E/kT} \exp\left[-(1/\theta\tau_0)\int_0^T e^{-E/kT}\, dT\right] \qquad (16\text{-}11)$$

where we have assumed throughout that E and τ_0 are independent of T. For further details we refer to Randall and Wilkins,[6] and to Garlick and Gibson.[7] It can be shown that the temperature at which maximum emission occurs is approximately proportional to the energy E. Also, the area under the curve is a measure for the number of electrons occupying the metastable levels at $t = 0$. An example of an experimental glow curve may be found in Fig. 16-5.

[7] G. F. J. Garlick and A. F. Gibson, *Proc. Phys. Soc. (London)*, **A60**, 574 (1948).

16-4. Thallium-activated alkali halides

When "pure" alkali halides are irradiated with X-rays one observes in the dark a faint luminescence. The decay of the phosphorescence may be followed with sensitive equipment for several hours and has been studied by a number of investigators.[8] The interpretation of these experiments is somewhat difficult in view of the possible role played by small amounts of unknown impurities. On the other hand, alkali halides activated with thallium frequently exhibit high efficiencies for luminescence; studies of these materials have provided a fairly detailed understanding of their luminescent properties. Although it is impossible to enter into a detailed discussion of this subject here, some of the most important features may be mentioned, in particular those of KCl:Tl (we shall adopt this notation to indicate the host crystal and the activator).

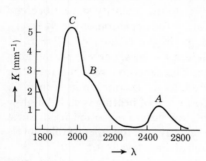

Fig. 16-4. Optical absorption spectrum of KCl containing 2×10^{-3} atomic percent Tl^+. [After P. D. Johnson and F. E. Williams, ref. 14]

The absorption spectra. The absorption spectra of the alkali halides without additives have been discussed in Chapter 15. When a small amount of thallous halide is added to the melt of an alkali halide, mixed crystals can be obtained with the usual growing techniques. Since the Tl^+ ion is fairly large (its radius is $\sim$1.5 Å as compared with 1.3 Å for K^+, for example), it seems reasonable to expect that the Tl^+ ions occupy positions normally occupied by the alkali ions rather than interstitial positions. Measurements of the lattice constant of these mixed crystals by X-ray diffraction methods seem to indicate that this is indeed the case.[9] The incorporation of the Tl^+ ions leads to new absorption bands, as illustrated in Fig. 16-4 for KCl:Tl, the Tl^+ ions being present in an atomic concentration of 2×10^{-3} per cent. Other thallium activated alkali halides give similar spectra, i.e., they all show two strong peaks indicated by A and C in Fig. 16-4 and a weak one, B. The rising part of the absorption curve at the extreme left of Fig. 16-4 marks the onset of the first characteristic absorption band of KCl. The positions of the peaks are roughly the

[8] M. L. Katz, *Phys. Z. Sowjetunion*, **12**, 273 (1937); H. N. Bose, *Indian J. Phys.*, **29**, 29 (1947); C. A. Boyd, *J. Chem. Phys.*, **17**, 1221 (1949); A. H. Morrish and A. J. Dekker, *Phys. Rev.*, **80**, 1030 (1950); G. W. Williams, S. R. Usiskin, and A. J. Dekker, *Phys. Rev.*, **92**, 1398 (1953).

[9] O. Stasiw and E. Saur, *Verhandl. deut. physik. Ges* , **19**, 4 (1938).

same in all alkali halide host crystals, the maximum shift being 1 ev.[10]
For KCl:Tl the bands measured at room temperature occur at the
following energies and wavelengths.

	A	B	C
E (ev).........	4.9	5.9	6.3
λ (Å)	2470	2060	1960
Transition...	$^1S_0 \to {}^3P_1$	—	$^1S_0 \to {}^1P_1$

The transitions associated with A and C have also been indicated. It is of
interest to note that similar bands are observed in solutions containing
Tl⁺ ions as well as in the thallous halides. This indicates that the transitions

occur in the Tl⁺ ions and that the
ions are fairly well screened from
their surroundings in this respect.
Seitz was the first to attempt an
interpretation of the luminescent
properties of these materials on the
basis of electronic transitions taking
place within the Tl⁺ ions.[11]	More
recently, Williams *et al.* have contributed a great deal to the understanding of many details of this
process.[12]	From a computation of
the radial charge density of the free
Tl⁺ ion in the ground state $^1S_0$ and
in the excited state $^3P_1$, Williams

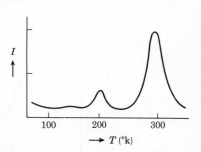

Fig. 16-5. Thermoluminescence curve
of KCl containing 0.05 atomic percent
Tl⁺. [After Johnson and Williams,
ref. 14]

found that the outer electron shell is quite localized in both cases; this
indicates that even in the excited state the ionic picture may be a good
approximation.[13] According to calculations by Johnson and Williams, the
ground state $^1S_0$ of the Tl⁺ ion in KCl lies approximately at the top of
the filled band.[14] Since the bottom of the conduction band in KCl lies
approximately 9.4 ev above the top of the valence band, the excited states
$^3P_1$ and $^1P_1$ lie several ev below the conduction band, i.e., the excited
electron is strongly bound to the activator atom.

Emission spectra. The two principal emission bands of KCl:Tl center
around 3050 Å and 4750 Å. The former has been identified with the
transition $^3P_1 \to {}^1S_0$; the 4750 emission is due to $^1P_1 \to {}^1S_0$. An example
of a glow curve obtained by Johnson and Williams is given in Fig. 16-5.[14]

[10] For a summary of data, see, for example, G. F. J. Garlick, *op. cit.*, p. 50.

[11] F. Seitz, *J. Chem. Phys.*, **6**, 150 (1938).

[12] For a brief review and references to this work see F. E. Williams, "Solid State
Luminescence," *Advances in Electronics*, **5**, 137 (1953).

[13] F. E. Williams, *J. Chem. Phys.*, **19**, 457 (1951).

[14] P. D. Johnson and F. E. Williams, *J. Chem. Phys.*, **21**, 125 (1953).

From the two peaks they conclude the existence of two metastable levels with activation energies of 0.35 ev and 0.72 ev; these must probably be ascribed to the $^3P_0$ and $^3P_2$ states. From these and other detailed studies Johnson and Williams suggest the energy diagram as function of the radial

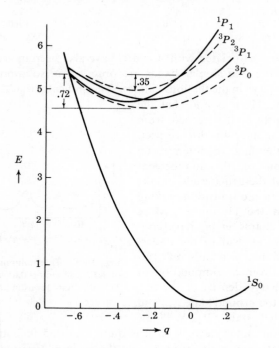

Fig. 16-6. Energy as function of configurational coordinate for the ground state ($^1S_0$), the emitting states ($^1P_1$ and $^3P_1$) and the metastable states ($^3P_2$ and $^3P_0$) of KCl:Tl. The configurational coordinate q corresponds to the radial displacement of the Cl⁻ ions relative to the perfect KCl lattice. [After Johnson and Williams, ref. 14]

displacement of the six neighboring Cl⁻ ions represented in Fig. 16-6. The metastable states are indicated by the dashed lines, which have been drawn in such a way as to obtain agreement with experiment.

Concentration-dependence of the luminescence efficiency. If one defines the luminescence efficiency η as the number of emitted photons per incident photon absorbed by the material, one obtains experimentally for many luminescent materials a curve for η versus atomic activator concentration c which exhibits a maximum for a certain activator concentration (Fig. 16-7). For the particular case in which the excitation of the luminescence center is achieved by the direct absorption of a photon, such as in the thallium-activated alkali halides, the efficiency versus concentration curve may be interpreted on the basis of a simple model.[15] Suppose that an activator atom, which has absorbed an incident photon, returns to the ground state with emission of a photon only if there is no other activator atom within a sphere of radius R around the central activator atom. In other words, we assume that the activator atoms interact with each other in such a way that if the distance between them is $\leqslant R$, they quench each other. Thus, around a given Tl^+ ion let there be Z metallic positions within the sphere of radius R; if any of these Z positions is occupied by another Tl^+ ion, we assume that neither of them will act as a luminescence center. Due to the quenching effect then, η will be proportional to $c(1 - c)^Z$, where

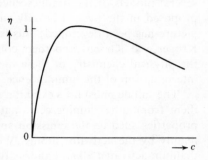

Fig. 16-7. Schematic representation of the luminescence efficiency as function of activator concentration.

c represents the probability that a given metallic site is occupied by a Tl^+ ion. Furthermore, η will be proportional to the probability that a photon absorbed by the material as a whole is actually absorbed by a Tl^+ ion; this probability is given by an expression of the type

$$\alpha c/[\alpha c + \beta(1 - c)] = c/[c + (\beta/\alpha)(1 - c)]$$

where β/α is the ratio of the capture cross section of a photon of given wavelength by a lattice atom and by a Tl^+ ion. Evidently, the ratio β/α will be a function of the wavelength of the exciting radiation; it also depends on temperature. Thus,

$$\eta = \frac{c(1 - c)^Z}{c + (\beta/\alpha)(1 - c)} \qquad (16\text{-}12)$$

For small concentrations of the activator, η increases proportionally with c; at high concentrations, the mutual quenching takes over, leading to a decrease in η. According to Johnson and Williams, KCl:Tl satisfies equation (16-12) quite well, with a value of $Z \simeq 70$ at room temperature.[16] The maximum efficiency is obtained for a mole fraction of approximately 0.002 Tl^+ ion.

---

[15] For the more complicated case of excitation by electrons or X-rays, see, for example, P. D. Johnson and F. E. Williams, *J. Chem. Phys.*, **18**, 1477 (1950).

[16] P. D. Johnson and F. E. Williams, *J. Chem. Phys.*, **18**, 1477 (1950).

16-5. The sulfide phosphors

Because of their practical importance, the zinc sulfide and cadmium sulfide phosphors have received a good deal of attention. Although several models of the luminescence centers in these materials have been proposed in the past, it is only since the last few years that a coherent picture has been developed; this is due in particular to the researches of Kröger and Klasens and their collaborators.[17] We shall see below that the physical chemistry of these materials plays an important role in the interpretation of the luminescence.

The sulfide phosphors exhibit a number of properties which distinguish them from other luminescent materials. In most luminescent materials properties such as the emission spectrum and the decay are determined mainly by the activator atoms. We have seen an example of this in the thallium-activated alkali halides. In the sulfide phosphors, however, these properties seem to be associated more with the lattice itself than with the activators. For example, when in zinc sulfide activated with Ag, Au, or Cu, the zinc atoms are gradually replaced by cadmium, the position of the emission bands gradually shifts to longer wavelengths in approximately the same manner as the forbidden gap between the valence band and the conduction band. Furthermore, the position of the emission peaks in ZnS activated with Ag, Cu, or Au vary only between about 4000 and 5000 Å. Incidentally, since the gap width in ZnS associated with optical transitions is 2.9 ev, it follows that the wavelength of the emission lies very close to the long-wavelength absorption edge. One speaks in this case of "edge emission." Such edge emissions are also observed in ZnO and CdS; the ultraviolet emissions from Al_2O_3 and certain silicates are probably also of this type.[18] The excited state from which emission occurs by return to the ground state lies presumably close to the bottom of the conduction band. This is confirmed by measurements on the luminescence efficiency as function of activator concentration; it seems that the efficiency can be represented by a formula of type (16-12) with $Z \simeq 4000$, indicating a large spatial extension of the excited states.[19]

The principle of charge compensation; coactivators. Zinc sulfide is usually obtained by precipitation from a solution of a zinc salt with H_2S or $(NH_4)_2S$. The actual phosphor is then prepared by firing the mixture of components at sufficiently high temperatures so that diffusion of the activators and recrystallization of the material may take place. To obtain

---

[17] For recent reviews and references see H. A. Klasens, *J. Electrochem. Soc.*, **100**, 72 (1953) and F. A. Kröger, *Proc. IRE*, December 1955 (solid state issue), p. 1941; *Brit. J. Appl. Phys.*, Supplement 4, 1954, p. 58.

[18] See, for example, F. A. Kröger, *op. cit.*, p. 49.

[19] F. E. Williams, *Advances in Electronics*, **5**, 153 (1953).

a reasonable rate of recrystallization, one requires under normal circumstances temperatures of the order of 1200°C. However, if one adds a flux, temperatures of, say, 800°C may be sufficient, and for practical reasons this is usually done. For example, for activation of ZnS with monovalent metals such as Cu, Ag, Au, salts like NaCl or $CaCl_2$ are found to be suitable fluxes. It seems that the important role played by the flux material in the preparation of sulfide phosphors was never fully realized until some years ago. In fact, Kröger and collaborators have shown that the incorporation of activators such as Ag, Cu, Au, Li, Na in zinc sulfide is governed by the so-called principle of charge compensation, which will now be explained.[20]

First consider what may occur when zinc sulfide is fired with another divalent sulfide, say MnS. Since the valences of the metal atoms are the same and since their radii do not differ too much (Mn^{2+} is approximately 10 per cent larger than Zn^{2+}), one may expect a substitutional mixed crystal to be formed in which Mn^{2+} ions have replaced Zn^{2+} ions. Consider now, however, a solid solution of ZnS and Ag_2S in which Ag^+ ions occupy positions normally occupied by Zn^{2+} ions. In order to conserve charge, the crystal must contain one sulfur vacancy for each two silver ions incorporated in the lattice. Since the creation of a vacancy requires a good deal of energy, the amount of silver incorporated in the lattice will be strongly limited. Similarly, a mixed crystal of ZnS and $ZnCl_2$, in which Cl^- ions occupy lattice sites normally occupied by S^{2-} ions, must contain positive ion vacancies. The formation of vacancies may be avoided, however, if in the case of ZnS:Ag a monovalent negative ion is incorporated for each Ag^+ ion. For example,

$$ZnS + \delta\ AgCl \rightarrow Zn^{2+}Ag_\delta^+ S^{2-}Cl_\delta^-$$

and no vacancies are required. One speaks here of charge compensation. The lack of positive charge associated with the Ag^+ ions is compensated by the lack of negative charge on the Cl^- ions. Since no vacancies have to be formed, this explains why a flux such as NaCl is so effective in producing good phosphors of ZnS activated with monovalent metals. The chlorine ions presumably enhance the solubility of the monovalent metallic activator ions, resulting in a good phosphor. Similar results are obtained with bromides as a flux. The Cl^- or Br^- ions are referred to as coactivators. From the principle of charge compensation it follows that trivalent metal ions such as Al^{3+} and Ga^{3+} should also be suitable coactivators for monovalent metal activators. This is indeed the case; the lack of positive charge is then compensated by an excess of positive charge.[20]

[20] F. A. Kröger and J. Dikhoff, *Physica*, **16**, 297 (1950); F. A. Kröger and J. E. Hellingman, *J. Electrochem. Soc.*, **93**, 156 (1948); **95**, 68 (1949).

The nature of the luminescence centers in impurity-activated sulfide phosphors. As mentioned above, the spectrum of the luminescence depends only slightly on the nature of the activator ions. This indicates that the activator ions themselves are probably not the luminescence centers, but that they disturb the host lattice in the immediate vicinity

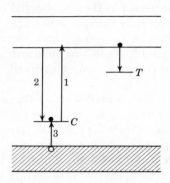

in such a way that levels for a luminescence center are created. Furthermore, the spectrum seems in many cases independent of the coactivator ion; this indicates that the activator and coactivator ions are relatively far apart. Since the activator and coactivator ions attract each other (the former has an effective negative charge, the latter an effective positive charge), the pair presumably dissociates at the firing temperature and this situation may remain frozen in to a large extent upon cooling. In some cases,

Fig. 16-8. Schematic representation of the electronic levels in a zinc sulfide phosphor; see text.

however, there seems to be a partial association between activator and coactivator ions. In any case, the facts given above lead one to suspect that the charge of the activator ions is more essential than their chemical species. One thus arrives at a model which is closely related to that employed in the discussion of the influence of lattice defects on the electronic levels in alkali halides (see Sec. 15-5). Consider, for example, a sulfur ion neighboring a monovalent metal ion such as Ag^+. Since the electrons of the S^{2-} ion are not so strongly bound as when the Ag^+ were replaced by a Zn^{2+} ion, localized electron levels will occur which lie somewhat above the valence band (see level C in Fig. 16-8). This picture is supported by the observation that after activation of ZnS, a new absorption band appears on the long-wavelength side of the fundamental absorption.[21] This absorption seems to give rise to photoconductivity, indicating that any excited states lie either just inside or very close to the conduction band. The excitation of C in Fig. 16-8 by direct absorption is indicated by arrow (1); emission corresponds to (2). The center may also be excited by capture of a hole from the valence band (3).

From the hyperbolic decay of the phosphorescence and from the thermoluminescence of the sulfide phosphors, one must conclude that the excited electrons may become trapped in the crystals. Since coactivator ions such as Al^{3+} or Cl^- have an effective positive charge, these may provide at least one type of electron trap; such traps have been represented by the level T in Fig. 16-8.

[21] F. A. Kröger and J. E. Hellingman, *J. Electrochem. Soc.*, **93**, 156 (1948); **95**, 68 (1949); J. H. Gisolf, W. de Groot, and F. A. Kröger, *Physica*, **8**, 805 (1941).

The presence of vacancies, even though they occur in relatively small concentrations, also leads to localized levels in the normally forbidden energy range. The production of positive ion vacancies in ZnS may be promoted by the incorporation of atoms such as aluminum or chlorine. For example, the blue emission band characteristic of self-activated ZnS is probably due to Zn^{2+} vacancies; it is observed particularly in ZnS phosphors prepared with the addition of $ZnCl_2$ or Al_2S_3. For a long time this emission was believed to be associated with interstitial zinc atoms. The reader is referred to the literature for a discussion of the present situation on this topic.[22]

16-6. Electroluminescence

The direct transformation of electrical energy into light is attractive from the practical standpoint and has a variety of applications. Since the last few years the subject has therefore become of much wider than purely academic interest. Although the theoretical interpretation of the details of electroluminescence is still in a state of flow, there are some basic ideas which seem generally accepted. The term electroluminescence covers a variety of phenomena which can occur when a luminescent material is subjected to an electric field and some of these will be discussed below.

The Gudden-Pohl effect. In 1920 Gudden and Pohl discovered that a momentary flash of light is emitted when an electric field is applied to a zinc sulfide phosphor during the after glow (phosphorescence).[23] When a d-c field is applied, a flash is observed; the same is true when the field is switched off. This indicates that after application of the field, an internal field is set up, due to polarization, which rapidly counteracts the external field. When the latter is removed, the polarization field itself produces a flash and decays rapidly to zero. The momentary flash may also be observed when the field is applied during excitation with photons. Luminescence associated with the application of a field during or after photo-excitation is referred to as electro-photoluminescence.

The Gudden-Pohl effect is evidently due to the emptying of electron traps. This may occur as a result of tunneling of electrons from the traps into the conduction band or it may be due to ionization of the filled traps by free electrons accelerated by the field in the conduction band. In any event, the effect is somewhat analogous to thermoluminescence, the

[22] See, for example, R. H. Bube, *Phys. Rev.*, **80**, 655 (1950); *J. Chem. Phys.*, **20**, 708 (1952); R. H. Rube and S. Larach, *J. Chem. Phys.*, **21**, 5 (1953); F. A. Kröger and H. J. Vink, *J. Chem. Phys.*, **22**, 250 (1954); F. A. Kröger, *Brit. J. Appl. Phys.*, Supplement 4, 58 (1954).
[23] B. Gudden and R. W. Pohl, *Z. Physik*, **2**, 192 (1920).

action of the field taking the place of the action of thermal vibrations. For further details of the present situation we refer the reader to the literature.[24]

The Destriau effect. The emission of light by a phosphor resulting solely from the action of an electric field applied to a suspension of luminescent particles in an insulator was first discovered by Destriau.[25] In this case one may speak of intrinsic electroluminescence, since the effect does not involve previous photo-excitation, nor the injection of charge carriers from an external source. An electroluminescent cell is usually made in the form of a parallel-plate capacitor of which at least one of the conducting plates is transparent. In order to transfer power to the dielectric consisting of the luminescent powder embedded in an insulator, alternating voltages or pulses must be used. For sinusoidal voltages the average brightness B increases rapidly with increasing amplitude. Several empirical formulas have been introduced to describe the observed brightness versus voltage curves, for example,

$$B = aV^n \exp\left(-b/V\right) \tag{16-13}$$

where a, b, and n are constants. The curve shown in Fig. 16-9 has been obtained by Roberts[26] for a copper-activated zinc sulfoselenide phosphor embedded as a powder in a variety of dielectric materials. If one assumes that the luminescent particles are spheres, one can show that the local field E_2 in the phosphor is given by the expression

$$E_2 = \frac{3\epsilon_1 E}{2\epsilon_1 + \epsilon_2 - f_1(\epsilon_2 - \epsilon_1)} \tag{16-14}$$

where E is the applied field, ϵ_1 is the dielectric constant of the phosphor, ϵ_2 is the dielectric constant of the matrix, and f_1 is the fraction of the volume occupied by the phosphor particles. By using various matrices of widely different dielectric constants, Roberts showed that the observed brightness is a function only of the local field E_2. The brightness varies only slightly with temperature, indicating that thermal excitation is of little importance in the mechanism. Electroluminescence becomes visible for fields of about 3000 volts per cm; for high brightness one requires fields approximately ten times as strong. A possible explanation of intrinsic electroluminescence presumably involves the emptying of traps by the field, subsequent acceleration of electrons in the conduction band, and excitation of centers by these electrons.

[24] For a review and many references to electroluminescence, see G. Destriau and H. F. Ivey, *Proc. IRE*, December 1955 (solid-state issue), p. 1911. In the same issue applications are discussed.

[25] G. Destriau, *J. chim. phys.*, **33**, 620 (1936); **34**, 117 (1937).

[26] S. Roberts, *J. Opt. Soc. Amer.*, **42**, 850 (1952).

Piper and Williams have studied the electroluminescence of single crystals of ZnS : Cu, clamped between two electrodes.[27]. From the non-ohmic behavior of this system they conclude that there exists a Schottky barrier at the crystal-metal interface. With an applied external field, the local field in the barrier may well be of the order of 10^6–10^7 volts per cm.

Although such fields are appreciably larger than the breakdown field of insulators ($\sim 10^5$ volts per cm), breakdown does not occur because the Schottky layer is thin ($\sim 10^{-5}$ cm). When electrons in the Schottky layer are accelerated by the field, they may produce luminescence by impact with luminescence centers.

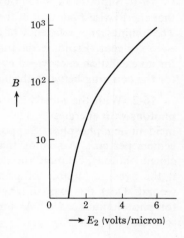

Carrier-injection luminescence. When a *p-n* junction of germanium or silicon is biased in the forward direction, electrons from the *n*-region penetrate into the *p*-region and holes flow from *p* to *n*. The minority carriers so injected will recombine with their counterparts and one might expect emission of photons. This has indeed been observed by Haynes and Briggs.[28] The emitted radiation has a wavelength which agrees well with the optical absorption associated with band-to-band transitions. For Ge and Si the radiation lies in the infrared ($\lambda = 1.77\ \mu$ and $1.12\ \mu$, respectively). The emission is localized in the junction region.

Fig. 16-9. The brightness in microlamberts as function of the local field strength for zinc sulfoselenide. The curve fits experimental data for the powdered phosphor in polystyrene ($\varepsilon = 2.56$), lucite ($\varepsilon = 3.59$) and polyvinyl chloride ($\varepsilon = 7.05$). [After Roberts, ref. 26]

REFERENCES

G. F. J. Garlick, *Luminescent Materials*, Oxford, New York, 1949.

F. A. Kröger, *Some Aspects of the Luminescence of Solids*, Elsevier, New York, 1948.

H. W. Leverenz, *Luminescence of Solids*, Wiley, New York, 1950.

P. Pringsheim and M. Vogel, *Luminescence of Liquids and Solids*, Interscience, New York, 1943.

F. E. Williams, "Solid State Luminescence," *Advances in Electronics.* Academic Press, New York, 1953, Vol. 5, p. 137.

[27] W. W. Piper and F. E. Williams, *Phys. Rev.*, **87**, 151 (1952).
[28] J. R. Haynes and H. B. Briggs, *Phys. Rev.*, **86**, 647 (1952).

Solid Luminescent Materials, Symposium held at Cornell University (1946), Wiley, New York, 1948.

PROBLEMS

16-1. Suppose an X-ray tube is operated at 60 kv and 10 ma. Assume that energywise 2 per cent of the electric energy is transformed into X-rays. The luminescence efficiency of a good phosphor under X-ray excitation is $\sim$10 per cent. Estimate the number of photons emitted by the phosphor for an excitation energy $\sim$5 ev; take into account a reasonable geometry for the coupling between the X-ray source and the phosphor.

16-2. With the most intense light sources one can obtain a beam of photons with energies $\geqslant$ 3 ev corresponding to $\sim$10^{19} per cm^2 per second incident on a phosphor. Suppose the phosphor contains 10^{18} luminescence centers per cm^3. Assuming that the host lattice does not absorb the incident photons, estimate the penetration depth of the photons and from it the average number of primary photons available per activator per second. Does this explain why saturation effects have not been observed for photoluminescence? Assume a lifetime of an excited center of 10^{-8} second.

16-3. Suppose a cathode-ray tube operating at 25 kv delivers 2.10^4 watts per cm^2 to a phosphor screen. Calculate the penetration depth of the electrons from the simplified Bethe formula [*Ann. Physik*, **5**, 325 (1930)], $x = E^2/4\pi NZe^4$, where E is the energy of the incident electrons, N is the number of atoms per unit volume, and Z is the average number of electrons per atom. Assume further that the primary electrons expend approximately 30 ev per excitation of a luminescence center (this includes losses of several kinds). Estimate the number of excitations available per center per second if the density of the latter is 10^{18} per cm^3. Show that this may lead to saturation effects, in contrast with the photoluminescence in the previous problem.

16-4. It was noted in this chapter that the concentration-dependence of the luminescence of KCl:Tl can be described by formula (16-12) with $Z \simeq 70$. What does this imply for the lower limit of the distance between two Tl^+ ions required to prevent quenching?

16-5. Suppose that the decay of a luminescent material may be described by a bimolecular mechanism of the type $dn/dt = -\alpha n^2$. If at $t = 0$ the exciting source is switched off and the luminescent intensity is then I_0, show that the time required for the intensity to reach half its initial intensity is given by $(\sqrt{2} - 1)/(I_0\alpha)^{1/2}$. (Note that $t_{1/2}$ depends on I_0). For the same phosphor discuss the build-up of the intensity of luminescence under constant illumination.

16-6. Give a proof of expression (16-14) for the local field in spherical particles of a luminescent material embedded in a homogeneous dielectric.

16-7. For spherical particles of dielectric constant ϵ_1 and resistivity ρ embedded in an insulator, show that the field in the particles leads the field in the insulator by an angle ϕ such that $\tan \phi = 2/\epsilon_1 \rho \nu$, where ν is the frequency of the applied field.

16-8. Discuss the properties of scintillation counters. These were first described by H. Kallmann, *Natur and Technik*, July 1947; for a review and references to the literature see G. A. Morton, *Advances in Electronics*, **4,** 69 (1952).

16-9. Discuss a model for the killer action of certain impurities, such as Ni in ZnS : Cu [see M. Schoen, *Naturwiss.*, **31,** 203 (1943); **38,** 235 (1951); W. Hoogenstraaten and H. A. Klasens, *J. Electrochem. Soc.*, **100,** 366 (1953)].

16-10. Discuss the topic of cathodoluminescence (see, for example, G. F. J. Garlick, *Proc. IRE*, December 1955, p. 1907).

16-11. Give a derivation of expression (16-9).

Chapter 17

SECONDARY ELECTRON EMISSION

When the surface of a solid is bombarded with charged particles of sufficient kinetic energy, emission of electrons by the solid may be observed. This phenomenon of secondary electron emission was discovered by Austin and Starke in 1902 in a study of the reflection of electrons by metals; they observed that under certain circumstances more electrons were emitted than were incident, indicating that the bombarding primary electrons liberate electrons from the solid.[1] Unless otherwise stated, it will be assumed in the present chapter that the bombarding particles are electrons. However, emission of electrons may also result from bombardment with heavy charged particles such as ions.[2] The theory of secondary emission under electron bombardment is completely different from that under ion bombardment. The reason is that in the former case the bombarding particles penetrate into the solid, thus producing a bulk effect; in the latter case, however, one deals essentially with a surface effect. For a survey of the field of secondary emission we refer to the bibliography at the end of this chapter. Some of the basic principles involved in the secondary emission process will now be discussed.

17-1. Secondary electrons

When a beam of primary electrons strikes the surface of a solid, a certain fraction is elastically reflected and the remainder penetrates into the solid. The primaries that enter the solid will lose energy by exciting lattice electrons into higher energy levels. The latter may then move toward the surface and a certain fraction will escape from the solid as secondaries. It is also possible that a primary electron, which has lost part of its energy inside the solid, returns to and escapes from the surface as a result of Rutherford scattering; such electrons are called inelastically reflected primaries. Although it is common to employ the term "secondary electrons" with reference to all electrons emitted by the surface and collected by a positive collector electrode, the above remarks

---

[1] L. Austin and H. Starke, *Ann. Physik*, **9**, 271 (1902).

[2] An extensive study of this topic has been made by H. D. Hagstrum, *Phys. Rev.*, **89**, 244 (1953); **91**, 543 (1953). See also J. H. Parker, Jr., *Phys. Rev.*, **93**, 1148 (1954) and L. J. Varnerin, Jr., *Phys. Rev.*, **91**, 859 (1953).

show that one may distinguish between three categories of electrons leaving the surface:

(a) Elastically reflected primaries

(b) Inelastically reflected primaries

(c) "True" secondaries

This may be illustrated by considering as an example the energy distribution of the electrons emitted by silver upon bombardment with primary electrons of 155 ev, as shown in Fig. 17-1 according to Rudberg.[3] (Such

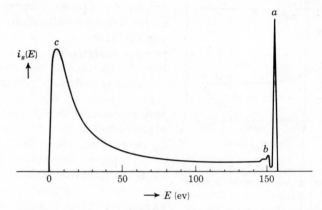

Fig. 17-1. The energy distribution of secondary electrons emitted by silver. [After Rudberg, ref. 3]

energy distributions may be determined either with a magnetic analyzer or with a retarding potential applied to a spherical collector with the target at the center.) The presence of the elastically reflected primaries is evident from the sharp peak (a) at the primary energy. Close to the peak (a) are a few small maxima (b), the positions of which relative to (a) are characteristic of the material and independent of the primary energy. These maxima evidently correspond to inelastically reflected primaries which have lost discrete amounts of energy before escaping from the surface. The majority of the emitted electrons have relatively low energies, corresponding to the broad peak (c). The maximum of this part of the curve lies for most solids in the vicinity of a few ev. It is important to note that the energy distribution of these slow electrons is practically independent of the primary energy. One therefore speaks of these slow electrons as true secondaries. On the other hand, it is impossible to draw a sharp distinction between true secondaries and inelastically reflected electrons; in fact, from Fig. 17-1 it is evident that the flat region of the curve consists

[3] E. Rudberg, *Proc. Roy. Soc.* (*London*), **A127**, 111 (1930); *Phys. Rev.*, **4**, 764 (1934).

of a mixture of the two categories. Somewhat arbitrarily, the term "true secondaries" usually refers to all those electrons with an energy below about 50 ev.

For primary energies below about 10 ev, no true secondaries are produced; i.e., 10 ev is roughly the threshold value for the secondary emission process. A considerable fraction of the incident primaries is elastically reflected in that case. As the primary energy increases, the number of reflected electrons decreases; for a primary energy of 100 ev for example only about 10 per cent is reflected. For very high primary energies, i.e., above say 50 kev, the fraction of elastically plus inelastically reflected primaries increases again. To illustrate this, we have reproduced in Fig. 17-2 results obtained by Trump and van de Graaff for tungsten and aluminum.[4] The full curves represent the ratio of the total secondary current and primary current as function of the primary energy E_{p0}. The dashed curves refer to the case where only electrons emitted with energies above 800 ev are collected. We note that the dashed curve increases with increasing E_{p0}.

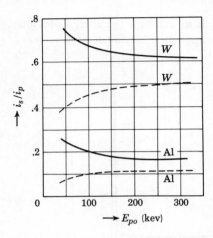

Fig. 17-2. Number of emitted electrons per incident primary versus primary energy for tungsten and aluminum. The full curves correspond to all emitted electrons; the broken curves to emitted electrons with an energy >800 ev. [After Trump and van de Graaf, ref. 4]

17-2. Experimental yield curves

The secondary yield δ is commonly defined as the number of emitted electrons per incident primary electron. According to this definition, the yield includes all three categories of emitted electrons discussed in the preceding section. If the experiment is set up in such a manner that the velocity distribution of the emitted electrons can be measured, a rough correction for the elastically and inelastically reflected primaries can be made.

One of the most important relationships in secondary emission, both from the experimental and theoretical point of view, is that between the secondary yield δ and the energy E_{p0} of the incident primaries. Examples of such yield curves are given in Figs. 17-3, 17-4, and 17-5 for magnesium

[4] J. G. Trump and R. J. van de Graaff, *J. Appl. Phys.*, **18**, 327 (1947).

oxide,[5] germanium,[6] and platinum.[7] Apart from quantitative differences the yield curves for all materials exhibit the same general shape. For low primary energies the yield increases, then goes through a maximum

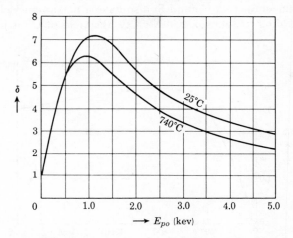

Fig. 17-3. Secondary yield δ versus primary energy (kev) for a single crystal of MgO. The upper curve refers to room temperature, the lower one to 740 C (see Sec. 17-9). [After Johnson and McKay, ref. 5]

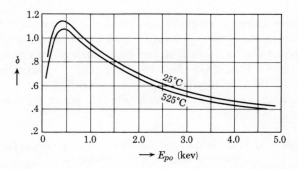

Fig. 17-4. Secondary yield δ versus primary energy in kev for a germanium single crystal. The upper curve refers to room temperature, the lower one to 525°C. [After Johnson and McKay, ref. 6]

value δ_m corresponding to a characteristic energy E_{pm} of the primaries, and finally decreases for high primary energies. In Table 17-1 we give values for δ_m and E_{pm} for some metals, semiconductors, and insulators by way of illustration. In all cases the primaries were incident perpendicular

[5] J. B. Johnson and K. G. McKay, *Phys. Rev.*, **91**, 582 (1953).
[6] J. B. Johnson and K. G. McKay, *Phys. Rev.*, **93**, 668 (1954).
[7] P. L. Copeland, *Thesis*, University of Iowa, 1931.

to the surface; the same is true for the examples given in Figs. 17-3, 17-4, 17-5. We note that the maximum yield of metals is of the order of unity, the largest value having been observed for platinum (1.8).[7] The intrinsic semiconductors Ge and Si also have a maximum yield of about unity; according to Johnson and McKay, the yield of Ge is independent

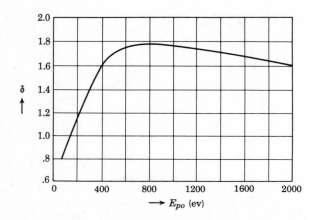

Fig. 17-5. Secondary yield δ versus primary energy in ev for platinum. [After Copeland, ref. 7]

of the donor or acceptor concentration up to $\sim 10^{19}$ per cm^3.[6] Insulators generally show a yield between about 3 and 10. The maximum yield of 21 for MgO, included in Table 17-1, has been obtained for crystals cleaved in vacuum (R. G. Lye, *Phys. Rev.* **99**, 1647 (1955). This value is considerably larger than δ_m for the crystal corresponding to Fig. 17-3, indicating that surface conditions (electron affinity!) are of great importance for the yield of insulators.

Table 17-1. Values of the Maximum Yield and the Corresponding Primary Energy for a Few Substances

Substances	δ_m	E_{pm} (ev)
Ag	1.5	800
Al	1.0	300
Cu	1.3	600
Fe	1.3	350
Pt	1.8	800
Ge	1.1	400
Si	1.1	250
NaCl	6	600
MgO	21	1100

17-3. Elementary theory of secondary emission; universal yield curves

In the theory of secondary emission it is convenient to distinguish between two stages in the process. In the first stage one considers the production of secondaries, resulting from the interaction between the primary beam and the lattice electrons. In the second stage one is interested in calculating the probability for the secondaries so produced to escape from the surface. Thus, in a simplified way and without paying attention to the velocity distribution of the secondaries, one may write for the secondary yield,[8]

$$\delta = \int n(x) f(x) \, dx \qquad (17\text{-}1)$$

Here $n(x) \, dx$ represents the number of secondaries produced by one primary at a depth between x and $x + dx$ below the surface; $f(x)$ represents the probability for such a secondary to move toward and escape from the surface. The integral extends over the thickness of the sample, although only a thin layer of the order of 100 Å participates in the process. To calculate δ the following assumptions will be made:

(a) The primaries, as they penetrate the solid, move along straight lines along the direction of incidence; this assumption thus neglects elastically and inelastically reflected primaries.

(b) The primaries are incident perpendicular to the surface.

(c) The energy loss of the primaries per unit path length is given by Whiddington's law[9]

$$-\frac{dE_p(x)}{dx} = \frac{A}{E_p(x)} \qquad (17\text{-}2)$$

where A is a constant characteristic of the material.

(d) The number of secondaries produced in layer dx by a single primary is proportional to dE_p/dx, i.e.,

$$n(x) = -\frac{1}{\epsilon_e} \cdot \frac{dE_p}{dx} \qquad (17\text{-}3)$$

where ϵ_e represents the average excitation energy required to produce a secondary.

(e) The probability for a secondary produced at a depth x to escape from the surface is determined by an exponential absorption law,

$$f(x) = f(0)e^{-\alpha x} = f(0)e^{-x/x_s} \qquad (17\text{-}4)$$

---

[8] See, for example, H. Bruining, *Physics and Applications of Secondary Electron Emission*, McGraw-Hill, New York, 1954; also H. Salow, *Z. tech. Phys.*, **21**, 8 (1940); *Phys. Z.*, **41**, 434 (1940).

[9] For relativistic energies, E_p should be replaced by $mv^2/2$, where m is the relativistic mass; this must be borne in mind in interpreting the secondary yield data obtained for high energies of the primaries, such as those of Trump and van de Graaff, Fig. 17-2.

where $f(0)$ represents the probability of escape for a secondary produced at or very near to the surface; $x_s = 1/\alpha$ may be considered as the range of the secondaries.

From (17-2) it follows that if E_{p0} is the energy of the primaries as they strike the surface, the primary energy as function of depth is given by

$$E_p^2(x) = E_{p0}^2 - 2Ax$$

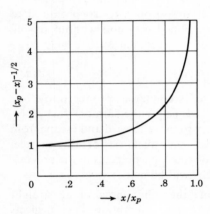

We note that the approximate maximum depth of penetration x_p of the primaries is obtained by putting $E_p = 0$, i.e.,

$$x_p = E_{p0}^2/2A \qquad (17-5)$$

Hence Whiddington's law leads to a primary range which is proportional to the square of the primary energy. The production of secondaries as function of depth is governed by (17-3), so that by making use of (17-5),

Fig. 17-6. The function $(x_p - x)^{-1/2}$ as function of x/x_p which determines the production of secondaries as function of depth according to equation (17-6).

$$n(x) = \left(\frac{A}{2}\right)^{1/2} \cdot \frac{1}{\epsilon_e(x_p - x)^{1/2}} \qquad (17-6)$$

The function $(x_p - x)^{-1/2}$ versus x/x_p has been plotted in Fig. 17-6. It is evident from (17-6) that most of the secondaries are produced at the end of the primary path.

For the moment we shall confine our attention to showing that the yield curve exhibits a maximum. For this purpose, let us first consider the case of very low primary energies such that $x_p \ll 1/\alpha = x_s$. In that case, the probability for escape for all secondaries produced may be taken equal to $f(0)$. Hence, in accordance with (17-1) and (17-3),

$$\delta = f(0) \int n(x)\, dx = f(0) \frac{E_{p0}}{\epsilon_e} \quad \text{for} \quad x_p \ll x_s \qquad (17-7)$$

Thus, for low primary energies the secondary yield should rise proportionally to E_{p0}. The other extreme case to be considered corresponds to a primary range very large compared with the range of the secondaries. Under these circumstances one is essentially interested in the function $n(x)$ for very small values of x/x_p, because the function $f(x)$ in (17-1) decreases strongly for values of $x > x_s = 1/\alpha$. From Fig. 17-6 it is evident that the production of secondaries as a function of depth may then be considered as approximately constant over the range of x-values of interest. In fact one may then employ in accordance with (17-5) and (17-6),

$$n(x) \simeq n(0) = \frac{A}{\epsilon_e E_{p0}}$$

Hence, from (17-1) it follows that

$$\delta = \frac{A}{\epsilon_e E_{p0}} \int_0^\infty f(x)\,dx = \frac{A}{\epsilon_e E_{p0}} \cdot \frac{f(0)}{\alpha} \quad \text{for} \quad x_p \gg x_s \qquad (17\text{-}8)$$

Thus, for high primary energies, δ decreases in inverse proportion to E_{p0}. From the above discussion it is clear that the yield curve should exhibit a maximum for primary energies at $x_p \simeq x_s$. It is of interest to note that the conclusions

$$\delta \text{ proportional to } E_p \quad \text{for} \quad x_p \ll x_s$$

$$\delta \text{ proportional to } E_p^{-1} \quad \text{for} \quad x_p \gg x_s$$

are independent of the particular mathematical form assumed for $f(x)$, as long as it decreases monotonically with x. This follows immediately from (17-8), because for a given solid under given external conditions, $\int f(x)\,dx$ is a constant.

Universal yield curves. Up to here we have considered only the extreme regions of low and high primary energies. We shall now show that the assumptions made above lead to the following interesting result. If one plots δ/δ_m as function of E_{p0}/E_{pm}, where δ_m represents the maximum yield and E_{pm} the corresponding primary energy, a universal curve is obtained which should be valid for all materials. This was first pointed out by Baroody, and can be shown in the following manner.[10] Substitution of (17-4) and (17-6) into (17-1) gives for the yield,

$$\delta = \left(\frac{A}{2} \right)^{1/2} \cdot \frac{1}{\epsilon_e} f(0) \int_0^{x_p} \frac{e^{-\alpha x}}{(x_p - x)^{1/2}}\,dx \qquad (17\text{-}9)$$

Introducing a new variable y such that

$$y^2 = \alpha(x_p - x)$$

expression (17-9) may be rewritten in the form,

$$\delta = \left(\frac{2A}{\alpha} \right)^{1/2} \frac{1}{\epsilon_e} f(0) \epsilon^{-\alpha x_p} \int_0^{\sqrt{\alpha x_p}} e^{y^2}\,dy$$

[10] E. M. Baroody, *Phys. Rev.*, **78**, 780 (1950).

Writing $\alpha x_p = E_{p0}^2 \alpha / 2A = z^2$, the last expression gives for the yield as function of the primary energy.

$$\delta = \left(\frac{2A}{\alpha}\right)^{1/2} \cdot \frac{1}{\epsilon_e} f(0) F(z) \quad \text{with} \quad F(z) = e^{-z^2} \int_0^z e^{y^2} \, dy \qquad (17\text{-}10)$$

The maximum yield can be obtained by putting $d\delta/dE_{p0}$ equal to zero; it is found that this maximum occurs for $z = 0.92$, so that

$$E_{pm} = 0.92 \left(\frac{2A}{\alpha}\right)^{1/2} \qquad (17\text{-}11)$$

It thus follows that the ratio δ/δ_m may be written

$$\frac{\delta}{\delta_m} = \frac{F(z)}{F(0.92)} = 1.85 F\left[E_{p0} \sqrt{\frac{\alpha}{2A}}\right] = 1.85 F\left[\frac{0.92 E_{p0}}{E_{pm}}\right] \qquad (17\text{-}12)$$

This expression is independent of the constants A and α which characterize the solid. The result is illustrated by the full curve in Fig. 17-7. It may be noted that for $z \ll 1$, the function $F(z) \simeq z$; this is in agreement with the conclusion drawn previously that the yield increases proportionally with E_{p0} for low primary energies. Similarly, for $z \gg 1$, $F(z) \simeq 1/2z$, i.e., for high primary energies δ varies as E_{p0}^{-1}, again in agreement with what has been said above.

A somewhat different universal curve has been obtained by Jonker.[11] In the theory given above, it was assumed that a secondary electron produced at a distance x below the surface had a probability $e^{-\alpha x}$ of arriving at the surface. Instead, Jonker employs the following model: he assumes that the secondaries move in straight lines from their point of origin toward the surface. Thus, if for an electron moving in a given direction, the distance between its point of origin and the surface, as measured along the direction of flight, is equal to l, he takes $e^{-\alpha l}$ as the probability for the electron to arrive at the surface. On the further assumption of an isotropic distribution of the directions of flight, he is then able to find an expression for δ as function of E_{p0}. Again, δ/δ_m as function of E_{p0}/E_{pm} is independent of the material. The broken curve in Fig. 17-7 represents the universal curve obtained by Jonker.

17-4. Comparison of the elementary theory with experiment

From the discussion in the preceding section it is evident that the general shape of the yield curve can be explained on the basis of some simple assumptions. It is further of interest to note that if one plots δ/δ_m versus E_{p0}/E_{pm} for a number of different metals, one obtains indeed a single curve which fits the metals investigated; experimental points are

---

[11] J. L. H. Jonker, *Philips Research Repts.*, **7**, 1 (1952).

represented in Fig. 17-7 by dots. It is observed that in the low primary energy region, Jonker's curve fits the experiments better than does Baroody's curve. On the other hand, it must be admitted that, physically speaking, Jonker's theory is not founded any better than the one due to Bruining-Baroody; this will become clear from our later discussions of the escape mechanism.

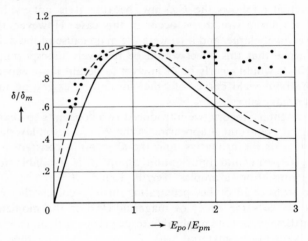

Fig. 17-7.   Universal yield curves representing δ/δ_m versus E_{po}/E_{pm}; the full curve represents equation (17-12), given by Baroody (ref. 10); the dashed line is according to Jonker, (ref. 11); the dots represent measured data for metals (see ref. 10).

Both theoretical curves show considerable deviation from the experimental one for primary energies $> E_{pm}$. In this connection it is interesting to note that for magnesium oxide, which is an insulator, the yield decreases as E_{p0}^{-1}, in agreement with the theoretically predicted behavior (Fig. 17-3).[12] Germanium (Fig. 17-4), on the other hand, shows deviations similar to those for metals. It has been suggested that the deviations from the E_{p0}^{-1} law for high primary energies result from the presence of inelastically reflected primaries. The influence of such primaries on the yield is twofold:

(i) They increase the yield simply because they are collected as emitted electrons.

(ii) They may increase the yield because they may produce more secondaries over a depth equal to the range of the secondaries than does a primary that penetrates deeply into the solid. The reason is that their path may pass twice or more through the same region of the solid close to the surface.

[12] A. J. Dekker, *Phys. Rev.*, **94**, 1179 (1954).

Neither of these effects explains the observed deviations unless one assumes that inelastic scattering becomes more probable with increasing values of E_{p0} beyond E_{pm}. That this is indeed the case for primary energies of the order of many kev is evident from the experiments of Trump and van de Graaff.[4] However, the energies involved here are only of the order of 1 kev. A difficulty in this explanation arises as a result of the fact that MgO actually follows the E_{p0}^{-1} law, because it is not evident why Rutherford scattering would not occur in this case. However, the yield of MgO is relatively large, and if (i) were the main cause of the deviations, one might argue that this effect would be relatively unimportant in the case of MgO. It would clearly be of interest to obtain more experimental information about yield curves of other insulators, extending to sufficiently high primary energies.

In the elementary theory, we introduced two constants to characterize the material: the constant A appearing in the Whiddington law describing the energy loss of the primaries, and the absorption constant α for the secondaries. Experimental information about A is available for high-energy electrons. For example, Terrill found $A = 4.5 \times 10^{12}$ volt^2 cm^{-1} for electrons of 25–50 kev penetrating through gold; other materials give values of the same order of magnitude.[13] For the moment let us assume that these values are applicable to primaries with an energy of the order of 1 kev. For a material with $E_{pm} = 1$ kev, one then obtains, according to (17-11), for the absorption constant, $\alpha \simeq 10^6$ cm^{-1}. In other words, this leads to a range of the secondaries of about 100 Angstroms. It should be noted that one expects A to decrease with decreasing E_{p0}, because slow primaries can excite only electrons from the outer electronic shells in the atoms. This would have the effect of lowering the value of α.

17-5. Variation of the secondary yield with angle of incidence

A large number of experiments show that if the primary beam is incident at an oblique angle with the surface, the yield is larger than for perpendicular incidence. For low primary energies, however, the effect is very small. As an example we give in Fig. 17-8 some results obtained by Bruining for a smooth (S) surface of nickel carbide.[14] The reason for the increase is that the secondaries are produced at smaller depths, and in terms of the elementary theory, are not so strongly absorbed before they reach the surface. That the effect for a rough surface would be much less pronounced is also evident and is illustrated by the curves R in Fig. 17-8, referring to soot. Bruining has interpreted his data in the following strongly simplified manner. Suppose n electrons are liberated

[13] H. M. Terrill, *Phys. Rev.*, **22**, 161 (1922).
[14] H. Bruining, *Physica*, **3**, 1046 (1936).

per primary electron inside the material. Then, if x_m is the mean depth of origin and $\exp(-\alpha x_m)$ is the probability for escape, the yield for perpendicular incidence $(\theta = 0)$ is given by

$$\delta_0 = ne^{-\alpha x_m}$$

For an angle of incidence θ with the normal, the yield should be equal to

$$\delta_0 = ne^{-\alpha x_m \cos\theta}$$

Hence

$$\alpha x_m = \frac{\ln(\delta_0/\delta_0)}{1 - \cos\theta} \quad (17\text{-}13)$$

He finds that αx_m as calculated from the experimental data is nearly independent of θ, indicating that the result may have significance. Assuming $\alpha = 1.5 \times 10^6$ cm^{-1} one finds $x_m \simeq 30$ Å.[15]

It is of interest to mention some results obtained by Jonker.[16] We have seen in Sec. 3 of this chapter that he employed a somewhat different model to calculate the escape probability. In the same paper he investigated the influence of the angle of incidence on the secondary yield by simply replacing x by $x \cos\theta$.

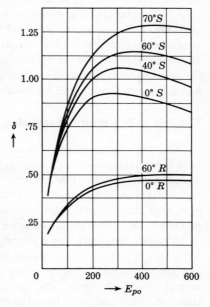

Fig. 17-8. Secondary yield δ as function of primary energy for different angles of incidence of the primary electrons. The S curves refer to a smooth surface of nickel carbide; the R curves to a rough surface of soot. The angle is measured relative to the normal. [After Bruining, ref. 14]

Without repeating his calculations here, he finds that

$$E_{pm} \cos\theta = \left(\frac{1.01A}{\alpha}\right)^{1/2} = \text{constant} \quad (17\text{-}14)$$

where A and α are the material constants introduced in Sec. 17-3. This relationship is in very good agreement with his measurements on nickel, nickel carbide, and lithium. Similarly, his theory permits establishment of a relation between the maximum yield δ_m and the angle of incidence, leading to

$$\delta_m (\cos\theta)^{1/2} = \text{constant} \quad (17\text{-}15)$$

[15] This value was found for nickel by A. Becker, *Ann. Physik*, **2**, 249 (1929).
[16] J. L. H. Jonker, *Philips Research Repts.*, **6**, 372 (1951).

This relation is in reasonable agreement with his results for the materials mentioned above. Finally, it is interesting that, according to his calculations, a universal yield curve is obtained by plotting δ versus const. $E_{p0} \cos \theta$, whereby the constant is chosen in such a manner that the maxima of the curves for different values of θ coincide. His experiments bear out the fact that such a universal curve for different θ's indeed exists. However, there is the same discrepancy between the experimental and the theoretical curves as discussed in the preceding section. On the other hand, it seems that Jonker has established an important experimental fact.

17-6. Baroody's theory of secondary emission for metals

Although the elementary theories provide a certain amount of insight into the phenomenon of secondary emission, it does not allow one to discuss many details. For example, one simply speaks about numbers of secondaries without paying attention to their energies. Also, the exponential absorption law for secondaries actually hides a very complicated mechanism by which the secondaries lose energy on their way to the surface.

Baroody in employing a Fermi model for the conduction electrons in metals, improved the situation considerably for this group of materials.[17] His theory shows, among other things, that the secondary yield for metals with high work function is larger than for those of low work function. This had been found experimentally but could not be explained by the elementary theory. In fact, one would expect metals of high work function to have a low yield because it is difficult for secondaries to escape in that case. It may be noted that Kadyschewitsch used a similar model as Baroody, but his calculations are complicated. The essential points of Baroody's theory will now be discussed.

It is assumed that the metal is at absolute zero so that in the momentum space all electrons lie within a sphere of radius p_F about the origin; all higher states are empty. This assumption does not restrict the application of the results, because no temperature effect of the yield has been detected for metals. The velocity of the primary electrons is assumed to be very high relative to that of the conduction electrons. Consider then, as represented in Fig. 17-9, the collision between a primary and a conduction electron. The instant at which the distance between the two electrons is b will be denoted by $t = 0$. Assuming the conduction electron to be at rest and the primary to move along a straight line, the component of the Coulomb force between the two particles perpendicular to the primary path is at any instant t given by

$$F = \frac{e^2 b}{(b^2 + v^2 t^2)^{3/2}} \qquad (17\text{-}16)$$

[17] E. M. Baroody, *Phys. Rev.*, **78**, 780 (1950).

where v is the velocity of the primary. The assumption of a simple Coulomb force in the case of metals is probably incorrect. The reason is that the highly mobile conduction electrons tend to prevent the field around the extra primary electron from penetrating far into space. Thus an exponentially decreasing screened potential would give a better representation of the interaction.[18] This point will be discussed further in Sec. (17-7), and for the moment (17-16) will be assumed to hold. The momentum transferred from the primary to the conduction electron perpendicular to the primary path is then equal to

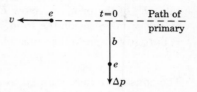

$$\Delta_p = \int_{-\infty}^{+\infty} F\, dt = \frac{2e^2}{bv} \quad (17\text{-}17)$$

Fig. 17-9. To illustrate the collision between a primary and a conduction electron; the momentum Δp transferred to the conduction electron is perpendicular to the path of the primary.

Thus, for all conduction electrons at a distance b, the center of the occupied momentum sphere will be displaced by an amount Δp. From this, it is possible to calculate the number of secondaries $N(\mu)$ produced per unit primary path length for which the momentum is larger than μp_F, where μ is a factor which we may choose. Obviously, for the secondary emission process one is interested in $\mu > 1$. As long as the velocity of the primary satisfies the relation $mv \gg (\mu + 1)p_F$, Baroody's calculation gives

$$N(\mu) = \frac{32\pi^2 e^4 p_F}{3h^3 v^2(\mu^2 - 1)} = \frac{BE_F^{1/2}}{E_p(\mu^2 - 1)} \quad (17\text{-}18)$$

where B is a constant, E_p is the primary energy, and E_F is the Fermi energy. We note that the number of secondaries produced with energies very close to the Fermi energy ($\mu \simeq 1$) becomes very large, and for $\mu = 1$, expression (17-18) becomes infinite. This is a consequence of the Coulomb law assumption, because the interaction with electrons far away from the primary, corresponding to large b values, leads to small energy losses. In a screened potential, such interactions would not occur and the difficulty would be removed. The derivative of (17-18), $-dN/d\mu$, gives the momentum distribution of the internal secondaries measured in terms of the Fermi momentum p_F. Both $N(\mu)$ and its derivative decrease rapidly with increasing μ. We also note that the number of secondaries

[18] R. Kronig and J. Korringa, *Physica*, **10**, 406, 800 (1943); H. A. Kramers, *Physica*, **13**, 401 (1947); D. Bohm and E. P. Gross, *Phys. Rev.*, **75**, 1851, 1864 (1949); D. Bohm and D. Pines, *Phys. Rev.*, **80**, 903 (1950); **82**, 625 (1951); D. Pines and D. Bohm, *Phys. Rev.*, **85**, 338 (1952); D. Pines, *Phys. Rev.*, **85**, 931 (1952); A. van der Ziel, *Phys. Rev.*, **92**, 35 (1953).

produced per unit primary path length with a momentum $> \mu p_F$ varies inversely as the primary energy. The assumption of a Whiddington law for the primaries, as used in the elementary theory discussed previously, is in agreement with this result.

Equation (17-18) gives the production of secondaries for a particular value E_p of the primary. Now E_p is a function of the path length covered by the primary inside the solid. Denoting the depth below the surface by x, Baroody employs the same relationship as that used in the older theories,

$$E_p^2(x) = E_{p0}^2 - ax \qquad (17\text{-}19)$$

The constant a here is equal to $A/2$ used in the preceding sections. From (17-19) and by differentiating (17-18) one thus obtains for the number of secondaries produced per primary in a slab dx and with a momentum between μp_F and $(\mu + d\mu)p_F$,

$$\frac{2BE_F^{1/2}\mu \, d\mu \, dx}{(E_{p0}^2 - ax)^{1/2}(\mu^2 - 1)^2} \qquad (17\text{-}20)$$

To describe the escape mechanism of the secondaries, Baroody introduces two mean free path lengths, λ_s and λ_a; λ_s refers to scattering of the secondaries by the lattice vibrations, and λ_a refers to "absorption," i.e., to inelastic collisions with other electrons. In the latter process the secondaries may lose appreciable amounts of energy in a single collision. It must be emphasized that because the secondaries have gained their momentum from the primary in a direction perpendicular to the primary path, i.e., parallel to the surface, a secondary must be scattered at least once before it can escape. Baroody discusses two extreme cases: $\lambda_s \gg \lambda_a$ and $\lambda_s \ll \lambda_a$, of which only the latter will be given attention here. When $\lambda_s \ll \lambda_a$, the secondaries carry out a large number of elastic collisions with the lattice before arriving at the surface. The escape mechanism may then be described as a diffusion process with absorption. As shown in elementary diffusion theory[19] the fraction of secondaries produced at a depth x which arrive at the surface is equal to $e^{-x/L}$, where L is the diffusion length defined by

$$L^2 = D\tau_a = \lambda_a\lambda_s/3 \qquad (17\text{-}21)$$

Here, $D = \lambda_s v/3$ is the diffusion coefficient of the secondaries and $\tau_a = \lambda_a/v$ is the lifetime associated with the absorption process (v is the velocity of the secondary). Note that the exponential absorption law used in the older theory is obtained here on the basis of an admittedly incomplete physical model. Now suppose $\mu_0 p_F$ is the minimum momentum perpendicular to the surface required for an electron to escape from the surface. Evidently, if ϕ is the work function of the metal,

$$\mu_0^2 p_F^2/2m = E_F + \phi \quad \text{or} \quad \mu_0^2 = 1 + \phi/E_F \qquad (17\text{-}22)$$

---

[19] See, for example, P. R. Wallace, *Nucleonics*, February 1949, p. 30.

Hence an electron at the surface with a momentum μp_F will escape only if the cosine of the angle with the normal is larger than μ_0/μ. For an isotropic velocity distribution, an electron at the surface with momentum

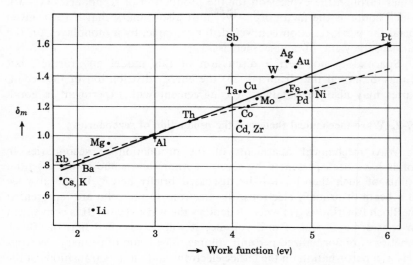

Fig. 17-10. Correlation between maximum yield and work function for various metals. The solid line is drawn to show the trend of experimental points. The dashed line is a plot of $\delta_m = (0.35\phi)^{1/2}$, according to Baroody, ref. 15.

μp_F has on the average a probability $(\mu - \mu_0)/\mu$ to escape from the surface (see Problem 17-7). One thus obtains finally for the secondary yield,

$$\delta = 2BE_F^{1/2} \int_0^{x_p} \frac{e^{-x/L}dx}{(E_{p0}^2 - ax)^{1/2}} \int_{\mu_0}^{\infty} \frac{(\mu - \mu_0)}{(\mu^2 - 1)^2} \, d\mu$$

The integral over x is the same as that in (17-9), so that

$$\delta = \frac{2BE_F^{1/2}}{a^{1/2}} F\left[\left(\frac{E_{p0}^2}{aL}\right)^{1/2} \right] \int_{\mu_0}^{\infty} \frac{(\mu - \mu_0)}{(\mu^2 - 1)^2} \, d\mu \qquad (17\text{-}23)$$

where the function F is defined by (17-10). We note that the dependence of δ on the primary energy is exactly the same as that obtained in Sec. 17-3, and that it follows the full curve in Fig. 17-7. The dependence of δ on the work function may be obtained as follows. According to (17-23), δ is proportional to $E_F^{1/2}$ times a function of μ_0. Furthermore, from (17-22) it follows that $E_F = \phi/(\mu_0^2 - 1)$. Therefore, if one makes the reasonable assumption that μ_0 and the other quantities in (17-23) do not depend on the work function in any systematic fashion, one concludes that the yield should be proportional to the root of the work function. In Fig. 17-10 we represent a number of data collected by McKay for the maximum yield of several metals.[20] The solid line is the one drawn by McKay, the dashed one represents $(0.35\phi)^{1/2}$ and is matched at thorium. We emphasize that the dependence on ϕ does not enter through the escape mechanism but rather through the expression for the production of secondaries (17-20), which contains the factor $E_P^{1/2}$. We must also remark that if for a given metal the work function is lowered, for example, by a monolayer on the surface, the yield, of course, increases.

Space does not permit discussion of this model any further, but it may be noted that from (17-23) the energy distribution of the secondaries may also be obtained; the agreement with experiment is good.

17-7. Wave-mechanical theory of the production of secondaries

Wave-mechanical treatments of the production of secondaries in solids have been presented by several authors and some of the essential points of such theories will be discussed briefly here.[21] In the absence of a beam of primary electrons, the electrons in the solid are represented by Bloch functions $\psi_k(r)$ where k denotes the wave vector. It is convenient to consider a crystal of unit volume; it will be assumed that the Bloch functions are normalized per unit volume. The beam of primary electrons acts as a perturbation on the lattice electrons and induces transitions of the latter to higher energy states. The wave vector and positional coordinates of a primary electron will be represented, respectively, by K and R. The basic problem in the theory of production consists in calculating the number of transitions per unit time $P(K,k \to K',k')\,d\Omega'$, for which the primary electron is scattered into a solid angle $d\Omega'$ around the vector K' and the lattice electron is excited into a new state k'. It is generally assumed that the primary electrons may be described by plane waves of the type $\exp i(K \cdot R)$, the reason being that their energy is large enough that they can be considered free. Such a representation, however, does not permit one to take into account Rutherford scattering, and the problem of elastic and inelastic reflection of primaries must therefore be investigated separately.

The next problem which arises is to decide on a law of interaction between a primary electron and a lattice electron. In insulators and semiconductors with relatively small densities of conduction electrons, it would seem that a simple Coulomb law would be suitable. In that case

$$V(R,r) = \frac{e^2}{|R - r|} \cdot \frac{1}{\epsilon} \qquad (17-24)$$

[20] H. G. McKay, *Advances in Electronics*, **1**, 66 (1948).

[21] H. Fröhlich, *Ann. Physik*, **13**, 229 (1932); D. A. Wooldridge, *Phys. Rev.*, **56**, 562, (1939); E. Rudberg and J. C. Slater, *Phys. Rev.*, **50**, 150 (1936); A. J. Dekker and A. van der Ziel, *Phys. Rev.*, **86**, 755 (1952); A. van der Ziel, *Phys. Rev.*, **92**, 35 (1953); J. F. Marshall, *Phys. Rev.*, **88**, 416 (1952); E. M. Baroody, *Phys. Rev.*, **89**, 910 (1953).

where ϵ is an effective dielectric constant. In metals and, in general for high densities of conduction electrons, the situation is different. The presence of the "extra" primary electron has the tendency to push the conduction electrons away from it. This results in the setting up of local space charges, because the positive ion cores are virtually at rest. Consequently, the field of the primary dies out over distances of the order of a few Angstroms. Without going into detail, it may suffice to say that the effect of the plasma[16] (conduction electrons plus positive ion cores) on the interaction between two electrons may be included by using instead of (17-24) a screened potential of the type,

$$V(\mathbf{R},\mathbf{r}) = \frac{e^2}{|\mathbf{R}-\mathbf{r}|}\exp\left[-\frac{\lambda}{|\mathbf{R}-\mathbf{r}|}\right]\qquad(17\text{-}25)$$

where $\lambda \simeq 10^8$ cm^{-1}. Because of its simplicity we shall assume (17-24) to be valid and quote the results for metals based on (17-25).

If there is no interaction, a primary electron plus a lattice electron can be represented by the wave function

$$u_0 = e^{i(\mathbf{K}\cdot\mathbf{R})}\psi_k(\mathbf{r})e^{-iEt/\hbar}\qquad(17\text{-}26)$$

where the total energy E is equal to

$$E = E(k) + \hbar^2 K^2/2m$$

Let us suppose that at the instant $t = 0$, the interaction between the primary and lattice electron is "switched on." The wave function of the system at the instant t may then be expanded as follows:

$$u(t) = \sum_{k'}\sum_{K'} a_{k'K'}(t)e^{i(\mathbf{K}\cdot\mathbf{R})}\psi_{k'}(\mathbf{r})e^{-iE't/\hbar}\qquad(17\text{-}27)$$

with

$$E' = E(k') + \hbar^2 K'^2/2m$$

According to the usual procedure of time dependent perturbation theory, the coefficients are given by

$$a_{k'K'}(t) = \frac{1}{i\hbar}\int_0^t\!\!\int_r\!\!\int_R e^{-i(\mathbf{K}'\cdot\mathbf{R})}\psi_{k'}(\mathbf{r})\frac{e^2}{\epsilon|\mathbf{R}-\mathbf{r}|}e^{i(\mathbf{K}\cdot\mathbf{R})}\psi_k(\mathbf{r})\,e^{-i(E-E')t/\hbar}\,d\mathbf{r}\,d\mathbf{R}\,dt$$

$$(17\text{-}28)$$

where the notations $d\mathbf{r}$ and $d\mathbf{R}$ refer to integrations over the volume of the crystal. The integration over $\mathbf{R}$ becomes

$$\int \frac{e^2}{\epsilon|\mathbf{R}-\mathbf{r}|}e^{i(\mathbf{K}-\mathbf{K}')\cdot\mathbf{R}}d\mathbf{R} = \frac{4\pi e^2}{\epsilon q^2}e^{i(\mathbf{q}\cdot\mathbf{r})}$$

where $q = K - K'$. If (17-28) is furthermore integrated over time, one obtains for the transition probabilities,

$$|a_{k'K'}(t)|^2 = \frac{16\pi^2 e^4}{\epsilon^2 q^4} \cdot \frac{2[1 - \cos (E' - E)t/\hbar]}{(E' - E)^2} |I|^2 \qquad (17\text{-}29)$$

where the integral I is defined by

$$I = \int e^{i(q \cdot r)} \psi_k(r) \psi_{k'}(r) \, dr \qquad (17\text{-}30)$$

To obtain an expression for $P(K,k \rightarrow K',k') \, d\Omega'$, defined at the beginning of this section, one proceeds as follows: Expression (17-29) is multiplied by the number of states in the range dK' within a solid angle $d\Omega'$ about K', i..e, by $K'^2 \, dK' \, d\Omega' = mK' \, dE' \, d\Omega'/\hbar^2$, and integrated over dE'; the time derivative of the resulting expression then gives the rate at which these transitions occur. Furthermore, if we consider a beam of primaries with a particle density $m/\hbar K$, so that one primary crosses unit area per unit time, we finally obtain

$$P(K,k \rightarrow K',k') \, d\Omega' = \frac{4m^2 e^4 K'}{\epsilon^2 \hbar^4 q^4 K} |I|^2 \, d\Omega' \qquad (17\text{-}31)$$

As far as the selection rules for possible transitions are concerned, we note that the time function in (17-29) has a strong maximum for $E' - E = 0$, i.e., only transitions for which energy is conserved will occur with relatively high probability. The selection rule governing the momenta of the primary and lattice electron is deduced from the integral I defined by (17-30). In fact, if one writes out the Bloch functions,

$$\psi_k(r) = e^{i(k \cdot r)} u_k(r)$$

where $u_k(r)$ has the periodicity of the lattice, i.e.,

$$u_k(r) = \sum_{b_1 b_2 b_3} c_b(k) e^{ib \cdot r}$$

with b representing 2π times a vector in the reciprocal lattice, one gets

$$I = \sum_b c_b(k) \int \exp [i(q + k - k' + b) \cdot r] \, dr \qquad (17\text{-}32)$$

The integral vanishes unless

$$q + k - k' + b = 0 \quad \text{or} \quad K + k + b = K' + k' \qquad (17\text{-}33)$$

This expresses the conservation of momentum before and after collision; the momentum $\hbar b$ is contributed by the lattice.

Production of secondaries in metals. For metals, as mentioned above, a screened potential of the type (17-25) may be expected to give more accurate results than a simple Coulomb interaction. If the same calculation as given above is carried through with (17-25), van der Ziel has shown that one obtains instead of (17-31),[22]

$$P(K,k \to K',k') \, d\Omega' = \frac{4m^2 e^4 K'}{K\hbar^4 (q^2 + \lambda^2)^2} \, |I|^2 \, d\Omega' \qquad (17\text{-}34)$$

so that essentially q^4 is now replaced by $(q^2 + \lambda^2)^2$, and of course, the dielectric constant ϵ must be left out. The basic problem has thus been solved and a number of quantities of interest may now be calculated from it. For metals, it may be shown that transitions for which b in (17-33) is different from zero contribute very little to the production of secondaries. Apart from other deficiencies, this indicates that the free electron model used by Baroody is probably justified. The number of secondaries produced per second in an energy range between E' and $E' + dE'$ is of particular interest. If N is the number of conduction electrons per unit volume, van der Ziel's calculations give

$$P(E') \, dE' \simeq \frac{\pi N e^4}{E_p} \cdot \frac{dE'}{(E' + E_\lambda)^2} \qquad (17\text{-}35)$$

where E_p is the primary energy and $E_\lambda = \hbar^2 \lambda^2 / 2m \simeq 40$ ev for $\lambda \simeq 10^8$ cm^{-1}. Note that the production increases as E_p decreases, in accordance with the ideas employed in the elementary theory. We also observe that (17-35) remains finite even for E' equal to the Fermi energy E_F; this is a consequence of the screened potential. Another quantity of interest is the energy loss of the primaries per unit path length. It turns out that in first approximation this quantity is given by a Bethe-type law,

$$-\frac{dE_p}{dx} \simeq \frac{\pi N e^4}{E_p} \log \left(\frac{E_p}{eE_\lambda} \right) \qquad (17\text{-}36)$$

where the factor e in the logarithm is the base of natural logarithms. It is evident that, because the logarithm varies slowly with E_p, Whiddington's law is a good approximation, at least over not too large intervals of E_p.

Production of secondaries in insulators. In insulators and intrinsic semiconductors, secondaries are produced by excitation of electrons in the occupied bands. The situation here is much more difficult than for metals for the following reasons. In the first place, if one assumes a Sommerfeld model for the conduction electrons, one knows the energy values as well as the wave vectors for the occupied states. For filled bands, on the other hand, the relation between energy and momentum is complicated

[22] See A. van der Ziel, *Phys. Rev.*, **92**, 35 (1953).

and not simply given by $E = \hbar^2 k^2 / 2m$. Furthermore, for electrons in the occupied bands one knows little about the periodic functions $u_k(r)$ occurring in the Bloch functions, whereas for the conduction electrons in a metal it is a good approximation to consider $u_k(r)$ a constant. Consequently, there is little or no information about the value of $|I|^2$ in (17-31) and hence about the energy distribution of the secondaries produced in insulators and semiconductors. For the general theory we refer to the literature.[23] It may be of interest to note that the energy losses of the primaries again lead to a law of the form given by (17-36), i.e., the energy loss per unit path length is proportional to $E_p^{-1} \log (E_p/E_0)$, where E_0 is an excitation energy, which varies with the primary energy as a result of the fact that only high-energy primaries are able to excite the deeper-lying electronic levels.

17-8. Interactions to be considered in the escape mechanism; factors determining high and low yields

As we have mentioned before, the description of the escape mechanism by a simple exponential absorption law is unsatisfactory in the sense that it does not give insight into the actual processes that determine the probability of escape. Recently, however, some attempts have been made to set up a theory for the escape mechanism based on our knowledge of the behavior of electrons in crystals. In general, a secondary produced at a certain depth x with a given energy E_0 may be expected to carry out a Brownian motion during which it may undergo the following types of interactions:

(i) Interaction with lattice electrons

(ii) Interaction with lattice vibrations

(iii) Interaction with electron traps

(iv) Interaction with occupied donor levels, if present

Consequently, the energy of a secondary gradually decreases, and as soon as it drops below a minimum value E_{min} required to escape from the surface, it is no longer of importance for the secondary emission process. In other words, for a secondary to have a nonvanishing escape probability it must have lost less than $(E_0 - E_{min})$ during the period required to drift from its point of origin to the surface. For metals $E_{min} = E_F + \phi \simeq 10$ ev, where E_F is the Fermi energy and ϕ is the work function. In insulators E_{min} is equal to the electron affinity of the crystal $\chi \simeq 1$ ev.

For metals, (i) refers essentially to interaction with the conduction electrons and may be expected to be practically independent of temperature.

[23] See, for example, A. J. Dekker and A. van der Ziel, *Phys. Rev.*, **86**, 755 (1952).

Any temperature effect of the secondary emission may be expected to result from (ii) because the mean free path for lattice scattering is temperature-dependent. However, for metals no temperature effect has been observed, indicating that (i) essentially determines the escape probability in this case. Interactions (iii) and (iv) are irrelevant in the case of metals. As a result of the strong interaction between secondaries and the conduction electrons in metals, and the relatively high average energy loss suffered by the secondaries in such collisions, the secondary yield of metals is in general small.

In insulators the density of electrons in the conduction band is so small that their presence may be neglected. This leaves, as far as (i) is concerned, only the possibility of energy losses due to excitation of electrons from the filled band. For such excitation processes, energies of the order of several ev are required. Thus if E_e is the minimum excitation energy involved, interactions of type (i) do not occur for secondaries of energies below E_e. Furthermore, because E_e for a good insulator is in general appreciably larger than the electron affinity χ of the crystal, secondaries in insulators have on the average a good chance of escaping from the surface, unless any of the other type of interaction would lead to relatively high energy losses. Neglecting for the moment (iii) and (iv), the escape mechanism for insulators is then essentially determined by the interaction with lattice vibrations. This leads to a temperature-dependence of the yield, as will be discussed in Sec. (17-9). The possible influence of traps and donor levels will be discussed briefly in Sec. (17-10). From these qualitative remarks and from the fact that in a collision with the lattice an electron of several ev energy loses on the average about 0.1 ev or less, it will be evident that relatively high yields may be expected for insulators. This is in agreement with the experimental data.

In intrinsic semiconductors such as germanium and silicon, the upper filled band is separated from the conduction band by only about 1 ev. Thus, electrons with energies > 1 ev are likely to lose appreciable amounts of energy by exciting lattice electrons from the filled band into the conduction band. This, combined with the fact that $\chi \simeq 1$ ev, leads one to the conclusion that the secondary yield for such materials should be relatively small and of the same order as for metals. This is in agreement with the observations. On the other hand, a small temperature effect of the yield is observed in germanium (Fig. (17-4)), showing its position to be intermediate between metals and insulators in this respect.

Before discussing some of the processes mentioned above, we may call attention to the following general formula for the probability of escape of electrons at the surface of a solid. Let E_{min} be the minimum energy required in the direction perpendicular to the surface for an electron to escape. For electrons of a total energy E and assuming an isotropic velocity distribution, the probability $P(E)$ of escape is then given by

$$P(E) = 1 - \left(\frac{E_{\min}}{E}\right)^{1/2} \tag{17-37}$$

as can readily be verified by the reader.

17-9. The temperature effect of the secondary yield in insulators

Although the production of secondaries in metals is well in hand according to the discussion of Sec. (17-7), the escape problem for metals is rather complicated because of the interaction of secondaries with conduction electrons.[24] The situation for insulators is just the reverse. The theory of the production of secondaries is too general to give quantitative results in specific cases, but certain aspects of the escape mechanism may be discussed by means of relatively simple concepts. We shall therefore discuss here the escape mechanism for insulators and in particular the influence of temperature on the secondary yield.[25] To begin with, the influence of temperature on the range of the secondaries will be calculated and from it one may then predict how the temperature should influence the secondary yield.

For simplicity let us for the moment consider only those secondaries which are produced with an initial energy E_0 and let us assume that the secondaries interact only with lattice vibrations, thus neglecting traps and donor levels. From the theory of the interaction between electrons and lattice vibrations it follows that the average energy lost by an electron of some ev per collision is independent of the energy of the electron and only a function of temperature.[26] Denoting the average energy loss per collision by $\alpha(T)$, the energy of a secondary as function of the number of collisions N it has suffered since it was produced is given by

$$E(N) = E_0 - N\alpha(T) \tag{17-38}$$

Also, the mean free path for collisions with lattice vibrations for electrons of several ev of energy is proportional to the energy times a function of temperature. We may therefore write for the mean free path,

$$\lambda(E,T) = \lambda_0 E f(T) \tag{17-39}$$

where λ_0 is a constant. According to (17-38) the energy decreases linearly with N, and therefore, so does λ. Now, we have seen in the preceding section that a certain minimum energy $E_{\min}$ is required for escape. Hence,

[24] For a discussion of this problem, see P. A. Wolff, *Phys. Rev.*, **95**, 56 (1954).

[25] A. J. Dekker, *Phys. Rev.*, **94**, 1179 (1954).

[26] See, for example, F. Seitz, *Phys. Rev.*, **73**, 549 (1948); **76**, 1376 (1949).

the "life" of a secondary is limited to a maximum number of collisions N_m such that

$$N_m \alpha(T) = E_0 - E_{\min} \tag{17-40}$$

If the motion of the secondaries is considered a Brownian motion in one dimension, the mean square displacement of a secondary during its "life" of N_m collisions is given by

$$\langle x^2 \rangle_{av} = N_m \langle \lambda^2 \rangle_{av} = N_m \lambda_0^2 [f(T)]^2 \langle E^2 \rangle_{av} \tag{17-41}$$

where the averages must be taken over the N_m collisions. Now, according to (17-38) we may write

$$\langle E^2 \rangle_{av} = E_0^2 + \alpha^2 \langle N^2 \rangle_{av} - 2\alpha E_0 \langle N \rangle_{av}$$

The average value of N is simply $N_m/2$, and if $N_m \gg 1$, which we shall assume to be the case,

$$\langle N^2 \rangle_{av} = \int_0^{N_m} \frac{N^2 \, dN}{N_m} = \frac{1}{3} N_m^2$$

Making use of (17-40), one readily finds that $\langle E^2 \rangle_{av}$ is independent of temperature and only determined by the constants E_0 and $E_{\min}$. Hence the temperature-dependence of the mean square displacement may be expressed by

$$\langle x^2 \rangle_{av} = \text{const. } N_m [f(T)]^2 = \text{const. } \frac{[f(T)]^2}{\alpha(T)} \tag{17-42}$$

Clearly, the square root of this expression may be considered a measure for the range of the secondaries. Although the range increases with increasing values of E_0, the temperature-dependence for any value of E_0 is evidently determined by (17-42). Let us now consider the case for which the primary energy is large, i.e., the range of the primaries is large compared with the range of the secondaries. From the discussion in Sec. 17-3 it follows that in this case the production of secondaries is nearly constant over a depth equal to the range of the secondaries. Thus to a first approximation, one expects the secondary yield to be proportional to the range of the secondaries. The ratio of the yields at two different temperatures T_1 and T_2 would then be given by

$$\frac{\delta_1}{\delta_2} \simeq \frac{f(T_1)}{f(T_2)} \left[\frac{\alpha(T_2)}{\alpha(T_1)} \right]^{1/2} \quad \text{for} \quad x_p \gg x_s \tag{17-43}$$

For ionic crystals, the mean free path for lattice scattering is given by[25]

$$\lambda = \frac{\lambda_0 E}{(2n_r + 1)} \quad \text{or} \quad f(T) = \frac{1}{(2n_r + 1)} \tag{17-44}$$

where $n_r = [\exp(h\nu/kT) - 1]^{-1}$ and ν is the frequency of the optical longitudinal vibrations of the lattice. Furthermore, the average energy loss per collision suffered by a secondary is given by

$$\alpha(T) = -\frac{dE}{dx}\lambda = \frac{h\nu}{2n_\nu + 1} \qquad (17\text{-}45)$$

Thus for ionic crystals, expression (17-43) may be written in the form

$$\frac{\delta_1}{\delta_2} \simeq \left[\frac{2n_{\nu 2} + 1}{2n_{\nu 1} + 1}\right]^{1/2} \quad \text{for} \quad x_p \gg x_s \qquad (17\text{-}46)$$

This result has been applied to explain the variation in yield as function of temperature for magnesium oxide single crystals.[25] For $T_1 = 1013°K$ and $T_2 = 298°K$, Johnson and McKay observed an average ratio $\delta_1/\delta_2 = 0.78$ for primary energies above 2 kev.[5] Now, from optical absorption measurements it follows that for MgO, $h\nu = 1300\,k$.[25] Employing this value, one obtains from (17-46) for the same ratio, $\delta_1/\delta_2 = 0.76$, in good agreement with the experimental value. It thus seems that the simple model used above gives a satisfactory explanation of the temperature effect in MgO. For nonpolar crystals a similar calculation may be carried out, starting from (17-43). However, no experimental data are available to check the theory further. It may be noted that a more general theory[27] based on the Boltzmann transport equation leads to the same result as obtained here.

It must be emphasized that as the temperature is raised the average energy loss suffered by the secondary per collision decreases. For MgO, for example,

$$\alpha\,(298°K) = 0.108\text{ ev} \qquad \alpha\,(1013°K) = 0.063\text{ ev}$$

The decrease of the yield with increasing temperature is thus a consequence of the reduction in the mean free path and of the fact that the path of the secondaries is curled up. In fact, if the secondaries moved in straight lines toward the surface, there would be no temperature effect, because dE/dx is temperature-independent for electrons of a few ev energy. (For thermal electrons this is not true).

For low primary energies, corresponding to the rising part of the yield curve, the influence of temperature on the yield is very slight, because most secondaries are then produced close to the surface and the energy losses resulting from scattering become less important.

17-10. The possible influence of donor levels on the secondary yield of insulators

The question may be raised as to whether it would be possible to increase the secondary yield of an insulator by introducing donor levels.

[27] A. J. Dekker, *Physica*, **21**, 29 (1955).

In principle, such donor levels may influence the production of secondary electrons as well as the escape mechanism of the secondaries. Let us first consider the possible influence of a certain concentration of donor levels on the escape mechanism. Qualitatively, one might argue that secondaries on their way to the surface may ionize the donors, thus leading to electron multiplication and an increase in the secondary yield. Quantitatively, however, it seems that the probability for this process to occur is very small, except if the donor concentration near the surface is extremely high. The reasons for this are the following. In the preceding section we have seen that as a result of the interaction with lattice vibrations the secondaries are slowed down gradually. Thus the escape mechanism can be influenced by imperfections only if the interaction with these imperfections takes place within the period required for a secondary to be slowed down to the minimum energy E_{min} required for escape. Thus, consider a secondary produced with an initial energy of $E_0 = 6$ ev, and let $E_{min} = 1$ ev. If the secondary loses on the average 0.05 ev per collision with the lattice, its slowing-down life extends over about 100 collisions. For a mean free path for scattering of, say, 10 Å, the actual path length covered by the secondary during life is then approximately 1000 Å. Let there be 10^{18} donors per cm^3; if σ is the cross section for ionization of a donor by a secondary, the minimum value for the cross section in order to obtain a measurable change in the yield must then be of the order of 10^{-14} cm^2. Although such cross sections are not impossible, they are very large indeed, and it seems that considerably higher donor concentrations would be required to produce an observable effect on the escape mechanism. Similar arguments hold for other lattice defects.

As far as the possible influence of donor levels on the production of secondaries in insulators is concerned, the following remarks may be made. First of all, the donor concentration is always small compared with that of the host atoms in the lattice. It seems, therefore, that any increase in the production of secondaries resulting from the direct interaction between the incident primaries and the donor levels would be very small. On the other hand, the incident primaries probably produce a considerable number of excitons in their wake; these excitons may diffuse about in the crystal and ultimately give up their energy by ionizing a donor electron as in the case of the photoelectric phenomena discussed in Sec. 15-9. The possible enhancement of the secondary emission resulting from ionization of donors by excitons has been discussed by the author.[28]

REFERENCES

H. Bruining, *Physics and Applications of Secondary Electron Emission*, McGraw-Hill, New York, 1954.

[28] A. J. Dekker, *Physica*, **22**, 361 (1956).

O. Hachenberg and W. Brauer, *Fortschr. Physik*, **1**, 439 (1954).

K. G. McKay, *Advances in Electronics*, **1**, 66 (1948).

R. Kollath, *Encyclopedia of Physics*, Springer, Berlin, vol. **21**, 232–291, (1956).

L. R. Koller, *Gen. Elec. Rev.*, **51**, 33, 50 (1948).

D. A. Wright, *Semi-Conductors*, Methuen, London, 1950, Chap. 5.

PROBLEMS

17-1. At first sight it may seem strange that the "range" of a primary electron may be smaller than that of a secondary, because the energy of the former is always larger than that of the latter. From the definitions of x_p and x_s used in the theory of secondary emission, explain that this difficulty actually does not exist.

17-2. Assuming $A = 10^{12}$ volt² cm⁻¹ in the Whiddington law (17-2), calculate the penetration depth of primaries of 500, 2000, and 5000 ev.

17-3. Plot dE_p/dx versus E_p for the range $E_p = 200$ ev to 5000 ev according to equation (17-36), assuming $N = 10^{22}$ cm⁻³ and $E_\lambda = 40$ ev. Approximate the high primary energy region by a Whiddington law and compare the value of A obtained in this way with the value given by H. M. Terrill, *Phys. Rev.*, **22**, 161 (1922).

17-4. Give a complete derivation of (17-12), filling in the steps omitted Sec. 17-3.

17-5. Explain why in Fig. 17-8 the primary energy for which the yield is a maximum shifts to larger values with increasing angles of incidence with the normal.

17-6. Give a derivation of equation (17-18).

17-7. Derive equation (17-37) for the escape probability; note that this equation is identical with the statement in Baroody's theory that $(\mu - \mu_0)/\mu$ is the probability of escape for an electron at the surface.

17-8. Calculate the mean square displacement for a secondary electron in MgO at room temperature, assuming it is slowed down by lattice vibrations from an energy of 5 ev to 2 ev. Employ the data for the mean free path given in A. J. Dekker, *Phys. Rev.*, **94**, 179 (1954). Carry out the same calculation for a temperature of 600°K.

17-9. Employing the data of A. J. Dekker, *loc. cit.*, calculate the diffusion coefficient for electrons with an energy of 4 ev in MgO. From it, calculate the mobility of such electrons by means of the Einstein relation.

17-10. According to recent measurements by J. R. Young, *Phys. Rev.*, **103**, 292 (1956) the range of primary electrons up to 5 kev in Al_2O_3 is given by $R = 0.0115\ E^{1.35}$, where R is expressed in mg/cm² and E in kev. Calculate the penetration depth of an electron of 1 kev. Show that $-dE/dx$ is proportional to $E^{-0.35}$; compare this result with Whiddington's law. Develop an elementary theory of secondary emission based on these new developments, assuming for simplicity that the primary range is proportional to $E_p^{4/3}$.

Chapter 18

DIAMAGNETISM AND PARAMAGNETISM

18-1. Introductory remarks

It is convenient to group the magnetic properties of solids under the following headings:

(i) diamagnetism

(ii) paramagnetism

(iii) ferromagnetism, antiferromagnetism, ferrimagnetism

In the present chapter we shall consider the dia- and paramagnetic behavior of solids for static applied fields; the properties corresponding to group (iii) will be discussed in the next chapter. Magnetic properties depending on the frequency of an alternating applied magnetic field are discussed in Chapter 20.

When a substance is placed in a magnetic field H, a magnetic moment M per unit volume results; M is called the magnetization. For isotropic materials, M and H are parallel vectors and the susceptibility χ defined by

$$M = \chi H \qquad (18\text{-}1)$$

is then a scalar quantity. In anisotropic substances, χ is a tensor. In case M refers to a gram molecule, one may introduce the molar susceptibility χ_m. All atoms or ions produce a diamagnetic contribution to the total susceptibility, although it may be masked by the other types; it is a consequence of the magnetic moment induced in the atoms by an external field. In this respect, diamagnetism may be compared with the electronic polarization in an electric field. Both are essentially independent of temperature. There exists, however, an essential difference: in the electrical case the induced moment lies along the direction of an applied field, leading to a positive electrical susceptibility; in the magnetic case the induced moment produces a negative susceptibility.

Paramagnetism requires the existence of permanent magnetic dipoles, and the paramagnetic susceptibility is the analogue of the orientational susceptibility associated with permanent electric dipoles. In both cases the susceptibility is positive and temperature-dependent. The properties corresponding to group (iii) above also require the existence of permanent magnetic dipoles, and moreover, a relatively strong interaction between

446

them. These properties are "cooperative" in the same sense as those encountered in ferroelectricity and order-disorder transitions in alloys.

The magnetic induction B may be defined as

$$B = H + 4\pi M = \mu H \qquad (18\text{-}2)$$

where μ is called the permeability; it should not be confused with the same symbol used below for the magnetic dipole moment of an atom. Unless stated otherwise, we shall assume H, M, and B to be parallel vectors, so that μ is a scalar. For para- and diamagnetic materials, the permeability is a constant, unless saturation conditions are approached (see below). For the properties mentioned under (iii) the relation between B and H is much more complicated and shows hysteresis, as will be further discussed in Chapter 19.

From (18-1) and (18-2) it follows that

$$\mu = 1 + 4\pi\chi \qquad (18\text{-}3)$$

This relation is the analogue of the expression for the dielectric constant ϵ when χ represents the ratio of the electric moment per unit volume and the applied electric field.

It is convenient to normalize the potential energy of a dipole μ in a magnetic field H in such a way that

$$E_{\text{pot}} = -\mu \cdot H \qquad (18\text{-}4)$$

In connection with the potential energy[1] of a substance in a magnetic field and its importance in experimental determinations of the susceptibility,[2] the reader is reminded that the proper thermodynamic formulas for magnetized materials can be obtained from the "normal" thermodynamic expressions for a gas by replacing

the pressure p by M

the volume V by H

Thus, for an adiabatic process in which the magnetic field to which a substance is subjected is varied from 0 to H, the change in energy per unit volume is given by

$$\int dE = -\int_0^H M\,dH = -\int_0^H \chi H\,dH = -\tfrac{1}{2}\chi H^2 \qquad (18\text{-}5)$$

[1] For a discussion of energy relations, see E. A. Guggenheim, *Proc. Roy. Soc. (London)*, **A155**, 49 (1936).

[2] For experimental methods, see L. F. Bates, *Modern Magnetism*, 3d ed., Cambridge, London, 1951; also P. W. Selwood, *Magnetochemistry*, Interscience, New York, 1943.

18-2. The origin of permanent magnetic dipoles

As stated in the hypothesis of Ampère, magnetic dipoles have their origin in the flow of electric currents. From electricity theory it is well known, for example, that a stationary loop current flowing in a plane produces a magnetic field which at large distances may be described as resulting from a magnetic dipole[3]

$$\mu = IS/c \qquad (18\text{-}6)$$

where I is the current and S is the area of the loop. The dipole direction is perpendicular to the plane of the loop. Employing this relation, let us consider the magnetic dipole moment associated with an electron describing a circular orbit of radius r, the angular velocity of the electron being ω_0. The loop current in this case is[4] $-e\omega_0/2\pi$ so that, according to (18-6), the magnetic dipole moment associated with the electron orbit is

$$\mu = -e\omega_0 r^2/2c \qquad (18\text{-}7)$$

It is of interest to relate the magnetic dipole moment to the angular momentum of the electron, which in this case is $m\omega_0 r^2$. According to (18-7) we have

$$\mu = -(e/2mc) \times \text{angular momentum} \qquad (18\text{-}8)$$

The minus sign indicates that the dipole moment points in a direction opposite to the vector representing the angular momentum. Relation (18-8) is valid for any electron orbit, as will be shown in Sec. 18-7; it is not valid, however, for the spin of an electron or nucleus, as we shall see below.

The use of quantum numbers.[5] A few remarks may be made here to refresh the reader's memory on the use of quantum numbers in the theory of atoms.

(a) The principal quantum number n determines the energy of the orbit; it can accept only the integer values $n = 1, 2, 3, \dots$. The corresponding electronic shells are called the K, L, M, N, ... shells.

(b) The angular momentum of the orbit is determined by the quantum number l, which is restricted to the set of values

$$l = 0, 1, 2, \dots, (n-1) \qquad (18\text{-}9)$$

---

[3] For a general proof, see, for example, R. Becker, *Theorie der Elektrizität*, Teubner, Leipzig, 1933, Vol. 2, p. 96. See also Problem 18-1 for a particularly simple example.

[4] Unless otherwise specified, the electronic charge will be represented by $-e$.

[5] A clear account may be found in G. Herzberg, *Atomic Spectra and Atomic Structure*, Dover, New York, 1944.

The total angular momentum associated with a given value of l is

$$\hbar[l(l+1)]^{1/2} \tag{18-10}$$

Electrons associated with states $l = 0, 1, 2, 3, \ldots$ are called, respectively, $s, p, d, f, g, \ldots$ electrons. Note that electrons in an s state always have zero angular momentum and thus a vanishing magnetic moment.

(c) The possible components of the angular momentum along any specified direction (such as the direction of an external magnetic field H)

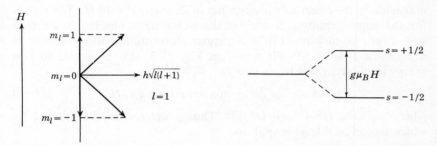

Fig. 18-1. Illustrating the three possible orientations of an angular momentum defined by the quantum number $l = 1$ in an external magnetic field.

Fig. 18-2. Illustrating the splitting of an energy level for an electron with a spin $\frac{1}{2}$ and zero orbital momentum in a magnetic field. For $s = +\frac{1}{2}$, the magnetic moment of 1 Bohr magneton is antiparallel; for $s = -\frac{1}{2}$ parallel to the field, in accordance with (18-12).

are determined by the magnetic quantum number m, where m is restricted to the set of values

$$m_l = l, (l-1), \ldots 0, \ldots -l(l-1), -l \tag{18-11}$$

For example, a p electron has the possible components of angular momentum along the direction of a magnetic field $\hbar$, 0, $-\hbar$. Consequently, the possible magnetic moment components along the direction of an applied magnetic field are (see Fig. 18-1)

$$-e\hbar/2mc, \quad 0, \quad +e\hbar/2mc$$

The quantity $e\hbar/2mc = 0.927 \times 10^{-20}$ erg/oersted is called the Bohr magneton; it will be denoted by μ_B.

(d) So far we have described an electron simply as a particle of charge e and mass m. However, the electron itself has an angular momentum known as the spin. The possible angular momentum components of the spin along an external field direction are $\pm\hbar/2$. This has led to the introduction of the spin quantum number $s = \pm\frac{1}{2}$.

On the basis of (18-8) one thus expects that the electron spin will give rise to a component of half a Bohr magneton. It must be emphasized, however, that for the spin, relation (18-8) is not valid. In fact the magnetic moment component μ_{sz} of the spin along an external field is given by

$$\mu_{sz} = g(e/2mc)(\hbar/2) \qquad (18\text{-}12)$$

where g is called the spectroscopic splitting factor, or the gyromagnetic ratio (actually, it is the inverse of the latter). For the electron spin $g = 2.0023$, i.e., the electron spin gives rise to very nearly one Bohr magneton in the direction (or opposite) of an external field H. The reason for the name "splitting factor" is the following. Consider an electron with a spin $\frac{1}{2}$ and without orbital angular momentum, under influence of a magnetic field H. As illustrated in Fig. 18-2, this gives rise to two energy levels separated by an energy

$$\Delta E = 2|\mu_{sz}|H = g(e/2mc)\hbar H = g\mu_B H \qquad (18\text{-}13)$$

where we used (18-4) and (18-12). Thus g determines the amount by which the original level is split up.

(e) The orbital angular momentum and the spin may be combined vectorially to give the total angular momentum; the latter is determined by the quantum number j. Thus, for an electron with a certain l and a spin of $\frac{1}{2}$, j can accept the values $l \pm \frac{1}{2}$. In atoms containing a number of electrons, the l vectors may be combined to form a resultant L, and the s vectors are combined to form a resultant S. This type of combination is called Russell-Saunders coupling; it is the only type of coupling that we shall consider. The resultants L and S then combine to form the total angular momentum J of the whole electron system of the atom. For such atoms, the spectroscopic splitting factor is given by the Landé formula,[6]

$$g = 1 + \frac{J(J+1) + S(S+1) - L(L+1)}{2J(J+1)} \qquad (18\text{-}14)$$

Hund's rules. In order to predict the magnetic dipole moment associated with the electronic system of a given atom, the above considerations must be combined with the Pauli principle and Hund's rules. According to the Pauli principle, only one electron can occupy a state defined by the set of quantum numbers n, l, m_l, and s. We leave it up to the reader to show that this leads immediately to the conclusion that filled electron shells do not contribute to the magnetic moment of an atom. Thus the magnetic moment in atoms must result from incompletely filled shells. With regard to the latter, Hund's rules state that for the ground state of such atoms:

(i) The electron spins add to give the maximum possible S consistent with the Pauli principle.

[6] For a derivation see G. Herzberg, *op. cit.*, p. 109.

(ii) The orbital momenta combine to give the maximum value for L that is consistent with (i).

(iii) For an incompletely filled shell, we have

$J = L - S$ for a shell less than half occupied,

$J = L + S$ for a shell more than half occupied.

For example, consider the Cr^{2+} ion, with an electron configuration $1s^2$; $2s^2$, $2p^6$, $3s^2$, $3p^6$, $3d^4$.[7] All shells are filled except the $3d$ shell, which contains four electrons. For a d shell, $l = 2$, so that according to (18-11) m_l has $2l + 1 = 5$ possible values. Each of these can accommodate 2 electrons ($s = \pm\frac{1}{2}$), so that the maximum number of electrons in the $3d$ level is 10. In the Cr^{2+} ion, the $3d$ shell is therefore less than half occupied. According to Hund's rule (i), we have $S = 2$. The possible m_l values are $+2$, $+1$, 0, -1, and -2. If we place the four electrons all with a spin of $+\frac{1}{2}$ in the first four of these, one obtains $L = 2$, which is the maximum value consistent with the spin distribution. Hence, according to (iii), we have in this case $J = 0$.

Other atoms or ions may be treated in a similar way and from the S, L, and J values, the magnetic moment may be calculated from (18-14) and (18-12).

Nuclear magnetic moments. So far we have mentioned only the orbital motion and the spin of the electrons as possible contributors to the magnetic moment of atoms. Another contribution may arise from the nuclear magnetic moment. The latter is expressed in nuclear magnetons, in analogy with the Bohr magneton defined by

$$\mu_n = e\hbar/2M_p c = 5.05 \times 10^{-24} \text{ erg/oersted} \qquad (18\text{-}15)$$

where M_p represents the mass of a proton. Thus nuclear magnetic moments are smaller than those associated with the electrons by a factor $\sim 10^3$. The nuclear magnetic moments are a result of the nuclear angular momentum (nuclear spin).

Summarizing, we see that atomic magnetic dipoles originate from: (a) the orbital motion of the electrons; (b) the electron spin; (c) the nuclear spin.

18-3. Diamagnetism and the Larmor precession

The basic principle of diamagnetic behavior may be illustrated readily with reference to the well-known law of Lenz in electricity theory.

---

[7] $1s^2$ means: two electrons in the $1s$ state ($n = 1$, $l = 0$), etc.

Consider a loop current with its associated magnetic field. When one attempts to change the magnetic flux enclosed by the loop by applying an external field H, a current is induced in such a direction that the magnetic field resulting from the induced current counteracts the field H. Suppose now that the electrical resistance of the loop is zero; the induced current will then persist as long as the external field is present. Such a

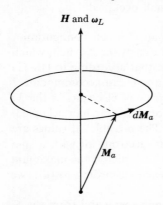

situation is realized in the loop current associated with the motion of an electron in an atom. It is also approached in superconductors. Consequently, any atomic orbit will produce a negative contribution to the magnetic susceptibility.

Fig. 18-3. The angular momentum vector M_a precesses about H with the Larmor frequency ω_L as a consequence of the torque exerted by the magnetic field on the magnetic dipole moment associated with M_a.

The Larmor precession. Let us now consider the influence of a magnetic field on the motion of an electron in an atom quantitatively. With reference to Fig. 18-3, we shall assume an arbitrary direction for the angular momentum vector M_a relative to the magnetic field H.

The magnetic dipole moment is in accordance with (18-8)

$$\mu = -(e/2mc)M_a \qquad (18\text{-}16)$$

The magnetic field produces a torque $\mu \times H$ on the dipole, so that, according to Newtonian mechanics, we may write

$$(d/dt)M_a = \mu \times H = -(e/2mc)M_a \times H \qquad (18\text{-}17)$$

This is the equation of motion of a vector M_a precessing about H with an angular frequency

$$\omega_L = eH/2mc \qquad (18\text{-}18)$$

where ω_L is called the Larmor frequency. That this is so can be seen from Fig. 18-3, from which it follows that for a precession of the type (18-18),

$$dM_a = \omega_L \times M_a \, dt = (e/2mc)H \times M_a$$

in agreement with (18-17). We note that $e/2mc = 1.40 \times 10^6$ sec^{-1} gauss^{-1}, so that even for a field of 10^5 gausses the Larmor frequency ω_L is much smaller than the angular frequency of the electron in its orbit ($\simeq 10^{14}$ to 10^{15} radians sec^{-1}). It should be realized that the derivation of (18-18) is based on the assumption that M_a is independent of H, i.e., it is assumed that the orbit is not deformed under influence of the magnetic field. To a first approximation this is correct.

From what has been said above, it follows that under the influence of an external field, the plane of the orbit is not stationary, but precesses about H. As a result of the charge of the electron, the precession produces an induced magnetic moment with a component opposite to that of H. In fact, in accordance with (18-8), this component is equal to

$$(\mu_{\text{ind}})_H = -(e/2mc)m\omega_L\langle\rho\rangle^2 = -(e^2/4mc^2)H\langle\rho\rangle^2 \qquad (18\text{-}19)$$

where $\langle\rho\rangle^2$ is the mean square radius of the projection of the orbit on a plane perpendicular to H. When this treatment is extended to a solid containing N atoms per cm³, each atom containing Z electrons, one obtains for the diamagnetic susceptibility defined as the induced moment per cm³ per gauss,

$$\chi_{\text{dia}} = -NZ(e^2/6mc^2)\langle r^2\rangle \qquad (18\text{-}20)$$

Here it has been assumed that the charge distribution of the atoms is spherically symmetric, so that $\langle r^2\rangle = \frac{3}{2}\langle\rho\rangle^2$ represents the mean square distance of the electrons from the nucleus.[8] The diamagnetic susceptibility is thus determined essentially by the charge distribution in the atoms. Note that χ is negative. With $\langle r^2\rangle \simeq 10^{-16}$ cm² and with $N \simeq 5.10^{22}$ cm⁻³, one obtains $\chi \simeq 10^{-7}Z \simeq 10^{-6}$.

Experimental values for the molar diamagnetic susceptibility of a number of ions in solids are given in Table 18-1.[9] It should be emphasized that the susceptibility of ions is determined to some extent by their environment and the values are therefore approximate. Note the increase in the absolute magnitude of χ_M with the number of electrons per ion. The reader may compare this table with that for the polarizabilities of these ions (Table 6-1).

Table 18-1. The Molar Diamagnetic Susceptibility $\times 10^6$ for a Number of Ions

Li⁺	−0.7	Mg²⁺	−4.3	F⁻	−9.4
Na⁺	−6.1	Ca²⁺	−10.7	Cl⁻	−24.2
K⁺	−14.6	Sr²⁺	−18.0	Br⁻	−34.5
Rb⁺	−22.0	Ba²⁺	−29.0	I⁻	−50.6
Cs⁺	−35.0				

[8] For a spherical charge distribution

$$\langle x^2\rangle = \langle y^2\rangle = \langle z^2\rangle;$$

furthermore

$$\langle r^2\rangle = \langle x^2\rangle + \langle y^2\rangle + \langle z^2\rangle \text{ and } \langle\rho\rangle^2 = \langle x^2\rangle + \langle y^2\rangle.$$

[9] G. W. Brindley and F. E. Hoare, *Trans. Faraday Soc.*, **33**, 268 (1937); *Proc. Phys. Soc. (London)*, **49**, 619 (1937).

For a discussion of the diamagnetism associated with the free electrons in metals, we refer the reader to the literature.[10] For a simple semi-classical theory of the diamagnetism of organic ring molecules, using electric circuit theory, see Pauling.[11]

18-4. The static paramagnetic susceptibility

The classical theory of paramagnetism. Consider a medium containing N magnetic dipole moments μ per unit volume. Suppose the interaction between the dipoles is weak, so that the field in which a given dipole finds itself is equal to the applied field H. We shall assume in this section that the magnetic field is constant or varies very slowly with time. In the classical theory, the dipoles are assumed to be freely rotating. Hence the resulting magnetic moment M per unit volume can be calculated in exactly the same way as the polarization P for a dipolar gas. Thus, according to the Langevin-Debye theory (see Sec. 6-3) we find

$$M = N\mu L(\mu H/kT) \tag{18-21}$$

where $L(x)$ is the Langevin function. As long as $\mu H \ll kT$ this reduces to the simple expression

$$M \simeq N\mu^2 H/3kT \quad \text{or} \quad \chi = N\mu^2/3kT \tag{18-22}$$

Note that μ is of the order of one Bohr magneton $\simeq 10^{-20}$ erg/gauss, so that for a field of 10^4 gausses, $\mu H \simeq 10^{-16}$ erg. At room temperature $kT/3 \simeq 10^{-14}$ erg, so that the condition $\mu H \ll kT$ is satisfied except for very low temperatures. The relation $\chi = \text{const.}/T$ is known as the Curie law.

The quantum theory of paramagnetism. According to the quantum theory, the permanent magnetic moment of a given atom or ion is not freely rotating, but restricted to a finite set of orientations relative to the applied field. Let us thus consider a medium containing N atoms per unit volume, the total angular momentum quantum number of each atom being J (this combines the total orbital angular momentum L and the total spin S of the electronic system per atom). According to the discussion of Sec. 18-2, this gives rise to the possible components of the magnetic moment,

$$M_J g \mu_B \quad \text{where} \quad M_J = J, (J-1), \ldots, -(J-1), -J \tag{18-23}$$

Here M_J is the magnetic quantum number associated with J. The potential energy of a magnetic dipole with a component $M_J g \mu_B$ along H

[10] See, for example, F. Seitz, *Modern Theory of Solids*, McGraw-Hill, New York, 1940, p. 583.
[11] L. Pauling, *J. Chem. Phys.*, **4**, 673 (1936).

is $-M_J g \mu_B H$, so that, according to statistical mechanics, the magnetization is given by

$$M = N \frac{\sum\limits_{-J}^{+J} M_J g \mu_B \exp (M_J g \mu_B H/kT)}{\sum\limits_{-J}^{+J} \exp (M_J g \mu_B H/kT)} \tag{18-24}$$

The coefficient of N on the right-hand side is the statistical average of the magnetic moment component per atom along H.

We may distinguish again between two cases:

(i) $M_J g \mu_B H/kT \ll 1$. Under these circumstances the exponentials in (18-24) may be approximated by $(1 + M_J g \mu_B H/kT)$, and by writing out the sums, one readily finds for the paramagnetic susceptibility,

$$\chi = M/H = Ng^2 J(J+1)\mu_B^2/3kT \tag{18-25}$$

This result is identical with the classical result (18-22) because the total magnetic moment μ_J associated with J is given by

$$\mu_J^2 = g^2 J(J+1)\mu_B^2 \tag{18-26}$$

See, for example, expression (18-10). We note that from susceptibility measurements in the range where the Curie law holds, it is possible to determine the effective number of Bohr magnetons.

$$p_{\text{eff}} = g[J(J+1)]^{1/2} \tag{18-27}$$

(ii) At low temperatures and strong magnetic fields the condition imposed under (i) may not be satisfied, and (18-24) must be calculated without approximating the exponentials. After some algebraic manipulation[12] one obtains the expression

$$M = NgJ\mu_B B_J(x) \tag{18-28}$$

where $x = gJ\mu_B H/kT$ and $B_J(x)$ is the Brillouin function defined by

$$B_J(x) = \frac{2J+1}{2J} \coth \left[\frac{(2J+1)x}{2J} \right] - \frac{1}{2J} \coth \left(\frac{x}{2J} \right) \tag{18-29}$$

Physically speaking, this result implies saturation of the magnetization at low temperatures, i.e., all dipoles ultimately will be directed along H. In this respect (18-28) is the analogue of the Langevin expression (18-21), the difference being that the latter holds for freely rotating dipoles only. In fact, if $J \to \infty$ (infinite number of possible orientations), the Brillouin expression (18-28) becomes identical with (18-21).

The order of magnitude of the paramagnetic susceptibility of a solid per cm³ may be estimated from (18-25). With $N \simeq 10^{22}$ and a dipole

---

[12] See, for example, L. F. Bates, op. cit., p. 43.

moment of one Bohr magneton, one obtains $\chi \simeq 1/300T$. At room temperature $\chi \simeq 10^{-5}$; at $1°K$, $\chi \simeq 10^{-3} - 10^{-2}$. These values are of importance in connection with the following question which may arise: in the theory of the dielectric polarization of a solid it was necessary to introduce the internal electric field, i.e., the actual field acting on a given

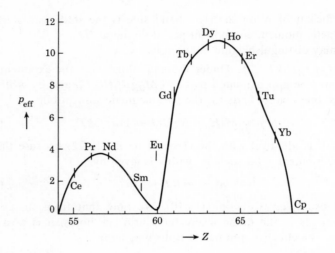

Fig. 18-4. The effective moment in Bohr magnetons as function of the number of electrons for the trivalent positive rare earth ions. The full curve represents the values calculated from (18-27); the vertical lines represent the range of experimental values. [After Bates, *Modern Magnetism*, Cambridge, 1951, p. 148]

atom was represented by the sum of the applied field and the field due to the polarization of the surroundings. On the other hand, in the derivation of the magnetic susceptibility above, the field acting on a dipole in a paramagnetic solid was assumed to be equal to the applied field H. The justification for this is the following: the order of magnitude of the internal field is given by $H + \gamma M = H(1 + \gamma\chi)$, where $\gamma \simeq 4$. Hence the fractional error made in neglecting the internal field correction is of the order of χ. As we have seen above, this is small for paramagnetic materials. For the electrical case, the susceptibility is $P/E = (\epsilon - 1)/4\pi$, and the internal field cannot be neglected in solids or liquids, since $(\epsilon - 1)$ is not small compared with unity.

It should finally be mentioned that there exists also a temperature-independent paramagnetic contribution to the susceptibility at low temperatures. This is called van Vleck paramagnetism. For its theoretical treatment we refer to van Vleck, *Theory of Electric and Magnetic Susceptibilities*, Oxford, New York, 1932.

18-5. Comparison of theory and experiment for paramagnetic salts

It was noted in Sec. 18-2 that paramagnetism requires the existence of partly filled electronic shells. Thus paramagnetic compounds are essentially those containing transition group elements. Of these, the rare earth group (incomplete $4f$ shell) and the iron group (incomplete $3d$ shell) have been investigated most extensively. The palladium group ($4d$), the platinum group ($5d$), and the uranium group ($5f$–$6d$) have received relatively little attention.

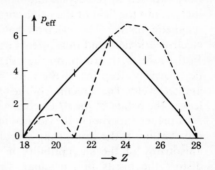

The rare earth ions. The theory outlined in the preceding section describes the behavior of most of the rare earth salts quite well. This may be seen from Fig. 18-4, where the full curve represents the effective number of Bohr magnetons calculated by van Vleck from expression (18-27); the J values and g were obtained from Hund's rules and from Landé's formula, as outlined in Sec. 18-2. The vertical lines correspond to observed values of p_{eff}, obtained from measurements of the temperature dependence of χ (see equation 18-25). The ions Sm^{3+} and Eu^{3+} evidently do not obey the simple theory.

Fig. 18-5. The effective moment in Bohr magnetons for the iron group as function of the number of electrons Z in the ions. The dashed curve represents the values calculated from (18-27); the full curve refers to the "spin-only" formula (18-30). The vertical lines represent the ranges of experimental values. [After Bates, *Modern Magnetism*, Cambridge, 1951, p. 152]

However, it has been shown by van Vleck and Frank[13] that these discrepancies can be explained satisfactorily if one considers the special situation with regard to the energy levels of these ions.

The iron group ions. If one calculates the effective number of Bohr magnetons for the ions of the iron group from expression (18-27), the results do not agree at all with the experimental values obtained from the Curie law. This may be seen from Fig. 18-5 where the vertical lines represent experimental values and the dashed curve represents (18-27). However, if one assumes that only the electron spins contribute to the magnetization, i.e., if one replaces (18-27) by

$$p_{\text{eff}} = 2[S(S+1)]^{1/2} \tag{18-30}$$

one obtains quite good agreement with experiment (full curve in Fig. 18-5). Thus the iron group ions behave as if the orbital magnetic moment

[13] A. Frank, *Phys. Rev.*, **39**, 119 (1932).

does not contribute at all. One speaks in this case of quenching of the orbital momentum. The quenching is not necessarily complete; it may be partial. Stoner suggested the following explanation for the different behavior of the rare earth and iron groups in this respect:[14] In the solid state, the paramagnetic ions find themselves in strong electric fields produced by neighboring diamagnetic ions. In the iron group, the paramagnetic $3d$ electrons are the outermost electrons and these are therefore fully exposed to the crystalline field. Consequently, the orbital motion is locked into the field of the neighbors and cannot orient itself in an external magnetic field.[15] The electron spin has no direct interaction with the electrostatic field and thus orients itself freely in an external magnetic field. In the rare earth group, on the other hand, the paramagnetic $4f$ electrons lie relatively deep inside the ions, because the outer electrons occupy $5s$ and $5p$ levels. The screening of the $4f$ electrons from the crystalline field thus leaves the orbits of the $4f$ electrons practically the same as in the free ion.

Further experimental evidence for the idea of quenching of the orbital momentum in the iron group salts has been obtained from studies of the anisotropy of the susceptibility in single crystals. The crystalline fields distort the orbits in particular directions and thus the magnetic field associated with these orbits has directional properties. The spin magnetic moment orients itself along the resultant of the external field plus the field associated with the orbits, and anisotropy results.

In connection with expression (18-28) it may be noted that at low temperatures saturation effects are observed which are described accurately by the Brillouin function;[16] for the iron salts one must, of course, use S rather than J in expression (18-28).

18-6. Nuclear paramagnetism

At the end of Sec. 18-2 it was mentioned that nuclear magnetic moments are smaller than the magnetic moments associated with electrons by a factor $\sim 10^3$. In paramagnetic substances, therefore, the static nuclear paramagnetism is masked by the electronic paramagnetism. Nuclear paramagnetism has been observed, however, in solid hydrogen,[17] which is diamagnetic as far as the electronic system is concerned. The magnetic moment obtained from these measurements is in agreement with the known proton magnetic moment of 2.793 nuclear magnetons. Nuclear magnetic moments are presently determined mainly by nuclear resonance methods, to be discussed in Chapter 20.

[14] E. C. Stoner, *Phil. Mag.*, **8**, 250 (1929).

[15] J. H. van Vleck, *Theory of Electric and Magnetic Susceptibilities*, Oxford, New York, 1932, p. 287.

[16] See, for example, W. E. Henry, *Phys. Rev.*, **88**, 559 (1952).

[17] B. Lasarew and L. Schubnikow, *Phys. Z. Sowjetunion*, **11**, 445 (1937).

18-7. The Hamiltonian for an electron in a magnetic field

It is of some interest to consider the problem of para- and diamagnetism from a somewhat different angle, starting from the Lorentz equation for the force on an electron moving in a combined electric and magnetic field.

$$F = -eE - (e/c)v \times H \tag{18-31}$$

The spin of the electron will be neglected in this section. Introducing the vector potential A by means of the relation $H = \text{curl } A$, it can be shown that (18-31) is equivalent with the following expression for the total energy (the Hamiltonian):[18]

$$\mathscr{H} = \frac{1}{2m}\left(p + \frac{e}{c}A\right)^2 + V \tag{18-32}$$

where V is the potential energy. Thus if we take

$$A_x = -\tfrac{1}{2}yH; \quad A_y = \tfrac{1}{2}xH; \quad A_z = 0$$

then $H_x = H_y = 0$ and $H = H_z$. Thus for a magnetic field in the z-direction, (18-32) becomes

$$\mathscr{H} = p^2/2m + (e/2mc)H(xp_y - yp_x) + (e^2/8mc^2)H^2(y^2 + x^2) + V \tag{18-33}$$

From this we may draw two important conclusions. First, if the electron motion were associated with a permanent magnetic dipole moment μ, this should give rise to a term $-\mu \cdot H = -\mu_z H$ in the Hamiltonian, in accordance with (18-4). Thus the second term on the right may be identified with $-\mu_z H$, so that

$$\mu_z = -(e/2mc)(xp_y - yp_x) \tag{18-34}$$

However, it follows from the definition of the angular momentum

$$M_a = r \times p \tag{18-35}$$

that (18-34) is related to the z-component of the angular momentum.

$$xp_y - yp_x = (M_a)_z \tag{18-36}$$

Hence relation (18-8) between the permanent dipole moment and the angular orbital momentum follows immediately in a general fashion from the Hamiltonian.

[18] See, for example, F. Seitz, *The Modern Theory of Solids*, McGraw-Hill, New York, 1940, p. 214; or N. F. Mott and I. N. Sneddon, *Wavemechanics and Its Applications*, Oxford, New York, 1948, p. 39.

Secondly, let us consider the term in H^2 in expression (18-33). Suppose we had written down the Hamiltonian for the electrons associated with a unit volume of a substance containing N atoms, each atom containing Z electrons. The term in H^2 would then read

$$N(e^2/8mc^2)H^2 \sum_{i=1}^{Z} (x_i^2 + y_i^2) = NZ(e^2/8mc^2)H^2\langle\rho^2\rangle \qquad (18\text{-}37)$$

where $\langle\rho^2\rangle$ represents the mean of the squares of the radii of the projections

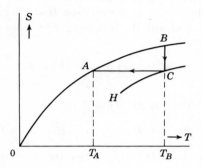

Fig. 18-6. Curves OAB and HC represent the entropy versus T without and with magnetic field, respectively. BC and CA are the first two steps in the cooling process employing adiabatic demagnetization.

of the orbits on a plane perpendicular to H. Now if the magnetic field induces a dipole moment in the material, the corresponding energy term should be quadratic in H. Thus (18-37) may be considered the energy term associated with the diamagnetism of the solid. Comparison of (18-37) and (18-5) thus yields

$$\chi_{\text{dia}} = -NZ(e^2/4mc^2)\langle\rho^2\rangle = -NZ(e^2/6mc^2)\langle r^2\rangle$$

where $\langle r^2\rangle$ represents the mean square distance of the electrons relative to the nucleus. It is observed that this result is identical with (18-20).

18-8. The principle of adiabatic demagnetization[19]

Because of its importance in obtaining temperatures below $1°K$, we may briefly indicate the principle of adiabatic demagnetization. The working substance in this process is a paramagnetic salt. In Fig. 18-6, let the curve OAB represent the entropy of the system as function of T, in the absence of an external field. Suppose now that at the temperature T_B

[19] This method was first suggested by P. Debye, *Ann. Physik*, **81**, 1154 (1926) and by W. F. Giauque, *J. Am. Chem. Soc.*, **49**, 1864 (1927).

a magnetic field H is applied isothermally (good thermal contact with a surrounding reservoir). Since the magnetic dipoles will tend to line up in parallel with the field, the spin system becomes more ordered, and hence the entropy decreases, say, from B to C. If now the specimen is isolated from its surroundings and the field is taken away, we move in Fig. 18-6 from C to A along an adiabatic ($dS = 0$). By successive steps of this kind, temperatures of 10^{-3} degree absolute have been obtained.

Thermodynamically, the problem may be treated as follows. According to the second law (see remarks in Sec. 18-1)

$$T\,dS = dE + M\,dH = \left(\frac{\partial E}{\partial T}\right)_H dT + \left[\left(\frac{\partial E}{\partial H}\right)_T + M\right] dH$$

Because dS is a total differential, it follows that

$$\frac{1}{T}\left[\left(\frac{\partial E}{\partial H}\right)_T + M\right] = \left(\frac{\partial S}{\partial H}\right)_T = \left(\frac{\partial M}{\partial T}\right)_H$$

where the last equality follows from one of the Maxwell relations. For an isothermal process (B to C) one may thus write

$$dS = \left(\frac{\partial M}{\partial T}\right)_H dH \quad \text{or} \quad S = S_{H=0} + \int_0^H \left(\frac{\partial M}{\partial T}\right)_H dH \qquad (18\text{-}38)$$

In the Curie region we have, according to (18-25) and (18-27),

$$M = N\mu_B^2 p_{\text{eff}}^2 H/3kT$$

so that then

$$S = S_{H=0} - N\mu_B^2 p_{\text{eff}}^2 H^2/6kT^2 \qquad (18\text{-}39)$$

For further details of this process we refer to the literature.[20]

REFERENCES

L. F. Bates, *Modern Magnetism*, 3d ed., Cambridge, London, 1951.

P. W. Selwood, *Magnetochemistry*, Interscience, New York, 1943.

E. C. Stoner, *Magnetism and Matter*, Methuen, London, 1934.

J. van den Handel, "Paramagnetism," *Advances in Electronics and Electron Physics*, **6**, 463 (1954).

J. H. van Vleck, *Theory of Electric and Magnetic Susceptibilities*, Oxford, New York, 1932.

J. H. van Vleck, "Landmarks in the Theory of Magnetism," *Amer. J. Phys.*, **18**, 495 (1950).

[20] See, for example, N. Kürti and F. Simon, *Proc. Roy. Soc. (London)*, **A149**, 152 (1935).

PROBLEMS

18-1. Consider a rectangular loop of wire carrying a current I. From the torque produced by a homogeneous magnetic field perpendicular to one pair of sides, show that the current is equivalent to a magnetic dipole moment $\mu = IS/c$, where S is the area of the loop. Do the same for a circular current.

18-2. Consider an electron moving in a circular orbit of radius r under influence of a nuclear charge Ze. From the equilibrium condition, find the angular frequency ω_0. Applying a magnetic field H perpendicular to the orbit and assuming that in first approximation r remains unaltered, show that the new angular frequency is

$$\omega = \pm\omega_0 + eH/2mc = \pm\omega_0 + \omega_L$$

when the Larmor frequency $\omega_L \ll \omega_0$.

18-3. Discuss the Gouy balance as an instrument for measuring the static susceptibility of a solid (see L. F. Bates or P. W. Selwood, *op. cit.*).

18-4. From the rules governing the use of quantum numbers, show that the K, L, and M shells in an atom can accommodate at most, respectively, 2, 8, and 18 electrons.

18-5. Consider a spinning spherical shell of charge e and mass m uniformly distributed over its surface. Show that the ratio of the magnetic moment to the angular momentum is $e/2mc$ (i.e., the g factor is unity).

18-6. Consider a system of N electron spins in an external field H. For $H = 10^4$ gausses and $T = 300°$K, calculate the excess number of spins oriented parallel to the field. Do the same for liquid helium temperature.

18-7. Discuss the diamagnetism of the conduction electrons in a metal on the assumption that they are free. (See for example F. Seitz, *Modern Theory of Solids*, McGraw-Hill, New York, 1940, p.583.)

18-8. Consider a system of N noninteracting spins of $\frac{1}{2}$ in a magnetic field H; the system is in equilibrium with a temperature bath T. Set up an expression for the free energy F of the system in terms of the excess number of aligned spins n, where n is for the moment undetermined. From the fact that F should be a minimum, rederive the proper expression for the susceptibility of the system.

18-9. When C_H and C_M represent, respectively, the specific heats at constant field and at constant magnetization, show from thermodynamics that for a substance which satisfies the Curie law, $M = CH/T$,

$$C_H - C_M = CH^2/T^2$$

18-10. Suppose a sphere of magnetic material finds itself in a magnetic field H. Show that when H is suddenly increased by an amount ΔH and when the energy absorbed by the sphere cannot leak away, the increase in temperature is given by

$$\Delta T = -\frac{T}{C_H}\left(\frac{\partial M(H,T)}{\partial T}\right)\Delta H$$

This is known as the magnetocaloric effect.

18-11. Suppose a beam of atoms is passed through an inhomogeneous magnetic field. Let μ_z be the component of the magnetic moment of a certain atom along the field direction. Show that the force on the atom is $F_z = \mu_z(dH/dz)$. This formula forms the basis of the Stern-Gerlach experiment in which an atomic beam is split up into a number of separate beams; this number is equal to the number of possible μ_z values.

Chapter 19

FERROMAGNETISM,
ANTIFERROMAGNETISM, AND
FERRIMAGNETISM

Ferromagnetism

19-1. Introductory remarks

In ferromagnetic materials the magnetization versus magnetic field relationship exhibits hysteresis similar to that encountered in Chapter 8 for the relationship between P and E in ferroelectric materials. Of the elements, only Fe, Ni, Co, Gd, and Dy are ferromagnetic, although there are a relatively large number of ferromagnetic alloys and oxides (see Table 19-2). Above a critical temperature θ_f, known as the *ferromagnetic Curie temperature*, the spontaneous magnetization vanishes and the material becomes paramagnetic. Well above the Curie temperature the susceptibility follows the Curie-Weiss law,

$$\chi = C/(T - \theta) \tag{19-1}$$

where C is the Curie constant; the temperature θ is called the *paramagnetic Curie temperature* and is usually some degrees higher than θ_f (see Fig. 19-4).

The theory of ferromagnetism is centered about the following two hypotheses put forward in 1907 by Weiss.[1]

(i) A ferromagnetic specimen of macroscopic dimensions contains, in general, a number of small regions (domains) which are spontaneously magnetized; the magnitude of the spontaneous magnetization of the specimen is determined by the vector sum of the magnetic moments of the individual domains.

(ii) Within each domain the spontaneous magnetization is due to the existence of a "molecular field" which tends to produce a parallel alignment of the atomic dipoles.

The occurrence of hysteresis in the magnetization versus field relationship can be explained on the basis of these hypotheses in a similar way as the hysteresis loop for P versus E in Sec. 8-1. The reader is reminded that

---

[1] P. Weiss, *J. Phys.*, **6**, 667 (1907).

the spontaneous magnetization refers to a single domain, whereas the remanent magnetization (for $H = 0$) refers to the specimen as a whole (see Sec. 8-1).

As a particular example of a hysteresis curve we give in Fig. 19-1 the magnetization curve for a single crystal of silicon-iron.[2] It is observed

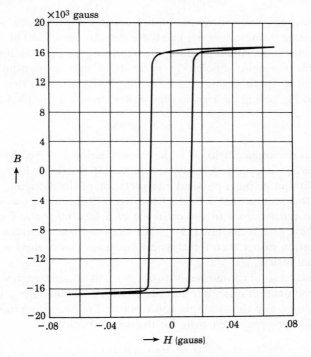

Fig. 19-1. The magnetization curve for a single crystal of silicon iron; the B scale is approximate. [After Williams and Shockley, ref. 2]

that for this particular case a very weak field (of the order of 10^{-2} gauss) is sufficient to produce a magnetization $M = B/4\pi = 10^3$ gausses. It should be mentioned that the coercive field for bulk materials may be several orders of magnitude larger than for the example in Fig. 19-1. Assuming atomic dipoles of the order of one Bohr magneton ($\sim 10^{-20}$ cgs unit) one verifies readily that values of M of the order of 10^3 gausses require essentially a parallel alignment of all the atomic dipoles in the specimen; hence the saturation of the magnetization in that region. By way of contrast this may be compared with a paramagnetic solid which in the same field of 10^{-2} gauss would give a magnetization $M \simeq N\mu_B^2 H/kT \simeq 10^{-6}$ gauss at room temperature; this is smaller by a factor of 10^9. Note

[2] H. J. Williams and W. Shockley, *Phys. Rev.*, **75**, 155 (1949).

that in a paramagnetic salt only one in 10^9 atomic dipoles is, on the average, lined up along the external field direction for the conditions specified above.

19-2. The Weiss molecular field

Spontaneous magnetization implies cooperation between the atomic dipoles within a single domain, i.e., there must be some kind of interaction between the atoms which produces the tendency for parallel alignment of the atomic magnetic dipoles. In order to obtain a phenomenological description of spontaneous magnetization, Weiss assumed that the molecular field H_m acting on a given dipole may be written in the form[3]

$$H_m = H + \gamma M \tag{19-2}$$

where H is the applied field, M is the magnetization and γ is the molecular field or Weiss constant. Clearly, the term γM provides the cooperative effect. Without giving a physical interpretation of the constant γ, we shall show in this section that a field of the type (19-2) indeed leads to spontaneous magnetization, to the existence of a ferromagnetic Curie point, and to the Curie-Weiss law (19-1). We shall use the quantum theory of magnetization rather than the classical Langevin theory used by Weiss in his original article.

Consider a solid containing N atoms per unit volume, each with a total angular momentum quantum number J (which includes the total orbital contribution L and the total spin contribution S). According to the results of Sec. 18-4 one may then write for the magnetization

$$M = Ng\mu_B J B_J(x) \tag{19-3}$$

where for paramagnetic solids $x = g\mu_B H J/kT$. For ferromagnetic materials we should replace H by H_m, in accordance with assumption (19-2), because H_m is the actual field seen by any given atomic dipole. Thus, in the present case

$$x = g\mu_B(H + \gamma M)J/kT \tag{19-4}$$

As long as we are interested in spontaneous magnetization, $H = 0$ and we may write

$$M = xkT/\gamma g\mu_B J \tag{19-5}$$

Since M must satisfy both (19-3) and (19-5), its value at a given temperature may be obtained from the point of intersection of the two corresponding

---

[3] Note that in the dipole theory of ferroelectricity, Sec. 8-3, a field of exactly the same form is assumed.

M versus x curves, as indicated schematically in Fig. 19-2. Note that (19-5) represents a straight line, the slope of the line being proportional to T. From Fig. 19-2 it follows that for $T < \theta_f$, one obtains a nonvanishing value for M, although the external field $H = 0$.[4] Hence for $T < \theta_f$, spontaneous magnetization results. For $T = \theta_f$, the slope of the straight line represented by (19-5) is equal to that of the tangent of curve (19-3) at the origin. Thus, for $T \geqslant \theta_f$ the spontaneous magnetization vanishes.

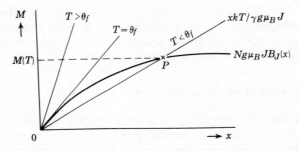

Fig. 19-2. Schematic representation of the method for finding the spontaneous magnetization at a temperature T. A point of intersection such as P determines $M(T)$.

It will be evident that there must exist a relation between the Curie temperature θ_f and the molecular field constant γ; in fact, one expects θ_f to increase with γ because the tendency for parallel alignment increases as γ becomes larger. In order to establish this relationship, we make use of the fact that for $x \ll 1$ (near the origin in Fig. 19-2), the Brillouin function is approximately given by

$$B_J(x) \simeq (J + 1)x/3J \qquad x \ll 1 \qquad (19\text{-}6)$$

Hence, the tangent of curve (19-3) at the origin has a slope equal to $Ng\mu_B(J + 1)/3$. Putting this equal to the slope of curve (19-5) for $T = \theta_f$, one obtains

$$3k\theta_f/\gamma = Ng^2\mu_B^2 J(J + 1) = N\mu^2 \qquad (19\text{-}7)$$

where μ is the total magnetic moment per atom. Hence θ_f is proportional to the molecular field constant.

Let us now consider the susceptibility in the region well above the ferromagnetic Curie temperature. In this region magnetization occurs only when an external field H is applied because there is no spontaneous magnetization. Thus, for fields low enough so that we are far away from

---

[4] Although the origin in Fig. 19-2 is also a point of intersection, it can be shown that the free energy of the state with nonvanishing M value is smaller than that for $M = 0$, i.e., the latter is unstable.

saturation, we may employ the approximation (19-6) for $B_J(x)$, and (19-3) becomes

$$M = Ng\mu_B(J + 1)x/3 \qquad (19\text{-}8)$$

where x is given by (19-4). Solving for M/H after substituting x into (19-8) one obtains readily the Curie-Weiss law

$$\chi = M/H = C/(T - \theta) \qquad (19\text{-}9)$$

where $C = N\mu^2/3k$ and $\theta = \gamma N\mu^2/3k = \gamma C$. Note that the value obtained here for θ is identical with that obtained for θ_f from expression (19-7). In other words, the Weiss theory does not distinguish between the para- and ferromagnetic Curie temperatures.

19-3. Comparison of the Weiss theory with experiment

Temperature dependence of the spontaneous magnetization. The maximum component of an atomic dipole associated with a quantum number J in any given direction is $gJ\mu_B$. Hence the maximum value of the spontaneous magnetization is given by $Ng\mu_BJ$, where N is the number of atoms per unit volume. This also follows from (19-3) because for $x \to \infty$ the Brillouin function $B_J(x) \to 1$. In accordance with Fig. 19-2, the maximum spontaneous magnetization occurs for $T = 0$, and we shall therefore write $Ng\mu_BJ = M(0)$. In order to describe the temperature dependence of the spontaneous magnetization in a convenient manner, we rewrite (19-3) in the form

$$M(T)/M(0) = B_J(x) \qquad (19\text{-}10)$$

where $M(T)$ is the magnetization at a temperature T. Similarly, we may write (19-5) in the form

$$M(T)/M(0) = xkT/\gamma Ng^2\mu_B^2 J^2 = xT(J + 1)/3J\theta_f \qquad (19\text{-}11)$$

where the last equality is obtained by substituting for γ in terms of θ_f by employing (19-7). The quantity $M(T)/M(0)$ must satisfy both (19-10) and (19-11); hence it can be obtained by the intersection method indicated in Fig. 19-2. It is important to note that for a given value of J, this procedure leads to a universal curve when $M(T)/M(0)$ is plotted as function of T/θ_f, as will be evident from (19-10) and (19-11). In Fig. 19-3 we have represented such curves for $J = \frac{1}{2}$, $J = 1$ and $J = \infty$; the latter case corresponds to classical freely rotating dipoles. In the same figure one finds experimental points for Fe, Ni, and Co. It is observed that the curve for $J = \frac{1}{2}$ fits the data best, indicating that the magnetization is essentially associated with the electron spins rather than with the orbital momentum of the electrons. That this is indeed the case has been confirmed by gyromagnetic experiments.[5] In such experiments one either reverses the magnetization of a freely suspended specimen and observes the resulting rotation, or one rotates the specimen and observes the resulting magnetization; the former is called the Einstein-de Haas method, the latter the Barnett method. From such experiments one obtains the g value,

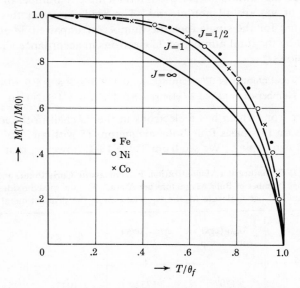

Fig. 19-3. The spontaneous magnetization for Fe, Ni, and Co as function of temperature. The curves for $J = \frac{1}{2}$, $J = 1$ and $J = \infty$ are those obtained from equation (19-10) and (19-11).

i.e., the ratio between the magnetic moment and the angular momentum; for the electron spin $g = 2$, for the orbital motion $g = 1$. Results of such experiments are given in Table 19-1; they show that the magnetization is largely due to the electron spins.[5]

Table 19-1. The Magnetomechanical Ratio g for Some Ferromagnetics[a]

	g		g
Fe	1.93	Fe_3O_4 (magnetite)	1.93
Co	1.87	Cu_2MnAl (Heusler alloy)	2.00
Ni	1.92	78% Ni, 22% Fe (permalloy)	1.91

[a] For references to the original literature, see C. KITTEL, *Introduction to Solid State Physics*, Wiley, New York, 1953, p. 168.

As in other order-disorder phenomena, the decrease of the spontaneous magnetization with temperature is associated with an anomalous specific heat; because of lack of space, this problem will not be discussed here.

[5] See, for example, S. J. Barnett, *Proc. Am. Acad. Arts Sci.*, **75**, 109 (1944); G. G. Scott, *Phys. Rev.*, **82**, 542 (1951); **87**, 697 (1952).

The effective number of Bohr magnetons per atom. From the saturation magnetization at $T = 0$ and the number of atoms per unit volume, one can calculate the effective number of Bohr magnetons n_{eff} per atom. Values of n_{eff} obtained in this way are given in Table 19-2, together with the ferromagnetic Curie temperature θ_f and the spontaneous magnetization. It is observed that although each atom has an integral number of electrons, the values of n_{eff} are all nonintegral. The reader may at this point be reminded that for the single ions the number of unpaired $3d$ electrons is determined by the total number of $3d$ electrons in accordance with Hund's rules as follows:[6]

Total number of $3d$ electrons:　　0 1 2 3 4 5 6 7 8 9 10
Number of unpaired $3d$ electrons: 0 1 2 3 4 5 4 3 2 1　0

Thus for iron, which has 6 electrons in the $3d$ shell in the ionic state, one expects on this basis four Bohr magnetons (5 with an "up" spin and 1 with a "down" spin). We see from Table 19-2, however, that n_{eff} is 2.2.

Table 19-2. **Saturation Magnetization, Ferromagnetic Curie Point, and the Effective Number of Bohr Magnetons per Atom.**[a] For the mixed oxides n_{eff} is calculated per molecule $MOFe_2O_3$, where M is the divalent metal ion.

Solid	M_{sat} (cgs) room temp.	M_{sat} (cgs) 0°K	θ_f (°K)	n_{eff} (0°K)
Fe	1707	1752	1043	2.221
Co	1400	1446	1400	1.716
Ni	485	510	631	0.606
Gd	...	1980	289	7.10
Dy	...	...	105	...
MnBi	600	675	630	3.52
Cu_2MnAl	430	(580)	603	(4.0)
Cu_2MnIn	500	(600)	506	(4.0)
MnAs	670	870	318	3.40
MnB	147	...	533	...
Mn_4N	183	...	745	0.24
MnSb	710	...	587	3.53
CrTe	240	...	336	2.39
CrO_2	...	...	...	2.07
$MnOFe_2O_3$	358	...	783	5.0
$FeOFe_2O_3$	458	...	848	4.2
$CoOFe_2O_3$	...	...	793	3.3
$NiOFe_2O_3$	240	...	863	2.3
$CuOFe_2O_3$	290	...	728	1.3
$MgOFe_2O_3$	143	...	583	1.1

[a] Reprinted with permission from C. KITTEL, *Introduction to Solid State Physics*, Wiley, New York, 1953, p. 166.

[6] See Sec. 18-2.

This discrepancy is not surprising if one recognizes that in the solid the atomic levels are broadened into bands and that the simple atomic picture cannot be valid.

Thus Mott[7] and Slater[8] explain the nonintegral values for n_{eff} on the basis of a wide $4s$ band overlapping with a narrow $3d$ band (Fig. 10-16). In general, there is on the average a certain fraction of the total number of $3d$ and $4s$ electrons in each band. For example, the fact that iron has $n_{\text{eff}} = 2.2$ indicates that in the $3d$ band there are 5 electron spins parallel and 2.8 antiparallel. Hence, of the total of 8 electrons, 7.8 reside on the average in the $3d$ band and 0.2 in the $4s$ band.

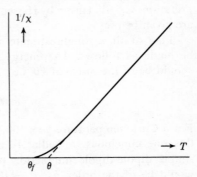

The paramagnetic region. Comprehensive experimental studies of the behavior of Fe, Co, and Ni above the Curie points have been made by Sucksmith and Pearce[9] and by Fallot.[10] According to the Curie-Weiss law (19-9), a plot of $1/\chi$ versus T should yield a straight line, the intercept along the T-axis

Fig. 19-4. Schematic representation of the behavior of the ferromagnetic metals above the Curie point; the slight curvature leads to the distinction between the ferromagnetic and paramagnetic Curie points.

being equal to θ. The experiments show that this law is indeed satisfied with considerable accuracy except in the region close to the Curie point. In fact, for all three metals there occurs a concave upward curvature near the Curie point, which leads to the distinction between the ferromagnetic and paramagnetic Curie temperatures θ_f and θ, respectively. This behavior is indicated schematically in Fig. 19-4. To illustrate this point, we give here θ_f and θ in degrees Kelvin for these metals. According to Stoner the observed curvature near the Curie point is consistent with his theory of ferromagnetism based on the collective electron treatment.[11]

	Fe	Co	Ni
θ_f	1043	1393	631
θ	1093	1428	650

[7] N. F. Mott, *Proc. Phys. Soc.* (*London*), **47**, 571 (1935).

[8] J. C. Slater, *J. Appl. Phys.*, **8**, 385 (1937); see also E. C. Stoner, *Proc. Roy. Soc.* (*London*), **A165**, 372 (1938); **A169**, 339 (1939); for an alternative explanation, see C. Zener, *Phys. Rev.*, **81**, 440 (1951); **83**, 299 (1951); **85**, 324 (1952).

[9] W. Sucksmith and R. R. Pearce, *Proc. Roy. Soc.* (*London*), **A167**, 189 (1938).

[10] M. Fallot, *Ann. Physik*, **10**, 291 (1938); *J. phys. radium*, **5**, 153 (1944).

[11] E. C. Stoner, *Proc. Leeds Phil. Lit. Soc.*, **3**, 457 (1938).

19-4. The interpretation of the Weiss field.

From what has been said in the preceding section one may conclude that, apart from certain details, the Weiss field describes the observations satisfactorily. So far, however, we have not touched upon the problem of the origin of this field. We shall limit the discussion here to one interpretation, viz., that given by Heisenberg; references to other interpretations are given below.

First of all, a rough estimate of the required molecular field H_m may be made as follows. The energy of a given atomic dipole in this field should be of the order of $k\theta$, i.e.,

$$\mu_B H_m \simeq k\theta \tag{19-12}$$

For a Curie temperature $\theta \simeq 1000°\mathrm{K}$ this gives $H_m \simeq 10^7$ gausses. From this one concludes immediately that the internal field is not due to a simple dipole-dipole interaction between neighbors, because such fields would be of the order $\mu_B/a^3 \simeq 10^3$ gausses. It may be pointed out here that in the case of ferroelectric materials the situation is quite different, because atomic electric dipoles are larger than magnetic ones by a factor of about 100;[12] thus, at least in principle, the molecular field in ferroelectrics may be due to dipole-dipole interaction. We may also point out that in the ferromagnetic solids the molecular field constant $\gamma = H_m/M \simeq 10^7/10^3 \simeq 10^4$, which is orders of magnitudes larger than the Lorentz factor $4\pi/3$ which one might expect for a simple model based on dipole-dipole interaction.

In 1928 Heisenberg showed that the large molecular field may be explained in terms of the so-called exchange interaction between the electrons.[13] The principle of this explanation may be illustrated by considering the hydrogen molecule. Let the nuclei be denoted by a and b, the atomic wave functions by ψ_a and ψ_b, the electrons by 1 and 2. The interaction potential between the two atoms is then, in a self-explanatory notation,

$$V_{ab} = e^2 \left(\frac{1}{r_{ab}} + \frac{1}{r_{12}} - \frac{1}{r_{b1}} - \frac{1}{r_{a2}} \right) \tag{19-13}$$

The reader familiar with the elementary Heitler-London theory of chemical binding knows that the energy of the system may be written in the form

$$E = K \pm J_e \tag{19-14}$$

---

[12] 1 Debye unit is 10^{-18} cgs unit, whereas $\mu_B = 0.92 \times 10^{-20}$ cgs unit.
[13] W. Heisenberg, Z. Physik, **49**, 619 (1928).

where K is the Coulomb interaction energy, which does not concern us here, and J_e is the exchange integral,

$$J_e = \int \psi_a^*(1)\psi_b^*(2)V_{ab}\psi_a(2)\psi_b(1) \, dv_1 \, dv_2 \qquad (19\text{-}15)$$

The plus sign in (19-14) refers to the nonmagnetic state of the molecule in which the two electronic spins are antiparallel. The minus sign corresponds to the case in which the two spins are parallel, i.e., to the magnetic state. It is evident from (19-14) that the magnetic state is stable only if J_e is positive, because then $(K - J_e) < (K + J_e)$. It can be shown[14] that (19-14) may be written in a more convenient form which contains the relative orientation of the two spins, viz.,

$$E = \text{const.} - 2J_e S_1 \cdot S_2 \qquad (19\text{-}16)$$

In other words, the exchange energy appears in the total energy as if there exists a direct coupling between the two spins. It must be emphasized, however, that the exchange interaction is fundamentally electrostatic and that the spin enters into the energy expression as a consequence of the Pauli exclusion principle.

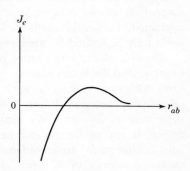

Fig. 19-5. Schematic representation of the behavior of the exchange integral as function of interatomic distance.

Making use of what has been said above, we shall thus assume from now on that for two atoms i and j the effective coupling between the spins due to exchange interaction is equivalent with a term

$$-2J_{ij}S_i \cdot S_j \qquad (19\text{-}17)$$

in the energy expression; J_{ij} is the exchange integral for the two atoms.

In general, the exchange integral is negative, i.e., in general the non-ferromagnetic state is favored. However, according to a qualitative analysis by Bethe, J_e is likely to be positive when the distance r_{ab} between the nuclei is fairly large compared with the orbital radii of the electrons involved; the behavior of J_e as function of r_{ab} is indicated in Fig. 19-5.[15] According to Slater, the ratio r_{ab}/r_0 where r_0 is the orbital radius, should be larger than 3 but not much larger.[16] Some pertinent data in this respect are given below.

	Fe	Co	Ni	Cr	Mn	Gd
r_{ab}/r_0	3.26	3.64	3.94	2.60	2.94	3.1

[14] See, for example, F. Seitz, *The Modern Theory of Solids*, McGraw-Hill, New York, 1940, p. 612.

[15] H. Bethe, *Handbuch der Physik*, Vol. 24/2.

[16] J. C. Slater, *Phys. Rev.*, **36**, 57 (1930).

Note that Cr and Mn are not ferromagnetic. One might raise the question here whether an element with uncompensated spins, which itself is not ferromagnetic because the r_{ab}/r_0 value is not favorable, may be combined with another nonferromagnetic element to form a compound for which the r_{ab}/r_0 value is suitable for ferromagnetism. That this seems indeed possible is illustrated by the fact that for example MnAs and MnSb are both ferromagnetic; the lattice constants of these compounds are, respectively, 2.85 and 2.89 Å, as compared with 2.58 Å for pure Mn. The ferromagnetism of the other alloys given in Table 19-2 can presumably be explained in a similar manner. We may also mention here that the Curie point may be shifted by applying high pressures.[17]

Because of the importance of the exchange integral, one would like to relate it to the Weiss constant γ and to the ferromagnetic Curie temperature. Although this is a very complicated problem, an approximate relationship between J_e and γ may be found by a simplified procedure suggested by Stoner.[18] We shall assume that the exchange integral is negligible except for nearest neighbors and that its value is J_e for all neighboring pairs. In accordance with (19-17) we may then write for the exchange energy of a given atom i with its neighbors,

$$V = -2J_e \sum_j \mathbf{S}_i \cdot \mathbf{S}_j \qquad (19\text{-}18)$$

where the summation is over the nearest neighbors of atom i. The essential assumption of Stoner is that the instantaneous values of the neighboring spins may be replaced by their time averages. Thus, if there are z nearest neighbors, we have

$$V = -2zJ_e(S_{xi}\langle S_{xj}\rangle + S_{yi}\langle S_{yj}\rangle + S_{zi}\langle S_{zj}\rangle) \qquad (19\text{-}19)$$

Assuming that the magnetization M is along the z-direction, we may write

$$\langle S_{xj}\rangle = \langle S_{yj}\rangle = 0 \quad \text{and} \quad \langle S_{zj}\rangle = M/g\mu_B N \qquad (19\text{-}20)$$

According to (19-19) and (19-20),

$$V = -2zJ_e S_{zi}M/gN\mu_B \qquad (19\text{-}21)$$

Now, this expression should be equal to the potential energy of spin i in the Weiss field γM, i.e.,

$$V = -gS_{zi}\mu_B\gamma M \qquad (19\text{-}22)$$

From the last two equations we obtain the following relation between γ and J_e:

$$\gamma = 2zJ_e/Ng^2\mu_B^2 \qquad (19\text{-}23)$$

[17] L. Patrick, *Phys. Rev.*, **93**, 384 (1954).
[18] E. C. Stoner, *Magnetism and Matter*, Methuen, London, 1934, p. 358.

Making use of (19-7), we obtain for the relation between θ_f and J_e,

$$\theta_f = 2zJ_eS(S + 1)/3k \tag{19-24}$$

Thus for a simple cubic lattice with $z = 6$ and with $S = \frac{1}{2}$, one finds

$$J_e/k\theta_f = \frac{1}{3} \tag{19-25}$$

More exact calculations by Opechowski[19] and P. R. Weiss[20] (not to be confused with Pierre Weiss) give, respectively, 0.518 and 0.540 for the ratio $J_e/k\theta_f$ for a simple cubic lattice.

Another method of calculating the magnetization in terms of the exchange integral was introduced by Bloch.[21] His so-called spin-wave method is applicable only in the low-temperature region, and leads to the result

$$M(T) = M(0)[1 - A(kT/J_e)^{3/2}] \quad \text{for} \quad T \ll \theta_f \tag{19-26}$$

where A is a numerical constant equal to 0.1174 for the simple cubic lattice. This result is known as the Bloch $T^{3/2}$ law and is in good agreement with low-temperature data. For further discussions of exchange interactions and objections against the Heisenberg theory of ferromagnetism we refer the reader to the literature.[22]

19-5. Qualitative remarks about domains

We mentioned in Sec. 19-1 that in order to explain the fact that a piece of ferromagnetic material may exist in the nonmagnetized state, whereas a weak magnetic field may produce saturation magnetization in the same specimen, Weiss introduced the domain hypothesis. Each domain is spontaneously magnetized, the magnetization being appropriate to the temperature T of the specimen. The over-all magnetization is given by the sum of the domain vectors, and thus may vanish under certain circumstances; an example is given in Fig. 19-6a. Magnetization of a specimen may occur either by the growth of one domain at the expense of another, i.e., by the motion of domain walls (Fig. 19-6b), or by rotation of domains (Fig. 19-6c). A representative magnetization curve is given in Fig. 19-7, indicating the predominant processes in the different regions. We may note here that originally it was thought that the well-known Barkhausen jumps were due to the rotation of a complete domain and that the size of the Barkhausen discontinuities was a measure of the size of the domains.

[19] W. Opechowski, *Physica*, **4**, 181 (1937); **6**, 1112 (1939).

[20] P. R. Weiss, *Phys. Rev.*, **74**, 1493 (1948).

[21] F. Bloch, *Z. Physik*, **61**, 206 (1930).

[22] See the papers by C. Kittel, C. Zener and R. R. Heikes, J. C. Slater, E. P. Wohlfarth, and J. H. van Vleck held at the Washington Conference on Magnetism, *Revs. Mod. Phys.*, **25** (1953); see also J. H. van Vleck, *Revs. Mod. Phys.*, **17**, 27 (1945).

However, experiments by Williams and Shockley show that the Barkhausen jumps are mainly associated with irregular fluctuations in the motion of the domain walls rather than with domain rotation.[23]

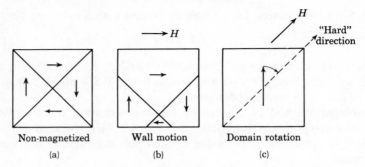

Fig. 19-6. The domain structure (a) corresponds to the non-magnetized state; (b) represents magnetization due to wall motion; in (c) the magnetization is due to rotation of the domain vectors from an "easy" to a "hard" direction (see Sec. 19-6).

The most direct experimental evidence for the existence of domains is provided by the so-called "Bitter powder patterns."[24] A drop of a colloidal suspension of ferromagnetic particles is placed on the carefully prepared

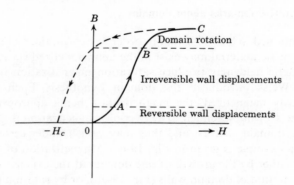

Fig. 19-7. Typical magnetization curve of a virgin specimen, indicating the predominant processes taking place in the different regions. When the field is reversed at C, the dashed curve is obtained; H_c is called the *coercive force*. [After C. Kittel, *Revs. Mod. Phys.*, **21**, 541 (1949)]

surface of the specimen; since there are strong local magnetic fields near the domain boundaries, the particles collect there and the domains may be observed under a microscope.

[23] H. J. Williams and W. Shockley, *Phys. Rev.*, **75**, 178 (1949).
[24] F. Bitter, *Phys. Rev.*, **38**, 1903 (1931).

The physical origin of domains may be understood from the general thermodynamic principle that the free energy $E - TS$ of a solid tends to reach a minimum value. As a result of the high degree of order in the magnetic system, except in the vicinity of the Curie temperature, the entropy term may be neglected for our purpose; thus, minimizing the energy E of the system should be sufficient to understand the existence of domains. To illustrate the essential features of this point of view, we refer to Fig. 19-8, representing a cross section through a ferromagnetic single

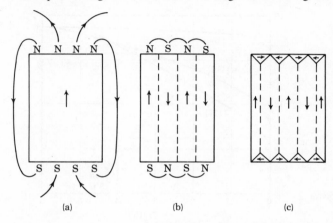

Fig. 19-8. The origin of domains (see text). [After C. Kittel, *Revs. Mod. Phys.*, **17**, 541 (1949)]

crystal. In (a) we have a single domain, i.e., saturation magnetization of the specimen. Because of the free magnetic poles at the ends of the specimen, the expression for the energy will contain a term $(1/8\pi) \int H^2 \, dV$ associated with the field outside the crystal. In a configuration such as in Fig. 19-8b on the other hand, the field energy is strongly reduced because the spatial extension of the field is much smaller. Now, as we shall see below, there is a certain amount of energy involved in producing a domain wall. Hence, one ultimately arrives at an equilibrium situation with a number of domains such that the energy required to produce one more domain boundary is equal to the resulting reduction of the field energy. The energy involved in building a domain wall is discussed in Sec. 19-7.

A domain structure such as in Fig. 19-8c has zero magnetic field energy. This is achieved by introducing the triangular prism domains at top and bottom of the crystal; such domains are called closure domains. Note that the wall between a closure domain and a vertical domain in Fig. 19-8c makes an angle of 45° with the magnetization directions in both types of domains. Hence the normal component of the magnetization in crossing such a wall is continuous, i.e., there are no free poles and there is no field energy. The energy required to produce a closure domain is essentially determined by the anisotropy of the crystal, i.e., by the fact that ferro-magnetic materials have "easy" and "hard" directions of magnetization. For example, from the magnetization curves represented in Fig. 19-9 one sees that in iron, which is cubic, the easy directions of magnetization are the cube edges.[25] In nickel, which is also cubic, the easy directions of magnetization are the body diagonals. In cobalt the hexagonal axis of the crystal is the only preferred direction; thus in a cobalt crystal with prominent domains magnetized along the hexagonal axis, the closure

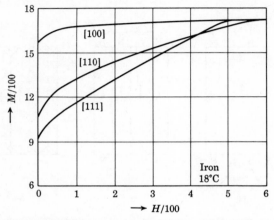

Fig. 19-9. Magnetization curves at 18°C for a single crystal of iron for different directions of the field relative to the crystal axes. [After Piety, ref. 25]

domains are necessarily magnetized along a hard direction. In iron and nickel, on the other hand, it is possible to have both the closure domains and the dominant domains magnetized along easy directions.

Summarizing the ideas discussed above we may say that domain structure has its origin in the principle of minimum energy. It will be evident that the number of domains and the domain structure will depend to a large extent on the shape and size of the crystal under consideration. The size of the domains for a particular domain structure may also be obtained from the principle of minimum energy. The volume of domains may vary between, say, 10^{-2} to 10^{-6} cm^3.

19-6. The anisotropy energy

Since ferromagnetic crystals have easy and hard directions of mag-netization, the energy associated with the magnetization depends on direction. In order to obtain the so-called anisotropy energy in terms of the direction of magnetization, one makes use of the crystal symmetry.

[25] R. G. Piety, *Phys. Rev.*, **50**, 1173 (1936).

Thus, for a cubic crystal, let α_1, α_2, and α_3 represent the direction cosines of the magnetization referred to the cubic crystal axes. Because of the cubic symmetry, the anisotropy energy should be an even power of each α; furthermore, it should be invariant for interchange between the α's. The lowest-order combination satisfying these conditions is $(\alpha_1^2 + \alpha_2^2 + \alpha_3^2)$ but since this is identically equal to unity, it does not enter in the anisotropy effects. The next order combination is $(\alpha_1^2\alpha_2^2 + \alpha_2^2\alpha_3^2 + \alpha_3^2\alpha_1^2)$; although this term by itself represents the experimental results for iron and nickel reasonably well, one usually adds one more term, viz., $\alpha_1^2\alpha_2^2\alpha_3^2$. Thus for cubic crystals the anisotropy energy may be written as

$$E_{an} = K_1(\alpha_1^2\alpha_2^2 + \alpha_2^2\alpha_3^2 + \alpha_3^2\alpha_1^2) + K_2\alpha_1^2\alpha_2^2\alpha_3^2 \qquad (19\text{-}27)$$

when higher terms are neglected. The constants K_1 and K_2 can be determined from experiment; for iron at room temperature,

$$K_1 = 4.2 \times 10^5 \text{ ergs/cm}^3; \qquad K_2 = 1.5 \times 10^5 \text{ ergs/cm}^3 \quad (19\text{-}28)$$

For crystals with a single preferred axis, such as cobalt, the anisotropy energy may be written in the form

$$E_{an} = K_1 \sin^2 \phi + K_2 \sin^4 \phi \qquad (19\text{-}29)$$

where ϕ is the angle between the magnetization and the easy axis; higher order terms are usually neglected. For cobalt at room temperature,

$$K_1 = 4.1 \times 10^6 \text{ ergs/cm}^3; \qquad K_2 = 1.0 \times 10^6 \text{ ergs/cm}^3 \quad (19\text{-}30)$$

It should be stated that the anisotropy constants depend strongly on temperature. The origin of the anisotropy is not immediately obvious. For example, the exchange interaction between the spins, given by (19-17), is completely independent of the geometrical anisotropy of the crystal, and hence does not lead to anisotropy effects. Furthermore, the anisotropy which arises from the interaction between the magnetic dipoles associated with the spins turns out to be much smaller than the observed anisotropy.

It is believed at present that the origin of the anisotropy must be sought along the following lines. We have seen before that the orbital angular momentum of the electrons is partially quenched as a result of inhomogeneous electric fields produced by neighboring atoms. On the other hand, because the quenching is incomplete, the electron spin will interact with the orbital momentum. Thus the electron spins are aware of the crystal lattice and its geometry as a result of the spin-orbit coupling. For further details, see a review paper by van Vleck.[26]

[26] J. H. van Vleck, *Annales de l'institut Henri Poincaré*, **10**, 57 (1947).

19-7. The thickness and energy of the Bloch wall

Although we have introduced the concept of a domain boundary before, we shall now consider this in some more detail. According to Bloch, the spin direction in going from one domain to another does not change abruptly, but gradually as indicated in the now classical Fig. 19-10; the domain walls are called Bloch walls.[27] The reason for the gradual rather than abrupt change in spin direction may be understood from the

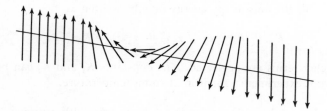

Fig. 19-10. Schematic representation of a 180° Bloch wall.

following argument. Consider two electrons with parallel spins; according to (19-18) the exchange energy is then $-2J_eS^2$. If we interpret the spin vectors in (19-18) as classical vectors[28] the exchange energy, when the two spins make a small angle ϕ, is equal to $-2J_eS^2 \cos \phi \simeq -2J_eS^2(1 - \phi^2/2)$. Thus in the process of changing the angle between the spins from zero to ϕ, the energy is increased by an amount $J_eS^2\phi^2$. Consider now a row of $(N + 1)$ spins within a Bloch wall separating two domains of which the magnetization directions make an angle ϕ_0. Let the angle between successive spins be $\phi = \phi_0/N$. The exchange energy of the row of spins, taking into account only nearest neighbor interaction, is then

$$(E_{ex})_{\text{row}} = NJ_eS^2\phi^2 = J_eS^2\phi_0^2/N \qquad (19\text{-}31)$$

Hence the energy decreases when N increases. This raises the question: Why does not the wall become infinitely thick? It is at this point that the influence of the anisotropy energy must be considered. Since the spins within the wall are nearly all directed away from the easy axes, one expects an anisotropy energy which is approximately proportional to the thickness of the wall. This has the effect of limiting the wall thickness, as may be seen from the following arguments. Let us consider a wall of 1 cm² area, the thickness being Na, where a is the lattice constant. The total wall energy per cm² may then be written in the form

$$\sigma = \sigma_{ex} + \sigma_{an} \qquad (19\text{-}32)$$

[27] F. Bloch, Z. Physik, **61**, 206 (1932).
[28] According to Kittel this is permitted as long as ϕ is small.

The exchange energy σ_{ex} is obtained by multiplying (19-31) by the number of rows of spins per cm², i.e., by $1/a^2$. The anisotropy energy σ_{an} is approximately equal to the anisotropy constant K times the volume Na of the wall. Hence (19-32) becomes

$$\sigma = J_e S^2 \phi_0^2 / Na^2 + KNa \qquad (19\text{-}33)$$

The equilibrium value of N may be obtained by minimizing σ with respect to N. Hence, putting $d\sigma/dN = 0$, one obtains

$$N = (J_e S^2 \phi_0^2 / Ka^3)^{1/2} \qquad (19\text{-}34)$$

As an example we may consider the case of iron; taking $J_e \simeq k\theta_f/3$ in accordance with (19-25), $\phi_0 = \pi$, $K \simeq 10^5$ ergs/cm³, $S = \frac{1}{2}$, one obtains

$$N \simeq 300 \quad \text{or} \quad t \simeq 1000 \text{ Å}$$

where t is the thickness of the wall. We may note that the domain walls in ferroelectric materials are only a few Angstroms thick, as we have seen in Chapter 8.

The total energy per cm² of a Bloch wall may be estimated by substituting for N from (19-34) into (19-33). This gives

$$\sigma = 2S\phi_0 (J_e K/a)^{1/2} \qquad (19\text{-}35)$$

which for iron turns out to be of the order of 1 erg per cm². We should emphasize that the above treatment is rather crude; for example, due to the anisotropy, the angle between successive spins is not constant throughout the Bloch wall.

We may mention here that there exists a critical size of ferromagnetic particles below which the single domain configuration is more stable than a multidomain structure; the critical size is determined by the anisotropy, the shape of the particles and the intensity of the magnetization. For spherical iron particles the critical radius is of the order of 10^{-6} cm. The calculations are given in C. Kittel, *Revs. Mod. Phys.*, **21**, 541 (1949). Similar calculations have been carried out for the critical single domain size of ferrites by Morrish and Yu.[29] For a more detailed and more complete treatment of the energy considerations entering in the discussion of domain formation we must refer the reader to Kittel's paper.

19-8. Coercive force and hysteresis

The coercive force H_c is the magnetic field required to produce zero magnetization in an initially saturated specimen (see Fig. 19-7). Its value varies widely from material to material and is of great practical importance.

[29] A. H. Morrish and S. P. Yu, *J. Appl. Phys.*, **26**, 1049 (1955).

In a good permanent magnet the coercive force may be of the order of 10^4 gausses (FePt), whereas a commercial power transformer may have a coercive force of 0.5 gauss. Note that the energy dissipated in going around the hysteresis loop is of the order of $B_{sat}H_c$, where B_{sat} is the saturation value of the magnetic inducton; hence the coercive force determines to a large extent the hysteresis losses.

We know that experimentally the part OA in the virgin curve of Fig. 19-7 is reversible, i.e., this must correspond to reversible motions of the

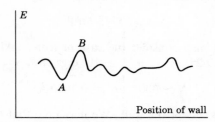

Fig. 19-11. Schematic representation of the energy of a ferromagnetic specimen as function of the position of a domain wall.

Bloch wall. Such motions may be vizualized with the aid of a potential curve, as indicated in Fig. 19-11; the curve represents the energy of a Bloch wall as function of its position in the crystal. The variations in energy are a consequence of local strains, impurities, lattice defects, etc. In the absence of an external field, the wall will be in a position corresponding to an energy minimum, say in A. Application of the field will modify this curve and unless the field is large enough to help the wall climb across a maximum such as B, only a small reversible wall displacement will result. For larger fields, the wall displacement may be large, but irreversible; this corresponds to the region AB in Fig. 19-7. The domain rotations occurring in the region BC of Fig. 19-7 take place when the applied magnetic field does not coincide with an easy direction of magnetization, i.e., work must be done against the anisotropy forces.

The above qualitative picture explains the fact that the coercive force increases with an increased intensity of local internal strains. The observation that alloys containing a precipitated phase are magnetically hard (high H_c) is also consistent with this picture. The quantitative aspects are, however, quite complicated.[30]

---

[30] For details, see R. Becker, *Physik. Z.*, **33**, 905 (1932); M. Kersten, *Grundlagen einer Theorie der ferromagnetischen Hysteresis und Koerzitivkraft*, Edwards, Ann Arbor, (1943) L. Néel, *Ann. univ. Grenoble*, **22**, 299 (1946); E. C. Stoner and E. P. Wohlfarth, *Phil. Trans.*, **A240**, 599 (1948).

Antiferromagnetism

19-9. Introductory remarks

In Sec. 19-4, we have seen that the Heisenberg theory of ferromagnetism is based on the assumption that the exchange integral is positive. When the exchange integral is negative, favoring an antiparallel orientation of neighboring spins, one has an antiferromagnetic substance. Such systems were first investigated theoretically by Néel[31] and Bitter[32]; the theory was later extended by van Vleck,[33] and his formulation is usually regarded as the basic theory of antiferromagnetism. Experimentally, antiferromagnetism was first discovered as a property of MnO by Bizette, Squire, and Tsai in 1938.[34]

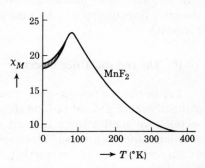

Fig. 19-12. The molar susceptibility χ_M of MnF_2 as function of temperature. At low temperatures χ_M depends slightly on the field strength; the upper branch corresponds to 2×10^4 gausses, the lower one to 400 gausses. [After de Haas, Schultz and Koolhaas, *Physica*, **7**, 57 (1940)]

The most characteristic property of a polycrystalline antiferromagnetic is that its susceptibility shows a maximum as function of temperature; an example of this behavior is given in Fig. 19-12. This characteristic feature may be explained qualitatively on the basis of the following model. Consider a crystal containing two types of atoms A and B distributed over two interlocking lattices; for example, let the A atoms occupy the corner points of an elementary cube, the B atoms being located at the centers of these cubes. Furthermore, let the interaction between the atoms be such that the A spins tend to line up antiparallel to the B spins. At low temperatures this interaction is very effective and in an external field the resulting magnetization will be small. As the temperature is raised, the efficiency of the interaction becomes less pronounced and the susceptibility increases. Finally, a critical temperature T_N (the Néel temperature) will be reached above which the spins are "free" and above this temperature the antiferromagnetic material becomes paramagnetic, i.e., χ decreases with further increase in T. This model will be further discussed below.

---

[31] L. Néel, *Ann. phys.*, **18**, 5 (1932); **5**, 232 (1936).

[32] F. Bitter, *Phys. Rev.*, **54**, 79 (1937).

[33] J. H. van Vleck, *J. Chem. Phys.*, **9**, 85 (1941).

[34] H. Bizette, C. F. Squire, and B. Tsai, *Compt. rend.*, **207**, 449 (1938).

The most direct experimental evidence for the basic picture of anti-ferromagnetism has been obtained from neutron diffraction experiments.[35] When neutrons are incident on a crystal they are scattered by the atomic nuclei but also by the interaction between the neutron spin and para-magnetic ions which may be present. Consequently, the ordered anti-ferromagnetic state gives rise to "extra" diffraction lines just as one observes extra X-ray diffraction lines for ordered alloys. The intensity of these extra lines decreases as the temperature increases because the anti-ferromagnetic order diminishes. Above the antiferromagnetic temperature the extra lines disappear. An example has been given already in Fig. 1-17 for MnO.

19-10. The two-sublattice model

Let us now pursue the two-sublattice model somewhat further and in a slightly more general fashion than outlined above. As in the preceding section, we shall assume that all nearest neighbors of an A atom are B atoms and vice versa. However, we shall assume that, besides an antiferromagnetic AB interaction, there are also antiferromagnetic AA and BB interactions. Thus let the molecular field at an A and a B site be given, respectively, by

$$H_{ma} = H - \alpha M_a - \beta M_b$$
$$H_{mb} = H - \beta M_a - \alpha M_b \tag{19-36}$$

where H is the applied field, and M_a and M_b represent the magnetization of the A and B lattices; α and β are positive Weiss constants. We shall consider two temperature regions:

(i) $T > T_N$. When the temperature is above the Néel temperature, we are far away from saturation, and the magnetization of the A lattice may be written

$$M_a = (N\mu^2/3kT)H_a \quad \text{with} \quad \mu^2 = \mu_B^2 g^2 J(J+1) \tag{19-37}$$

where N is the number of A atoms per unit volume. If we assume that the dipoles on the B sites are identical with those of the A sites and that there are equal numbers of A and B sites, we may write similarly,

$$M_b = (N\mu^2/3kT)H_b \tag{19-38}$$

Substituting equations (19-36) into the last two equations leads, upon addition, to

$$M = M_a + M_b = (N\mu^2/3kT)[2H - (\alpha + \beta)M] \tag{19-39}$$

[35] C. G. Shull and J. S. Smart, *Phys. Rev.*, **76**, 1256 (1949).

This equation becomes a scalar equation if we assume that M and H are parallel. On this assumption we can solve for the susceptibility, leading to

$$\chi = M/H = \frac{2N\mu^2/3k}{T + N\mu^2(\alpha + \beta)/3k} = \frac{C}{T + \theta} \qquad (19\text{-}40)$$

This may be compared with expression (19-9) for the susceptibility of a ferromagnetic material above the critical temperature. It is observed that

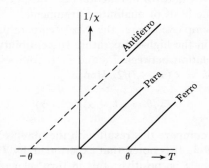

Fig. 19-13. The reciprocal susceptibility versus temperature for a para-, ferro- and antiferromagnetic material above the critical temperature.

the antiferromagnetic case contains $T + \theta$ rather than $T - \theta$; moreover, the Curie constant C is twice the Curie constant of the individual A or B lattice. In order to illustrate the difference between the paramagnetic, the ferromagnetic, and the antiferromagnetic behavior in the high-temperature region, we have plotted in Fig. 19-13 $1/\chi$ versus T. For the three cases one obtains

para	*ferro*	*antiferro*	
$1/\chi = T/C$	$1/\chi = (T-\theta)/C$	$1/\chi = (T+\theta)/C$	(19-41)

(ii) *The region below the Néel temperature.* At the Néel temperature T_N itself, one is still sufficiently far away from saturation effects to employ the equations given above for M_a and M_b. Thus in the absence of an applied magnetic field we may write for $T = T_N$ in accordance with (19-37),

$$M_a = -(N\mu^2/3kT_N)(\alpha M_a + \beta M_b)$$

or

$$[(1 + N\mu^2/3kT_N)\alpha]M_a + (N\mu^2/3kT_N)\beta M_b = 0 \qquad (19\text{-}42)$$

Similarly,

$$(N\mu^2/3kT_N)\beta M_a + [1 + (N\mu^2/3kT_N)\alpha]M_b = 0 \qquad (19\text{-}43)$$

The last two equations have a nonvanishing solution for M_a and M_b only if the determinant of their coefficients vanishes. Making use of the fact that $2N\mu^2/3k = C$ one finds that

$$T_N = C(\beta - \alpha)/2 \qquad (19\text{-}44)$$

Note that the Néel temperature increases as the antiferromagnetic AB interaction (β) becomes stronger, whereas it decreases with increasing antiferromagnetic AA and BB interaction (α); this, of course, is what one would expect on the basis of qualitative arguments.

In the model employed here, the Néel temperature is not identical with θ, appearing in the high-temperature susceptibility. In fact, one can readily set up a relation between T_N and θ. It follows from (19-40) that $\theta = N\mu^2(\alpha + \beta)/3k = C(\alpha + \beta)/2$. Hence

$$T_N/\theta = (\beta - \alpha)/(\beta + \alpha) \qquad (19\text{-}45)$$

It is of interest to compare this result with the observed values of T_N and θ given in Table 19-3. It is noted that experimentally $T_N < \theta$ in all cases, indicating that α must be positive; this in turn seems to indicate that in so far as the present model is applicable, there is indeed an antiferromagnetic AA and BB interaction.

Table 19-3. **Some Parameters of Selected Antiferromagnetics.**[a] (After A. B. Lidiard, *Repts. Progr. Phys.*, **17**, 201 (1954)

Compound	Crystal structure	Cation lattice structure	T_N (°K)	θ (°K)	χ_0/χ_{T_N}
MnF_2	rutile	b.c. tetragonal	72	113	0.76
FeF_2	rutile	b.c. tetragonal	79	117	0.72
CoF_2	rutile	b.c. tetragonal	38	53	...
NiF_2	rutile	b.c. tetragonal	73	116	...
MnO_2	rutile	b.c. tetragonal	84	316	0.94
MnO	NaCl	f.c.c.	122	610	0.67
MnS	NaCl	f.c.c.	165	528	0.82
FeO	NaCl	f.c.c.	198	570	0.79
CoO	NaCl	f.c.c.	292	280	...

[a] Reproduced with kind permission of the Physical Society.

Let us now consider the susceptibility of an antiferromagnetic material below the Néel temperature; for simplicity we shall assume only AB interaction, i.e., we shall assume $\alpha = 0$. First, as a result of crystalline anisotropy, there will be one or more "natural" spin directions along which the spins will tend to align themselves. There are therefore two cases of special interest;

(a) An applied magnetic field *perpendicular* to the natural spin direction.

(b) An applied field *parallel* to the natural spin direction.

Case (a) has been represented schematically in Fig. 19-14a; the calculation of the susceptibility in this case is analogous to the calculation of the polarizability of an elastically bound charge, in which the equilibrium is determined by the balance of the external force and a restoring force.

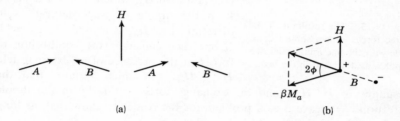

Fig. 19-14. Illustrating the calculation of $\chi_\perp$, as described in the text, for an antiferromagnetic arrangement of dipoles.

In the present case, the field tends to line up the dipoles along the field direction, but as a result of the tendency for the A and B dipoles to remain antiparallel, a compromise is obtained in which the dipoles make a certain angle ϕ with the original spin direction. To calculate the susceptibility $\chi_\perp$ for this case, we proceed as follows. Consider one of the dipoles B as made up of two unit poles, as indicated in Fig. 19-14b. The forces on the positive pole are H and $-\beta M_a$, as indicated; the forces on the negative pole are equal but of opposite sign. In equilibrium, the resultant forces should lie along the line joining the poles, so that for small angles ϕ we must have

$$2\beta M_a \phi = H$$

Since $M_a = M_b$, the total magnetization along the external field direction is equal to

$$M = (M_a + M_b)\phi = H/\beta$$

so that

$$\chi_\perp = 1/\beta \qquad (19\text{-}46)$$

Thus for the model under discussion, $\chi_\perp$ is independent of temperature. It can readily be shown that $\chi_\perp$ is equal to the susceptibility at the Néel temperature when approached from the high-temperature region. We may note that (19-46) is still obtained, even if $\alpha \neq 0$, as shown in Problem 19-8.

The reader will have noticed that nowhere in the above derivation for $\chi_\perp$ did we introduce an argument that explicitly referred to the existence of a natural spin direction; we considered only the balance between the force produced by the external field and the exchange force between nearest neighbors. A simple way in which the existence of a natural spin direction might be introduced is indicated in Fig. 19-15 for one of the B dipoles. It is assumed that there exists a constant field H_{an} which by itself tends to keep the dipole in the "natural" spin direction, i.e., H_{an} is an anisotropy field. If one then considers the equilibrium of forces in the presence of an external field $H \perp H_{an}$, one must require that the resultant of H, H_{an}, and the exchange force $-\beta M_a$ lie in the dipole direction. We leave it as a problem for the reader to show that, as long as the angle ϕ is small, one finds in this case

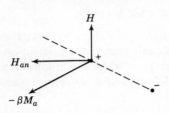

Fig. 19-15. The resultant of the three forces shown should coincide with the line joining the two poles, as described in the text.

$$\chi_\perp = \frac{1}{\beta + H_{an}/2M_a} \tag{19-47}$$

Since M_a increases as T decreases, this model leads to an increasing value of $\chi_\perp$ with decreasing temperature; this is indeed observed on single crystals of MnF_2.[36]

(b) The calculation of the susceptibility $\chi_{\parallel}$ corresponding to an applied field along the natural spin direction is much more complicated, since statistical methods involving Brillouin functions must be employed. Calculations by van Vleck give the curves as represented in Fig. 19-16 for different J values: the susceptibility rises smoothly from zero to $\chi(T_N)$ as the temperature increases. That $\chi_{\parallel} = 0$ for $T = 0$ can be understood qualitatively on the basis of the discussion of Sec. 19-9. The measurements by Stout and Griffel on MnF_2 indicate that the theory is at least qualitatively correct.

The susceptibility below the Néel temperature in polycrystalline materials is given by an average value lying between $\chi_\perp$ and $\chi_{\parallel}$; as a result, one obtains in such cases a susceptibility versus temperature curve of the type indicated in Fig. 19-12.

19-11. Superexchange interaction

A few remarks may be made here about the nature of the interaction in antiferromagnetics of the NaCl structure, such as MnO. From the neutron diffraction experiments by Shull and Smart[35] on MnO one

---

[36] J. W. Stout and M. Griffel, *J. Chem. Phys.*, **18**, 1455 (1950).

concludes (see Fig. 19-17) that the strongest negative interaction for a given Mn^{2+} ion does not come from its nearest Mn^{2+} neighbors but from those Mn^{2+} ions which are at a distance $\sqrt{2}$ times as far. In fact, the

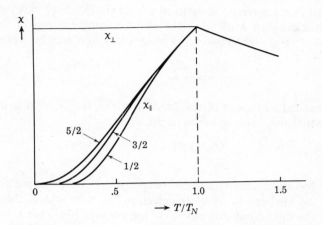

Fig. 19-16. The susceptibility of an antiferromagnetic substance as function of temperature, for spin values of $\frac{1}{2}$, $\frac{3}{2}$, and $\frac{5}{2}$. [After van Vleck, ref. 33]

negative interaction takes place between those Mn^{2+} ions which are separated by an O^{2-} ion such that the angle $Mn^{2+} - O^{2-} - Mn^{2+}$ is $180°$. Since the overlap between the $3d$ electrons of these Mn^{2+} ions is negligible

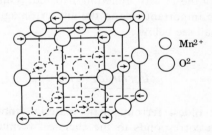

Mn^{2+}

O^{2-}

Fig. 19-17. The antiferromagnetic arrangement of spins in MnO; note that the spins in {111} planes are parallel to each other.

one concludes that the antiferromagnetism of MnO is not due to a direct exchange interaction. Néel suggested that Kramers' theory of super exchange may provide an answer for the interaction between the Mn^{2+} ions through an intermediate O^{2-} ion.[37] This theory has been discussed by

[37] H. A. Kramers, *Physica*, **1**, 182 (1934).

Anderson[38] and van Vleck;[39] in simple terms, the nature of this type of interaction may be understood qualitatively as follows: the description of manganese oxide as a completely divalent ionic compound of the type $Mn^{2+}O^{2-}$ is inadequate in the sense that one should include in the wave functions terms corresponding to Mn^+ and O^- ions; we may call Mn^+O^- an excited state of $Mn^{2+}O^{2-}$. The electron configuration of the ground state ($Mn^{2+}O^{2-}$) for the two types of ions involved may be represented by

$$Mn^{2+}(3d^5) \qquad\qquad O^{2-}(2p^6)$$
$$\rightarrow \rightarrow \rightarrow \rightarrow \rightarrow \qquad\qquad \begin{array}{c}\rightarrow \rightarrow \rightarrow\\ \leftarrow \leftarrow \leftarrow\end{array}$$

In the excited state, one of the $2p$ electrons of the O^{2-} ion is transferred to the Mn^{2+} ion, leading to the configuration

$$Mn^+(3d^6) \qquad\qquad O^-(2p^5)$$
$$\begin{array}{c}\rightarrow \rightarrow \rightarrow \rightarrow \rightarrow\\ \leftarrow\end{array} \qquad\qquad \begin{array}{c}\rightarrow \rightarrow \rightarrow\\ \leftarrow \leftarrow\end{array}$$

The O^- ion has evidently a resulting spin which has the same direction as that of the Mn^+ ion to which the electron has been added. Suppose now that on the right-hand side of the O^- ion another Mn^{2+} ion is located; as a result of the spin of the O^- ion the magnetic moment of this Mn^{2+} ion will have a tendency to be lined up antiparallel to that of the O^- ion if the interaction between these ions is antiferromagnetic (negative exchange integral, i.e., not too large separation between the ions). Hence, on this assumption one obtains an antiparallel alignment between the two Mn^{2+} ions as a result of the presence of the O^{2-} ion between them. The angle of 180° is particularly suitable for this type of interaction because of the dumbbell shape of the $2p$ wave function involved. This type of interaction may also play an important role in the antiferromagnetic interactions in ferrites, as we shall see below.

Ferrimagnetism

Probably the oldest ferromagnetic material known to mankind is magnetite, which corresponds to the chemical formula Fe_3O_4 or, more specifically, to $Fe^{2+}Fe_2^{3+}O_4$. When one replaces the divalent ferrous ion by another divalent metal such as Mn, Co, Ni, Cu, Mg, Zn, or Cd, one obtains a ferrite of the general composition $Me^{2+}Fe_2^{3+}O_4$ where Me^{2+} is the divalent metal ion. In mixed ferrites the Fe^{2+} ion is replaced by a mixture of ions. In searching for ferromagnetic materials for use at high frequencies, Snoek, Verwey, and others at the Philips Research Laboratories in Holland developed a number of such ferrites which are known under

[38] P. W. Anderson, *Phys. Rev.*, **79**, 350 (1950).

[39] J. H. van Vleck, *J. phys. radium*, **12**, 262 (1951).

the trade name Ferroxcube.[40] The most important of these are the MnZn ferrites (Ferroxcube IV). The d-c resistivity of ferrites is 10^4 to 10^{11} times as large as that of iron. Thus in transformer cores they can be used up to much higher frequencies than iron.

19-12. The structure of ferrites[41]

The physical properties of ferrites are intimately related to the structure of these solids. They belong to the large class of compounds which have the spinel structure (after the mineral spinel, $MgAl_2O_4$). The oxygen ions, with a radius of 1.32 Å form, to a good approximation, a close-packed cubic structure. The unit cell contains 32 oxygen ions, 16 Fe^{3+} ions, and 8 divalent metal ions. The total of 24 metal ions, ranging in radius between 0.4 and 1 Å, are distributed amongst eight tetrahedral interstices (surrounded by four O^{2-} ions) and sixteen octahedral interstices (surrounded by six O^{2-} ions). The distribution of the metal ions is very important for an understanding of the magnetic properties of these materials; the following distributions may occur.

(i) In the "normal" spinel structure of a ferrite the 8 divalent metal ions occupy tetrahedral positions; the 16 trivalent iron ions occupy octahedral positions. We shall follow a usual notation for this structure: $Me^{2+}[Fe_2^{3+}]O_4$ the brackets around the Fe^{3+} ions indicating that they occupy octahedral sites.

(ii) In the "inverse" spinel structure of a ferrite, the divalent Me^{2+} ions occupy octahedral sites; the Fe^{3+} ions are distributed in equal numbers over the tetrahedral and octahedral sites. The arrangement may thus be represented by $Fe^{3+}[Fe^{3+}Me^{2+}]O_4$.

(iii) In the intermediate case we have arrangements of the type

$$Fe_x^{3+}\, Me_{1-x}^{2+}[Fe_{2-x}^{3+}\, Me_x^{2+}]O_4$$

19-13. The saturation magnetization

The importance of the distribution of the metallic ions over the tetrahedral and octahedral sites may be illustrated with reference to the saturation magnetization for simple and mixed ferrites; data for the saturation magnetization obtained by Gorter are given in Fig. 19-18 for various mixed crystals of the type $Me^{2+}Fe_2^{3+}O_4$—$ZnFe_2^{3+}O_4$.[42]

[40] See J. J. Went and E. W. Gorter, *Philips Tech. Rev.*, **13**, 181 (1952); J. J. Went, G. W. Rathenau, E. W. Gorter, and G. W. Oosterhout, *Philips Tech. Rev.*, **13**, 194 (1952).

[41] For a comprehensive review, see E. W. Gorter, *Philips Research Repts.*, **9**, 295 (1954); also F. C. Romeyn, "Physical and Crystallographic Properties of Some Spinels," Thesis, Leiden, 1953.

[42] E. W. Gorter, *Philips Research Repts.*, **9**, 321 (1954).

Since the ferrites are essentially ionic compounds, one would expect that the saturation magnetization may be calculated from the number of unpaired spins of the ions. For example, in magnetite ($Fe^{2+}Fe_2^{3+}O_4$) the Fe^{2+} and Fe^{3+} ions have, respectively, six and five $3d$ electrons. Thus, according to the discussion on page 470 these ions have, respectively, four and five unpaired spins. For normal ferromagnetic behavior one thus expects a saturation magnetic moment of $4 + 2 \times 5 = 14$ Bohr magnetons per molecule Fe_3O_4. However, experiments by Weiss and Forrer give $4.08\mu_B$; it looks as if only the Fe^{2+} ions contribute to the magnetization. It is worth while to point out here that Fe_3O_4 is an inverse spinel.

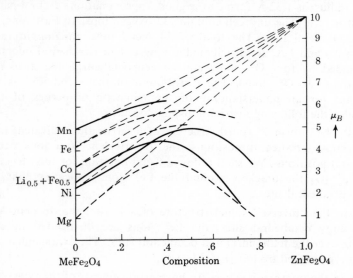

Fig. 19-18. Saturation magnetization in Bohr magnetons of various mixed series of $MeFe_2O_4$ and $ZnFe_2O_4$. [After E. W. Gorter, ref. 42]

Zinc ferrite and cadmium ferrite, which are known to have the normal spinel structure, are paramagnetic. All other known simple ferrites which are ferromagnetic have the inverted spinel structure, and it thus seems that ferromagnetism is associated with the inverted structure. The rather peculiar magnetic properties may further be illustrated by noting that according to Fig. 19-18 the replacement of paramagnetic ions such as Fe^{2+}, Co^{2+}, Mn^{2+} by the diamagnetic Zn^{2+} ions leads to an increase in the saturation magnetization, at least for small zinc concentrations.

We may also mention that when one plots the reciprocal of the susceptibility versus temperature above the Curie point, one frequently obtains a concave curvature towards the T-axis, rather than a straight line predicted by the normal Curie-Weiss law.

19-14. Elements of Néel's theory

In order to explain the magnetic properties of ferrites, Néel in 1948 put forward the hypothesis that there exists a "negative" interaction between the ions on the tetrahedral sites (A sites) and the octahedral sites (B sites) which tends to promote an antiparallel spin alignment of the A and B ions.[43] Thus, in magnetite, which may be represented by $Fe^{3+}[Fe^{2+}Fe^{3+}]O_4$, the saturation magnetization per molecule Fe_3O_4 should be $(4 + 5) - 5 = 4\mu_B$, in close agreement with the experimental value quoted above. Besides the negative AB interaction just mentioned, one must take into account an AA and a BB interaction. These turn out (see below) to be negative as well, but are considerably weaker than the AB interaction. One thus arrives at the rather remarkable situation in which ferromagnetic behavior is explained in terms of three antiferromagnetic interactions. Néel coined the term "ferrimagnetism" for this type of behavior.

In order to give the essential features of Néel's theory, we shall consider the relatively simple case of a ferrite represented by the formula

$$Fe_x^{3+}Me_{1-x}^{2+}[Fe_{2-x}^{3+}Me_x^{2+}]O_4 \tag{19-48}$$

where Me^{2+} is a diamagnetic ion. We shall assume, to begin with, a negative AB interaction; the AA and BB interactions will be represented by a factor $-\alpha$ and $-\beta$, respectively, giving the sign and strength of these interactions relative to the AB interaction. Thus, when α turns out to be negative, it indicates that the AA interaction is antiferromagnetic. It is convenient for the problem at hand to introduce the magnetizations M_a and M_b associated with the A and B sites per gram ion rather than per cm³. The total magnetization per mole is then

$$M = xM_a + (2 - x)M_b \tag{19-49}$$

Consider now the molecular field H_a acting on an ion occupying an A site; according to Néel this may be written in the form

$$H_a = H - \gamma[(2 - x)M_b - \alpha x M_a] \tag{19-50}$$

where H is the applied field, $-\gamma(2 - x)M_b$ is due to the negative AB interaction, and $\gamma\alpha x M_a$ is due to the AA interaction. Thus Néel assumes a molecular field linear in the magnetization, as did Weiss in the theory of ferromagnetism. Similarly, the molecular field acting on a B atom is given by

$$H_b = H - \gamma[xM_a - \beta(2 - x)M_b] \tag{19-51}$$

We shall first consider the paramagnetic region above the Curie point.

[43] L. Néel, Ann. phys., 3, 137 (1948).

Under these circumstances the partial magnetizations may be assumed to follow a Curie-Weiss law, i.e.,

$$M_a = C_m H_a/T \quad \text{and} \quad M_b = C_m H_b/T \tag{19-52}$$

where C_m is the Curie constant per mole; the C_m's are the same for the A and B lattices, because for the example chosen here, the Fe^{3+} ions are the only magnetic ions. Substituting H_a and H_b from (19-50) and (19-51) into the two equations (19-52) one obtains for the paramagnetic behavior

$$\frac{H}{M} = \frac{1}{\chi_{\text{mole}}} = \frac{T}{C_m} + \frac{1}{\chi_0} - \frac{\sigma}{T - \theta} \tag{19-53}$$

where

$$\frac{1}{\chi_0} = (\gamma/4)[2x(2 - x) - \alpha x^2 - \beta(2 - x)^2]$$

$$\sigma = \tfrac{1}{16}\gamma^2 C_m x(2 - x)[x(1 + \alpha) - (2 - x)(1 + \beta)]^2$$

$$\theta = \tfrac{1}{4}\gamma C_m x(2 - x)(2 + \alpha + \beta)$$

Note that according to (19-53) there exists a concave curvature toward the T-axis when $1/\chi_{\text{mole}}$ is plotted versus T, in agreement with experiment. From the shape of the experimental curves one can find χ_0, σ, and θ; hence x, α, β, and γ can also be obtained, at least qualitatively. Néel found for several ferrites that both α and β are negative (i.e., the AA and BB interactions are also antiferromagnetic). Furthermore, $|\alpha|$ and $|\beta|$ are both $\ll 1$, indicating that the AB interaction predominates.

In order to obtain the spontaneous magnetization in the region below the Néel point, we put $H = 0$ in (19-50) and (19-51). Since there are saturation effects, we cannot employ the Curie-Weiss law, and we therefore must replace equations (19-52) by the general expressions (see 19-3).

$$M_a = NgS\mu_B B_S(gS\mu_B H_a/kT) \tag{19-54}$$

$$M_b = NgS\mu_B B_S(gS\mu_B H_b/kT) \tag{19-55}$$

where now N is the number of Avogadro, since M_a and M_b refer to a mole. From these expressions together with (19-50) and (19-51) (with $H = 0$) one can obtain M_a and M_b, i.e., the total magnetization

$$M = (2 - x)M_b - xM_a$$

as function of T. The solutions depend of course on x and are given in Fig. 19-19. Thus, even for the relatively simple example given here, the situation is quite complicated. For further details of the theory we refer the reader to the literature. Apart from certain details, it seems that Néel's theory describes the observations quite well.

For the possible explanation of the nature of the antiferromagnetic interaction in terms of superexchange we refer to Gorter.[44] In certain cases one observes a weakly positive BB interaction; this has been explained by Zener in terms of a "double exchange" mechanism.[45]

We may make here some further remarks on the curves given in Fig. 19-18. From X-ray diffraction data it follows that in the mixed zinc ferrites the Zn^{2+} ions occupy tetrahedral (A) sites, as they do in the pure

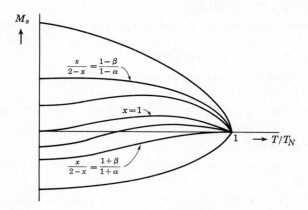

Fig. 19-19. The theoretical spontaneous magnetization as function of temperature for varying ratio of ferric ions in A and B sites, according to Néel's theory. [After E. W. Gorter, ref. 42]

zinc ferrite (which has the normal spinel structure). The other divalent ions Mn^{2+}, Ni^{2+}, etc. occupy octahedral sites, and the Fe^{3+} ions are distributed over the remaining tetrahedral and octahedral sites. Thus the mixed zinc ferrites satisfy the representation

$$Z_x^{2+} \ Fe_{1-x}^{3+}[Fe_{1+x}^{3+} \ Me_{1-x}^{2+}]O_4$$

For low zinc concentration there are a sufficient number of Fe^{3+} ions in the A sites to cause all the magnetic moments in the B sites to remain parallel (due to AB interaction). Hence for low zinc concentrations the saturation magnetization will increase with increasing Zn^{2+} concentration (because M_A decreases relative to M_b). In fact, the slope of the magnetization versus composition (x) should be such that for $x = 1$ the intercept should give $10\mu_B$. This is represented by the dashed straight lines in the figure. The fact that the actual magnetization falls below these curves is a result of the continually reduced AB interaction; the BB interactions then take over, favoring an antiparallel alignment of the B atoms. Finally, for $x = 1$, we have the pure zinc ferrite with vanishing saturation moment.

[44] E. W. Gorter, *Philips Research Repts.*, **9**, 321 (1954).
[45] C. Zener, *Phys. Rev.*, **81**, 440 (1951); **82**, 403 (1951).

REFERENCES

L. F. Bates, *Modern Magnetism*, 3d ed., Cambridge, London, 1951.

R. Becker and W. Döring, *Ferromagnetismus*, Springer, Berlin, 1939.

R. M. Bozorth, *Ferromagnetism*, Van Nostrand, New York, 1951.

A. Fairweather, F. F. Roberts, and A. J. E. Welch, "Ferrites," *Repts. Progr. Phys.*, **15**, 142 (1952).

E. W. Gorter, "Saturation Magnetization and Crystal Chemistry of Ferrimagnetic Oxides," *Philips Research Repts.* **9**, 295, 321, 403 (1954). See also *Proc. IRE*, **43**, 1945 (1955).

C. Kittel, "Physical Theory of Ferromagnetic Domains," *Revs. Mod. Phys.*, **21**, 541 (1949).

A. B. Lidiard, "Antiferromagnetism," *Repts. Progr. Phys.*, **17**, 201 (1954).

J. L. Snoek, *New Developments in Ferromagnetic Materials*, Elsevier, New York, 1947.

E. C. Stoner, "Ferromagnetism," *Repts. Progr. Phys.*, **11**, 43 (1948); **13**, 83 (1950).

J. H. van Vleck, "A Survey of the Theory of Ferromagnetism," *Revs. Mod. Phys.*, **17**, 27 (1945).

"Report on Washington Conference on Magnetism," *Revs. Mod. Phys.*, January 1953.

"Report on Grenoble Conference on Magnetism," *J. phys. rad.*, March 1951.

PROBLEMS

19-1. Consider a system of classical freely rotating magnetic dipoles, all of the same magnitude μ; there are N dipoles per cm³. Assume that the local field acting on a given dipole is equal to $H_{applied} + \gamma M$, where M is the magnetization. Show that this leads to ferromagnetic behavior below a critical temperature $\theta = \gamma N \mu^2 / 3k$. Show that above this temperature the susceptibility is given by $\chi = (\theta/\gamma)/(T - \theta)$. Compare these results with those obtained in Sec. 19-2.

19-2. A system consists of N freely rotating dipoles of magnitude μ_1 and an equal number of dipoles μ_2. Suppose the dipoles interact in such a way that the local field at the position of any given dipole is equal to $H_{applied} + \gamma M$, where M is the total magnetization per cm³. Discuss the behavior of this system.

19-3. Show that equation (19-14) can actually be written in the form (19-16). See for example F. Seitz, *Modern Theory of Solids*, McGraw-Hill, New York, 1940, p. 612.

19-4. Give a discussion of the collective electron theory of ferromagnetism. See, for example, J. C. Slater, *Quantum Theory of Matter*, McGraw-Hill, New York, 1951, Chap. 14, Appendix 22.

19-5. Magnetostriction may be thought of as resulting from the dependence of the anisotropy energy on the state of strain in a crystal; discuss magnetostriction on this basis. See C. Kittel, *Revs. Mod. Phys.*. **21**, 541 (1949).

19-6. Show that for iron the critical size for spherical single-domain particles is of the order of 10^{-6} cm. See C. Kittel, *Revs. Mod. Phys.*, **21**, 541 (1949).

19-7. For a ferromagnetic crystal let $M_s(T)$ be the spontaneous magnetization at a temperature T; let γ be the Weiss constant. Show that the extra specific heat is given by $\Delta C = -(\gamma/2)(dM_s^2/dT)$. Make a qualitative plot of ΔC versus temperature.

19-8. Consider a two sublattice model of A and B sites, the dipoles on the two types of sites being equal. Assuming that the local field at an A site is given by $H_{ma} = H_{\text{applied}} - \beta M_b - \alpha M_a$, with a similar expression for H_{mb}, show that the susceptibility $\chi_\perp$ is equal to $1/\beta$ and independent of α. Compare Sec. 19-10.

Chapter 20

MAGNETIC RELAXATION AND
RESONANCE PHENOMENA

There are numerous frequency-dependent effects associated with the magnetic properties of solids. Since it is impossible to deal with all of these within the scope of this volume, we have chosen paramagnetic relaxation and nuclear magnetic resonance as particular examples in order to illustrate certain aspects of these phenomena. Other frequency-dependent effects are mentioned briefly. Cyclotron resonance has been mentioned already in Sec. 13-6 in connection with the determination of the effective mass of electrons in semiconductors; it will therefore not be discussed here.

Paramagnetic Relaxation

20-1. Phenomenological description

In Chapter 18 the discussion of paramagnetic substances was limited to static magnetic fields. Presently we shall be concerned with phenomena occurring in oscillating magnetic fields. Consider a paramagnetic material in the absence of an external field. The magnetic dipoles are then oriented at random and there is no resultant magnetization. Suppose now that suddenly a magnetic field H is applied. One then expects that a certain period will elapse before the magnetization has reached its equilibrium value M_e. In analogy with the time effects in dielectrics it is found experimentally that the build-up of the magnetization may be described by one or more relaxation times τ such that the equation

$$dM/dt = (M_e - M)/\tau \qquad (20\text{-}1)$$

determines the rate of growth of M.[1]

From this it follows that if one applies instead of a constant magnetic field H_c a field of the type

$$H(t) = H_c + H_0 \cos \omega t \qquad (20\text{-}2)$$

the magnetization M per unit volume will in general lag behind in phase, i.e.,

$$M(t) = M_c + M_0 \cos (\omega t - \varphi) \qquad (20\text{-}3)$$

[1] It is useful to compare what follows with Secs. 6-7 and 6-8.

This phenomenon is called paramagnetic relaxation and was first observed by Gorter.[2] Usually the constant field H_c is parallel to the oscillating field, but it may also be perpendicular to it. Unless stated otherwise, the two fields will be assumed parallel.

Denoting the static susceptibility by χ_s, one may write (20-3) in the form

$$M(t) = \chi_s H_c + \chi' H_0 \cos \omega t + \chi'' H_0 \sin \omega t \qquad (20\text{-}4)$$

where $\chi''/\chi' = \tan \varphi$. For low frequencies $\chi'' = 0$ and $\chi' = \chi_s$. The frequency-dependence of χ' is called dispersion, in analogy with the optical case; χ' is referred to as the high-frequency susceptibility, for obvious reasons. The quantity χ'' determines the absorption of energy by the specimen. In fact, making use of (20-2) and (20-3), one finds for the absorption per second per unit volume,[3]

$$A = (\omega/2\pi) \oint M \, dH = (\omega/2)\chi'' H_0^2 \qquad (20\text{-}5)$$

It is usually convenient to employ complex notation. Thus if one writes

$$H(t) = H_c + H_0 e^{i\omega t} \qquad (20\text{-}6)$$

it follows that

$$M(t) = M_c + \chi^* H_0 e^{i\omega t} \qquad (20\text{-}7)$$

where

$$\chi^* = \chi' - i\chi''$$

is the complex susceptibility. We may note in passing that χ' and χ'' are related to each other by the so called Kramers-Kronig relations[4] (see Problem 20-3). Also, both χ' and χ'' are functions of H_c as well as of frequency.

So far, the description has been completely phenomenological. The task of the theory of paramagnetic relaxation is twofold:

(a) The quantities χ' and χ'' should be related to the relaxation times mentioned above.

(b) The relaxation times must find an interpretation based on the properties of the magnetic atoms and the lattice in which they are incorporated.

20-2. Relaxation mechanisms

In order to get an insight into the problem, consider a system of free magnetic dipoles, oriented at random. Suppose the dipoles have no

[2] C. J. Gorter, *Physica*, **3**, 503 (1936).

[3] The reader is reminded that by replacing in the "normal" thermodynamic expressions the pressure by M and the volume by H, one obtains expressions appropriate to the magnetic case.

[4] H. A. Kramers, *Atti congr. fis., Como*, 545 (1927); R. Kronig, *J. Opt. Soc. Amer.* **12**, 547 (1926).

interaction with each other, nor with their surroundings. When an external field H is applied, the dipoles will precess about the field direction, as explained in Sec. 18-3. In fact, this is the only influence that can be attributed to the field. Thus the component of a given dipole along the field direction will remain unaltered, and no magnetization will result. If magnetization is to occur, there must be a mechanism by which the dipoles can exchange energy with their surroundings, because only then does it become possible for them to orient themselves along the field direction. For example, if a dipole μ_B shifts from an antiparallel to a parallel position in the external field H, the system must dispose of an energy $2\mu_B H$. It is illustrative at this point to note that it requires several hours for the magnetic moments of the protons in ice, at liquid air temperature, to orient themselves in a magnetic field.[5] This is simply a consequence of the fact that the nuclei are in very poor energy contact with each other and with their surroundings. If the ice is melted, the relaxation time reduces to a few seconds. In substances where the paramagnetism is due to electrons, the relaxation times vary between 10^{-11} to 10^{-6} second at room temperature. It is essentially with these substances that we are concerned here.

In 1932, before paramagnetic relaxation had been observed, Waller wrote a remarkable theoretical paper on the subject.[6] He came to the conclusion that a distinction should be made between two relaxation mechanisms:

(i) The spin-lattice relaxation, corresponding to applied fields which are large compared with the internal magnetic field (see below).

(ii) The spin-spin relaxation, corresponding to applied fields small compared with the internal magnetic field.

Before discussing these mechanisms we may emphasize the essential difference between them.[7] In any paramagnetic material, each spin finds itself in a fluctuating magnetic field due to neighboring dipoles. This internal field H_i is of the order of μ_B/a^3, where a is a few Angstroms, i.e., $H_i \simeq 1000$ gausses. For example, in iron alum, H_i is 450 gausses.[8] Suppose now that an external field $\ll H_i$ is applied to the system. The effect of the applied field is then to change slightly the direction of the field seen by a dipole, but the magnitude remains essentially unaltered. The dipoles will thus precess about a slightly different direction, and as a result a net magnetization in the direction of the applied field occurs. The magnetization in this case does not require any energy exchange between the spins and the lattice. There is, however, an energy exchange between the spin system and the field. The mechanism described here corresponds to (ii) above.

[5] E. A. Turner, A. M. Sachs, and E. M. Purcell, *Phys. Rev.*, **76**, 465 (1949).

[6] I. Waller, *Z. Physik*, **79**, 370 (1932).

[7] See also A. H. Cooke, *Repts. Progr. Phys.*, **13**, 276 (1950), footnote, p. 279.

[8] J. Volger, F. W. de Vrijer, and C. J. Gorter, *Physica*, **13**, 621 (1947).

When, on the other hand, a constant field $H_c \gg H_i$ is applied and H_c is increased by a small amount, the direction of the field seen by the dipoles remains unaltered whereas the magnitude varies. In this case an increase of the magnetization can occur only if the number of dipoles parallel to the field increases. Thus some dipoles must flip over from the antiparallel to the parallel orientation. This requires a change in energy, which is brought about by an energy exchange with the lattice.

Experiments on paramagnetic relaxation are interpreted in terms of the sum of mechanisms (i) and (ii). It is fortunate that they can be separated readily: spin-spin relaxation is measured in small magnetic fields; the relaxation times are of the order of 10^{-10} sec and measurements are made with frequencies of many megacycles. Spin-lattice relaxation is measured in strong fields at frequencies low enough so that spin-spin relaxation can be neglected. The spin-lattice relaxation times are strongly temperature dependent, increasing with decreasing T, whereas the spin-spin relaxation times are temperature independent.

20-3. Spin-lattice relaxation

The first theory of spin-lattice relaxation, based on a model in which the magnetic interaction between the spins is neglected, was developed by Gorter and Kronig.[9] They obtained the well-known Debye relaxation equations (see Problem 20-4)

$$\chi' = \chi_s/(1 + \omega^2\tau^2) \quad \text{and} \quad \chi'' = \chi_s\omega\tau/(1 + \omega^2\tau^2) \qquad (20\text{-}9)$$

Although these equations describe the observations qualitatively, better agreement is obtained with a thermodynamic theory developed by Casimir and DuPré.[10] The basis of this theory is that the relaxation time associated with the spin-lattice interaction is so long compared to the spin-spin relaxation time that the spin system can be considered to be always in thermodynamic equilibrium. Thus the spin system is treated as a thermodynamic system, separate from but in energy contact with the lattice. The spin system has its own specific heat, temperature, etc. In contrast with this, the previous theories mentioned above considered the individual spins in energy contact with the lattice. That the temperature T_s of the spin system is not necessarily the same as that of the lattice may be seen as follows. Consider a system of spins of $\frac{1}{2}$ in thermal equilibrium with the lattice in an external field H at a temperature T. According to Boltzmann statistics we then have $N_p/N_a = \exp(2\mu_B H/kT)$, where N_p and N_a refer, respectively, to the number of spins parallel and antiparallel to H.

[9] C. J. Gorter and R. Kronig, *Physica*, **3**, 1009 (1936); R. Kronig, *Physica*, **5**, 65 (1938).

[10] H. B. G. Casimir and F. K. DuPré, *Physica*, **5**, 507 (1938).

When H is suddenly increased to H', the temperature of the lattice remaining T, it takes some time for the ratio N_p/N_a to adjust itself to the new field. However, substituting H' for H in the Boltzmann distribution above, one can define a certain temperature T_s such that the instantaneous populations satisfy the Boltzmann expression; in this case, T_s would be the spin temperature. In the above example $T_s > T$ immediately after the increase of the field; as time goes on, T_s approaches T. In an oscillating field, the difference $\theta = T_s - T$ will also oscillate, the amplitude of the oscillation becoming smaller as the heat contact between the spin system and the lattice becomes better. As long as θ is not too large, the heat transferred from the lattice to the spin system during a short time interval dt may be written

$$dQ = -\alpha\theta \, dt \qquad (20\text{-}10)$$

where the quantity α may be called the coefficient of heat contact between the spin system and the lattice. On the other hand, the first law of thermodynamics for the spin system may be written in the form

$$dQ = C_H(\partial T/\partial M)_H \, dM + C_M(\partial T/\partial H)_M \, dH \qquad (20\text{-}11)$$

where C_H and C_M are the specific heats at constant H and M, respectively. For a field of the type (20-6) we may write

$$H(t) = H_c + H_0 e^{i\omega t}$$
$$M(t) = M_c + M_0 e^{i\omega t}$$
$$\theta = \theta_0 e^{i\omega t}$$

so that

$$-\alpha\theta_0 = i\omega[C_H(\partial T/\partial M)_H M_0 + C_M(\partial T/\partial H)_M H_0] \qquad (20\text{-}12)$$

On the other hand,

$$\theta_0 = (\partial T/\partial M)_H M_0 + (\partial T/\partial H)_M H_0 \qquad (20\text{-}13)$$

By eliminating θ_0 from the last two equations one obtains for the complex susceptibility,

$$\chi^* = \frac{M_0}{H_0} = \left(\frac{\partial M}{\partial H}\right)_T \frac{1 + (i\omega/\alpha)C_M}{1 + (i\omega/\alpha)C_H} \qquad (20\text{-}14)$$

Recognizing that $(\partial M/\partial H)_T$ is the static susceptibility χ_s, one may write the real and imaginary parts as

$$\frac{\chi'}{\chi_s} = \frac{C_M}{C_H} + \frac{1 - C_M/C_H}{1 + \omega^2\tau^2} \qquad (20\text{-}15)$$

$$\frac{\chi''}{\chi_s} = \frac{(1 - C_M/C_H)\omega\tau}{1 + \omega^2\tau^2} \qquad (20\text{-}16)$$

where the relaxation time $\tau = C_H/\alpha$ is determined by the coefficient of heat contact between the spin system and the lattice. Note that the high-frequency susceptibility χ' contains, besides the Debye function (20-9), a constant part equal to C_M/C_H. A typical example of a set of dispersion

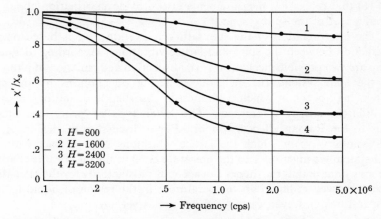

Fig. 20-1. Paramagnetic dispersion of $Gd_2(SO_4)_3 \cdot 8H_2O$ at 77°K. The numbers refer to the constant parallel field H_c. [After Broer and Gorter, ref. 11]

measurements is given in Fig. 20-1 for the octahydrate of gadolinium sulfate at 77°K.[11] The dots are measured points, the curves correspond to equation (20-15); there is thus good agreement with the Casimir-DuPré

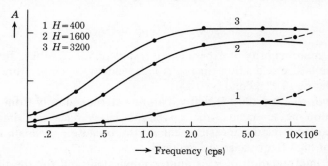

Fig. 20-2. Paramagnetic absorption in $Gd_2(SO_4)_3 \cdot 8H_2O$ at 77°K, in arbitrary units for various values of the constant parallel field H_c. The dashed part of the curve is interpreted as spin-spin relaxation. [After Broer and Gorter, ref. 11]

theory. The absorption (equation 20-16) of the same material is given in Fig. 20-2, and again good agreement is obtained. The deviations at high frequencies (dashed curve) are due to the onset of spin-spin relaxation. We note here that recent experiments at liquid helium temperatures

[11] L. J. F. Broer and C. J. Gorter, *Physica*, **10**, 621 (1943).

indicate that the relaxation effects at such temperatures cannot be described by a single relaxation time.[12]

Without going into details, it is evident from equations (20-15) and (20-16) that relaxation measurements also provide information about the specific heat of the spin system.[13]

The interpretation of the spin-lattice relaxation time is based on the interaction between the spins and lattice vibrations. According to Waller there are two possible mechanisms; (i) absorption and emission of phonons by the spin system, (ii) inelastic scattering of phonons by the spin system may occur in which a phonon is absorbed and another phonon of different energy is emitted. The latter type of process is analogous to the Raman effect in optics. For a discussion of the details of the various ways in which the lattice vibrations may interact with the spin system we must refer to the literature cited at the end of this chapter. We may remark that the theory can account satisfactorily for the relaxation times observed at liquid air temperatures; in the region of liquid helium temperatures, however, certain aspects are as yet unexplained.

20-4. Spin-spin relaxation

We have seen in Fig. 20-2 that at high frequencies absorption is observed (dashed curve) over and above the spin-lattice absorption. This absorption is interpreted as due to spin-spin relaxation and can be described by the formula

$$A_{\text{spin}} = \tfrac{1}{2}\omega^2 \tau_s \chi_s C_M / C_H \tag{20-17}$$

for the great majority of experimental results obtained so far. In contrast with the lattice relaxation time τ_s is independent of temperature; it is of the order of 10^{-10} second.

It follows from (20-17) that τ_s can be determined only from absolute absorption measurements, whereas the spin-lattice relaxation time may be obtained from relative measurements. Also, because τ_s is small, measurements at high frequencies are required.

The interpretation of τ_s is quite complicated, and for the theory we must refer the reader to the literature.[14] It may suffice here to give a rough estimate of its value. Let H_i be the rms value of the internal magnetic field at the position of any dipole due to the other dipoles. If the dipoles are free spins, the Larmor precession frequency associated with H_i is equal to $\omega_L = (e/mc)H_i$. One thus expects that the time required for the

[12] H. C. Kramers, D. Bijl, and C. J. Gorter, *Physica*, **16**, 65 (1950).

[13] R. J. Benzie and A. H. Cooke, *Proc. Phys. Soc.* (*London*), **A63**, 201 (1950).

[14] See, for example, L. J. F. Broer, *Physica*, **10**, 801 (1943); A. Wright, *Phys. Rev.*, **76**, 1826 (1949); J. H. van Vleck, *Phys. Rev.*, **74**, 1168 (1948).

spin to change its axis of precession will be of the order of $\tau_s \simeq 1/\omega_L$. That this gives indeed the order of magnitude can be seen from the table below.

Table 20-1. Some Spin-Spin Relaxation Times and Internal Fields[a]

Solid	H_i (gausses)	τ_s exp (in 10^{-10} sec)	$1/\omega_L$ calc (in 10^{-10} sec)
$Fe(NH_4)(SO_4)_2 \cdot 12H_2O$	450	1.1	1.2
$Gd_2(SO_4)_3 \cdot 8H_2O$	1380	0.57	0.4
$Cu(NH_4)_2(SO_4)_2 \cdot 6H_2O$	200	9.1	2.7
$CuSO_4 \cdot 5H_2O$	370	6.7	1.5

[a] Reproduced with kind permission of the Physical Society, London, from A. H. Cooke, *Repts. Progr. Phys.*, 13, 276 (1950).

Nuclear Magnetic Resonance

20-5. Nuclear magnetic moments

In general, atomic nuclei have an angular momentum and associated with it a magnetic moment. When one speaks of the "nuclear spin" I, one refers to the largest observable value of the component of the angular momentum in units of $\hbar$ along any specified direction. This direction may be that of an applied magnetic field; in general, we shall refer to the specified direction as the z-direction. The total angular momentum is in analogy with (18-10) given by

$$M_a = \hbar[I(I+1)]^{1/2} \tag{20-18}$$

The possible components along the z-direction are again determined by a magnetic quantum number m_I, which can accept the values

$$m_I = I, (I-1), ..., -(I-1), -I \tag{20-19}$$

(compare 18-11).

The magnetic moment μ associated with M_a is given by

$$\mu = g(e/2M_p c)M_a \tag{20-20}$$

in analogy with (18-12). Here M_p is the proton mass and g is the inverse of the gyromagnetic ratio. The maximum component of μ along an applied field H is thus equal to

$$(\mu_z)_{max} = g(e/2M_p c)\hbar I = g\mu_n I \tag{20-21}$$

where $\mu_n = 5.049 \times 10^{-24}$ erg/gauss is called the nuclear magneton. It serves a purpose similar to the Bohr magneton in the magnetic moments associated with electrons.

In an external field H, the magnetic moment will precess with the Larmor frequency,

$$\omega_L = -g(e/2M_pc)H \qquad (20\text{-}22)$$

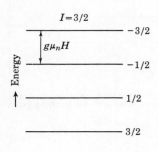

Fig. 20-3. The four Zeeman levels for $I = \frac{3}{2}$ in a magnetic field H; transitions are possible only between successive levels, leading to the resonance condition (20-23).

The proof is essentially the same as that given in Sec. 18-3 for the precession of an electron orbit, and will not be repeated here. Note the minus sign, indicating that the precession vector has a direction opposite to H.

An applied magnetic field also produces a splitting of the energy levels. Consider for example the isotope Na[23] with $I = \frac{3}{2}$. The possible components of μ along the field direction are then, in units of $g\mu_n$,

$$\tfrac{3}{2}, \quad \tfrac{1}{2}, \quad -\tfrac{1}{2}, \quad -\tfrac{3}{2}$$

Since the energy of a dipole μ in a magnetic field is equal to $-\mu_z H$, we obtain four levels, as indicated in Fig. 20-3.

20-6. Conditions required for resonance absorption

Transitions between these levels are, for magnetic dipole radiation, governed by the selection rule $\Delta m_I = \pm 1$; hence transitions are possible only between successive levels. From what has been said above, it thus follows that resonance may be observed in an alternating magnetic field of angular frequency ω, such that

$$\hbar\omega = g\mu_n H = g(e/2M_p c)\hbar H \qquad (20\text{-}23)$$

It follows immediately from (20-22) and (20-23) that the required frequency is identical with the Larmor frequency. For a field of 10^4 gausses, the nuclear resonance frequencies $\omega_L/2\pi$ lie in the radio frequency range between 1 and 50 megacycles (see Table 20-2). Resonance of this type was first observed by Purcell's group[15] and, independently, by Bloch and collaborators.[16]

The experiments are carried out by applying a variable static magnetic field H_c in the z-direction and a radio frequency field of amplitude $H_0 \ll H_c$

[15] Purcell, Torrey, and Pound, *Phys. Rev.*, **69**, 37 (1946); Bloembergen, Purcell, and Pound, *Phys. Rev.*, **73**, 679 (1948).

[16] Bloch, Hansen, and Packard, *Phys. Rev.*, **69**, 127 (1946); **70**, 474 (1946); F. Bloch, *Phys. Rev.*, **70**, 460 (1946).

perpendicular to H_c. One then observes absorption of radio frequency energy by the spin system when the resonance condition (20-23) is satisfied. The reason for the perpendicular field arrangement may be explained with reference to Fig. 20-4. For simplicity, consider a spin $I = \tfrac{1}{2}$, leading to two energy levels in the constant field H_c. In the lower level, the orientation of the dipole is as indi-cated in the figure. At the same time, the dipole precesses with the Larmor frequency about H_c. Clearly, when absorption is observed, tran-sitions between the lower and upper level must occur, i.e., the radio frequency field must have a chance to tip the dipoles from the parallel to the antiparallel position and vice versa. That this is indeed achieved by employing the oscillating field perpendicular to H_c may be seen as follows. Let the oscillating field be represented by

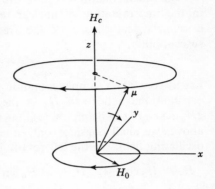

Fig. 20-4. Illustrating the constant torque acting on a precessing dipole due to a field rotating with the Larmor frequency.

$$H_x = 2H_0 \cos \omega t; \qquad H_y = H_z = 0$$
$$(20\text{-}24)$$

For our purpose it is convenient to consider this oscillating field as the sum of two rotating fields, one rotating to the right, the other to the left:

right $H_x = H_0 \cos \omega t; \qquad H_y = H_0 \sin \omega t; \qquad H_z = 0$

left $H_x = H_0 \cos \omega t; \qquad H_y = -H_0 \sin \omega t; \qquad H_z = 0$

$$(20\text{-}25)$$

If $\omega = \omega_L$, one of these rotating components will follow the precessing dipole and the dipole will eventually tip over as a result of the constant torque exerted on it.[17] The other rotating component is evidently of little consequence. The reader can convince himself readily that the probability for tipping from the parallel to the antiparallel position is equal to that for tipping in the opposite direction. Hence, in order to observe absorption of radio frequency energy by the spin system it is essential that the lower level be more heavily populated than the upper one. In thermal equilibrium this is indeed the case, because according to Boltzmann, for the case $I = \tfrac{1}{2}$, we have for the ratio of the number of parallel to antiparallel spins,

$$N_p/N_a = \exp\left(g\mu_n H/kT\right) \simeq 1 + g\mu_n H/kT$$

It must be realized that the excess number in the lower level is usually

---

[17] For the transition probabilities, see N. Bloembergen, E. M. Purcell, and R. V. Pound, *Phys. Rev.*, **73**, 679 (1948).

very small indeed; for protons for example $g = 5.58$ and one finds with $H \simeq 10^4$ gausses at room temperature, $N_p/N_a \simeq 1 + 7 \times 10^{-6}$.

20-7. The Bloch equations and the complex susceptibility

The Bloch equations [16] to be discussed below occupy a central position in the interpretation of nuclear resonance experiments. They provide a semiclassical theory of the frequency dependence of the complex susceptibility,

$$\chi^* = \chi' - i\chi'' \tag{20-26}$$

Let us consider a sample containing magnetic nuclei under influence of a constant magnetic field H_0 in the z-direction plus an oscillating field $2H_0 \cos \omega t$ of small amplitude along the x-direction. For reasons explained above, we shall consider only one of the rotating components of the oscillating field, say the left-rotating component in (20-25). Hence

$$H_x = H_0 \cos \omega t; \quad H_y = -H_0 \sin \omega t; \quad H_z = H_c; \quad H_0 \ll H_c \tag{20-27}$$

Consider first the influence of a field H alone, on a single nuclear dipole μ. In accordance with (18-17) we may write

$$(\partial \mu / \partial t)_{\text{field}} = g(e/2M_p c)\mu \times H \tag{20-28}$$

i.e., the field alone simply leads to a Larmor precession of μ about H. Adding the effect of all dipoles per unit volume, we may write for the rate of change of M due to the field alone,

$$(\partial M/\partial t)_{\text{field}} = g(e/2M_p c)M \times H = \gamma M \times H \tag{20-29}$$

For the field defined by (20-27) we have

$$\gamma = g(e/2M_p c) \simeq \omega_L/H_c \tag{20-30}$$

Besides the influence of the field, two other sources contribute to the rate of change of M, viz.,

(i) The spin-lattice interaction

(ii) The spin-spin interaction

Their influence will now be considered. Suppose that M_c represents the magnetization along the z-direction if the system is in thermal equilibrium when only the constant field H_c is applied. When this field is suddenly switched off, the magnetization will gradually approach zero. Similarly, when the field is suddenly switched on, a certain time interval is required to obtain the equilibrium value M_c. During this build-up, a certain fraction of the dipoles must flip over from an antiparallel to a parallel orientation relative to the field. Since this process requires a change in energy of the spin system, the build-up time is determined by the heat contact between the spin system and the lattice. Thus, as a result of the spin-lattice interaction the rate of change of the z-component of M is assumed to be given by

$$(\partial M_z/\partial t)_{sl} = -(M_z - M_c)/\tau_1 \qquad (20\text{-}31)$$

where the subscripts sl refer to the spin-lattice interaction; the characteristic time τ_1 is the spin-lattice relaxation time. Combining (20-31) with the z-component of equation (20-29) we obtain for the total rate of change of M_z,

$$dM_z/dt = \gamma[-M_x H_0 \sin \omega t - M_y H_0 \cos \omega t] + (M_c - M_z)/\tau_1 \qquad (20\text{-}32)$$

This is one of the Bloch equations; the two others provide expressions for the rate of change of the transverse components M_x and M_y. In order to set up the expressions for M_x and M_y, it is important to realize that if there were a completely random distribution of the x and y components of the nuclear dipoles, M_x and M_y would be zero. In other words, one is interested in the lifetime associated with a certain M_x or M_y value in the absence of an applied oscillating field. Now, consider two neighboring identical dipoles i and j. Since both are precessing about H_c, then j will produce an oscillating field of the Larmor frequency at the position of i and vice versa. Consequently, transitions may take place in which i and j simultaneously reverse their orientation (spin exchange), thus limiting the lifetime of each state. Since the interaction energy ΔE is of the order of μ_n^2/r^3, the lifetime τ_2 as given by the Heisenberg uncertainty principle is $\tau_2 \simeq \hbar/\Delta E = \hbar r^3/\mu_n^2$. The characteristic time τ_2 was introduced by Bloch as the spin-spin relaxation time. He thus assumed that the rate of change of M_x and M_y as determined by the spin-spin interaction is given by

$$(\partial M_x/\partial t)_{ss} = -M_x/\tau_2 \quad \text{and} \quad (\partial M_y/\partial t)_{ss} = -M_y/\tau_2 \qquad (20\text{-}33)$$

From a different point of view, one may argue that a given dipole sees, besides the applied field, an internal field $H_i \simeq \mu_n/r^3$ produced by its neighbors. Thus one expects a spread in the precession frequencies $\Delta\omega_L$ where, according to the resonance condition (20-23),

$$\Delta\omega_L \simeq g\mu_n H_i/\hbar \simeq g\mu_n^2/\hbar r^3 \qquad (20\text{-}34)$$

Thus the width of the absorption band corresponds to a characteristic time $2\pi/\Delta\omega_L$ which is essentially the same as τ_2 introduced above. It must be noted, however, that the two effects mentioned here in connection with τ_2 are not identical; for example, spin exchange is possible only between identical nuclei, whereas the internal field point of view is always valid.

When we add to the equations (20-33) the corresponding component equations of (20-29), we obtain the following two Bloch equations

$$dM_x/dt = \gamma(M_y H_c + M_z H_0 \sin \omega t) - M_x/\tau_2 \qquad (20\text{-}35)$$

$$dM_y/dt = \gamma(M_z H_0 \cos \omega t - M_x H_c) - M_y/\tau_2 \qquad (20\text{-}36)$$

Since the constant field and the oscillating field are applied, respectively, in the z and x-directions, one is particularly interested in solutions of the Bloch equations (20-32), (20-35), and (20-36) for M_z and M_x. Without giving the mathematical details here, one obtains[18]

$$M_z = \chi_C H_c \frac{1 + (\omega_L - \omega)^2 \tau_2^2}{1 + (\omega_L - \omega)^2 \tau_2^2 + \gamma^2 H_0^2 \tau_1 \tau_2} \qquad (20\text{-}37)$$

$$M_x = \tfrac{1}{2} \chi_C \omega_L \tau_2 \frac{(\omega_L - \omega)\tau_2(2H_0 \cos \omega t) + 2H_0 \sin \omega t}{1 + (\omega_L - \omega)^2 \tau_2^2 + \gamma^2 H_0^2 \tau_1 \tau_2} \qquad (20\text{-}38)$$

where χ_C is the static susceptibility given by the Curie law. From the definition of the complex susceptibility it follows (see 20-4) that

$$M_x(t) = \chi'(2H_0 \cos \omega t) + \chi''(2H_0 \sin \omega t) \qquad (20\text{-}39)$$

Comparison of (20-39) and (20-38) thus leads to the expressions

$$\chi' = \tfrac{1}{2} \chi_C \omega_L \tau_2 \frac{(\omega_L - \omega)\tau_2}{1 + (\omega_L - \omega)^2 \tau_2^2 + \gamma^2 H_0^2 \tau_1 \tau_2} \qquad (20\text{-}40)$$

$$\chi'' = \tfrac{1}{2} \chi_C \omega_L \tau_2 \frac{1}{1 + (\omega_L - \omega)^2 \tau_2^2 + \gamma^2 H_0^2 \tau_1 \tau_2} \qquad (20\text{-}41)$$

The reader is reminded that the absorption of radio frequency energy is determined by χ'', as expressed by formula (20-5).

In discussing the results obtained, one may distinguish between two cases;

(i) The amplitude H_0 of the oscillating field is so small that $\gamma^2 H_0^2 \tau_1 \tau_2 \ll 1$. In this case M_z is simply equal to $\chi_C H_c$, i.e., equal to the static equilibrium value. This means that the spin-lattice relaxation is rapid enough to maintain a Boltzmann distribution of the population in the various energy levels, notwithstanding the fact that, because of radio frequency absorption, an excess is thrown from lower to higher levels. For this case, the frequency-dependence of χ' and χ'' is represented in Fig. 20·5. Note that the half width of the absorption line under these circumstances is determined by the spin-spin relaxation time τ_2; it is, in fact, equal to $1/\tau_2$ in terms of an angular frequency.

(ii) When $\gamma^2 H_0^2 \tau_1 \tau_2$ is not negligible compared to unity, $M_z < \chi_C H_c$ and both χ' and χ'' are reduced in magnitude. In this case one speaks of saturation of the spin system; the spin-lattice relaxation is not able to maintain a Boltzmann distribution of the populations in the energy levels under these circumstances. In other words, the spin temperature increases beyond the lattice temperature as a result of the rapid rate of absorption

[18] See F. Bloch, *Phys. Rev.*, **70**, 460 (1946); G. E. Pake, *Am. J. Phys.*, **18**, 438 (1950).

of radio frequency energy. Also, the absorption line becomes weaker and broader.

The Bloch equations given above were obtained from macroscopic considerations. However, somewhat more complex but essentially similar relations may be derived from a microscopic viewpoint, employing statistical mechanics.[19]

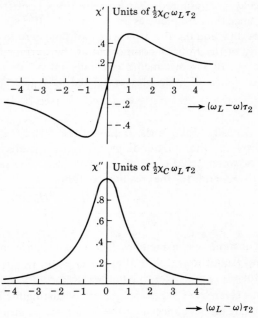

Fig. 20-5. The real (χ') and imaginary (χ'') part of the complex susceptibility as function of ($\omega_L - \omega)\tau_2$, pertaining to the case of negligible saturation.

20-8. The influence of molecular motion on the relaxation times

Several methods have been described in the literature for measuring the relaxation times τ_1 and τ_2.[20] Measurements of τ_1 are based on the competition between resonance absorption (which tends to equalize the populations in the different levels) and spin-lattice interaction (which tends to maintain a Boltzmann distribution). The values of τ_1 obtained experimentally vary between 10^{-5} and 10^4 seconds, the latter value being

[19] R. K. Wangsness and F. Bloch, *Phys. Rev.*, **89**, 728 (1953).

[20] See, for example, N. Bloembergen, E. M. Purcell, and R. V. Pound, *Phys. Rev.*, **73**, 679 (1948); M. Soutif and R. Gabillard, *Physica*, **17**, 319 (1951); R. L. Conger and P. W. Selwood, *J. Chem. Phys.*, **20**, 383 (1952); H. C. Torrey, *Phys. Rev.*, **76**, 1059 (1949); E. E. Salpeter, *Proc. Phys. Soc.* (*London*), **A63**, 337 (1949); E. L. Hahn, *Phys. Rev.*, **80**, 580 (1950).

obtained for ice at low temperatures.[5] In order to interpret experimental results it is important to realize that both τ_1 and τ_2 are strongly influenced by the migration or motion of atoms. Consider for example the build-up of the magnetization of a system of nuclear dipoles which is suddenly exposed to a static field H_c. The build-up requires dipolar transitions, and for these to occur, oscillating magnetic fields of a frequency equal to the Larmor frequency are required. Lattice vibrations contribute very little in this respect, since their frequencies are too high ($\sim 10^{13}$ sec^{-1}). However, at least in gases and liquids, the atoms or molecules are in rapid motion and the intensity of the Fourier component at the Larmor frequency will thus determine τ_1. In viscous media one may introduce a "correlation time" which, for spherical molecules, is defined by[21]

$$\tau_c = 4\pi\eta a^3/3kT \qquad (20\text{-}42)$$

where η is the viscosity and a is the radius of the molecules; τ_c measures the time required for the surroundings of a given molecule to change appreciably. For water at 20°C, $\tau_c \simeq 3 \times 10^{-12}$ sec. The relaxation time τ_1 is related to τ_c and to the resonance frequency ω_L by

$$\frac{1}{\tau_1} = C\left(\frac{\tau_c}{1+\omega_L^2\tau_c^2} + \frac{2\tau_c}{1+4\omega_L^2\tau_c^2}\right) \qquad (20\text{-}43)$$

where C is a constant which includes factors which are independent of temperature and frequency.[21] Note that for $\omega_L\tau_c \ll 1$, $1/\tau_1 \simeq 3C\tau_c$, and for $\omega_L\tau_c \gg 1$, then $1/\tau_1 \simeq 3C/2\omega_L^2\tau_c$; in the intermediate region τ_1 exhibits a minimum value given by $(\tau_1)_{min} = 3\omega_L/2^{3/2}C$, occurring for $\omega_L\tau_c = 1/\sqrt{2}$.

For a particular model concerning the molecular or atomic motion, C can be calculated; C can also be determined experimentally from the minimum value of τ_1. An example of τ_1 as function of τ_c is given in Fig. 20-6. Experimental verification of expression (20-43) has been obtained for liquids as well as for solids over a wide range of τ_1 and τ_c values. In the case of solids, τ_c is determined by the diffusion of atoms or vacancies; this makes it possible to determine diffusion coefficients from nuclear resonance experiments. We shall return to this point below.

As an example of the influence of molecular motion on τ_1 we may mention that for water at 20°C, $\tau_1 = 3.6 \pm 0.2$ seconds[22] (the calculated value,[21] on the basis of a diffusion mechanism is 3.4 seconds); on the other hand, for ice at 80°K one obtains $\tau_1 \simeq 2.5$ hours, and the line becomes much broader and weaker (compare 20-41).[23] It should be stated that τ_1 may be strongly reduced if paramagnetic ions are present; these ions have an effective moment which is 10^3 times as large as the nuclear

[21] See Bloembergen, Purcell, and Pound, *loc. cit.*
[22] G. Chiarotti and L. Giulotto, *Phys. Rev.*, **93**, 1241 (1954).
[23] E. A. Turner, A. M. Sachs, and E. M. Purcell, *Phys. Rev.*, **76**, 465 (1949).

moments, and are a very efficient medium for establishing heat contact between the nuclear spins and their surroundings.

The spin-spin relaxation time also depends on τ_c, as is illustrated in Fig. 20-6. Let us consider a solid at very low temperature where τ_c is long because atomic jumps are rare. The spin-spin relaxation time will then have some small limiting value, say 10^{-6} sec. As the temperature is raised, τ_2 will remain constant, and so will the line width in accordance with (20-41), until τ_c has been reduced to a value of the same order as τ_2. As the temperature is increased further, the number of spin exchanges per unit time decreases, since atoms are nearest neighbors for a time τ_c, which is smaller than the lifetime of the spin states. Hence τ_2 begins to increase and will continue to do so as τ_c decreases; in the region of τ_c values where both τ_1 and τ_2 increase with decreasing τ_c, the values of τ_1 and τ_2 are approximately equal.

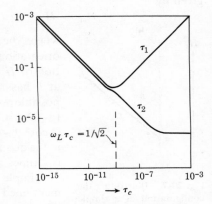

Fig. 20-6. τ_1 and τ_2 as function of the correlation time τ_c; τ_1 is given by (20-43). [After Bloembergen, Purcell, and Pound, ref. 17]

20-9. Some applications to solid state physics

Nuclear magnetic resonance experiments have become a powerful tool in studying the physical properties of solids. Although it is not possible to go into details here, a few examples may be given here to illustrate this.

(i) *Structural studies.*[24] The width and structure of a resonance absorption line are influenced by the magnetic interaction between the dipoles. Since this interaction is determined by the relative positions of the nuclei, the width and shape of the lines provide information about the structure of solids. The simplest case is encountered in solids where the nuclei occur in single pairs, so that the effective magnetic field at the position of a given nucleus is determined by the applied magnetic field H_c plus the internal field produced by its partner. With reference to Fig. 20-7 let the vector r, joining two such nuclei, make an angle θ with the applied field H_c in the z-direction. In order to calculate the effective magnetic field at the site of nucleus b we shall start from the classical formula for the field produced by a dipole μ_a at a point r:

$$H_a = 3r^{-5}(\mu_a \cdot r)r - \mu_a r^{-3} \tag{20-44}$$

[24] Gutowski, Kistiakowski, Pake, and Purcell, *J. Chem. Phys.*, **17**, 972 (1949).

Since $H_a \ll H_c$ the effective field seen by nucleus b is still essentially parallel to H_c, i.e., we are interested only in the z-component of H_a produced at b. Furthermore, let the spins be $\frac{1}{2}$ so that μ_a can be taken as $\frac{1}{2}g\mu_n$, its direction being either parallel or antiparallel to H_c. The reader will convince himself readily that the effective field at b is then given by

$$H_{\text{eff}} = H_c \pm (g\mu_n/2r^3)(3\cos^2\theta - 1) \qquad (20\text{-}45)$$

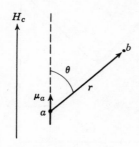

Fig. 20-7. Illustrating the configuration of a simple two-spin system in an external field H_c.

where the $\pm$ sign is due to the two possible orientations of spin a. Thus, for a given direction of H_c relative to the crystal axes, the field at b has two possible values, leading to two possible resonance frequencies. In fact, according to (20-45), the splitting corresponds to $(g\mu_n/r^3)$ $|3\cos^2\theta - 1|$ gausses. We must note here that in the quantum mechanical theory the separation is $\frac{3}{2}$ times as large.[25]

Simple two-spin systems of the type just mentioned occur to a good approximation for the protons in hydrates, such as $CaSO_4 \cdot 2H_2O$, $CuCl_2 \cdot 2H_2O$ etc., and in solid 1,2-dichloroethane. As an example, we give in Fig. 20-8 the resonance line for the latter compound in the solid state, measured at 90°K. The full curve represents the observed absorption line; the open circles represent the smoothed-out absorption line for $r = 1.70$ Å, taking into account additional broadening due to other neighboring nuclei and field inhomogeneity. The dots on the right-hand side are for $r = 1.72$ Å. For more complicated cases we refer to the literature cited in the bibliography. We may mention here that nuclei with $I > \frac{1}{2}$ have electric quadrupole moments which give rise to a quadrupole energy term in the expression for the total energy when electric field gradients occur at the nucleus. In solids this gives rise to splitting of the resonance lines from which information about the symmetry of the crystalline electric field gradients may be obtained.[26]

(ii) *Molecular rotation in solids.*[27] In the liquid and gaseous states one usually deals with narrow absorption lines, which are generally well resolved; this is a result of the fact that in these cases τ_c is small, resulting in a large value of τ_2 (and τ_1). In solids on the other hand, τ_c is large, τ_2 is small and therefore the bands are broad. In certain solids, however,

[25] G. E. Pake, *J. Chem. Phys.*, **16**, 327 (1948).

[26] H. E. Petch, D. W. L. Smellie and G. M. Volkoff, *Phys. Rev.*, **84**, 602 (1951); *Can. J. Phys.*, **30**, 270 (1952); G. M. Volkoff, *Can. J. Phys.*, **31**, 820 (1953); H. E. Petch, N. G. Crana, and G. M. Volkoff, *Can. J. Phys.*, **31**, 837 (1953).

[27] H. S. Gutowski and G. E. Pake, *J. Chem. Phys.*, **18**, 162 (1950).

molecular groups may carry out rotations when the temperature is sufficiently high. It is thus possible by measuring the narrowing of the line width as function of temperature to observe the onset of such rotations.

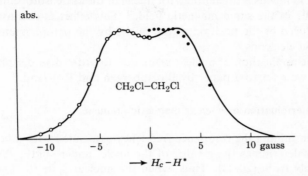

Fig. 20-8. The proton magnetic resonance absorption for solid 1,2-dichloroethane (CH_2Cl—CH_2Cl) at 90°K. The solid line represents the experimental data. The open circles are computed for $r = 1.70$ Å, the dots for $r = 1.72$ Å. [After Gutowski, *et al.*, ref. 24]

   (iii) *Nuclear resonance in metals.* In Fig. 20-9 we have represented the width of the resonance line of Na^{23} in metallic sodium. The width at high temperatures is 0.05 gauss and is presumably due to field inhomogeneity. The transition at 190°K is interpreted to be associated with the diffusion

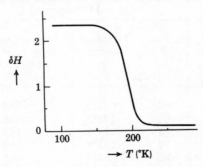

Fig. 20-9. The Na^{23} nuclear resonance line width as function of T in metallic sodium. [After Gutowski, ref. 27]

of vacancies in the sodium lattice for reasons explained above. From the transition temperature and the slope of the curve, Gutowski arrives at an activation energy for the self-diffusion of 9.5 ± 1.5 kcal.[28] According to an analysis by Norberg and Slichter, the diffusion coefficient and its temperature dependence determined from nuclear resonance experiments

[28] H. S. Gutowski, *Phys. Rev.*, **83**, 1073 (1951).

are in good agreement with direct diffusion measurements.[29] A detailed theory of diffusion effects has been given by Torrey.[30]

We may mention here that Knight discovered that the resonance frequency in metals is higher than for nuclei of the same isotope in chemical compounds in the same magnetic field.[31] This effect is due to the local field produced at the position of the nuclei by the paramagnetism of the conduction electrons.[32]

For the application of nuclear resonance to order-disorder phenomena in alloys, we refer to a paper by Bloembergen and Rowland.[33]

20-10. Determination of nuclear magnetic moments

By determining the resonance frequency associated with a field H one essentially determines the g-value of the nuclei under study; this follows immediately from (20-23). Thus, when the nuclear spin I is known, one can calculate the maximum component of the magnetic dipole moment from the relation $(\mu_z)_{max} = g\mu_n I$; this component is usually referred to as the nuclear magnetic moment when expressed in units of the nuclear magneton μ_n. (Actually, the magnetic moment is equal to $g\mu_n[I(I+1)]^{1/2}$.) Magnetic moments for a number of nuclei are given in Table 20-2, together with the resonance frequency ν_L in megacycles/sec for a field of 10^4 gausses. Presently, the resonance method is the most accurate one for determining magnetic moments.

Table 20-2. **Nuclear Magnetic Moments in Units of the Nuclear Magneton**
$\mu_n = 5.049 \times 10^{-24}$ erg/gauss

Nucleus	I	Magnetic moment gI	Resonant frequency for $H = 10^4$ gausses in megacycles/sec.
neutron	1/2	-1.9135	29.1
H^1	1/2	2.7935	42.6
Li^7	3/2	3.2571	16.5
Na^{23}	3/2	2.2178	11.3
Al^{27}	5/2	3.6419	11.1
Cu^{63}	3/2	2.2266	11.3
Cu^{65}	3/2	2.3850	12.1
Cl^{35}	3/2	0.8222	4.2

[29] R. E. Norberg and C. P. Slichter, *Phys. Rev.*, **83**, 1074 (1951); see also R. E. Norberg, *Phys. Rev.*, **86**, 745 (1952).

[30] H. C. Torrey, *Phys. Rev.*, **92**, 962 (1953).

[31] W. D. Knight, *Phys. Rev.*, **76**, 1259 (1949).

[32] Townes, Herring and Knight, *Phys. Rev.*, **77**, 852 (1950).

[33] N. Bloembergen and T. J. Rowland, *Acta Metallurgica*, **1**, 731 (1953).

Other Resonance and Relaxation Effects

20-11. Paramagnetic resonance

Paramagnetic or electron spin resonance is the analogue of nuclear spin resonance. The resonance condition is obtained by replacing M_p in expression (20-23) by the electron mass, so that

$$\omega_L = g(e/2mc)H_c \tag{20-46}$$

Since the electron mass is $\sim 10^3$ times smaller than M_p, the resonance frequencies for the same field are $\sim 10^3$ higher than for nuclear resonance. For a free electron $g = 2.0023$, and in that case $\omega_L = 2.8026H$ megacycles per second when H is expressed in gausses. Paramagnetic resonance was first observed by Zavoisky on the paramagnetic salt $CuCl_2 \cdot 2H_2O$.[34] Studies of paramagnetic resonance in crystalline solids have provided a great deal of accurate information about the crystalline electric fields. A summary of this has been given in a paper by Bleany and Stevens.[35] Other investigations have been concerned with free radicals, trapped electrons, conduction electrons in metals, and excited molecules. We shall confine ourselves to some remarks in connection with color centers and donor levels.

We have seen in Sec. 15-6 that an F center in an alkali halide crystal is considered an electron trapped at a negative ion vacancy, the electron being shared by the six surrounding positive ions. Such electrons may be expected to exhibit the electron spin resonance phenomenon and this is indeed the case. The absorption lines are quite broad. For example, in KCl colored additively with excess potassium, one observes a resonance line of 54 gausses wide (one usually employs a fixed frequency of the transverse a-c field and sweeps the constant part H_c slowly through resonance) and a g factor of 1.995.[36] Now, when one calculates the width of the line on the basis of dipolar interaction between randomly distributed F centers, the width would be only 0.1 gauss. However, attempts to ascribe the observed line width to the interaction between the F center electron and the surrounding nuclei K^{39} and K^{41} have been successful. For example, from the fact that K^{39} has a nuclear magnetic moment of $0.3910\mu_n$ and K^{41} of -0.2145, one would expect on the basis of this notion that replacing K^{39} by K^{41} should produce a narrower line. One finds for $K^{41}Cl$ (containing

[34] E. Zavoisky, *J. Phys. U.S.S.R.*, **9**, 211, 245, 447 (1945).

[35] B. Bleany and K. W. H. Stevens, *Repts. Progr. Phys.*, **16**, 108 (1953).

[36] A. F. Kip, C. Kittel, R. A. Levy, and A. M. Portis, *Phys. Rev.*, **91**, 1066 (1953); see also C. A. Hutchinson, Jr., *Phys. Rev.*, **75**, 1769 (1949).

99.2 per cent K[41]) irradiated with X-rays, a line width of 36 gausses. If only the immediately neighboring K ions were the source of interaction, the line width would have been 31 gausses; presumably the interaction with the next shell of chlorine ions also contributes to some extent to the line width.

We also mentioned in Sec. 15-6 that from the observed g factor and line width one has concluded that the F center electron is not accurately described by a pure s-state wave function; the wave function also contains components with nonvanishing orbital momentum.

Electron spin resonance lines have also been observed in n- and p-type silicon.[37] The lines exhibit a hyperfine structure resulting from the interaction between the electron spin and the nuclear spin of the atom to which it belongs. In general, for a nuclear spin I, one obtains $(2I + 1)$ lines; the number of lines observed is in agreement with this rule. At high donor concentrations the lines become narrow and the splitting disappears; this is a result of the ionization of the donor levels, the remaining line being attributed to the conduction electrons.

20-12. Ferromagnetic resonance and relaxation

In principle, ferromagnetic resonance experiments are very similar to nuclear and electron spin resonance experiments. A specimen of the material, usually in the form of the thin disk, is placed in a microwave cavity so that the specimen is acted upon by an oscillating magnetic field of angular frequency ω and small amplitude H_0. At the same time, a relatively strong d-c field H_c is applied parallel to the disk, so that the magnetization is saturated. The magnetization vector M_s may be considered as precessing about H_c, and for a fixed frequency ω, H_c may be varied such that the precession frequency equals ω; energy is then absorbed from the microwave field.

Ferromagnetic resonance was first observed by Griffiths.[38] At first sight one is tempted to interpret the results on the basis of the resonance condition (20-46) for paramagnetic resonance. However, one then obtains values for g which are much larger than the free electron value $g \simeq 2$. It was shown by Kittel[39] that for a sample in the form of a disk with H_c parallel to the disk, the resonance condition is given by

$$\omega_L = g(e/2mc)(BH_c)^{1/2} \tag{20-47}$$

($B =$ magnetic induction). When this formula is used, the g values obtained

[37] See, for example, A. M. Portis, A. F. Kip, C. Kittel, and W. H. Brattain, *Phys. Rev.*, **90**, 988 (1953).

[38] J. H. E. Griffiths, *Nature*, **158**, 670 (1946).

[39] C. Kittel, *Phys. Rev.*, **71**, 270 (1947); **73**, 155 (1948).

are close to the free electron value. As an example, we give in Fig. 20-10 the ferromagnetic absorption line for nickel ferrite, measured at 24,000 megacycles/sec.

In general, the theory of ferromagnetic resonance is in good agreement with experiments; however, the explanation for the very large line widths (~100 gausses) which are observed is still in doubt.[40] Since the line width is determined by relaxation effects (compare 20-41), this difficulty has stimulated studies of ferromagnetic relaxation; references on this topic may be found in E. Abrahams, *Advances in Electronics and Electron Physics*, **7**, 47 (1955).

For antiferromagnetic solids, the resonance frequencies lie just beyond the limit of the experimentally accessible region. The reason for this may be found in Kittel's theory of antiferromagnetic resonance.[41] On the basis of a two sublattice model, he finds that below the Curie point the resonance frequency is a doublet determined by

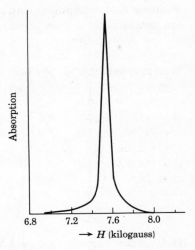

Fig. 20-10. The ferromagnetic resonance line in Ni-ferrite at 24,000 megacycles/sec. [After Yager, Galt, Merrit, and Wood, *Phys. Rev.*, **80**, 744 (1950)]

$$\omega_0/\gamma = H \pm [H_A(H_A + H_{mf})]^{1/2} \tag{20-48}$$

where $\gamma = g(e/2mc)$, H is the applied field, H_A is the anisotropy field for one sublattice, and H_{mf} is the molecular field. Thus for MnF_2 for which $H_A \simeq 9000$ gausses and $H_{mf} \simeq 10^6$ gausses, one obtains $\omega_0 \simeq 10$ cm^{-1}.[42]

The antiferromagnetic doublet has, however, been observed for $CuCl_2 \cdot 2H_2O$, which has an antiferromagnetic Curie point of 4·3°K and thus a relatively weak molecular field.[43]

20-13. Frequency-dependence of the initial permeability in ferrites

Because of the great interest in ferromagnetic insulators, such as the ferrites, for high-frequency applications, extensive investigations are being made of the high-frequency behavior of these materials. In particular, one

[40] C. Kittel, *J. phys. rad.*, **12**, 291 (1951); J. H. Van Vleck, *Physica*, **17**, 234 (1951).

[41] C. Kittel, *Phys. Rev.*, **82**, 565 (1951).

[42] F. Keffer, *Phys. Rev.*, **87**, 608 (1952).

[43] Ubbink, Poulis, Gerritsen, and Gorter, *Physica*, **18**, 361 (1952); for the theory, see J. Ubbink, *Physica*, **19**, 9 (1953).

is interested in the frequency-dependence of the initial permeability because the latter determines essentially the propagation of electromagnetic waves in the material. In such experiments there is no applied static magnetic field, in contrast with the ferromagnetic resonance experiments; one measures for a demagnetized sample the complex permeability

$$\mu^* = \mu' - i\mu'' = B/H \tag{20 49}$$

in an alternating field. We note that the complex permeability is related to

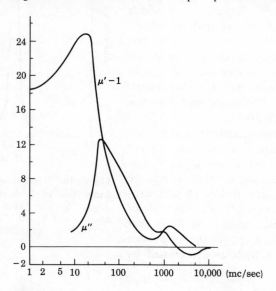

Fig. 20-11. The frequency dependence of $(\mu' - 1)$ and μ'' for ferramic A in the demagnetized state. [After Rado, Wright, and Emerson, ref. 47]

the complex susceptibility χ^* by the relation $\chi^* = (\mu^* - 1)/4\pi$. The frequencies of interest range between zero and 10^4 megacycles per second.

In such measurements on sintered Ni-Zn and Mn-Zn ferrites, Snoek found that the losses of these materials above a frequency of the order of 5–100 megacycles/sec become very high.[44] The shape of the curves for μ' versus frequency are similar to those given in Fig. 20-11, except that he found only one maximum. The fact that μ' first increases indicates a resonance phenomenon, although the fact that the μ'-values did not become <1 (i.e., $\chi' < 0$), indicates a relaxation effect at the same time. The resonance was explained by Snoek in the following way. According to Landau and Lifshitz the crystalline anisotropy field is equivalent with

[44] J. L. Snoek, *New Developments in Ferromagnetic Materials*, Elsevier, New York, 1947.

an internal field H_i.[45] Thus the electron spins precess about H_i with the Larmor frequency within each crystallite of the polycrystalline material. When an alternating magnetic field of the Larmor frequency is applied, ferromagnetic resonance occurs when this field has a component perpendicular to H_i. This has been called "natural" resonance, in contrast with the "induced" resonance obtained with an applied static magnetic field.[46]

More recently, Rado *et al.* carried out some interesting experiments of the same type on "ferramic A," which is a sintered mixture of several oxides, but containing mainly magnesium ferrite.[47] The curves obtained for $(\mu' - 1)$ and μ'' are given in Fig. 20-11. It is observed that in this case two resonances occur, one at about 50 megacycles/sec and another in the vicinity of 1000 megacycles/sec. When they carried out the same experiment with small particles ($\sim 0.5\ \mu$) embedded in wax, they observed that the 50-megacycle resonance was absent. Also, they had shown previously that particles of this size behave essentially as single-domain particles. They conclude from these results that the 50-megacycle resonance is associated with domain-wall displacements, and that the 100-megacycle resonance is due to domain rotations. The theory of these phenomena is still in a state of flux and will not be discussed here.[48]

REFERENCES

E. Abrahams, "Relaxation Processes in Ferromagnetism," *Advances in Electronics and Electron Physics*, **7**, 47 (1955).

A. H. Cooke, "Paramagnetic Relaxation Effects," *Repts. Progr. Phys.*, **13**, 276 (1950).

K. K. Darrow, "Magnetic Resonance," *Bell System Tech. J.*, **32**, 74, 384 (1953).

C. J. Gorter, *Paramagnetic Relaxation*, Elsevier, New York, 1947.

H. S. Gutowski, "Nuclear magnetic resonance," *Ann. Revs. Phys. Chem.*, **5**, 333 (1954).

J. Van den Handel, "Paramagnetism," *Advances in Electronics and Electron Physics*, **6**, 463 (1954).

W. D. Knight, "Electron Paramagnetism and Nuclear Magnetic Resonance in Metals," in *Solid State Physics*, Academic Press, New York, vol. **2**, 1956.

[45] L. Landau and E. Lifshitz, *Phys. Z. Sowjetunion*, **8**, 153 (1935).
[46] G. T. Rado, *Revs. Mod. Phys.*, **25**, 81 (1953).
[47] G. T. Rado, R. W. Wright, and W. H. Emerson, *Phys. Rev.*, **80**, 273 (1950).
[48] The present situation has been reviewed by E. Abrahams, *Advances in Electronics and Electron Physics*, **7**, 47 (1955).

G. E. Pake, "Nuclear Magnetic Resonance Absorption," I and II, *Am. J. Phys.*, **18**, 438, 473 (1950).

G. E Pake, "Nuclear Magnetic Resonance," in *Solid State Physics*, Academic Press, New York, vol. **2**, 1956.

G. T. Rado, "Ferromagnetic Phenomena at Microwave Frequencies," *Advances in Electronics*, **2**, 251 (1950).

J. Smit and H. P. J. Wijn, "Physical Properties of Ferrites," *Advances in Electronics and Electron Physics*, **6**, 70 (1954).

J. L. Snoek, *New Developments in Ferromagnetic Materials*, Elsevier, New York, 1947.

"International Conference on Spectroscopy at Radiofrequencies," *Physica*, **17**, 169–484 (1951).

"Washington Conference on Magnetism," *Revs. Mod. Phys.*, January 1953.

Conference on Defects in Crystalline Solids, held at the H. H. Wills Physical Laboratory, University of Bristol, July 1954.

PROBLEMS

20-1. Consider a series arrangement of a self-inductance L and a resistance R; show that the conductance G of the system as function of frequency is given by

$$G(\omega) = \frac{G(0)}{1 + \omega^2\tau^2} - i\,\frac{G(0)\omega\tau}{1 + \omega^2\tau^2}$$

with $\tau = L/R$. Note that this expression is similar to that for χ according to the Debye equations (20-9).

20-2. Show that at low frequencies the paramagnetic absorption is one order of magnitude more sensitive than the dispersion.

20-3. As mentioned in Sec. 20-1, χ' and χ'' are not independent of each other; in fact if one of them is known for all angular frequencies ω, the other may be calculated from one of the Kramers relations:

$$\chi'(\omega_0) = \frac{2}{\pi} \int_0^\infty \frac{\omega\chi''(\omega)\,d\omega}{(\omega^2 - \omega_0^2)} \quad \text{and} \quad \chi''(\omega_0) = -\frac{2}{\pi} \int_0^\infty \frac{\omega_0\chi'(\omega)\,d\omega}{(\omega^2 - \omega_0^2)}$$

(a) Show that the Debye equations (20-9) satisfy these relations; do the same for the Casimir-Dupré equations (20-15) and (20-16).

(b) Give a proof of the Kramers relations by following these hints: Apply a magnetic field in the form of a delta function

$$H(t) = \delta(t) = \frac{1}{\pi} \int_0^\infty \cos \omega t \, d\omega$$

The corresponding magnetization is then

$$M(t) = \frac{1}{\pi} \int_0^\infty (\chi' \cos \omega t + \chi'' \sin \omega t) \, d\omega$$

Now, for $t < 0$ we must have $M(t) = 0$; also $\cos \omega t$ is an even and $\sin \omega t$ is an odd function of t. Hence, we must require for $t > 0$ that

$$\int_0^\infty \chi' \cos \omega t \, d\omega = \int_0^\infty \chi'' \sin \omega t \, d\omega = f(t)$$

From this information, derive the Kramers relations by inversion of the Fourier integrals.

20-4. This problem refers to the theory of Gorter and Kronig of paramagnetic relaxation, leading to the Debye equations. Consider N noninteracting spins of $\frac{1}{2}$. Apply a constant field H_c. In equilibrium $N_a P_{ap} = N_p P_{pa}$ where N_a is the number of spins parallel to H_c and P_{ap} is the probability for a transition from the antiparallel to the parallel orientation. First show that if $\mu_B H_c \ll kT$

$$P_{ap} - P_{pa} = (\mu_B H_c / kT) P \quad \text{with} \quad P = P_{ap} + P_{pa}$$

(Note that the P's depend on H_c.) Next assume that

$$H(t) = H_c + H_0 e^{i\omega t} \quad \text{and} \quad P_{ap} = (P_{ap})_{H_0=0} + \left(\frac{\partial P_{ap}}{\partial H} \right)_T H_0 e^{i\omega t}$$

where $H_0 \ll H_c$. Set up the equations for $(\partial N_p / \partial t)$ and $(\partial N_a / \partial t)$ appropriate to the field $H(t)$. Calculate the magnetization M_0 corresponding to the a-c field and show that

$$\chi = M_0 / H_0 = \chi_{\text{static}} (1 + i\omega t)^{-1} \quad \text{with} \quad \tau = 1/P$$

This expression gives the Debye equations (20-9).

APPENDIX

A. Thermodynamic conditions for equilibrium

When a physical system is not in thermal equilibrium, it will in time proceed to equilibrium by means of a number of irreversible processes. The second law of thermodynamics in its general form reads

$$T \, dS \geqslant dE + p \, dV \qquad \text{(A-1)}$$

where $p \, dV$ represents the work done by the system. If the work is of a mechanical nature, p and V stand for pressure and volume, but in other types of work they may represent other quantities, such as polarization and field strength, etc. The equality sign in (A-1) holds only in the state of equilibrium. From (A-1) one may derive conditions for equilibrium, depending on the external quantities one choses to keep constant. It should be emphasized that the first law of thermodynamics, which expresses the conservation of energy, holds for reversible as well as for irreversible processes, i.e.,

$$\delta Q = dE + p \, dV \qquad \text{(A-2)}$$

The following cases arise:

(a) $\delta Q = 0$. This refers to systems which are isolated from the rest of the universe so that no heat exchange with the surroundings is possible. This gives,

$$T \, dS \geqslant 0 \quad \text{for} \quad \delta Q = 0 \qquad \text{(A-3)}$$

Thus, for such a system the entropy can only increase or remain constant; i.e., in equilibrium the entropy of such a system reaches its maximum value.

(b) *Systems held at constant volume and temperature.* Under these conditions one concludes from (A-1) that $T \, dS - dE \geqslant 0$, or

$$dF = d(E - TS) \leqslant 0 \quad \text{for constant } V,T \qquad \text{(A-4)}$$

Here F is called the Helmholtz free energy or, as in this book, simply the free energy. Note that in this case F must be a minimum when equilibrium has been reached.

(c) *Systems held at constant pressure and temperature.* In the physics of solids this is the most frequently occurring case. It follows from (A-1) that

$$dG = d(E + pV - TS) \leqslant 0 \quad \text{for constant } p, T \qquad \text{(A-5)}$$

Here G is called the Gibbs free energy, or the thermodynamic potential. The reason that in so many of the problems discussed in this book F is minimized rather than G, is that when p is the atmospheric pressure, the term $p \, dV$ is usually negligible compared with dE and $T \, dS$. In other words, this procedure is justified as long as the pressure is low enough as to have no influence on the properties of the crystal. In fact, for $p = 0$, conditions (A-4) and (A-5) become identical.

B. Particle in a box according to wave mechanics

Consider a particle allowed to move in one dimension. Let the potential energy of the particle be zero for $0 < x < L$ and let it be infinite for $x \leqslant 0$ and $x \geqslant L$. The Schrödinger equation is

$$d^2\psi/dx^2 + (2m/\hbar^2)E\psi = 0 \qquad (B-1)$$

where E is the total energy of the particle, i.e., in our case the kinetic energy. The general solution is

$$\psi(x) = Ae^{ikx} + Be^{-ikx} \quad \text{with} \quad k^2 = (2m/\hbar^2)E$$

The boundary conditions require

$$\psi = 0 \quad \text{for} \quad x = 0 \quad \text{and for} \quad x = L$$

The first condition yields $A = -B$; this leaves only solutions of the type $\sin kx$. Applying the second boundary condition, one singles out only those solutions for which

$$\sin kL = 0 \quad \text{or} \quad k_n = n\pi/L \quad \text{with} \quad n = 1, 2, 3, \ldots$$

The solutions

$$\psi_n = C \sin (n\pi x/L) \qquad (B-2)$$

are standing waves. For each value of n there is a wave function ψ_n corresponding to an energy

$$E_n = \hbar^2 k_n^2/2m = \hbar^2\pi^2 n^2/2mL^2 \qquad (B-3)$$

Note that $\hbar k_n$ represents the momentum of the particle. The energy spectrum evidently consists of discrete levels, the separation depending on L^2 and n^2. The constant C in (B-2) may be obtained from the requirement that for a particle known to be in the state ψ_n, the probability to be found anywhere between $x = 0$ and $x = L$ must be equal to unity, i.e.,

$$\int_0^L |\psi_n(x)|^2 \, dx = 1 \qquad (B-4)$$

For a particle in a 3-dimensional cubic potential box of edge L, the solutions are again standing waves:

$$\psi(x,y,z) = C \sin (n_x \pi x/L) \sin (n_y \pi y/L) \sin (n_z \pi z/L) \qquad \text{(B-5)}$$

where n_x, n_y, n_z are integers $\geqslant 1$. The energy levels are

$$E_{n_x n_y n_z} = (\hbar^2 \pi^2 / 2mL^2)(n_x^2 + n_y^2 + n_z^2) \qquad \text{(B-6)}$$

A particle described by one of the wave functions (B-5) is said to be in a given "state." Note that one energy level may correspond to various states; for example, the integer values (112), (121), (211) all correspond to the same energy level, although they represent different wave functions. The energy level is then said to be 3-fold degenerate.

What is the number of possible wave functions corresponding to a momentum between p and $p + dp$? This may be found by realizing that (B-6) represents $p^2/2m$. We may then write (B-6) as

$$p^2 L^2 / \hbar^2 \pi^2 = n_x^2 + n_y^2 + n_z^2 \equiv R^2$$

The number of different sets of integers corresponding to a range between R and $R + dR$ is

$$\tfrac{1}{8} 4\pi R^2 \, dR = 4\pi p^2 \, dp \, L^3/h^3 \qquad \text{(B-7)}$$

where the factor $\tfrac{1}{8}$ arises from the fact that the integers are positive. For each set of integers n_x, n_y, n_z there is one wave function, i.e., one state; the spin is not included in this case. Note that (B-7) may be interpreted as follows: divide the momentum space into cells of h^3; each cell then corresponds to a possible wave function per unit volume.

C. Indistinguishable particles and the Pauli principle

Consider two weakly interacting particles in a 1-dimensional potential box and let the potential energy inside the box be taken as zero. For a single particle in the box, the Schrödinger equation is

$$d^2\psi/dx^2 + (2m/\hbar^2)E\psi = 0 \qquad \text{(C-1)}$$

Let the solutions of this equation be ψ_a, ψ_b, ψ_c, ..., corresponding to the energies E_a, E_b, E_c, ... For the system of two particles we have

$$\left(\frac{\partial^2}{\partial x_1^2} + \frac{\partial^2}{\partial x_2^2} + \frac{2m}{\hbar^2} E \right) \psi(x_1, x_2) = 0 \qquad \text{(C-2)}$$

We leave it to the reader to show that possible solutions of this equation are the product of the single particle solutions:

$$\psi_a(x_1)\psi_b(x_2) \quad \text{and} \quad \psi_b(x_1)\psi_a(x_2) \qquad \text{(C-3)}$$

The former describes the situation in which particle 1 is in state ψ_a and particle 2 is in state ψ_b; the latter corresponds to particle 1 in ψ_b and particle 2 in ψ_a. Note that both solutions correspond to the same energy $E = E_a + E_b$. From the mathematical point of view any linear combination of the solutions (C-3) is a satisfactory solution of (C-2). From the point of view of physics, however, there are only two acceptable linear combinations, viz.,

$$\psi_{\text{sym}} = \psi_a(x_1)\psi_b(x_2) + \psi_b(x_1)\psi_a(x_2) \tag{C-4}$$

and
$$\psi_{\text{anti}} = \psi_a(x_1)\psi_b(x_2) - \psi_b(x_1)\psi_a(x_2) \tag{C-5}$$

In (C-4) an interchange of the coordinates of the particles leaves the wave function unaltered and one speaks of the symmetric wave function. In the antisymmetric wave function (C-5) an interchange of the coordinates x_1 and x_2 produces a change of sign. The physical reason for selecting only (C-4) and (C-5) from an infinite number of possible mathematical solutions is based on the principle of indistinguishability of the two particles. In other words, from a physical experiment we may ascertain that one of the particles is in state ψ_a and the other in state ψ_b; but it is impossible to distinguish experimentally between the possible solutions $\psi_a(x_1)\psi_b(x_2)$ and $\psi_b(x_1)\psi_a(x_2)$. The principle thus rejects the possibility of "painting" numbers on the particles. Mathematically, the principle may be expressed as follows: let $\psi_{1,2}$ represent a wave function describing the system of two particles, and let $\psi_{2,1}$ be obtained from $\psi_{1,2}$ by interchanging the coordinates x_1 and x_2. We then require that

$$\left|\psi_{1,2}\right|^2 dx_1 \, dx_2 = \left|\psi_{2,1}\right|^2 dx_1 \, dx_2 \tag{C-6}$$

because each of these expressions gives us the probability of finding one particle in the range dx_1 and the other in the range dx_2. The principle of indistinguishability thus imposes the following symmetry conditions on the two-particle wave functions:

$$\text{either} \qquad \psi_{1,2} = \psi_{2,1} \tag{C-7}$$

$$\text{or} \qquad \psi_{1,2} = -\psi_{2,1} \tag{C-8}$$

Note that (C-4) and (C-5) satisfy, respectively, (C-7) and (C-8); it can be shown that (C-4) and (C-5) are the only solutions with these properties.

In nature there are two types of particles: those for which the two-particle wave function is always symmetric and those for which the two-particle wave function is always antisymmetric. To which group a particular type of particles belongs must be decided from experiment. Electrons, protons, and neutrons require antisymmetric wave functions. Particles described by antisymmetric wave functions have the following fundamental peculiarity: from (C-5) it follows that if $\psi_a = \psi_b$, i.e., if both particles are in the same state, ψ_{anti} vanishes, i.e., such a situation does not exist. By extending the above treatment to many particles, one arrives at the following conclusion:

In a system of particles described by antisymmetric wave functions, such as electrons, only one particle can occupy any one "state." This is the Pauli exclusion principle.

The word "state" must be amended here in the following sense: the complete wave function of an electron does not contain only the spatial coordinates x, y, z but also the spin, which can accept two possible values. Thus if the spin is included in the wave functions ψ_a and ψ_b, the wording of the conclusion is correct. If a state is considered to be described by its spacial coordinates only, the Pauli principle should read that no more than two electrons can occupy a given state. Particles obeying the Pauli exclusion principle give rise to Fermi-Dirac statistics. Particles described by symmetric wave functions give rise to Bose-Einstein statistics, and for them no limitation exists on the number of particles occupying a given state.

D. Fermi statistics

Consider a system of particles for which the possible wave functions (states) and energy levels are known. Let the energy levels be denoted by $\epsilon_1, \epsilon_2, \ldots, \epsilon_i \ldots$ and let the number of possible states (including the spin) corresponding to these energy levels be denoted by $Z_1, Z_2, \ldots, Z_i, \ldots$. The interaction between the particles is assumed to be weak, so that the total energy of the system E is equal to the sum of the separate energies of the particles. The fundamental problem of statistical mechanics is this: given the total number of particles N and the total energy E, what is the most probable population $n_1, n_2, \ldots, n_i, \ldots$ of the energy levels? Evidently,

$$\sum_i n_i = N \quad \text{and} \quad \sum_i n_i \epsilon_i = E \tag{D-1}$$

Also, the levels of interest for the problem are only those below the value E; this limits the total number of possible states involved to

$$Z_{\text{total}} = Z_1 + Z_2 + \ldots + Z_i + \ldots + Z_E \tag{D-2}$$

where Z_E is the number of possible states of the level E.

To solve the problem just stated, it is necessary to decide upon the probability for a single particle to be in a given state. We shall accept the postulate of "equal a priori probabilities," in which it is assumed that there is no preference for any of the Z_{total} possible states. In other words, the probability for any one particle to be in a given state is simply

$$p = 1/Z_{\text{total}} \tag{D-3}$$

Furthermore, we shall restrict the discussion to particles for which the Pauli exclusion principle holds, i.e., to Fermi-Dirac statistics.

What is the probability $P(n_1, n_2, ...)$ that the populations in the energy levels are $n_1, n_2, ...$? Consider Z_i boxes and n_i indistinguishable balls and assume that each box can contain either one or no ball ($Z_i \geqslant n_i$). The probability for a specific distribution (say box 1 empty, box 2 filled, box 3 filled etc.) is evidently p^{n_i}. However, there are in general many ways W_i in which the balls can be distributed, viz., just as many ways as there are possible arrangements of n_i occupied and ($Z_i - n_i$) empty boxes. Hence

$$W_i = Z_i!/[n_i!(Z_i - n_i)!]$$

Thus the probability of finding n_i particles in ϵ_i is

$$P(n_i) = p^{n_i} W_i = p^{n_i} Z_i!/[n_i!(Z_i - n_i)!]$$

For the other levels, similar arguments hold, so that

$$P(n_1, n_2, ...) = p^N W_1 W_2 ... \equiv p^N W \qquad \text{(D-4)}$$

Note that p^N is a constant and that the most probable state of affairs is determined by the maximum value of W. One thus has to find that set of values $n_1, n_2, n_3, ...$ for which W obtains its maximum value. It is more convenient, however, to maximize log W. By applying Stirling's theorem, assuming all quantities involved to be $\gg 1$, one may write

$$\log W = \sum_i \log W_i = \sum_i [Z_i \log Z_i - n_i \log n_i - (Z_i - n_i) \log (Z_i - n_i)] \qquad \text{(D-5)}$$

When W is a maximum, we must have for small variations δn_i in the numbers n_i,

$$\delta \log W = \sum_i [-\log n_i + \log (Z_i - n_i)] \, \delta n_i = 0 \qquad \text{(D-6)}$$

However, the variations δn_i are not independent of each other, but should satisfy the following auxiliary conditions derived from (D-1):

$$\delta N = \sum_i \delta n_i = 0 \quad \text{and} \quad \delta E = \sum_i \epsilon_i \, \delta n_i = 0 \qquad \text{(D-7)}$$

Using the method of undetermined multipliers of Lagrange, we may write from (D-6) and (D-7),

$$\delta \log W - \alpha \sum_i \delta n_i - \beta \sum_i \epsilon_i \, \delta n_i = 0 \qquad \text{(D-8)}$$

where α and β are undetermined constants. Suppose now we choose α and β such that of the sum (D-8) the coefficients of δn_k and δn_j are zero, i.e.,

$$\log [(Z_k' - n_k)/n_k] - \alpha - \beta \epsilon_k = 0$$

$$\log [(Z_j - n_j)/n_j] - \alpha - \beta \epsilon_j = 0$$

This is always possible, because we have two equations from which β and α may be found. Now the variations δn_i are independent except for two of them (because there are two auxiliary conditions). If we consider δn_k and δn_j as the dependent ones, it is evident that (D-8) can be satisfied only if for all values of i,

$$\log\left[(Z_i - n_i)/n_i\right] - \alpha - \beta\epsilon_i = 0 \tag{D-9}$$

Hence
$$n_i = Z_i/(e^{\alpha + \beta\epsilon_i} + 1) \equiv Z_i F(\epsilon_i) \tag{D-10}$$

As shown in appendix E, β must be identified with $1/kT$, where k is Boltzmann's constant. Expression (D-10) is the Fermi-Dirac distribution. The value of α is determined by the condition $\sum_i n_i = N$.

Note that if $e^\alpha \gg 1$, then the term of unity in the denominator of (D-10) may be neglected for all values of ϵ_i, and the Fermi distribution reduces to the Boltzmann distribution; in this case one speaks of a nondegenerate gas. If $0 < e^\alpha < 1$, i.e., for α negative, the gas is degenerate and the term of unity in the denominator must be retained at least for the low energy range; this is the case for the conduction electrons in a metal.

E. The Boltzmann relation

It will be shown that the number of possible arrangements W introduced in appendix D is related to the entropy of the system. Suppose a small amount of heat δQ is added to a system. According to the first law of thermodynamics, this will produce a change in the energy of the system equal to

$$\delta E = \delta Q - p\,\delta V \tag{E-1}$$

where $p\,\delta V$ is the work done by the system. On the other hand, if the total energy is E, we may write

$$\delta E = \sum_i \epsilon_i\,\delta n_i + \sum_i n_i\,\delta\epsilon_i \tag{E-2}$$

It must be emphasized that any changes $\delta\epsilon_i$ in the energy levels are possible only if the volume changes; this follows from the discussion in appendix B. Hence the last term in (E-2) may be written

$$\sum_i n_i\,\delta\epsilon_i = \sum_i n_i \frac{\partial\epsilon_i}{\partial V}\,\delta V = -p\,\delta V \tag{E-3}$$

because $p = -\partial E/\partial V$. We thus conclude that

$$\delta Q = \sum_i \epsilon_i\,\delta n_i \tag{E-4}$$

Consider this question: When a small amount of heat δQ is added reversibly to a system, what is the corresponding change in log W? The term "reversibly" means that the system is continuously in thermal equilibrium, i.e., during the whole process of adding δQ, W is a maximum. Employing (D-8), while keeping the total number of particles constant, we obtain

$$\delta \log W = \beta \sum_i \epsilon_i \, \delta n_i = \beta \, \delta Q \qquad \text{(E-5)}$$

There evidently exists a simple relation between a small amount of heat added to the system and the resulting change in log W. Now $\delta \log W$ is a complete differential, i.e.,

$$\delta \log W = \sum_i \frac{\partial}{\partial n_i} (\log W) \, \delta n_i$$

Hence, $\beta \, \delta Q$ must also be a complete differential. We know from thermodynamics that δQ itself is not a complete differential, but that $1/T$ is an integrating factor. Therefore $\beta = 1/kT$, where k is a constant, and instead of (E-5) we may write

$$k \, \delta \log W = \delta S \quad \text{or} \quad S = k \log W + \text{const.} \qquad \text{(E-6)}$$

This is the famous Boltzmann relation between the entropy S and log W. The value of k must be obtained by comparison with experiment, and turns out to be Boltzmann's constant $k = 1.38 \times 10^{-16}$ erg degree^{-1}.

The above W and entropy are associated with the distribution of energy and in this volume are written W_{th} and S_{th}. The subscripts stand for "thermal" and distinguish them from W_{cf} and S_{cf}, which refer to configurational or mixing entropy which results from possible arrangements of particles in space.

INDEX

533

2